P9-BYG-925

PROJECTIVE *and Related* GEOMETRIES

A series of advanced mathematics texts under
the editorship of CARL B. ALLENDOERFER

MEASURE AND INTEGRATION
by Sterling K. Berberian
TOPICS IN HIGHER ANALYSIS
by Harold K. Crowder and S. W. McCuskey
ABSTRACT ALGEBRA
by W. E. Deskins
THEORY AND SOLUTION OF ORDINARY DIFFERENTIAL EQUATIONS
by Donald Greenspan
RETRACING ELEMENTARY MATHEMATICS
by Leon Henkin, W. Norman Smith, Verne J. Varineau, and Michael J. Walsh
INTRODUCTION TO MATHEMATICAL STATISTICS
by Robert V. Hogg and Allen T. Craig
ELEMENTARY MATRIX ALGEBRA, *Second Edition*
by Franz E. Hohn
METHODS IN ANALYSIS
by Jack Indrits
PROJECTIVE AND RELATED GEOMETRIES
by Harry Levy
STATISTICAL THEORY
by B. W. Lindgren
INTRODUCTION TO PROBABILITY THEORY
by James R. McCord, III, and Richard M. Moroney, Jr.
ELEMENTS OF ABSTRACT ALGEBRA
by John T. Moore

PROJECTIVE *and Related* GEOMETRIES

HARRY LEVY
Professor of Mathematics
University of Illinois
Urbana

THE MACMILLAN COMPANY, NEW YORK
COLLIER-MACMILLAN LIMITED, LONDON

First Printing

Library of Congress catalog card number: 64-10968

THE MACMILLAN COMPANY, NEW YORK
COLLIER-MACMILLAN CANADA, LTD., TORONTO, ONTARIO

PRINTED IN THE UNITED STATES OF AMERICA

Preface

This book has developed out of mimeographed notes for the introductory course in geometry given at the University of Illinois for many years by myself and by many of my colleagues. It is designed for students at the intermediate level, that is, for undergraduate mathematics majors and for beginning graduate students with minimal preparation in geometry.

I have adopted Klein's formulation of geometry as the invariant theory of a given set under a given group of transformations, and I have developed this point of view consistently and systematically, using (and developing) the student's knowledge of algebra and analysis as the occasion requires. There are many advantages, both pedagogical and mathematical, in this type of development. It permits the introduction of the axiomatic method in a form that clarifies the generality of the geometric structure that is being defined without calling upon the student for a premature appreciation of different projective geometries. On the other hand, in this setting the student recognizes the necessity of a mathematical formulation of intuitive geometrical concepts which, in the setting of Euclidean geometry, he has never analyzed. Experience has shown that this kind of presentation makes for a natural transition from elementary mathematics to the highly developed abstractions of today.

Chapter I is largely introductory, designed to introduce the student to ideas and ways of thinking which generally are new to him and which help to bridge the gap between analytic geometry and the present subject matter. However, the material relating to linear algebra and matrices, in Sections 4 and 5, is presented in more general form than is actually needed for the subsequent development. The student and teacher who wish to press on with the study of geometry could limit consideration of these two sections to the cases $n = 2,3$. The treatment of Euclidean geometry and its group of motions in Section 6 and the discussion of central projections in Section 7, important for their own sake, orient the student to the point of view that I have adopted.

In Chapter II, I state the axioms in terms of which I define $S_1(\mathsf{F})$, a projective space of dimension one over F, a commutative field not of characteristic two. I develop a minimal set of properties, including, however, the theorem of Von Staudt and Darboux that in the real case preservation of harmonic sets by a one-to-one map implies that the map is a projectivity. The definition given of $S_1(\mathsf{F})$ is used frequently in the rest of the book. For example, in Chapters III and IV it is proved that $S_2(\mathsf{F})$, a projective plane, creates one-dimensional projective structures on its pencils of lines and on its conics as well as on its lines. Later it is proved that in E_2, the Euclidean metric plane, and in K_2, the similarity plane, pencils of lines possess one-dimensional elliptic structures, whereas in the hyperbolic plane the structure of a pencil of lines may be that of a one-dimensional affine, elliptic, or hyperbolic space. As this suggests, I have placed a great deal of emphasis throughout on the concept of geometric structure.

Projective spaces of dimension two over F are defined in Chapter III. This chapter contains the usual material on linear geometry, and Chapter IV develops the geometry of the conic and of quadratic forms. In addition to the standard topics, I have included a brief study of elementary topological properties of the real projective plane, and of projective order in $S_1(\mathsf{R})$. Unfortunately, these important ideas are often neglected in a first course in projective geometry, whereas they enter naturally into our development. However, it has seemed desirable to postpone the more difficult problems relating to sense and orientation until later in the book. In Section 5 of Chapter V, I develop these ideas for the affine plane in full detail. By using Veblen and Young's sense classes in $S_1(\mathsf{R})$ rather than strictly affine concepts, this treatment (with only minor extensions) serves subsequently for the orientation of the Euclidean and hyperbolic planes as well as for the local orientation of the elliptic plane.

Probably one of the more difficult problems encountered in a treatment of geometry at the level of this book centers around the question, "What is a projective plane, and how is it related to the Euclidean plane?" Although there are many ways of handling this problem, I have found that premature identification of distinct planes tends to obfuscate rather than to clarify. My development emphasizes that $S_2(\mathsf{R})$ and E_2, for example, exist side by side as two independent geometric structures. The student learns how to pass from theorems in one to theorems in the other by "embedding" E_2 in $S_2(\mathsf{R})$, and he recognizes that in applying projective theorems to the Euclidean plane (or vice versa) there may enter three categories of relations: those in each of the two planes and, thirdly, the properties of a particular embedding. Although a definition of an embedding is not given in full until Chapter V, it is desirable for pedagogical reasons to introduce the idea early, and in Chapter II, I give an incomplete though usable definition of an embedding of a Euclidean line and of a Euclidean pencil of lines in $S_1(\mathsf{R})$.

I have tried to make the choice of the ground field a secondary matter, one that does not intrude itself into the subject matter at the expense of other, more important, ideas. Except in a few instances, a less mature student could on his first reading of Chapters II and III think primarily in terms of real projective spaces. Similarly I hope that I have kept my treatment of the limit concept sufficiently elementary to meet the needs of the beginning student and sufficiently advanced to stimulate him to independent thinking.

By the time he reaches Chapter V, the student is ready for a new range of problems. His understanding of geometry as an abstract mathematical system has grown considerably, and he is ready to grapple with the idea that new geometries are created by studying the action of a given geometry on different subsets. Many concepts introduced earlier take on a richer meaning as they are examined in a new context, and a great variety of new ideas are presented for the first time. I have already noted that I have based the orientation of the several planes that I consider in this chapter on the concept of sense classes in $S_1(\mathsf{R})$. Normal subgroups naturally play an important role in the geometric development, and the concept of isomorphic geometries permeates the entire chapter. The affine plane is studied in considerable detail in Sections 2, 3, and 5, and enough is done with the Euclidean plane to place its geometry on a sound footing. The last three sections treat the hyperbolic, inversive, and elliptic planes, respectively. Section 9 includes an analysis of the hyperbolic group of motions, and introduces the student to orbits of one-parameter groups. In Section 10 the emphasis is on a projective space of complex dimension one, with applications to the Euclidean sphere and to hyperbolic geometry. The final section includes proofs of the connectedness and compactness of the elliptic group of motions.

There is more material in this book than can normally be covered in a year's course. Although most sections are interrelated, Sections 8 and 11 of Chapter IV can be omitted in their entirety. The instructor who would like to include most of Chapter V in the year's work could plan to deal sparingly with Sections 9, 10, and 11 of III and 7 and 10 of IV, returning when cross references suggest it to appropriate theorems of those sections. On the other hand, the student who expects that he may shortly be teaching analytic geometry (either to high school seniors or to college freshmen) should accord the highest priority to all except possibly Sections 8, 10, and 11 of Chapter IV and 6, 9, 10, and 11 of Chapter V.

Although I have been reluctant to introduce unusual notation, I believe it is mathematically desirable to have a symbol for the elements of the algebraic structure onto which one ordinarily maps the points of a projective space. I have written $[a, b, c]$ for the equivalence class of ordered triples that are nonzero multiples of (a, b, c), and throughout I have used square brackets to denote the class of nonzero scalar multiples of the object within the brackets. Thus when $\mathbf{X}$, $\mathbf{Y}$ are column matrices over R, $[\mathbf{Y}] = \{\mathbf{X} \mid \mathbf{X} = \rho\mathbf{Y},\ \rho \in \mathsf{R},\ \rho \neq 0\}$. It would seem to be premature at this stage to insist on the concept of a quotient space. I have denoted the line incident to distinct points A, B by $A \oplus B$ rather than by much overworked juxtaposition of letters. Although the notation used has no other unfamiliar tones, symbols used frequently with a constant meaning are listed on pages 396, 397.

There are about 750 exercises, with a wide range of difficulty. Some are referred to (or solved) later in the text, and these are indicated by an asterisk. Those of a more difficult nature are identified by the symbol $^{\#}$.

Many of my colleagues have participated in the making of this book, and I am glad to take this opportunity to express my appreciation for their helpful suggestions. In particular, it is my pleasure to thank C. W. Mendel; I have availed myself extensively of his critical capacities, his judgment, and his eye for detail. If for no other reason, professional courtesy would require that I acknowledge the special contribution made by Lucretia Levy; for instance, Section 3 of Chapter III and Section 4 of Chapter V were largely of her composition. However, any attempt to isolate her contribution would be foreign to the character of our personal relationship. Finally, I should like to thank A. H. McLeod of The Macmillan Company for his kindly patience and invaluable assistance.

HARRY LEVY

Urbana, Illinois.

Contents

CHAPTER I

Introduction

1 Point Transformations

The development of geometrical systems may follow various patterns and may be based on a variety of methods. In this book we propose to study geometry by methods that are largely analytical; in the pattern of our development the concept of a *point transformation* will play a central role.

To clarify this concept, let us first suppose that we are dealing with the ordinary plane and that we represent its points by means of a definite rectangular Cartesian coordinate system. We read the symbol $P:(x,y)$ the point P with coordinates (x,y). As (x,y) varies over all ordered pairs of real numbers, the point P varies over the entire plane. A relation such as

$$x' = x + 1, \qquad y' = 2y \tag{1.1}$$

can be interpreted as an association of $P':(x',y')$ with $P:(x,y)$. Each point P of the plane determines uniquely a point P' with coordinates determined by equations (1.1). Thus the points $A:(1,2)$ and $B:(-2,0)$ determine, in the presence of (1.1), the points $A':(2,4)$ and $B':(-1,0)$, respectively. We say that (1.1) represents a *point transformation*, and that A, B, and P are *transformed* or *mapped* by the transformation (1.1) into A', B', and P', respectively. The points A', B', P' are called the *transforms* or *maps*, under the transformation, of A, B, P.

In this case, we have described the transformation analytically by giving for *every* point P the coordinates of the transform of P, as functions of the coordinates of P. But the concept of transformation does not depend on the presentation of an analytical description of the relationship between a point and its transform; it suffices merely that there be a determinate relationship. Again, the transformation (1.1) operates on all the points of the plane. This aspect of the transformation (1.1) is not to be regarded as an attribute of all point transformations. Thus, for example, Figure 1.1 suggests a particular transformation of the points of a given circle onto the points of a given ellipse by associating with any point P of the circle the point in which the half-line, from the center of the circle, through P, intersects the ellipse. For the circle and ellipse of Figure 1.1 (where the center of the circle is an

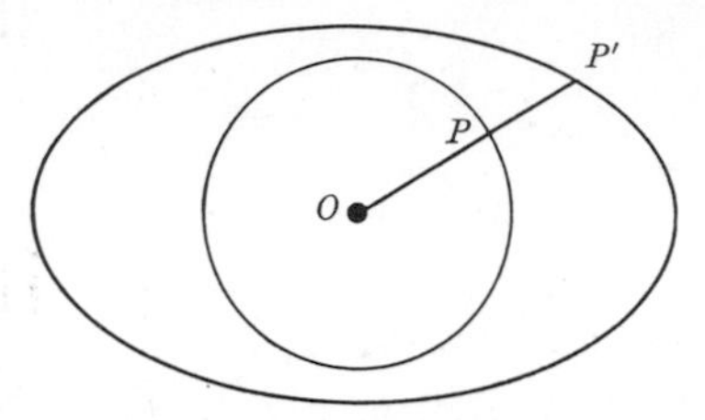

FIGURE 1.1

interior point of the ellipse), P' on the ellipse is determined whenever P, on the circle, is specified. Thus we have a transformation of the points of the circle onto points of the ellipse. We formalize these ideas with the following definition.

DEFINITION 1.1. Any law that associates with each point of a given set of points, a point of the same or another set of points is a *point transformation* or a *map* of the first point set into the second point set. The point associated with a given point is called the *transform* or the *map* of the given point under the transformation.

The point set on which a transformation operates is called the *domain of definition* of the transformation, and the point set consisting of all transforms, the *range* of the transformation. Thus the transformation that transforms a point P of space into the foot of the perpendicular from P to a given line has for its domain of definition all points of space, and the set of transforms, that is, the range, is the set of all points of the given line.

If τ is a given transformation, we can ask what point, or points, are transformed by τ onto a given point. If for each P (in the range of τ) there exists one and only one point Q (depending on P) whose transform is P, we say that τ is *one-to-one.* Thus the transformation (1.1) transforms $Q:(x-1, y/2)$, and no other point, into $P:(x, y)$ for all x, y, so that (1.1) is one-to-one, but the orthogonal projection of points of space onto a line is not one-to-one.

When (x, y) are interpreted as coordinates in the plane, equations of the type

$$x' = f(x, y), \qquad y' = g(x, y) \tag{1.2}$$

represent a point transformation whose domain of definition is the common domain of definition of the functions f and g, and whose range is either all the points of the plane or some subset thereof. If equations (1.2) possess a unique solution for x, y as functions of x', y' for all x', y' in the range, the transformation is one-to-one.

Conversely, if τ is a transformation of the plane, there exist functions f and g such that equations (1.2) represent τ; if τ is one-to-one, equations (1.2) possess a unique solution

$$x = F(x', y'), \qquad y = G(x', y') \tag{1.3}$$

defined for all x', y' for which $P'\!:(x', y')$ lies in the range of τ.

If τ is a point transformation with domain of definition a set of points $\mathscr{D}$, we shall say that τ is a transformation *of* or *from* $\mathscr{D}$ *onto* the range of τ; the terminology, a transformation from $\mathscr{D}$ *to* or *into* $\mathscr{D}'$ carries the meaning that the range of τ is contained in $\mathscr{D}'$, but need not consist of all points of $\mathscr{D}'$.

We shall use the symbols τ, τ_1, τ_2, σ, σ_1, σ_2 to denote point transformations, and later we shall need additional symbols. On some occasions we shall make explicit use of equations of the form (1.2), but equally frequently we shall work directly with symbols representing the transformation.

If P is a point, we shall denote by τP the transform or map of P. If $\mathscr{C}$ is any point set contained in the domain of definition of τ, we shall denote by $\tau\mathscr{C}$ the set of transforms of all points of $\mathscr{C}$, and we call $\tau\mathscr{C}$ the *transform* or *map* of $\mathscr{C}$. We shall also say that τ *maps* P and $\mathscr{C}$ *onto* τP and $\tau\mathscr{C}$. If $\mathscr{C}$ is a curve, $\tau\mathscr{C}$ will generally be a curve. If $\mathscr{C}$ is given parametrically,

$$x = \Phi(t), \qquad y = \Psi(t), \tag{1.4}$$

we find a parametric representation of $\tau\mathscr{C}$, when τ is given by (1.2), directly by replacing x, y in (1.2) by their values in terms of t from (1.4), and then dropping the primes in order to conform to the usual practice of representing the coordinates of an arbitrary point by (x, y). Thus if $\mathscr{C}$ is given by (1.4), its transform under (1.2) is given by

$$x = f(\Phi(t), \Psi(t)), \qquad y = g(\Phi(t), \Psi(t)).$$

If $\mathscr{C}$ is given by an equation

$$\phi(x, y) = 0, \tag{1.5}$$

it would be necessary to solve equations (1.2) for x, y in terms of x', y'; if a solution exists and is given by (1.3), we can now require that $P\!:(x, y)$ given by (1.3) satisfy (1.5); it then follows that $\tau P\!:(x', y')$ satisfies

$$\phi(F(x', y'), G(x', y')) = 0. \tag{1.6}$$

Finally if we drop the primes to conform to custom, (1.6) becomes the equation of $\tau\mathscr{C}$, or of a locus containing $\tau\mathscr{C}$.

If a set of points is subjected to a transformation τ, and their transforms are then subjected to a second transformation σ, we can obtain a new transformation by going directly from the original set of points to their final transforms (Figure 1.2). If we denote by P a variable point of the original

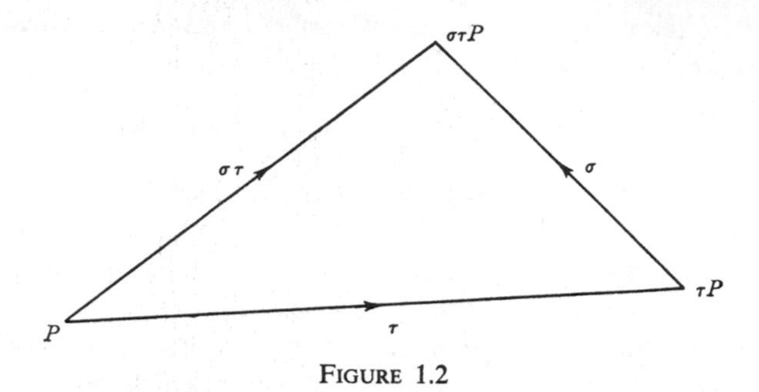

FIGURE 1.2

point set, we can formulate the idea of *product* of two transformations as follows:

DEFINITION 1.2. Let σ and τ be two point transformations such that the range of τ is contained in the domain of definition of σ. The *product* of σ by τ is the transformation which maps a point P onto the point $\sigma(\tau P)$, for all points P in the domain of τ. We denote the product of σ by τ by $\sigma\tau$.†

Hence, by definition $(\sigma\tau)P = \sigma(\tau P)$, and the parentheses are superfluous.

Let e, f, and θ be real numbers, and let τ_1 and τ_2 be the two particular point transformations of the plane onto itself defined by the equations

$$\tau_1: \quad \begin{aligned} x' &= x + e, \\ y' &= y + f, \end{aligned} \tag{1.7}$$

$$\tau_2: \quad \begin{aligned} x' &= x \cos\theta - y \sin\theta, \\ y' &= x \sin\theta + y \cos\theta. \end{aligned} \tag{1.8}$$

To find the product $\tau_2\tau_1$, let us denote $\tau_1 P$ (the transform of $P:(x, y)$ under τ_1) by $P'':(x'', y'')$; then

$$x'' = x + e, \qquad y'' = y + f.$$

If, similarly, the point $P':(x', y')$ is $\tau_2 P''$, then

$$\begin{aligned} x' &= x'' \cos\theta - y'' \sin\theta, \\ y' &= x'' \sin\theta + y'' \cos\theta; \end{aligned}$$

substituting for x'', y'' their values in terms of x and y, we obtain the transformation (Figure 1.3)

$$\tau_3: \quad \begin{aligned} x' &= (x + e)\cos\theta - (y + f)\sin\theta, \\ y' &= (x + e)\sin\theta + (y + f)\cos\theta. \end{aligned} \tag{1.9}$$

† Some authors denote by $\tau\sigma$ the product we denote by $\sigma\tau$, and by $P\tau$, rather than τP, the transform of P under τ.

From the definition of the product of two transformations,

$$\tau_3 = \tau_2 \tau_1 .$$

If we carry out these transformations in the other order, first τ_2, then τ_1, and denote this product by τ_4, we have

$$\tau_4 : \begin{array}{l} x' = x \cos \theta - y \sin \theta + e, \\ y' = x \sin \theta + y \cos \theta + f. \end{array} \tag{1.10}$$

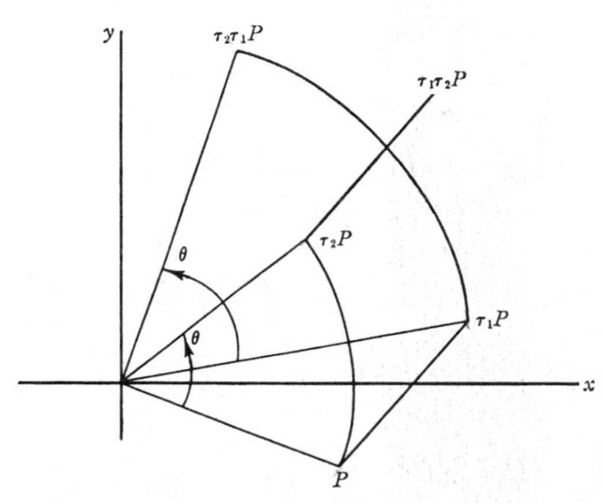

FIGURE 1.3

We see that $\tau_4 = \tau_1 \tau_2$ is not the same transformation as $\tau_3 = \tau_2 \tau_1$, so that the order of multiplication is material.

More generally, if the transformation τ given by equations (1.2), and the transformation σ given by

$$\sigma : \begin{array}{l} x' = \xi(x, y), \\ y' = \eta(x, y) \end{array} \tag{1.11}$$

represent any two transformations of the plane into itself, the product $\sigma\tau$ is given by

$$\sigma\tau : \begin{array}{l} x' = \xi(f(x, y), g(x, y)), \\ y' = \eta(f(x, y), g(x, y)), \end{array}$$

while the product $\tau\sigma$ is given by

$$\tau\sigma : \begin{array}{l} x' = f(\xi(x, y), \eta(x, y)), \\ y' = g(\xi(x, y), \eta(x, y)). \end{array}$$

We shall find it convenient to use the equality sign as a symbol of relation, not only between numbers, but also between points, between point sets, and between transformations. Thus when P and P' are points, the relation $P = P'$ asserts that P and P' are the same point. When $\mathscr{C}$ and $\mathscr{C}'$ are point sets, the relation $\mathscr{C} = \mathscr{C}'$ asserts that every point belonging to $\mathscr{C}$ belongs to $\mathscr{C}'$, and that every point belonging to $\mathscr{C}'$ belongs to $\mathscr{C}$. When τ and τ' are point transformations, the relation $\tau = \tau'$ asserts that τ and τ' have a common domain of definition and that the equality $\tau P = \tau' P$ holds for all P in the domain of definition.

Although the multiplication of point transformations, defined in Definition 1.2, is not necessarily commutative, that is, $\sigma\tau$ is generally not equal to $\tau\sigma$, it is always associative.

THEOREM 1.1. *Multiplication of point transformations is associative, that is,* $(\tau_3 \tau_2)\tau_1 = \tau_3(\tau_2 \tau_1)$, *where* τ_1, τ_2, τ_3 *are any point transformations for which the products are defined.*

Proof. Let P be a variable point, and let

$$\tau_1 P = P_1, \qquad \tau_2 P_1 = P_2, \qquad \tau_3 P_2 = P_3.$$

Then

$$\tau_2 \tau_1 P = P_2, \qquad \tau_3 \tau_2 P_1 = P_3,$$

and therefore

$$\tau_3(\tau_2 \tau_1)P = \tau_3 P_2 = P_3,$$

$$(\tau_3 \tau_2)\tau_1 P = (\tau_3 \tau_2)P_1 = P_3,$$

so that

$$(\tau_3 \tau_2)\tau_1 P = \tau_3(\tau_2 \tau_1)P, \qquad \text{for all } P.$$

Therefore

$$(\tau_3 \tau_2)\tau_1 = \tau_3(\tau_2 \tau_1). \tag{1.12}$$

DEFINITION. 1.3. The point transformation that maps every point of a given domain of definition onto itself is known as the *identity* transformation, and we denote it by I.

Clearly for every point transformation τ,

$$\tau I = I\tau = \tau.$$

For transformations of the plane onto itself, I is given by

$$x' = x, \qquad y' = y. \tag{1.13}$$

DEFINITION 1.4. If τ is a point transformation, and if there exists a point transformation σ such that $\sigma\tau = I$, σ is called the *inverse* of τ. We denote the inverse of τ by τ^{-1}.

If τ is one-to-one, the inverse of τ necessarily exists; if, moreover, τ maps P onto P', τ^{-1} maps P' onto P. Hence τ, mapping P back to P', is the inverse of τ^{-1}:

$$\tau = (\tau^{-1})^{-1},$$

and from Definition 1.4, we obtain

$$\tau\tau^{-1} = \tau^{-1}\tau = I. \tag{1.14}$$

If equations (1.2) can be solved for x and y, and the solution is given by (1.3), then the transformation

$$x' = F(x, y), \qquad y' = G(x, y) \tag{1.15}$$

is the inverse of (1.2). The inverses of τ_1 and τ_2 (defined by (1.7) and (1.8)) are

$$\tau_1^{-1}: \begin{array}{l} x' = x - e, \\ y' = y - f, \end{array} \tag{1.16}$$

$$\tau_2^{-1}: \begin{array}{l} x' = x \cos\theta + y \sin\theta, \\ y' = -x \sin\theta + y \cos\theta. \end{array} \tag{1.17}$$

There exist transformations that are their own inverses, for example,

$$x' = y, \qquad y' = x.$$

Such a transformation, that is, one whose square is the identity transformation, is said to be *involutory*.

Equations (1.7) and (1.8) are probably not unfamiliar to the reader who has met them in analytic geometry as the equations defining a coordinate transformation. But we note the quite different interpretation we have placed on these equations; we have a fixed rectangular Cartesian coordinate system, and here equations (1.7) and (1.8) define point transformations, so that (1.7) is a *translation*; under it every point is moved a constant distance in a fixed direction. It can be verified that (1.8) is a *rotation* about the origin, through the angle θ; under it a point P is transformed into P' where the distances OP and OP' are equal, and the directed angle from the ray OP to the ray OP' is equal to the constant $\theta \pmod{2\pi}$.

EXERCISES

In Exercises 1 *to* 6, *let* τ_1 *be the transformation* (1.1), *let* τ_2 *be the translation* $x' = x - 1$, $y' = y + 2$, *and let* τ_3 *be the rotation* $x' = -y$, $y' = x$.

1. Find the curve into which $x = t^3 + 1$, $y = t^2 - 1$ is transformed by τ_1; by τ_2; by τ_3. ANS. $\tau_1\mathscr{C}: x = t^3 + 2$, $y = 2t^2 - 2$.

2. Find the curve into which $y^2 = x$ is transformed by τ_1; by τ_2; by τ_3. ANS. $\tau_2\mathscr{C}: y^2 - 4y - x + 3 = 0$.

3. If $\mathscr{C}$ is the curve $(x - 1)^2 + (y + 2)^2 = 1$, find $\tau_1\mathscr{C}$; $\tau_2\mathscr{C}$; $\tau_3\mathscr{C}$. ANS. $\tau_3\mathscr{C}: (x - 2)^2 + (y - 1)^2 = 1$.

4. Compute the products: $\tau_1\tau_2$; $\tau_2\tau_1$; τ_1^2; $\tau_1\tau_3$; $\tau_3\tau_1$. ANS. $\tau_1\tau_2: x' = x$, $y' = 2y + 4$.

5. Find τ_1^{-1}, τ_2^{-1}, τ_3^{-1}, if they exist. ANS. $\tau_2^{-1}: x' = x + 1$, $y' = y - 2$.

6. Verify the associative law by computing $\tau_1 \tau_2 \tau_3$ in two ways.

7. Let $\mathscr{C}$ be a circle with center at A and radius a. A transformation τ is defined as follows: The transform of a point P ($\neq A$) of the plane is the point P' such that A, P, P' are collinear, and the product of the directed distances AP and AP' is equal to a^2. Find the equations of τ (a) referred to rectangular Cartesian coordinates with origin at A; (b) referred to polar coordinates with pole at A. What is the domain of definition and range of τ?

ANS. (a) $x' = \dfrac{a^2x}{x^2 + y^2}, \; y' = \dfrac{a^2y}{x^2 + y^2}.$

8. The points of a line are subjected to a transformation defined as follows: Let A be a given point of the line, and let P vary over all the points of the line except A; the transform of P is the point P' on the given line such that the product of the directed distances AP and AP' is 1. Find an analytical representation of the transformation in terms of a suitably chosen coordinate system. What is the domain of definition and range of this transformation?

9. Let P be a variable point with Cartesian coordinates (x, y), and let the line joining P to the origin intersect the line $x = 2$ in the point R. A transformation is defined by selecting as the transform of P the point P', on the line OP, such that the ratio of directed distances $OP/PR = -OP'/P'R$. Find equations of the transformation, the domain of definition, and the range.

ANS. $x' = \dfrac{x}{x - 1}, \; y' = \dfrac{y}{x - 1}.$

10. Show that the transformation of Exercise 9 carries the circle $x^2 + y^2 = 1$ into a parabola, and the circle $x^2 + y^2 = 4$ into a hyperbola whose asymptotes are the transforms of the tangents to the circle at its intersections with the line $x = 1$.

11. Find the inverses, when they exist, of each of the following transformations:

$$\text{(a)} \quad x' = 2x - y + 1, \qquad y' = x + y + 1;$$

$$\text{(b)} \quad x' = x/(x^2 + y^2), \qquad y' = y/(x^2 + y^2);$$

$$\text{(c)} \quad x' = 3x - y + 1, \qquad y' = 6x - 2y + 1.$$

Are any of these transformations involutory? What is the domain of definition and range of each?

12. Under the transformation of Exercise 11(b), what are the transforms of straight lines? Of circles? Of what curves are straight lines and circles respectively the transforms?

In Exercises 13 *to* 18, *let* τ, τ_1, τ_2, τ_3, τ_4 *be given point transformations all of whose domains of definition and ranges coincide.*

13. Solve $\tau_3 = \tau_1 \tau_2 \tau_1^{-1}$ for τ_2.

14. If $\tau_3 = \tau_1\tau_2$ and $\tau_4 = \tau_2\tau_1$, show that $\tau_4 = \tau_2\tau_3\tau_2^{-1} = \tau_1^{-1}\tau_3\tau_1$ and $\tau_3 = \tau_2^{-1}\tau_4\tau_2 = \tau_1\tau_4\tau_1^{-1}$.

***15.** Prove that $(\tau_2\tau_1)^{-1} = \tau_1^{-1}\tau_2^{-1}$. State this theorem in words.

***16.** We define $\tau^2 = \tau\tau$ and $\tau^n = \tau^{n-1}\tau$; show that $\tau^k\tau^m = \tau^{k+m}$, where k, m are positive integers.

***17.** Prove that $(\tau^{-1})^n = (\tau^n)^{-1}$. State this theorem in words. Note that this theorem permits the notation τ^{-n}.

***18.** Extend Exercise 16 to the case where k, m are any integers.

2 Groups of Transformations

So far we have considered equations such as (1.2) as representing a single point transformation. Now we wish to consider collections or sets of transformations. For example, let us denote by T the set consisting of all the transformations given by (1.7) when the constants e, f in (1.7) are allowed to vary over the set of real numbers. Thus $x' = x + 1$, $y' = y + 2$ is one transformation belonging to the set T, and $x' = x - 1/2$, $y' = y + \sqrt{3}$ is another. Just as $x^2 + y^2 = a^2$ represents both the circle with center at (0, 0) and radius a (when a is regarded as fixed) and the set of all circles with center at (0, 0) (when a varies), so (1.7) represents both a specific transformation (for e, f fixed) and a set of transformations (for e, f variable). The reader will need to keep constantly in mind which of these two interpretations is meant, that is, whether at a given moment we are considering all the transformations of a given set or an individual transformation of the set. We shall usually represent sets of transformations by capital letters.

We shall be primarily interested in sets of point transformations that constitute *groups*.

DEFINITION 2.1. A set of point transformations is a *group* if it possesses both of the following properties:

(a) the product of every two transformations of the set exists and is a transformation of the set;

(b) the inverse of each transformation of the set exists and is in the set.

Let us return to the set T,

$$T: \quad \begin{aligned} x' &= x + e, \\ y' &= y + f, \end{aligned} \qquad e, f \text{ real.} \tag{2.1}$$

We can show that this set is a group as follows: Two arbitrary transformations τ_1, τ_2 of T can be represented by

$$\tau_1: \quad \begin{aligned} x' &= x + e_1, \\ y' &= y + f_1, \end{aligned} \qquad \tau_2: \quad \begin{aligned} x' &= x + e_2, \\ y' &= y + f_2, \end{aligned}$$

where e_1, e_2, f_1, f_2 are arbitrary but fixed real numbers. We find upon computing the product, that $\tau_2 \tau_1$ is represented by

$$\tau_2 \tau_1: \quad \begin{aligned} x' &= x + e_1 + e_2, \\ y' &= y + f_1 + f_2. \end{aligned}$$

Since the sum of real numbers is real, $\tau_2 \tau_1$ is in T. Since τ_1, τ_2 were arbitrary transformations of T, the product of every two transformations of T is in T, and property (a) of Definition 2.1 is satisfied. The inverse of τ_1 is seen from (1.16) to be the transformation of T given by $e = -e_1, f = -f_1$. Again since τ_1 is arbitrary, condition (b) is satisfied, and the set T given by (2.1) is a group. We call this group the *translation group.*

The translations (1.7) for which e and f are positive integers do not form a group, but those for which e and f are *any* integers do; the set of rotations (1.8) $(0 \leqq \theta < 2\pi)$ form a group called the *rotation group*; the set of six rotations through angles 0°, 60°, 120°, 180°, 240°, 300°, respectively, form a *finite* group. These statements require proofs, which the reader should carry out.

The translation group (2.1) is an example of a continuous group of two parameters; the rotation group is a continuous group of one parameter.

We shall give some further examples of groups in this section, but first let us return to the definition of a group and note some of its consequences:

First, *every group contains the identity transformation*, for if it contains τ, it contains τ^{-1} by (b), and by (a) it contains $\tau\tau^{-1} = I$.

Second, *if a transformation belongs to a group it is one-to-one* by property (b).

Finally, *all the transformations of a group have a common domain of definition, and this domain coincides with the range.*

Proof. If τ and σ are two arbitrary transformations of a group, the product $\sigma\tau^{-1}$ exists, and therefore the domain of definition σ contains the range of τ^{-1}, which in turn is equal to the domain of definition of τ, that is, the domain of σ contains the domain of τ. By interchanging the roles of τ and σ, we see that the domain of τ contains the domain of σ, and hence the two domains coincide. Since τ and σ were arbitrary, all the transformations of the groups have a common domain of definition. Since the ranges of τ and σ are the domains of definition of τ^{-1} and σ^{-1}, respectively, the ranges of τ and σ coincide; hence all the transformations of the group have a common range, and this range coincides with the common domain of definition.

We digress briefly to state the following algebraic theorem which we shall use very frequently.

THEOREM 2.1. *The product of two determinants of order two can be expressed as a determinant whose elements are obtained from the elements of the given determinants in accordance with the following rule:*

$$\begin{vmatrix} a_1 & a_2 \\ b_1 & b_2 \end{vmatrix} \cdot \begin{vmatrix} c_1 & c_2 \\ d_1 & d_2 \end{vmatrix} = \begin{vmatrix} a_1 c_1 + a_2 d_1 & a_1 c_2 + a_2 d_2 \\ b_1 c_1 + b_2 d_1 & b_1 c_2 + b_2 d_2 \end{vmatrix}. \tag{2.2}$$

The reader can prove the theorem by carrying out the indicated operations. To remember the identity (2.2), we note that to obtain the element in the ith row and j^{th} column of the product determinant, we form the sum of the products of the elements in the ith row of the first factor by the corresponding elements in the jth column of the second factor.

We now give several further examples of groups. First let us consider the *linear group L* defined by the equations

$$L: \quad \begin{aligned} x' &= ax + by, \\ y' &= cx + dy, \end{aligned} \tag{2.3a}$$

where a, b, c, d vary over the set of all real numbers for which

$$\Delta = \begin{vmatrix} a & b \\ c & d \end{vmatrix} \neq 0. \tag{2.3b}$$

We shall prove that this set of transformations is a group by showing that it meets both conditions of Definition 2.1. Let σ_1 be an arbitrary transformation of the set L, and let it be given by

$$\sigma_1: \quad \begin{aligned} x' &= a_1 x + b_1 y, \\ y' &= c_1 x + d_1 y, \end{aligned} \qquad \Delta_1 = \begin{vmatrix} a_1 & b_1 \\ c_1 & d_1 \end{vmatrix} \neq 0. \tag{2.4}$$

Since $\Delta_1 \neq 0$, we can solve equations (2.4) for x, y, so that the inverse exists; it is given by

$$\sigma_1^{-1}: \quad \begin{aligned} x' &= \frac{1}{\Delta_1}(d_1 x - b_1 y), \\ y' &= \frac{1}{\Delta_1}(-c_1 x + a_1 y). \end{aligned} \tag{2.5}$$

We find upon calculating the determinant of σ_1^{-1} that it is $1/\Delta_1$, and therefore is not zero. Hence σ_1^{-1} exists and belongs to the set L. To show that property (a) of Definition 2.1 holds, we choose two arbitrary transformations of the set, say σ_1 and σ_2, given by (2.4) and

$$\sigma_2: \quad \begin{aligned} x' &= a_2 x + b_2 y, \\ y' &= c_2 x + d_2 y, \end{aligned} \qquad \Delta_2 = \begin{vmatrix} a_2 & b_2 \\ c_2 & d_2 \end{vmatrix} \neq 0. \tag{2.6}$$

We compute the product in accordance with Definition 1.2, and we find that $\sigma_2 \sigma_1$ is given by

$$\sigma_2 \sigma_1: \quad \begin{aligned} x' &= a_2(a_1 x + b_1 y) + b_2(c_1 x + d_1 y), \\ y' &= c_2(a_1 x + b_1 y) + d_2(c_1 x + d_1 y). \end{aligned} \tag{2.7}$$

We see that $\sigma_2 \sigma_1$ is a linear transformation with determinant Δ_{21} given by

$$\Delta_{21} = \begin{vmatrix} a_2 a_1 + b_2 c_1 & a_2 b_1 + b_2 d_1 \\ c_2 a_1 + d_2 c_1 & c_2 b_1 + d_2 d_1 \end{vmatrix}.$$

By means of Theorem 2.1 we can write this determinant as a product,

$$\Delta_{21} = \Delta_2 \Delta_1, \tag{2.8}$$

and since the determinants Δ_1 and Δ_2 do not vanish, neither does their product. Hence the product belongs to L. Thus the set L satisfies both requirements of Definition 2.1 and therefore is a group.

Transformations of the linear group (2.3) can be represented by the array of coefficients; thus the arrays

$$\begin{pmatrix} a_1 & b_1 \\ c_1 & d_1 \end{pmatrix}, \qquad \begin{pmatrix} a_2 & b_2 \\ c_2 & d_2 \end{pmatrix}$$

represent the transformations σ_1 and σ_2. If we agree to *multiply* such arrays by the procedure described in Theorem 2.1 for the multiplication of determinants, that is, if we define

$$\begin{pmatrix} a_2 & b_2 \\ c_2 & d_2 \end{pmatrix}\begin{pmatrix} a_1 & b_1 \\ c_1 & d_1 \end{pmatrix} = \begin{pmatrix} a_2 a_1 + b_2 c_1 & a_2 b_1 + b_2 d_1 \\ c_2 a_1 + d_2 c_1 & c_2 b_1 + d_2 d_1 \end{pmatrix}, \tag{2.9}$$

then the array representing the product of two transformations of L is the product, in the same order, of the arrays representing the transformations. We shall return to this idea in Section 4.

The *affine group*, which we shall denote by G_6, is defined by the equations:

$$G_6: \quad \begin{aligned} x' &= ax + by + e, \\ y' &= cx + dy + f, \end{aligned} \tag{2.10a}$$

where the coefficients a, b, c, d, e, f vary over the set of all real numbers for which

$$\Delta = \begin{vmatrix} a & b \\ c & d \end{vmatrix} \neq 0. \tag{2.10b}$$

We leave to the reader to prove that the set G_6 is a group (Exercise 5 below).

Of special importance in Euclidean geometry is the three-parameter group of *direct motions*; they are the affine transformations (2.10) for which

$$a^2 + c^2 = 1, \qquad d = a, \qquad b = -c. \tag{2.11}$$

By virtue of the first of these conditions, the equations

$$a = \cos\theta, \qquad c = \sin\theta \tag{2.12}$$

determine uniquely a real number θ in the interval $0 \leqq \theta < 2\pi$; we can then write the equations of M, the group of direct motions,

$$(2.13) \qquad M: \begin{array}{l} x' = x \cos \theta - y \sin \theta + e, \\ y' = x \sin \theta + y \cos \theta + f, \end{array}$$

where e, f are any real numbers and $0 \leqq \theta < 2\pi$. The proof that M is a group is left to the reader (Exercise 6 below).

DEFINITION 2.2. A group G of transformations is an *Abelian* (or *commutative*) group if every two transformations g_1, g_2 of G satisfy the condition

$$(2.14) \qquad g_1 g_2 = g_2 g_1 .$$

DEFINITION. 2.3. A group of transformations H is a *subgroup* of a group G, if every transformation of H belongs to G.

To illustrate these definitions, we exhibit the set of transformations

$$(2.15) \qquad x' = ax, \qquad y' = y, \qquad a \neq 0,$$

where a varies over all real numbers except zero. The reader can easily verify that this set of transformations is a group, that it is a subgroup of L, and that it is Abelian.

The group M is not Abelian, for the transformations τ_1, τ_2 given by (1·7), (1.8), respectively, clearly belong to M, and their two products $\tau_2 \tau_1$ and $\tau_1 \tau_2$ given by (1.9), (1.10) are distinct (except for the trivial cases $\tau_1 = I$, or $\tau_2 = I$). However, among the subgroups of M are the translation group and the rotation group, and these subgroups are Abelian (see Exercise 2 below).

We shall, when it is useful, use the notation of set theory. Let $\mathscr{C}$ and $\mathscr{D}$ represent sets, that is, collections of points, of curves, of point transformations, of functions, or of any kind of mathematical objects. Then $a \in \mathscr{C}$ is read "a is an element, or a member, of $\mathscr{C}$."† Thus $g \in L$ and $g' \in G_6$ assert that g is a linear transformation, and g' an affine one. The relation $\mathscr{C} \subset \mathscr{D}$ is read "$\mathscr{C}$ is contained in $\mathscr{D}$," and means that every element in $\mathscr{C}$ is an element in $\mathscr{D}$. Thus we have $T \subset M \subset G_6$. The notation $\mathscr{C} \times \mathscr{D}$ is read "the Cartesian product of $\mathscr{C}$ by $\mathscr{D}$"; it denotes the set consisting of all ordered pairs (x, y) where $x \in \mathscr{C}$ and $y \in \mathscr{D}$. Thus, if R denotes the set of all real numbers, $\mathsf{R} \times \mathsf{R}$ denotes the set of all ordered pairs of real numbers.

We shall use T, M, L, and G_6 to denote the groups specified earlier in this section. We shall denote both the ordinary plane, and the point set of that plane, by the symbol E_2. We shall call this plane the Euclidean plane, and we give a formal definition of it in Section 6 of this chapter.

† We shall also use $\in$ and $\subset$ in other grammatical constructions: thus in "Let $a \in \mathscr{C}$," $\in$ must be read "*be* an element of." On some occasions the symbols will be used in a modifying phrase, for example, "for all $a \in \mathscr{C}$."

EXERCISES

1. Prove that M given by (2.13) is a group.

***2.** Show that the translation group and the rotation group are Abelian subgroups of M.

3. Does the set of transformations given by $x' = ax$, $y' = -y$, where a takes on all real values except zero, form a group?

4. Is the group L (given by (2.3)) Abelian?

5. Prove that the set of transformations given by (2.10) is a group.

6. Show that both the linear group and the group of direct motions are subgroups of the affine group.

***7.** Is the subset of the group L, where a, b, c, d are any real numbers such that $\Delta = 1$, a group? Answer the same question for $\Delta = -1$, for $\Delta = \pm 1$, for $\Delta = 2$.

#****8.** Let the transform of P be P' defined as in Exercise 9, Section 1 except that the ratio into which the segment OR is divided by P' is k times the ratio in which it is divided by P. Find the equations of the transformation. Now let k vary. Does the set of transformations form a group (a) if k takes on all real values, (b) if k takes on all positive rational values? What other possible ranges for k will give a group?

9. Show that there exists just one transformation of the group of translations which maps one given point onto a second given point.

10. Show that each of the circles $x^2 + y^2 = a^2$ is mapped onto itself by every transformation of the rotation group.

#****11.** Let G be a group of point transformations. Show that the set of all transformations in G which map a particular point Q onto itself is a group.

#****12.** Find the transformations of the affine group G_6 which map the points of the line $x = 1$ onto points of the same line. Prove that these transformations form a group without using explicitly the equations of the transformations.

3 Invariance

The concept of invariance is one of the most important ideas that we encounter. It is found in many areas of mathematics, and it assumes a variety of forms. We shall describe some of these forms, but we shall not try to be exhaustive.

We note first that in a given geometrical framework, as for example in the geometry of E_2 (the geometry studied in high school), the very vocabulary is built on the concept of invariance. The words *circles*, *parabolas*, *straight lines*, all denote collections of curves such that each of these collections possesses some property that permeates the entire collection. Let us use the phraseology *the space of all circles, the space of all parabolas, the space of all lines*, to mean these respective collections of curves together with the interrelations that flow, in each case, out of the nature of the curves in the collection. For brevity, let us denote one of these spaces, say the space of all parabolas, by the letter W. Then $w \in W$ means that w is a parabola. Recalling that M is the group of motions defined by (2.13), we assert the following:

(i) If $w \in W$, and $m \in M$, then $mw \in W$.

(ii) If $mw \in W$, and $m \in M$, then $w \in W$.

We have written in mathematical notation the familiar fact that every motion of the ordinary plane maps a parabola onto a parabola, and conversely, that if a given mathematical object is mapped by a motion onto a parabola, the given object must be a parabola. Thus the group of motions operating, by extension, on the space of all parabolas leaves that space intact. The space of all straight lines and the space of all circles are equally unchanged when operated on by the group of motions.

We are now ready to define our first form of the invariance concept, namely, an *invariant space*. For purposes of simplicity we suppose that our group of transformations operates on the points of the ordinary plane, but this restriction could be omitted were we to formulate a general concept of *space*.

DEFINITION 3.1. Let W be a definite collection, each element of W being a set of points of the Euclidean plane, and let G be any group of point transformations on that plane. W is an *invariant space* under G if $gw \in W$ for all $w \in W$ and $g \in G$.

Our definition guarantees that the transformations of G map an element of an invariant space onto an element of that space; we can prove that an object not contained in the invariant space remains outside under all transformations of G by using the fact that G is a group, so that each $g \in G$ possesses an inverse: If $gw \in W$, and W is an invariant space, then $g^{-1}(gw) \in W$. But $g^{-1}(gw) = (g^{-1}g)\, w = w$, and thus $w \in W$.

If V and W are two invariant spaces under G, and if $V \subset W$, we say that V is an *invariant subspace* of W under G. As an example, the space of all circles in E_2 of radius, say 5, is an invariant subspace of the space of all circles in E_2 under M.

Let us give another example of invariant spaces. Recall that $E_2 \times E_2$ means the collection of all ordered pairs of points of E_2. Then any group G of transformations whose domain of definition is E_2 possesses $E_2 \times E_2$ as an invariant space: Ordered pairs of points of E_2 are mapped, by $g \in G$, onto ordered pairs of points.

Let us now consider the linear group L, given by (2.3); let $P:(x_1, y_1)$,

$Q:(x_2, y_2)$ be any two points, and $P':(x_1', y_1')$, $Q':(x_2', y_2')$ their maps under an arbitrary transformation of L. We have from (2.3)

$$\begin{aligned} x_1' &= ax_1 + by_1, \qquad & y_1' &= cx_1 + dy_1; \\ x_2' &= ax_2 + by_2, \qquad & y_2' &= cx_2 + dy_2. \end{aligned} \tag{3.1}$$

Let us denote the determinant of the coordinates of P, Q by $f(P, Q)$,

$$f(P,Q) = \begin{vmatrix} x_1 & x_2 \\ y_1 & y_2 \end{vmatrix}, \tag{3.2}$$

so that

$$f(P',Q') = \begin{vmatrix} x_1' & x_2' \\ y_1' & y_2' \end{vmatrix}; \tag{3.3}$$

if we make use of equations (3.1) to express $f(P', Q')$ in terms of x_1, y_1, x_2, y_2, we find (by means of Theorem 2.1) that

$$f(P',Q') = \Delta\, f(P,Q), \tag{3.4}$$

where Δ is given by (2.3b).

Consequently two points for which $f(P, Q) = 0$ are transformed by every transformation of L into two points which likewise have this property. Thus the equation $f(P, Q) = 0$ determines an invariant subspace of $E_2 \times E_2$, under L. From the definition of f in (3.2), we note that $f(P, Q) = 0$ if and only if O (the origin), P, and Q lie on a line. Thus all transformations of L preserve collinearity with the origin.

We speak of the property of being an element of an invariant space as an *invariant property*, under the group.

Although the domain of definition of $g \in G$ was initially supposed to be E_2, we have extended the domain of definition in a natural way by our definition of $g\mathscr{C}$ when $\mathscr{C}$ is any point set of E_2. If V and W are any two collections of point sets, and if $d \in (V \times W)$, we can write $d = (v, w)$ where $v \in V$, $w \in W$. We naturally define gd to be the ordered pair (gv, gw). Then if V and W are invariant spaces, $gv \in V$, $gw \in W$, and therefore $gd \in (V \times W)$. Hence we have proved the following theorem.

THEOREM 3.1. *The Cartesian product of two invariant spaces, under a group G, is an invariant space under G.*

We turn next to a different aspect of invariance.

Consider in E_2 the group of motions M defined by (2.13). Let $P:(x_1, y_1)$ and $Q:(x_2, y_2)$ be any two points, and let $P':(x_1', y_1')$, $Q':(x_2', y_2')$ be the transforms of P, Q, respectively, under an arbitrary transformation m of M. Then

$$\begin{aligned} x_1' &= x_1 \cos\theta - y_1 \sin\theta + e, \\ y_1' &= x_1 \sin\theta + y_1 \cos\theta + f; \\ x_2' &= x_2 \cos\theta - y_2 \sin\theta + e, \\ y_2' &= x_2 \sin\theta + y_2 \cos\theta + f. \end{aligned} \tag{3.5}$$

If we define the function d determined by the pair of points P, Q by

$$d(P,Q) = \sqrt{(x_2 - x_1)^2 + (y_2 - y_1)^2}, \qquad P, Q \in E_2, \tag{3.6}$$

so that

$$d(P',Q') = \sqrt{(x_2' - x_1')^2 + (y_2' - y_1')^2}, \tag{3.7}$$

we find by a straightforward calculation which makes use of equations (3.5) that

$$d(P',Q') = d(P,Q). \tag{3.8}$$

If we use a single letter, say p, to denote an ordered pair of points, we can regard (3.6) as defining a function d of p, and (3.8) can be written

$$d(mp) = d(p), \qquad \text{for all } p \in E_2 \times E_2, \quad m \in M. \tag{3.9}$$

We see then that the function d given by (3.6) has these two properties:

(1) The domain of definition of d, namely $E_2 \times E_2$, is an invariant space, under M.

(2) The value of d, for a given pair of points, is equal to the value for any pair onto which the given pair can be mapped by some transformation of M.

The reader has of course recognized that $d(p)$ is the distance between the two points P, Q that constitute p, and that (3.9) expresses the fact that distance between pairs of points is preserved by the group M.

The definition of an *invariant* follows along the lines suggested by the preceding example.

DEFINITION 3.2. Let W be an invariant space under a group G, and let f be a real-valued function whose domain of definition is W. If $f(gw) = f(w)$ for all $w \in W$ and $g \in G$, f is an *invariant* of W.

This concept of invariant includes all of the mensuration formulas of elementary geometry. Thus the radius, the circumference, and the area of a circle are real-valued functions defined over the space of all circles in E_2, and the value of one of these functions for one circle is equal to the value of that function for any circle onto which the first can be mapped by a motion.

The next theorem merely summarizes what we have already said about distance.

THEOREM 3.2. *Distance between pairs of points in E_2 is an invariant under the group of direct motions.*

Let us recall that by an *algebraic curve* in the Euclidean plane we mean the locus of points whose Cartesian coordinates satisfy an equation $F(x,y) = 0$, where F is a polynomial in x, y; the degree of F is called the *order* of the curve.

The affine group G_6 was defined by equations (2.10).

THEOREM 3.3. *The order of an algebraic curve is an invariant under the affine group.*

Proof. Since G_6 is a group, when we solve the equations (2.10), representing an arbitrary transformation of the group, for x, y in terms of x', y', we must obtain equations of the same form. We can therefore write

$$x = a_1 x' + b_1 y' + e_1, \qquad y = c_1 x' + d_1 y' + f_1. \tag{3.10}$$

Let the given curve have an equation $F(x, y) = 0$, where $F(x, y)$ is a polynomial in x, y. The equation of the transformed curve is obtained by replacing x, y in F by their values from (3.10). Since equations (3.10) are linear, we obtain a polynomial equation in x', y', and the degree of the new equation cannot be greater than the degree of F itself. Is it possible that the terms of highest degree cancel out? Suppose they did. The inverse transformation would then increase the degree. But we have already seen that no transformation of the group can increase the degree. Consequently the degree of the equation is unchanged, and the order of an algebraic curve is an invariant under the affine group.

Thus there exist invariants that take on only positive integral values.

The reader should note where in the preceding argument we proved that the space of all algebraic curves is an invariant space.

THEOREM 3.4. *If A is an invariant space under a group G, A is an invariant space under any subgroup of G.*

Proof. Denote the subgroup by H, and let $h \in H$. Then, by the definition of subgroup, $h \in G$; since A is an invariant space under G, $ha \in A$ for $a \in A$, $h \in H$. Hence A is an invariant space under H.

We shall leave the proof of the next theorem to the reader.

THEOREM 3.5. *If f is an invariant of A under a group G, and if H is a subgroup of G, then f is an invariant of A under H.*

We shall use the following theorem very frequently; it is a clear consequence of the three preceding theorems.

THEOREM 3.6. *The space of lines of E_2 is an invariant space under the affine group G_6, under the linear group L, under the group of motions M, under the translation group T, and under the rotation group.*

THEOREM 3.7. *Parallelism is an invariant property of pairs of lines under the affine group.*

Proof. The theorem asserts that any pair of parallel lines is mapped, by an affine transformation, onto a pair of parallel lines, that is, that the space of pairs of parallel lines is an invariant space under G_6. We let p_1, p_2 be lines with equations

$$p_1: \quad A_1 x + B_1 y + C_1 = 0, \tag{3.11}$$

$$p_2: \quad A_2 x + B_2 y + C_2 = 0. \tag{3.12}$$

Since two lines are parallel† if and only if

$$A_1 B_2 - A_2 B_1 = 0, \tag{3.13}$$

we consider the function $f(A_1, A_2, B_1, B_2)$ given by

$$f(A_1, A_2, B_1, B_2) = A_1 B_2 - A_2 B_1. \tag{3.14}$$

Let us investigate the behavior of f under the group G_6. If $g \in G_6$, gp_1 is necessarily a line; let its equation be

$$A_1' x + B_1' y + C_1' = 0. \tag{3.15}$$

The coefficients entering in this equation can be computed by noting that if g is given by (2.10), then (3.15) is the transform of

$$A_1'(ax + by + e) + B_1'(cx + dy + f) + C_1' = 0.$$

If this is to be an equation of p_1 itself, we must have

$$\begin{aligned} \rho_1 A_1 &= aA_1' + cB_1', \\ \rho_1 B_1 &= bA_1' + dB_1', \\ \rho_1 C_1 &= eA_1' + fB_1' + C_1', \end{aligned} \qquad \rho_1 \neq 0, \tag{3.16}$$

where ρ_1 is a factor of proportionality which must be introduced into equations (3.16) since the coefficients in the equation of a line are determined only to within a factor of proportionality. If we denote by $A_2' x + B_2' y + C_2' = 0$ the transform of (3.12), it follows from (3.16) that

$$\begin{aligned} \rho_2 A_2 &= aA_2' + cB_2', \\ \rho_2 B_2 &= bA_2' + dB_2', \end{aligned} \qquad \rho_2 \neq 0.$$

We have a situation similar to that met in equations (3.1) to (3.4), and we can conclude

$$\rho_1 \rho_2 \begin{vmatrix} A_1 & B_1 \\ A_2 & B_2 \end{vmatrix} = \begin{vmatrix} A_1' & B_1' \\ A_2' & B_2' \end{vmatrix} \Delta. \tag{3.17}$$

Since $\rho_1 \rho_2 \Delta \neq 0$, it follows that every pair of lines satisfying (3.13) will transform, under the affine group, onto a pair which likewise satisfies (3.13), and the theorem itself follows from the remark immediately preceding equation (3.13) and Definition 3.1.

We may here note that even in a given coordinatization of E_2, the function f defined in (3.14) fails to be a function whose domain of definition

† We include in the set of lines parallel to a given line, the given line itself.

is the space of pairs of lines because of the indeterminateness of the coefficients in the equation of a line. Nevertheless equation (3.13) does determine in the space of all pairs of lines, an invariant subspace consisting of pairs of parallel lines.

THEOREM 3.8. *The (undirected) distance between a point and a line is an invariant under the group of direct motions.*

Proof. Let $D(P,p)$ be the distance between a point $P:(x,y)$ and a line p with normal equation

$$x \cos \alpha + y \sin \alpha + r = 0. \tag{3.18}$$

Then the function D is defined over the Cartesian product of E_2 and the space of all lines, and this product space is an invariant space by Theorems 3.1. and 3.6. The value of D is given by

$$D(P, p) = |x \cos \alpha + y \sin \alpha + r|. \tag{3.19}$$

Let m be an arbitrary motion, given by (2.13). From (1.10) we have $m = \tau_1 \tau_2$, where τ_1 is the translation (1.7) and τ_2 the rotation (1.8). We compute the coordinates of $\tau_1 P$, and find the equation of $\tau_1 p$:

$$\tau_1 P:(x + e, y + f); \qquad \tau_1 p:(x - e) \cos \alpha + (y - f) \sin \alpha + r = 0.$$

From (3.19), we find that $D(\tau_1 P, \tau_1 p) = D(P,p)$ for all (P,p). A similar computation yields that the equation of $\tau_2 p$ is

$$x \cos (\theta + \alpha) + y \sin (\theta + \alpha) + r = 0;$$

direct computation yields $D(\tau_2 P, \tau_2 p) = D(P,p)$. Therefore

$$D(mP, mp) = D(\tau_1(\tau_2 P), \tau_1(\tau_2 p)) = D(\tau_2 P, \tau_2 p) = D(P, p),$$

and our theorem is proved.

There is still another form of the invariance concept that we shall discuss. This form involves a broadening of the function concept. At his present stage, the student's contact with function theory has probably been restricted to the consideration of functions whose values are numbers; generally these have been real numbers, but the student has met functions whose values are integers, and may have studied functions that take on complex values. Yet there is nothing in the function concept that requires such a restriction. Elementary geometry is replete with illustrations of functions in a broader sense: the perpendicular bisector of a segment, the circle circumscribing a triangle, the foci of an ellipse, the centroid of an arc—all have in common the property that each element of a given space determines uniquely an element of another space.

Consider, in particular, the directrix of a parabola. For a given parabola, the directrix is a line; as the parabola varies over the space of all parabolas in E_2, the directrix relationship is best thought of as a function whose values lie in the space of all lines in E_2. If we denote this function by f, the notation $v = f(w)$ then implies that w is a parabola, that is, an element of the space of all parabolas, and that v is a line, that is, an element in the range of the function f.

Let G be any group of point transformations in E_2 which possesses the space of parabolas as an invariant space; then $g \in G$ and w a parabola imply that gw is a parabola. Thus gw possesses a directrix $f(gw)$, and we can ask: Is the directrix of the transformed parabola, the transform, under g, of the directrix of the original parabola? In symbolism, we are asking whether

$$gf(w) = f(gw). \tag{3.20}$$

We are interested primarily in the general rather than the particular; (3.20) might hold for a special parabola without holding for all. If (3.20) holds for all parabolas, we can write it as

$$gf = fg. \tag{3.21}$$

The reader would probably guess (correctly) that (3.21) holds when G is the group of motions M (see Theorem 3.9 below); that it does not hold for G_6 is less obvious (see Exercises 2, 3 below).

DEFINITION 3.3. Let V and W be invariant spaces under a group G, and let f be a function whose domain of definition is W and whose range is contained in V. We say that $f(w)$ is *invariantly related* to w *under* G if $gf(w) = f(gw)$ whenever $g \in G$ and $w \in W$. We call f an *invariant relation* in $V \times W$.

THEOREM 3.9. *The focus and directrix of a parabola are invariantly related to the parabola under the group of motions.*

Proof. Let w, $f_1(w)$, and $f_2(w)$ be, respectively, a parabola, its directrix, and its focus, and let mw, $mf_1(w)$, and $mf_2(w)$ be their respective transforms under an arbitrary motion $m \in M$. To prove the theorem, we must show that mw is a parabola, that $mf_1(w)$ is its directrix, and $mf_2(w)$ its focus. We know that $mf_2(w)$ is a point since $f_2(w)$ is a point, and $mf_1(w)$ is a line by Theorem 3.6. Let $P \in w$, and let mP be its transform under m. Then from a well-known defining property of parabolas and the definition of the functions d and D (equations (3.6) and (3.19)), we have

$$d(P, f_2(w)) = D(P, f_1(w)). \tag{3.22}$$

But by Theorems 3.2 and 3.8, d and D are invariants under M, and hence

$$d(P, f_2(w)) = d(mP, mf_2(w)),$$
$$D(P, f_1(w)) = D(mP, mf_1(w));$$

therefore

$$d(mP, mf_2(w)) = D(mP, mf_1(w)). \tag{3.23}$$

This equation asserts that mP is equidistant from the point $mf_2(w)$ and the line $mf_1(w)$; therefore mP lies on the parabola w' whose focus is $mf_2(w)$ and whose directrix is $mf_1(w)$. That is, $mw \subset w'$. All that remains is to show that $mw = w'$, that is, that every point of w' is a point of mw. Let $Q \in w'$; then

$$d(Q, mf_2(w)) = D(Q, mf_1(w)). \tag{3.24}$$

Now subject E_2 to the motion m^{-1}. It follows that $m^{-1}Q \in w$, so that $Q \in mw$. Hence $w' \subset mw$ and $w' = mw$.

We consider next two closely related theorems.

THEOREM 3.10a. *The ratio in which a point P divides a directed segment P_1P_2 (that is, the ratio of directed distances P_1P/PP_2) is an invariant under the affine group.*

THEOREM 3.10b. *The point P which divides a directed segment in a given ratio is invariantly related to the segment under the affine group.*

We shall prove the second of these two theorems, leaving the proof of the first to the reader.

Proof. Let w be an arbitrary segment, and let us denote its initial point by $P_1:(x_1, y_1)$ and its terminal point by $P_2:(x_2, y_2)$. Let $P = f(w)$ be the point which divides w in the ratio k, and let (x, y) be the coordinates of P. Then

$$x = \frac{x_1 + kx_2}{1 + k}, \qquad y = \frac{y_1 + ky_2}{1 + k}.$$

Let $g \in G_6$, and let us use primes to denote the coordinates of gP_1, gP_2, and gP. Then

$$\begin{aligned} x' &= ax + by + e \\ &= \frac{1}{1+k}(a(x_1 + kx_2) + b(y_1 + ky_2)) + e \\ &= \frac{1}{1+k}(ax_1 + by_1 + e + k(ax_2 + by_2 + e)) \\ &= \frac{1}{1+k}(x_1' + kx_2'). \end{aligned}$$

We obtain similarly that

$$y' = \frac{1}{1+k}(y_1' + ky_2').$$

Thus $gf(w)$ is the point that divides the segment gw in the ratio k, so that $gf(w) = f(gw)$. Hence the point $f(w)$ is invariantly related to the segment w, for all w, as was to have been proved.†

These two theorems suggest that there is a close interrelation between invariants and invariant relations. Frequently in mathematical literature, the word *invariant* is used adjectivally to denote not only what we have called invariants, but also invariant spaces and invariant relations. We shall do likewise when no confusion can arise.

We close this section with a companion theorem to Theorems 3.4 and 3.5.

THEOREM 3.11. *If f is an invariant relation under a group G, f is an invariant relation under any subgroup of G.*

EXERCISES

1. List about a dozen invariant spaces, invariants, and invariant relations under M that have not been mentioned in the text. Do not prove that they are invariant, but specify all items in your list carefully.

2. Show that there exists at least one $g \in G_6$ such that $gf(w) \neq f(gw)$, where w is a parabola, and $f(w)$ is its directrix.

3. Prove that the focus of a parabola is not invariantly related to the parabola under G_6.

4. A transformation in E_2 given by

$$x' = ax + e, \qquad y' = ay + f,$$

where a, e, and f are real numbers and $a > 0$, is called a homothetic transformation. Prove that the set of all homothetic transformations is a group.

5. Prove that the set of transformations

$$x' = ax, \qquad y' = ay, \qquad a > 0,$$

is a group, and that this group preserves the focus and directrix of a parabola.

6. Show that perpendicularity is not an invariant property of two lines under G_6. Is it under the group of Exercise 4? Of Exercise 5?

7. Prove that the medians of a triangle are invariantly related to the triangle under (i) the affine group, (ii) the linear group.

8. Prove Theorem 3.10a.

9. Prove Theorem 3.5.

10. Prove Theorem 3.11.

11. Prove the following theorem: If f is a (real-valued) invariant of a space W, under a group G, the set of all elements of W at which f takes on a preassigned value is an invariant subspace of W.

† In this proof we have avoided the main question, what is a directed segment, and is the space of directed segments an invariant space under G_6? These questions will be discussed, in part, in Section 6, and more fully in Chapter V.

#12. Let f be an invariant relation on $V \times W$ (see Definition 3.3), $v_0 \in V$, and $W_0 = \{w \mid f(w) = v_0, w \in W\}$. Show that W_0 need not be an invariant space, and find the analogue of the theorem of Exercise 11 in this situation.

#13. If x_n and y_n $(n = 1, 2, 3, \ldots)$ are sequences of real numbers that converge to x and y, respectively, we say that the sequence of points $P_n : (x_n, y_n)$ converges to $P : (x, y)$, and we write $P = \lim P_n$. Prove that this limit operation is invariant under G_6. Is this form of invariance related to any of those discussed in the text?

#14. Using the definition of the tangent line to a curve $y = f(x)$, as the line whose slope is dy/dx, analyze the invariantive character of the tangency relation under the affine group. Can the relationship be obtained directly as an invariantive limit operation?

4 Fields and Linear Transformations

In this and the following section we interrupt our development of geometric ideas to introduce several algebraic concepts. We develop some of this material in a more general form than we shall actually need. The reader who is eager to press on with the study of geometrical ideas can omit the discussion for n an arbitrary integer that begins with equations (4.7) and work only the first eight exercises at the end of this section. He should also note the comment on page 35.

In any development of geometry by analytical methods, one must at an early stage specify the domain of the variables of the geometry. Thus far we have supposed that variables that represent numbers represent real numbers. We might ask why real, and not complex? If we were to specify that our numbers are complex, we could, for example, always be certain that a quadratic polynomial $ax^2 + bx + c$ could be factored into linear factors. By the introduction of complex elements in our geometry, we would frequently find a unity that is not present in real geometry. But if we were to do this, we would at the same time destroy distinctions which we would often prefer to preserve. Many interesting results in real geometry are not valid in complex geometry. On the other hand, many of the geometrical properties that we shall develop in later chapters hold not only for both real and complex spaces, but also for spaces based on a more general number concept. It is important that at every stage we should know what kind of numbers are admissible as values of the variables. For this reason we shall first discuss briefly a generalization of the concept of number.

We suppose that we have a set of elements which we denote by F and of which a, b, c, x, ... are arbitrary members. We suppose further that we have two functions, each of two variables, defined in F × F with functional values elements of F. We call one of these functions the sum function and the function operation addition; the other we call the product function and the function operation multiplication. We denote these two operations by the symbols used for ordinary addition and multiplication.

DEFINITION 4.1. The set of elements F is a *field* with respect to the given operations of addition and multiplication provided that the following properties hold for all elements in F.

(1) Commutative Laws: $a + b = b + a, \quad ab = ba.$

(2) Associative Laws: $(a + b) + c = a + (b + c), \quad (ab)c = a(bc).$

(3) Distributive Law: $a(b + c) = ab + ac.$

(4) Existence of unit elements: There exist two elements in F, which we call the additive unit and the multiplicative unit and which we denote by 0 and 1, respectively, that satisfy

$$0 \neq 1, \quad a + 0 = a, \quad a \cdot 1 = a, \qquad \text{for all } a \in \mathsf{F}.$$

(5) Existence of additive inverses: For every element a in F, the equation $a + x = 0$ has a solution in F. We denote it by $-a$, and call it the additive inverse or the negative of a.

(6) Existence of multiplicative inverses: For every $a \neq 0$ in F, the equation $ax = 1$ has a solution in F. We denote it by a^{-1} (or $1/a$) and call it the multiplicative inverse or the reciprocal of a.

The set of all real numbers with the usual operations of addition and multiplication constitutes a field, called the *real* field. Similarly the *complex* field consists of all complex numbers and the *rational* field of all rational numbers, with the usual operations of addition and multiplication. As a less familiar example, we can cite the field consisting of just five elements: We denote them by the marks, 0, 1, 2, 3, 4, and the operations on these symbols are taken to be ordinary addition and multiplication reduced modulo 5. Thus in this field, the units are 0 and 1, the additive inverses of 1, 2, 3, 4 are 4, 3, 2, 1, respectively, and the mutliplicative inverses of 1, 2, 3, 4 are 1, 3, 2, 4, respectively. This last field is a special case of a field with elements represented by the marks 0, 1, 2, 3, . . . , $p - 1$, where p is a prime integer, and whose operations are ordinary addition and multiplication modulo p. We shall denote this field by F_p.†

By property (4), every field possesses an additive unit; is this unit unique? Suppose there were two elements 0 and 0′, such that $a + 0 = a$, $a + 0' = a$ for all a; then the first would surely hold for $a = 0'$ and the second for $a = 0$, so that $0' + 0 = 0'$ and $0 + 0' = 0$. But by the commutativity of addition, $0' + 0 = 0 + 0'$ so that $0 = 0'$. Similar arguments can be used to show that the multiplicative unit 1, and the inverses $-a$ and a^{-1} are unique.

† For a proof that F_p is a field, see Birkhoff and Maclane, *A Survey of Modern Algebra*, New York, The Macmillan Co., 1953, pp. 28, 35.

We agree to write $a - b$ for $a + (-b)$, and a/b for $ab^{-1} = b^{-1}a$. We shall show that the following properties are consequences of Definition 4.1:

$$c(a - b) = ca - cb. \tag{4.1}$$

$$c(-b) = -cb. \tag{4.2}$$

$$a(-1) = -a. \tag{4.3}$$

$$a \cdot 0 = 0. \tag{4.4}$$

Proof of (4.1).

$c(a - b) + cb = c((a - b) + b)$	by the Distributive Law
$= c(a + (-b + b))$	by the definition of $a - b$ and the Associative Law
$= c(a + 0)$	by the Commutative Law and the definition of additive inverses
$= ca.$	

By adding $-(cb)$ to both sides, we obtain (4.1).

(4.2) follows from (4.1) by letting $a = 0$; we obtain (4.3) from (4.2) by writing $-a = -(a \cdot 1)$, and (4.4) from (4.1) by writing $a \cdot 0 = a(1 - 1)$.

Every field contains the elements 0 and 1, and therefore the element $1 + 1$. If $1 + 1 \neq 0$, we denote this element by 2. If $1 + 1 = 0$, the field is said to be of *characteristic* 2. In our later work, we shall find it convenient to restrict ourselves to fields not of characteristic 2.

Throughout the rest of this book we shall use the following notation:
R denotes the field of real numbers.
C denotes the field of complex numbers.
F denotes an arbitrary field not of characteristic 2.
F_p denotes the field of residues mod p, where p is a prime, not 2.

We can solve linear equations with coefficients in a given field exactly as we solve such equations in the real field. Thus if the equation

$$ax = b, \qquad a \neq 0$$

possesses a solution, we can multiply both sides of the equation by a^{-1} to obtain the necessary condition

$$x = a^{-1}b = b/a,$$

and by direct substitution we verify that b/a is actually a solution. From (4.4) we have that $0 \cdot a = 0$ for all a, and hence for $a = 0$, $ax = b$ either has no solution or is satisfied by all x in F, according as $b \neq 0$ or $b = 0$.

Similar results hold for systems of linear equations in two or more unknowns. Thus we can show that the equations

$$\begin{aligned} a_{11}x_1 + a_{12}x_2 &= b_1, \\ a_{21}x_1 + a_{22}x_2 &= b_2, \end{aligned} \tag{4.5}$$

with coefficients in a field† F, possess a unique solution given by Cramer's Rule

$$x_1 = \frac{\begin{vmatrix} b_1 & a_{12} \\ b_2 & a_{22} \end{vmatrix}}{\begin{vmatrix} a_{11} & a_{12} \\ a_{21} & a_{22} \end{vmatrix}}, \qquad x_2 = \frac{\begin{vmatrix} a_{11} & b_1 \\ a_{21} & b_2 \end{vmatrix}}{\begin{vmatrix} a_{11} & a_{12} \\ a_{21} & a_{22} \end{vmatrix}} \tag{4.6}$$

whenever the determinant in the denominator does not vanish.

Although we shall be primarily interested in systems of linear equations in two or three unknowns, it is more convenient to discuss the general case involving an arbitrary but finite number of unknowns. The student can treat the case $n = 3$ independently of what follows (see Exercises 4–8 below). Consider n equations in n unknowns

$$\begin{aligned} a_{11}x_1 + a_{12}x_2 + \ldots + a_{1n}x_n &= b_1, \\ a_{21}x_1 + a_{22}x_2 + \ldots + a_{2n}x_n &= b_2, \\ \ldots\ldots\ldots\ldots\ldots\ldots&\ldots\ldots \\ a_{n1}x_1 + a_{n2}x_2 + \ldots + a_{nn}x_n &= b_n, \end{aligned} \qquad a_{ij}, b_i \in \mathsf{F}. \tag{4.7}$$

We can write a system (4.7) more compactly as

$$\sum_{j=1}^{n} a_{ij}x_j = b_i, \qquad i = 1, 2, \ldots, n \tag{4.7'}$$

Let $\mathbf{A}$ denote the array of coefficients

$$\mathbf{A} = \begin{pmatrix} a_{11} & a_{12} & \ldots & a_{1n} \\ a_{21} & a_{22} & \ldots & a_{2n} \\ \ldots & \ldots & \ldots & \ldots \\ a_{n1} & a_{n2} & \ldots & a_{nn} \end{pmatrix}, \tag{4.8}$$

where the order of the elements a_{ij} in $\mathbf{A}$ is that given in (4.7). We let det $\mathbf{A}$ denote the determinant of the a's, and we let A_{ji} denote $(-1)^{i+j}$ multiplied by the determinant obtained from $\mathbf{A}$ by deleting the ith row and the jth column; for example, if $n = 3$,

$$A_{12} = -\begin{vmatrix} a_{12} & a_{13} \\ a_{32} & a_{33} \end{vmatrix}.$$

We call A_{ji} the *cofactor* of a_{ij} in $\mathbf{A}$.

The expansion of a determinant by the cofactors of the ith row gives us the relation

$$a_{i1}A_{1i} + a_{i2}A_{2i} + \ldots + a_{in}A_{ni} = \det \mathbf{A},$$

and the expansion in terms of the cofactors of the jth column yields that

$$A_{j1}a_{1j} + A_{j2}a_{2j} + \ldots + A_{jn}a_{nj} = \det \mathbf{A}.$$

† The restriction on F that it not be of characteristic 2 is unnecessary both in this section and in the next one.

If, in $\mathbf{A}$, we replace the jth row by the ith row, for $j \neq i$, the resulting array has two identical rows, and its determinant is zero; we expand this determinant by the cofactors of its jth row, and we find that

$$a_{i1} A_{1j} + a_{i2} A_{2j} + \dots + a_{in} A_{nj} = 0, \qquad i \neq j.$$

A similar result holds for the columns. We can write these relations more compactly

$$\begin{aligned}(4.9) \qquad \sum_{k=1}^{n} a_{ik} A_{kj} = \sum_{k=1}^{n} A_{ik} a_{kj} &= 0 \quad \text{if} \quad i \neq j,\\ &= \det \mathbf{A} \quad \text{if} \quad i = j.\end{aligned}$$

To solve (4.7), say for x_1, we multiply successive equations of (4.7) by $A_{11}, A_{12}, \dots, A_{1n}$ and add. Using (4.9), we obtain

$$(\det \mathbf{A}) x_1 = \sum_{k=1}^{n} A_{1k} b_k .$$

More generally, to solve for x_j we multiply the kth equation by A_{jk} and sum on k. We find by using (4.9) that

$$(4.10) \qquad (\det \mathbf{A}) x_j = \sum_{k=1}^{n} A_{jk} b_k , \qquad j = 1, 2, \dots, n.$$

Thus if $\det \mathbf{A} \neq 0$, and if (4.7) possesses a solution, the solution is unique and is given by Cramer's Rule

$$(4.11) \qquad x_j = (1/\det \mathbf{A}) \sum_{k=1}^{n} A_{jk} b_k , \qquad j = 1, 2, \dots, n.$$

Finally, it should be shown that (4.11) is actually a solution of (4.7) (Exercise 12 below).

We shall find it useful to interpret these results somewhat differently. For a_{ij} fixed elements of F and (x_1, x_2) varying over $\mathsf{F} \times \mathsf{F}$, equations (4.5) determine (b_1, b_2) as varying over $\mathsf{F} \times \mathsf{F}$. We would prefer to use (x_1', x_2') rather than (b_1, b_2) to represent the map of (x_1, x_2), but the essential idea is that (4.5) can be regarded as establishing a map from $\mathsf{F} \times \mathsf{F}$ onto itself. When F is the real field, the set of all maps for which $\det \mathbf{A} \neq 0$ has already been shown to be the linear group L (see Section 2). We now define a *linear transformation*, over F, in n variables to be a map from $\mathsf{F} \times \mathsf{F} \times \dots \times \mathsf{F}$ (n factors) onto itself expressible by the equations

$$(4.12a) \qquad x_i' = \sum_{j=1}^{n} a_{ij} x_j , \qquad i = 1, 2, \dots, n,$$

where the constants a_{ij} and the variables x_i, x_i' are elements of F. We denote by $L(\mathsf{F}, n)$ the set of all transformations (4.12a) for which

$$(4.12b) \qquad \det \mathbf{A} \neq 0.$$

The existence and uniqueness of the solution (4.11) of (4.7) can now be stated as follows:

THEOREM 4.1. *If* $g \in L(\mathsf{F}, n)$, *g maps* $\mathsf{F} \times \mathsf{F} \times \ldots \times \mathsf{F}$ (*n factors*) *onto itself, and the map is one-to-one. If g is given by* (4.12), *the inverse map is given by*

$$x'_i = (1/\det \mathbf{A}) \sum_{j=1}^{n} A_{ij} x_j, \qquad i = 1, 2, \ldots, n. \tag{4.13}$$

We should expect next to show that the set $L(\mathsf{F}, n)$ is a group. For $n = 2$, and F the real field, this was done in Section 2. That proof made use of two important ideas:

(i) the representation of $g \in L$ by the array $\mathbf{A}$ (with $n = 2$) of the coefficients and the relation (2.9) between the arrays of two maps in L and that of the product map;

(ii) the relation between the determinant of two maps and that of their product (Theorem 2.1).

We have already denoted the array of coefficients of $g \in L(\mathsf{F}, n)$ by $\mathbf{A}$, where g is given by (4.12) and $\mathbf{A}$ by (4.8). Let $h \in L(\mathsf{F}, n)$, and let $\mathbf{B} = (b_{ij})$ denote the array of coefficients corresponding to h. To compute the transformation gh, we let $(x''_1, x''_2, \ldots, x''_n)$ denote the map of $(x_1, x_2, \ldots, x_n)$ under h, and $(x'_1, x'_2, \ldots, x'_n)$ that of $(x''_1, x''_2, \ldots, x''_n)$ under g. Then we can write

$$x''_k = \sum_{j=1}^{n} b_{kj} x_j, \qquad x'_i = \sum_{k=1}^{n} a_{ik} x''_k. \tag{4.14}$$

If we eliminate $(x''_1, x''_2, \ldots, x''_n)$, we find

$$x'_i = \sum_{k=1}^{n} a_{ik} \left(\sum_{j=1}^{n} b_{kj} x_j \right).$$

By the associative and distributive laws of Definition 4.1, this becomes

$$x'_i = \sum_{j=1}^{n} \left(\sum_{k=1}^{n} a_{ik} b_{kj} \right) x_j. \tag{4.15}$$

We have not so far used (4.12b); therefore we have shown that if g, h are any two maps of the set (4.12a), and if they are represented by arrays $\mathbf{A}$ and $\mathbf{B} = (b_{ij})$, respectively, the product gh also belongs to the set (4.12a); letting $\mathbf{C} = (c_{ij})$ be the array representing gh, we have that

$$c_{ij} = \sum_{k=1}^{n} a_{ik} b_{kj}. \tag{4.16}$$

Thus the array corresponding to the product gh is formed from the arrays of the individual factors by the process described verbally on page 11.

Theorem 2.1 is a special case of the following theorem.

THEOREM 4.2. *If* $\mathbf{C} = (c_{ij})$ *is given by* (4.16), *then det* $\mathbf{C}$ = (*det* $\mathbf{A}$) (*det* $\mathbf{B}$).

For $n = 2$, our earlier proof is valid. For $n > 2$, the reader is referred to the literature (for example, Birkhoff and Mac Lane, *op. cit.*, p. 305).

Theorem 4.2 guarantees that $gh \in L(\mathsf{F}, n)$ whenever $g, h \in L(\mathsf{F}, n)$. Thus both ideas (i) and (ii) mentioned earlier can be extended from the special case of L of Section 2 to the set $L(\mathsf{F}, n)$. Consequently the earlier proof that L is a group can be adapted to our present situation, and we have the following theorem.

THEOREM 4.3. *The set of transformations* $L(\mathsf{F}, n)$ *is a group.*

We call $L(\mathsf{F}, n)$ the linear group over (the field) F, of dimension n.

EXERCISES

1. Show that the set of elements $a + b\sqrt{2}$, where a, b are rational, with the usual operations of addition and multiplication, is a field.

2. Let (a, b) be an element of $\mathsf{R} \times \mathsf{R}$, where R is the real field. We define operations in $\mathsf{R} \times \mathsf{R}$ by the relations

$$(a, b) + (c, d) = (a + c, b + d),$$
$$(a, b) \cdot (c, d) = (ac - bd, ad + bc).$$

Show that under these operations $\mathsf{R} \times \mathsf{R}$ is a field. (This field is essentially the complex field, and this definition shows that the existence of complex numbers is a consequence of the existence of real numbers.)

3. Reformulate the definition of the field of Exercise 1 in terms of operations on ordered pairs of rational numbers.

4. Solve the system of three equations

$$x_1' = x_1 + x_2, \qquad x_2' = 2x_1 - x_2 + x_3, \qquad x_3' = 3x_1 + x_2 + x_3$$

for the x's in terms of the x''s, and identify the coefficients of the x''s with the cofactors (of the original array of coefficients) divided by their determinant.

5. Find the product of the determinants of the two arrays, that of the coefficients of Exercise 4 and that of their cofactors; write the product as a single determinant by using (4.16) and thereby verify Theorem 4.2 in this instance.

6. Interpret the equations

$$x_1' = a_{11}x_1 + a_{12}x_2 + a_{13}x_3,$$
$$x_2' = a_{21}x_1 + a_{22}x_2 + a_{23}x_3,$$
$$x_3' = a_{31}x_1 + a_{32}x_2 + a_{33}x_3,$$

as determining a map from $\mathsf{F} \times \mathsf{F} \times \mathsf{F}$ to itself. Find the inverse map, when it exists; identify the array of coefficients of the inverse map with the cofactors in the given array of coefficients, divided by the determinant.

7. Show that the product of two maps of Exercise 6 is linear, with coefficients that are formed from the arrays of coefficients of the given maps in the way described verbally on page 11, that is, by (4.16) for $n = 3$. What else is needed to prove Theorem 4.3 for $n = 3$?

***8.** State and prove the theorems of Exercises 14 and 15 below for $n = 2, 3$.

#9. Prove that the system (4.7), with det $\mathbf{A} = 0$ and the b's such that not all the sums $\sum_{k=1}^{n} A_{jk}\, b_k$ vanish, has no solution.

#10. Prove that if det $\mathbf{A} = 0$, if at least one cofactor A_{ij} is not zero, and if $\sum_{k=1}^{n} A_{jk}\, b_k = 0$ for all j, one of the equations (4.7) is redundant.

11. Show that if det $\mathbf{A} \neq 0$, either one of the two systems (4.9) can be used to define the cofactors A_{ij}.

12. Verify that (4.11) is a solution of (4.7).

13. The choice of subscripts in (4.14) was based on hindsight rather than foresight, and it made the derivation of (4.15) seem easier than is actually the case. Write (4.14) as

$$x_i'' = \sum_{j=1}^{n} b_{ij} x_j, \qquad x_i' = \sum_{j=1}^{n} a_{ij} x_j'',$$

and derive (4.15), changing notation only as the need arises.

#14. Prove the following theorem: If the determinant of $n + 1$ linear equations in n unknowns is zero, and if some set of n of the $n + 1$ equations possesses a unique solution, that solution satisfies the remaining equation.

#15. State the converse of the theorem of Exercise 14.

5 Matrices and Homogeneous Equations

To define a matrix and a matrix algebra over a field F, we start with ordered rectangular arrays of elements of a field F. Let $\mathbf{A}$ denote such an array, and let the positive integers m and n denote the number of rows and columns, respectively. If $a_{ij} \in$ F with $i = 1, 2, \ldots, m$ and $j = 1, 2, \ldots, n$, we write (as we did in (4.8) where $m = n$)

$$\mathbf{A} = \begin{pmatrix} a_{11} & a_{12} & \cdots & a_{1n} \\ a_{21} & a_{22} & \cdots & a_{2n} \\ \cdots & \cdots & \cdots & \cdots \\ a_{m1} & a_{m2} & \cdots & a_{mn} \end{pmatrix}. \tag{5.1}$$

Let $(\mathbf{A})_{ij}$ denote the entry in the ith row and j^{th} column of $\mathbf{A}$. We call $(\mathbf{A})_{ij}$ the (i, j)-element of $\mathbf{A}$ so that for (5.1)

$$(\mathbf{A})_{ij} = a_{ij}, \qquad i = 1, 2, \ldots, m; \quad j = 1, 2, \ldots, n. \tag{5.2}$$

We call m the *row order* and n the *column order* of $\mathbf{A}$, and we say that $\mathbf{A}$ is of *order* $m \times n$.

Let $\mathbf{B}$ be another such array, of order $m' \times n'$, with

$$(\mathbf{B})_{ij} = b_{ij}, \qquad i = 1, 2, \ldots, m'; \quad j = 1, 2, \ldots, n'.$$

We define the *sum*, $\mathbf{A} + \mathbf{B}$, only if $m' = m$ and $n' = n$. Then $\mathbf{A} + \mathbf{B}$ is the $m \times n$ array defined by

$$(5.3) \qquad (\mathbf{A} + \mathbf{B})_{ij} = a_{ij} + b_{ij}.$$

We define the *product*, $\mathbf{AB}$, only if $n = m'$. Then $\mathbf{AB}$ is an array of order $m \times n'$ defined by

$$(5.4) \qquad (\mathbf{AB})_{ij} = \sum_{k=1}^{n} a_{ik} b_{kj}, \qquad i = 1, 2, \ldots, m; \quad j = 1, 2, \ldots, n'.$$

Two arrays $\mathbf{A}$ and $\mathbf{B}$ are *equal* if they have equal row orders, equal column orders, and if their (i, j)-elements are equal throughout the range of i and j:

$$(5.5) \qquad \begin{aligned} &\mathbf{A} = \mathbf{B} \quad \text{if and only if} \quad a_{ij} = b_{ij}, \\ &i = 1, 2, \ldots, m; \quad j = 1, 2, \ldots, n; \quad m' = m; \quad n' = n. \end{aligned}$$

Lastly, we define scalar multiplication. If $\rho \in \mathsf{F}$, $\rho\mathbf{A}$ is defined by

$$(5.6) \qquad (\rho\mathbf{A})_{ij} = \rho a_{ij}.$$

Since multiplication in F is commutative, $\rho a_{ij} = a_{ij}\rho$; it is therefore useful to define $\mathbf{A}\rho$ by

$$(5.7) \qquad \mathbf{A}\rho = \rho\mathbf{A}.$$

Ordered rectangular arrays subjected to the operations we have just defined are called *matrices*, and the algebra of such sets is called a matrix algebra over F. It is not our intention to develop matrix algebra; we shall use matrices primarily as a computational device, and we shall here summarize the properties that we shall need in later chapters. Thus if $\mathbf{X}$ and $\mathbf{X}'$ represent the column matrices

$$(5.8) \qquad \mathbf{X} = \begin{pmatrix} x_1 \\ x_2 \\ \cdot \\ \cdot \\ \cdot \\ x_n \end{pmatrix}, \qquad \mathbf{X}' = \begin{pmatrix} x'_1 \\ x'_2 \\ \cdot \\ \cdot \\ \cdot \\ x'_n \end{pmatrix},$$

our definition of multiplication enables us to write the transformation (4.12a) as

$$(5.9) \qquad \mathbf{X}' = \mathbf{AX},$$

where $\mathbf{A}$ is the square matrix (4.8).

Matrix addition and multiplication and scalar multiplication can be shown to satisfy the following associative and distributive laws for all matrices **A**, **B**, **C** for which the operations are defined, and for all $\rho \in \mathsf{F}$:

$$\mathbf{A} + (\mathbf{B} + \mathbf{C}) = (\mathbf{A} + \mathbf{B}) + \mathbf{C}, \tag{5.10a}$$

$$\mathbf{A}(\mathbf{BC}) = (\mathbf{AB})\mathbf{C}, \tag{5.10b}$$

$$\mathbf{A}(\mathbf{B} + \mathbf{C}) = \mathbf{AB} + \mathbf{AC}, \qquad (\mathbf{B} + \mathbf{C})\mathbf{A} = \mathbf{BA} + \mathbf{CA}, \tag{5.11a}$$

$$\rho(\mathbf{AB}) = (\rho\mathbf{A})\mathbf{B} = \mathbf{A}(\rho\mathbf{B}). \tag{5.11b}$$

Thus if $g, h \in L(\mathsf{F}, n)$ (see (4.12)), and if g, h are represented by the $n \times n$ matrices **A**, **B**, respectively, the product map gh is represented by the product matrix **AB**. The proof of this, already given in Section 4, can now be repeated using matrix notation: In place of (4.14) we can write

$$\mathbf{X}'' = \mathbf{BX}, \qquad \mathbf{X}' = \mathbf{AX}''.$$

Hence $\mathbf{X}' = \mathbf{A}(\mathbf{BX})$, and by (5.10), $\mathbf{A}(\mathbf{BX}) = (\mathbf{AB})\mathbf{X}$.

The $n \times n$ matrix **I** defined by

$$(\mathbf{I})_{ii} = 1, \qquad (\mathbf{I})_{ij} = 0 \quad \text{for } i \neq j, \qquad i,j = 1, 2, \ldots, n, \tag{5.12}$$

is called the *unit matrix* of order n. It is the matrix corresponding to the identity transformation in $L(\mathsf{F}, n)$. Since the product of matrices corresponds to the product of the corresponding linear transformations, we have that for any square matrix **A** of order n

$$\mathbf{AI} = \mathbf{IA} = \mathbf{A}. \tag{5.13}$$

A matrix of order $m \times n$ all of whose elements are zero is called the *zero matrix* of that order. We denote it by $\mathbf{0}_{mn}$, and when the values of m and n need not be specified, we shall write $\mathbf{0}$ for $\mathbf{0}_{mn}$. From (5.3) and (5.4) we have

$$\mathbf{A} + \mathbf{0} = \mathbf{A}, \qquad \mathbf{A0} = \mathbf{0A} = \mathbf{0}. \tag{5.14}$$

We denote by det **A** the determinant of a square matrix **A**. From the properties of determinants and (5.6), we have that for a square matrix of order n

$$\det(\rho\mathbf{A}) = \rho^n \det \mathbf{A}. \tag{5.15}$$

If **A** is the square matrix (4.8), we call the matrix whose (i,j)-element is the cofactor of a_{ji} the *adjoint* of **A**. We denote the *adjoint* of **A** by $\mathbf{A}^a$; in the notation following (4.8),

$$(\mathbf{A}^a)_{ij} = A_{ij}. \tag{5.16}$$

We can now write equations (4.9) as

$$\mathbf{AA}^a = \mathbf{A}^a\mathbf{A} = (\det \mathbf{A})\mathbf{I}. \tag{5.17}$$

By Theorem 4.2 and equation (4.9) we have, at least if $\det \mathbf{A} \neq 0$,

$$\det(\mathbf{A}^a) = (\det \mathbf{A})^{n-1}. \tag{5.18}$$

A square matrix with determinant different from zero is said to be *nonsingular*. If $\mathbf{A}$ is such a matrix, we denote by $\mathbf{A}^{-1}$ the matrix defined by

$$\mathbf{A}^{-1} = (1/\det \mathbf{A})\mathbf{A}^a; \tag{5.19}$$

we call $\mathbf{A}^{-1}$ the (multiplicative) *inverse* of $\mathbf{A}$. From (5.17) and (5.6) it follows that

$$\mathbf{A}\mathbf{A}^{-1} = \mathbf{A}^{-1}\mathbf{A} = \mathbf{I}. \tag{5.20}$$

If $\mathbf{A}$ is the matrix of $g \in L(\mathsf{F}, n)$, then $\mathbf{A}^{-1}$ is the matrix of g^{-1}. Since $(g^{-1})^{-1} = g$, we have $(\mathbf{A}^{-1})^{-1} = \mathbf{A}$. If $\mathbf{B}$ is the matrix of $h \in L(\mathsf{F}, n)$, we have (see I, 1, Exercise 15)† $(gh)^{-1} = h^{-1}g^{-1}$. Hence for nonsingular matrices

$$(\mathbf{AB})^{-1} = \mathbf{B}^{-1}\mathbf{A}^{-1}, \tag{5.21}$$

and if $\mathbf{A} = \mathbf{B}$, it follows, by induction, that for any positive integer k

$$(\mathbf{A}^k)^{-1} = (\mathbf{A}^{-1})^k. \tag{5.22}$$

We can therefore write $\mathbf{A}^{-k}$ for either $(\mathbf{A}^k)^{-1}$ or $(\mathbf{A}^{-1})^k$.

From (5.20) and Theorem 4.2 we have

$$\det(\mathbf{A}^{-1}) = (\det \mathbf{A})^{-1} \tag{5.23}$$

From (5.19), $\mathbf{A}^a = (\det \mathbf{A})\mathbf{A}^{-1}$; hence $(\mathbf{A}^a)^a = (\det \mathbf{A}^a)(\mathbf{A}^a)^{-1}$. But from (5.17), $(\mathbf{A}^a)^{-1} = (1/\det \mathbf{A})\mathbf{A}$. Taking this together with (5.18), we obtain that for nonsingular matrices

$$(\mathbf{A}^a)^a = (\det \mathbf{A})^{n-2}\mathbf{A}, \tag{5.24}$$

so that *the cofactors in the matrix of cofactors are proportional to the original elements.*

For any $m \times n$ matrix (5.1), we denote by $\mathbf{A}^T$ the matrix obtained by interchanging rows and columns:

$$(\mathbf{A}^T)_{ij} = a_{ji} = (\mathbf{A})_{ji}. \tag{5.25}$$

We call $\mathbf{A}^T$ the *transpose* of $\mathbf{A}$. Clearly $(\mathbf{A}^T)^T = \mathbf{A}$. To find the transpose of a product $(\mathbf{AB})^T$, we write

$$\begin{aligned}((\mathbf{AB})^T)_{ij} &= (\mathbf{AB})_{ji} \\ &= \sum_k a_{jk} b_{ki} = \sum_k b_{ki} a_{jk} \\ &= \sum_k (\mathbf{B}^T)_{ik}(\mathbf{A}^T)_{kj} = (\mathbf{B}^T\mathbf{A}^T)_{ij}.\end{aligned}$$

Hence

$$(\mathbf{AB})^T = \mathbf{B}^T\mathbf{A}^T, \tag{5.26}$$

† In this reference the Roman numeral denotes the chapter, and the Arabic numeral the section. We shall frequently use this style of reference. However, the chapter designation is often omitted in references to the chapter at hand.

and it follows, by induction, that the transpose of the product of a finite number of matrices is the product of their transposes taken in the reverse order.

We define the *rank* of a matrix (5.1) as follows: If in **A** we delete any $m - p$ rows and any $n - p$ columns (where $1 \leqq p \leqq \min(m, n)$),† there remains a square array of order p; the determinant of such an array, we call a *minor* of **A** of order p. It is understood that the minors of order 1 are the elements a_{ij} themselves. It follows from the properties of determinants that if all minors of some specified order vanish, then all minors of higher order (if any exist) also vanish. If $\mathbf{A} \neq \mathbf{0}_{mn}$, the orders of nonvanishing minors of **A** vary over a finite set of consecutive integers, and there exists a largest integer in the set. We call this integer the *rank* of **A**; we denote it by $r(\mathbf{A})$, or simply r. If $\mathbf{A} = \mathbf{0}_{mn}$, the set of integers referred to above is empty; in this case we define the rank to be the integer 0: $r(\mathbf{0}_{mn}) = 0$. Clearly, $r(\mathbf{A}) = 0$ implies that **A** is a zero matrix. If $r(\mathbf{A}) \neq 0$, there exists a minor of **A** of order $r(\mathbf{A})$ which does not vanish, and every minor of greater order (if any exist) does vanish.

We shall be greatly concerned in later chapters with systems of homogeneous linear equations, and although our major concern will be with equations in two or three unknowns, there is an advantage to be gained both in generality and in simplicity in developing the general theory. But here as in Section 4 we have taken account of the student who prefers to pursue his study of geometry with minimum interruption. Such a student should write out equations (5.27a, b) for the cases $n = 2$ and 3 and study the text material through Theorem 5.1, and the concepts of rank and independence that follow it, for these two values of n. From there, he can omit the text material entirely. The problems at the end of this section deal only with the cases $n = 2$ and $n = 3$, and they have been arranged to furnish the student with the theory needed later in this book.

A system of m homogeneous linear equations in n unknowns is a system that can be written, with the summation notation, as

$$\sum_{j=1}^{n} a_{ij} x_j = 0, \qquad i = 1, 2, \ldots, m. \tag{5.27a}$$

The a's are to be regarded as given elements belonging to a field F.‡ If we use the $m \times n$ matrix **A** given by (5.1) and the $n \times 1$ matrix **X** given in (5.8), we can write (5.27a) in matrix notation as

$$\mathbf{AX} = \mathbf{0}_{m1}. \tag{5.27b}$$

† If $m = n$, $\min(m, n) = m$; otherwise $\min(m, n)$ is the smaller of m and n.

‡ Here, as in Section 4, we could forego the restriction on F that it not be of characteristic 2.

From the point of view of (5.27a), a solution is an ordered set of n elements of F that satisfy (5.27a); from the point of view of (5.27b), a solution is a column matrix. We shall generally use the latter point of view.

Throughout the rest of this section we shall use the symbols $\mathbf{X}, \mathbf{Y}, \mathbf{Z}, \mathbf{Y}_i$, to represent $n \times 1$ matrices, such as are given by (5.8). If such a matrix $\mathbf{Y}$ is a solution of (5.27b), we have $\mathbf{AY} = \mathbf{0}_{m1}$. It then follows by (5.6) and (5.11b) that for all $k \in F$, $\mathbf{A}(k\mathbf{Y}) = k(\mathbf{AY}) = \mathbf{0}_{m1}$, and therefore $k\mathbf{Y}$ is also a solution of (5.27). If $\mathbf{Z}$ is another solution, $\mathbf{AZ} = \mathbf{0}_{m1}$. Hence $\mathbf{A}(\mathbf{Y} + \mathbf{Z}) = \mathbf{AY} + \mathbf{AZ} = \mathbf{0}_{m1}$, and $\mathbf{Y} + \mathbf{Z}$ is another solution. Thus we have proved a basic theorem.

THEOREM 5.1. *Any scalar multiple of a solution of* (5.27) *is a solution; the sum of any two solutions is a solution.*

By combining these operations, we obtain from a given set of solutions $\mathbf{Y}_1, \mathbf{Y}_2, \ldots, \mathbf{Y}_p$ a solution $\mathbf{Y} = k_1\mathbf{Y}_1 + k_2\mathbf{Y}_2 + \ldots + k_p\mathbf{Y}_p$, for any choice of the scalar multipliers k_i in F. We say that the solution $\mathbf{Y}$ is *linearly dependent on*, or *a linear combination of*, the solutions $\mathbf{Y}_1, \ldots, \mathbf{Y}_p$. Because we can *generate* more solutions from a given set of solutions, it suffices for many purposes to find the smallest set that generates all solutions, if such a set exists. We shall find it convenient to form a *matrix of solutions*; a matrix of solutions of order $n \times p$ is a matrix each of whose p columns regarded as an $n \times 1$ matrix is a solution.

We mean by the *rank* of a system (5.27) the rank of the matrix of coefficients; clearly the rank of (5.27) is unchanged when the order of the unknowns $x_1, x_2, \ldots, x_n$ or the order of enumeration of the equations in (5.27a) is changed. Similarly, we mean by the *rank* of a set of solutions of (5.27) the rank of their matrix. We shall say that a set of equations, or a set of solutions, is an *independent set* if the number of equations, or the number of solutions, in the set is equal to its rank.

If the rank of a matrix is its row order, no row can be a linear combination of other rows, because a determinant in which one row is a linear combination of other rows must vanish. Therefore in an independent set of equations, no equation is a linear combination of other equations of the set. Similarly, in an independent set of solutions, no solution is a linear combination of the other solutions. Although $\mathbf{X} = \mathbf{0}_{n1}$ is a solution of (5.27) regardless of the choice of $\mathbf{A}$, an independent set of one or more solutions cannot contain the solution $\mathbf{0}_{n1}$. We shall refer to $\mathbf{0}_{n1}$ as the trivial solution.

THEOREM 5.2. *If the rank of a system* (5.27) *is r, it contains an independent set of r equations; the remaining equations are linear combinations of these r equations.*

Proof. Since the rank is r, there exists a minor of $\mathbf{A}$ of order r which is not zero. Let us first suppose that this minor contains the first r rows and first r columns of $\mathbf{A}$, so that

$$(5.28)\qquad \begin{vmatrix} a_{11} & a_{12} & \dots & a_{1r} \\ a_{21} & a_{22} & \dots & a_{2r} \\ \dots & \dots & \dots & \dots \\ a_{r1} & a_{r2} & \dots & a_{rr} \end{vmatrix} \neq 0.$$

For simplicity, let

$$(5.29)\qquad a_1 x_1 + a_2 x_2 + \dots + a_n x_n = 0$$

represent an arbitrary one of the last $n-r$ equations. (5.29) is a linear combination of the first r equations if and only if we can find multipliers $k_1, k_2, \dots, k_r$ such that

$$(5.30)\qquad a_i = k_1 a_{1i} + k_2 a_{2i} + \dots + k_r a_{ri}, \qquad i = 1, 2, \dots, n.$$

These equations in the unknown k's are nonhomogeneous, and the first r of them have, by (5.28), a nonvanishing determinant; hence $k_1, k_2, \dots k_r$ are determined uniquely by (5.30) for $i = 1, 2, \dots, r$. Do the values of k so determined satisfy (5.30) for $i = r+1, \dots, n$? Yes, by virtue of the theorem stated in (I, 4, Exercise 14); the determinant formed from the $r+1$ equations (5.30) for which $i = 1, 2, \dots, r$ and any other value is a minor of $\mathbf{A}$ of order $r+1$ and hence vanishes. Thus the solution of (5.30) for $i = 1, 2, \dots, r$ satisfies each of the remaining equations, and our theorem is proved in the special case when (5.28) holds.

If the nonvanishing minor of $\mathbf{A}$ of order r is not in the upper left corner, we can rewrite (5.27) by permuting the equations, and by permuting $x_1, x_2, \dots, x_n$ so that for the new ordering we have a system satisfying (5.28). Then our conclusion is valid for the newly ordered system, and we can return to our original ordering without violating the conclusion.

THEOREM 5.3. *A system* (5.27) *of rank r possesses an independent set of n − r solutions.*†

Proof. Using the device employed at the end of the proof of Theorem 5.2, we can suppose that (5.28) holds, and that (5.27) is equivalent to the system

$$(5.31)\qquad \sum_{j=1}^{n} a_{ij} x_j = 0, \qquad i = 1, 2, \dots, r.$$

Then we can assign arbitrary values to $x_{r+1}, x_{r+2}, \dots, x_n$, and for each such choice of values (5.31) becomes a system of r equations in the r unknowns $x_1, x_2, \dots, x_r$ with nonvanishing determinant; hence each set of

† It is customary to regard an empty set of solutions as independent, and in this sense the theorem holds for $r = n$.

values $x_{r+1}, x_{r+2}, \ldots, x_n$ determines uniquely the set $x_1, x_2, \ldots, x_r$ such that $(x_1, x_2, \ldots, x_n)$ is a solution† of (5.31). Let us now denote by $\mathbf{Y}_\sigma$ ($\sigma = 1, 2, \ldots, p$, where $p = n - r$) the p particular solutions which have zero in all but one of the last p rows, the $(r + \sigma)^{\text{th}}$ row being equal to 1. Then this solution matrix can be written:

$$(5.32) \qquad (\mathbf{Y}_1 \quad \mathbf{Y}_2 \quad \ldots \quad \mathbf{Y}_p) = \begin{pmatrix} * & * & \cdots & * \\ \vdots & \vdots & & \vdots \\ * & * & \cdots & * \\ 1 & 0 & \ldots & 0 \\ 0 & 1 & \ldots & 0 \\ \vdots & \vdots & & \vdots \\ 0 & 0 & \ldots & 1 \end{pmatrix},$$

where the last $n - r$ rows of (5.32) form the unit matrix of order $n - r$, and the actual values of the elements in the first r rows need not concern us. The minor of (5.32) determined by its last $n - r$ rows is not zero, and the set of $n - r$ $\mathbf{Y}$'s is a solution set of rank $n - r$.

LEMMA 5.1. *Every solution of* (5.27) *is a linear combination of the solutions* (5.32) *exhibited in Theorem* 5.3.‡

Proof. Let $\mathbf{Y} = (y_1, y_2, \ldots, y_n)^T$ be any solution of (5.27), and construct the solution $\mathbf{Z}$ given by

$$(5.33) \qquad \mathbf{Z} = \mathbf{Y} - \sum_{\sigma=1}^{n-r} y_{r+\sigma} \mathbf{Y}_\sigma,$$

where $\mathbf{Y}_\sigma$ are the solutions (5.32). Then

$$\mathbf{Z} = (z_1, z_2, \ldots, z_r, 0, 0, \ldots, 0)^T,$$

where the values of $z_1, z_2, \ldots, z_r$ are momentarily unknown. But $\mathbf{Z}$ is a solution of the equivalent system (5.31), and we find by substitution therein that

$$\sum_{j=1}^{r} a_{ij} z_j = 0, \qquad i = 1, 2, \ldots, r.$$

Since (5.28) holds, we must have $z_1 = z_2 = \ldots = z_r = 0$, so that $\mathbf{Z} = \mathbf{0}_{n1}$. From (5.33) we have that $\mathbf{Y}$ is a linear combination of $\mathbf{Y}_1, \mathbf{Y}_2, \ldots, \mathbf{Y}_p$, and the lemma is proved.

† A solution of (5.27a) or (5.31) is an ordered set of elements of F, and we write such a set $(x_1, x_2, \ldots, x_n)$. But a solution of (5.27b) is a column matrix and although $\mathbf{X} = (x_1 \ x_2 \ \ldots \ x_n)^T$ without commas is the more consistent notation, we shall find it convenient to introduce commas to set off the elements of the column matrix and thus write $\mathbf{X} = (x_1, x_2, \ldots, x_n)^T$.

‡ If $r = n$, there is no solution set given by Theorem 5.3, and in this case we interpret the lemma as asserting that (5.27) possesses no solution other than the trivial one $\mathbf{0}_{n1}$.

We next shall show how to construct other independent sets of solutions, and prove that all solutions are linear combinations of any independent set of $n - r$ solutions.

Let $\mathbf{Z}_1, \mathbf{Z}_2, \ldots, \mathbf{Z}_p$ be any set of $p = n - r$ solutions. By the lemma each of these solutions is a linear combination of the solutions (5.32),

$$\mathbf{Z}_\sigma = \sum_{\tau=1}^{p} \mathbf{Y}_\tau k_{\tau\sigma}, \qquad \sigma = 1, 2, \ldots, p; \tag{5.34}$$

if for convenience we let $\mathbf{Y}_\sigma = (y_{1\sigma}, y_{2\sigma}, \ldots, y_{n\sigma})^T$ and $\mathbf{Z}_\sigma = (z_{1\sigma}, z_{2\sigma}, \ldots, z_{n\sigma})^T$, (5.34) becomes

$$z_{i\sigma} = \sum_{\tau=1}^{p} y_{i\tau} k_{\tau\sigma}, \qquad i = 1, 2, \ldots, n; \quad \sigma = 1, 2, \ldots, p. \tag{5.35}$$

In matrix notation, (5.35) can be written

$$(\mathbf{Z}_1 \quad \mathbf{Z}_2 \quad \ldots \quad \mathbf{Z}_p) = (\mathbf{Y}_1 \quad \mathbf{Y}_2 \quad \ldots \quad \mathbf{Y}_p)\mathbf{K}, \tag{5.36}$$

where $(\mathbf{K})_{\tau\sigma} = k_{\tau\sigma}$. A minor of $(\mathbf{Z}_1 \quad \mathbf{Z}_2 \quad \ldots \quad \mathbf{Z}_p)$ of order p is the determinant whose elements are $z_{i\sigma}$ where $\sigma = 1, 2, \ldots, p$, and i ranges over any set of p distinct integers of the set $1, 2, \ldots, n$. From (5.35) and Theorem 4.2, it follows that the minors of order p of $(\mathbf{Z}_1 \quad \ldots \quad \mathbf{Z}_p)$ are obtained from the corresponding minors of $(\mathbf{Y}_1 \quad \ldots \quad \mathbf{Y}_p)$ by multiplying the latter by det $\mathbf{K}$. The solution matrix (5.32) has already been proved to be of rank $p = n - r$. Then if $(\mathbf{Z}_1 \quad \ldots \quad \mathbf{Z}_p)$ is also of rank $p = n - r$, we must have det $\mathbf{K} \neq 0$. Conversely, if det $\mathbf{K} \neq 0$, $(\mathbf{Z}_1 \quad \ldots \quad \mathbf{Z}_p)$ possesses a nonvanishing minor of order p, and therefore is of rank $p = n - r$.

If det $\mathbf{K} \neq 0$, $\mathbf{K}^{-1}$ exists, and from (5.36) we obtain that

$$(\mathbf{Z}_1 \quad \mathbf{Z}_2 \quad \ldots \quad \mathbf{Z}_p)\mathbf{K}^{-1} = (\mathbf{Y}_1 \quad \mathbf{Y}_2 \quad \ldots \quad \mathbf{Y}_p). \tag{5.37}$$

These equations assert that the solutions $\mathbf{Y}_\sigma$ are linear combinations of $\mathbf{Z}_1, \mathbf{Z}_2, \ldots, \mathbf{Z}_p$; using the lemma, we see that every solution of (5.27) is a linear combination of a given independent set of $p = n - r$ solutions. Finally, we could repeat the derivation of (5.36) and the discussion following it for any two independent sets of $n - r$ solutions. Thus we have proved the following theorem.

THEOREM 5.4. *If the rank of* (5.27) *is* r, *the set of all solutions of* (5.27) *is the set of all linear combinations of the solutions of an independent set of* $n - r$ *solutions. If* $(\mathbf{Y}_1 \quad \mathbf{Y}_2 \quad \ldots \quad \mathbf{Y}_{n-r})$ *is the matrix of any independent set of* $n - r$ *solutions, the matrix of any other independent set of* $n - r$ *solutions is found by, and only by, multiplying* $(\mathbf{Y}_1 \quad \mathbf{Y}_2 \quad \ldots \quad \mathbf{Y}_{n-r})$ *on the right by a nonsingular matrix of order* $n - r$.

We shall need two further theorems.

THEOREM 5.5. *If the rank of a system of linear equations is* r, *the rank of a set of solutions cannot exceed* $n - r$.

Proof. Consider a solution matrix $(\mathbf{Z}_1 \quad \mathbf{Z}_2 \quad \ldots \quad \mathbf{Z}_k)$; if $k \leqq n - r$, there is nothing to prove. Let us suppose that $k = n - r + 1$. If there exists a minor of order $k - 1 = n - r$ that does not vanish, $k - 1$ of the solutions are independent, and one of the columns is, by Theorem 5.4, a linear combination of the remaining columns. Hence the rank of $(\mathbf{Z}_1 \quad \mathbf{Z}_2 \quad \ldots \quad \mathbf{Z}_k)$ in this case can not exceed $n - r$. If all minors of order $k - 1$ vanish, there is nothing to prove. Finally, if $k > n - r + 1$, it follows by the preceding argument that every minor of order $n - r + 1$ must vanish.

The relationship between the coefficients of (5.27) and its solutions is reciprocal. If $\mathbf{B}$ is any matrix of order $n \times m$, the columns of $\mathbf{B}$ are solutions of an equation

$$a_1 x_1 + a_2 x_2 + \ldots + a_n x_n = 0$$

if and only if the row matrix $\mathbf{U} = (a_1, a_2, \ldots, a_n)$ is a solution of

$$\mathbf{UB} = \mathbf{0}_{1m}. \tag{5.38}$$

Since $(\mathbf{UB})^T = \mathbf{B}^T\mathbf{U}^T$, (5.38) is equivalent to

$$\mathbf{B}^T\mathbf{U}^T = \mathbf{0}_{m1}. \tag{5.39}$$

We can apply our preceding theory; Theorem 5.4 gives us the following new theorem.

THEOREM 5.6. *If* $\mathbf{B}$ *is a matrix of order* $n \times m$ *and rank* p, *there exist independent sets of* $r = n - p$ *equations of which the columns of* $\mathbf{B}$ *are solutions. One such independent set of* r *equations is obtained from another by, and only by, left multiplication by a nonsingular matrix. Any equation satisfied by the columns of* $\mathbf{B}$ *is a linear combination of the* r *equations of an independent set.*

EXERCISES

1. Let $\mathbf{A}$, $\mathbf{B}$, $\mathbf{C}$, $\mathbf{D}$ be the matrices over the real field R,

$$\mathbf{A} = \begin{pmatrix} 2 & 3 \\ 4 & 1 \end{pmatrix}, \quad \mathbf{B} = \begin{pmatrix} 1 & 1 \\ 2 & 2 \end{pmatrix}, \quad \mathbf{C} = \begin{pmatrix} 1 & 0 \\ 1 & -1 \end{pmatrix}, \quad \mathbf{D} = \begin{pmatrix} 1 & 2 \\ 2 & 4 \end{pmatrix}.$$

Find $\mathbf{AB}$, $\mathbf{BA}$, $\mathbf{AC}$, $\mathbf{A}^a$, $\mathbf{B}^a$, $\mathbf{C}^T$; determine the rank of $\mathbf{A}$, $\mathbf{B}$, $\mathbf{C}$, and $\mathbf{D}$, and the inverses when they exist.

2. Let each of the matrices of Exercise 1 be regarded as the coefficient matrix of a system of homogeneous linear equations; verify, for each system, Theorems 5.2 and 5.3, and Lemma 5.1.

3. Let a, b, c, d be any four real numbers; find all solutions (x_1, x_2) of $ax_1 + bx_2 = 0$, $cx_1 + dx_2 = 0$ without reference to the theorems of the text. Treat all essential cases, and show that your conclusions are those of the text for $n = 2$.

***4.** Let **Y** and **Z** be two independent column matrices of order 2; show that every column matrix of order 2 is expressible as a linear combination of **Y** and **Z**.

5. Repeat Exercise 1 for the matrices **A**, **B**, **C**, **D** (over R) given by

$$\begin{pmatrix} 1 & 2 & 3 \\ 2 & 1 & 1 \\ 1 & -4 & 7 \end{pmatrix}, \quad \begin{pmatrix} 1 & 1 & 1 \\ 2 & 1 & -1 \\ 3 & 2 & 1 \end{pmatrix}, \quad \begin{pmatrix} 1 & 2 & -1 \\ 2 & 4 & -2 \\ -1 & -2 & 1 \end{pmatrix}, \quad \begin{pmatrix} 1 & -1 \\ 0 & 0 \\ 1 & 2 \end{pmatrix},$$

respectively.

6. Repeat Exercise 2 for the matrices of Exercise 5.

7. Find all possible coefficients of a linear equation in three variables that has $(1, -1, 2)$ as a solution; show that all can be expressed as linear combinations of two particular ones. Will any two do?

8. Solve the equation $\mathbf{X}' = \mathbf{BX}$ for **X**, where **X** is a column matrix and **B** is the matrix of Exercise 5.

9. Verify (5.24) for the matrix **B** of Exercise 5.

10. If a system of one or more equations has the columns of the matrix **A** of Exercise 5 as solutions, determine the coefficients of the equations. Repeat by replacing **A** in turn by **B**, **C**, and **D**. Verify in these cases that the number of independent equations in the system is 3 decreased by the rank of the matrix.

***11.** Prove without reference to the theorems of the text that if $a_1 x_1 + a_2 x_2 + a_3 x_3 = 0$, $b_1 x_1 + b_2 x_2 + b_3 x_3 = 0$ are two independent equations every solution is a scalar multiple of the particular solution $(a_2 b_3 - a_3 b_2, a_3 b_1 - a_1 b_3, a_1 b_2 - a_2 b_1)$. Note the relation of this solution to the minors of order 2 of the matrix of coefficients of the given equations.

***12.** If $\mathbf{Y} = (y_1, y_2, y_3)^T$, $\mathbf{Z} = (z_1, z_2, z_3)^T$ are two independent column matrices, find the coefficient of all nontrivial equations that have $(\mathbf{Y} \;\; \mathbf{Z})$ as a solution matrix by using the theorem stated in Exercise 11. Is the restriction "nontrivial" needed?

***13.** Prove that the determinant of any three solutions of a nontrivial homogeneous linear equation in three unknowns must vanish. Of what theorem stated in the text is this a special case?

***14.** Prove that three homogeneous linear equations in three unknowns have a nontrivial solution if and only if the determinant of their coefficients vanishes.

15. Show that if a 3×3 matrix has rank 2, one of its rows is a linear combination of the other two rows, and one of its columns is a linear combination of the other two columns.

***16.** Show that every homogeneous linear equation in three unknowns which is satisfied by a solution of two independent equations must be a linear combination of those two equations. Is the restriction imposed by *independent* essential?

17. Three solutions of $a_1 x_1 + a_2 x_2 + a_3 x_3 = 0$ are $(0, a_3, -a_2)$, $(-a_3, 0, a_1)$, and $(a_2, -a_1, 0)$. Show that if each $a_i \neq 0$, each of these solutions is a linear combination of the other two.

***18.** Prove that every solution of a single linear equation in three variables is a linear combination of any two independent solutions (see Exercise 17).

***19.** Prove that the solution sets of each of two linear homogeneous equations in three variables are identical if and only if the coefficients of either are nonzero multiples of the coefficients of the other.

#****20.** Let $\mathbf{A}, \mathbf{B}$ be $n \times n$ matrices, with $r(\mathbf{A}) = n$. Prove that $r(\mathbf{B}) = r(\mathbf{AB}) = r(\mathbf{BA})$. (*Hint*: consider the solution set of each of the systems $\mathbf{BX} = 0$, $\mathbf{ABX} = 0$, etc.)

21. Prove that G_6 is a group by writing (2.6) in the form $\mathbf{X}' = \mathbf{AX} + \mathbf{B}$, where $\mathbf{A}$ is a 2×2 matrix, and $\mathbf{B}$, $\mathbf{X}$, and $\mathbf{X}'$ are column matrices.

22. Evaluate

$$\begin{pmatrix} \cos\theta & -\sin\theta \\ \sin\theta & \cos\theta \end{pmatrix} \begin{pmatrix} \cos\phi & -\sin\phi \\ \sin\phi & \cos\phi \end{pmatrix},$$

and use this to prove with matrix notation that M is a group.

6 The Group of Motions

In 1872, Felix Klein in his Erlangen Programm first formulated the idea that a geometry can be characterized by a group of transformations, and that the definitions and theorems of the geometry are simply the invariants, invariant properties, and invariant relations under the group. Before this time, many different geometries had been invented, but their inventors had usually characterized them by the different sets of axioms or postulates with which they had started.

Klein's point of view brought a new clarity to the relationships between different geometries. Since the essential thing is the group of transformations, and not the objects transformed, two sets of objects which are transformed by the same group are essentially the same. Further, the geometry of a given group will possess a well-defined relationship to the geometries of its subgroups by which we can translate the more general results into the more particular.

In this book we shall adopt Klein's point of view, and our main concern will be to develop projective geometry as the geometry of the projective group. We have not so far mentioned the projective group of two dimensions; it is a group of which both the affine group and therefore the group of direct motions are subgroups, and we shall see that there exists a close relationship between the geometry of the projective plane and that of the

Euclidean plane. But for the present we wish to suggest how a geometry can be developed from a group of transformations, and we shall illustrate such a development by sketching the development of Euclidean geometry from this point of view.

The underlying group of Euclidean geometry contains, besides the group of direct motions M, given by (2.13), *reflections* in lines. The reflection, in the line $y = 0$, is the transformation

$$x' = x, \qquad y' = -y. \tag{6.1}$$

In this section, we shall denote this transformation by μ. Let us denote by $M\mu$ the set of all maps $m\mu$, for $m \in M$,

$$M\mu = \{g \mid g = m\mu, m \in M\}, \tag{6.2a}$$

and by M^* the set of all maps which belong to at least one of the sets M or $M\mu$,†

$$M^* = M \cup M\mu \tag{6.2b}$$

Thus an element in M^* is either a direct motion or the product map obtained by following the reflection μ by a direct motion. Since $\mu^2 = I$, $m^* \in M\mu$ implies that $m^*\mu \in M$; conversely, if m^* is a map such that $m^*\mu \in M$, it follows that $m^* \in M\mu$, and therefore $m^* \in M^*$. If M is represented by (2.13), $M\mu$ is represented by

$$x' = x \cos\theta + y \sin\theta + e, \qquad y' = x \sin\theta - y \cos\theta + f. \tag{6.3}$$

Hence (2.13) and (6.3) together represent, for variable e, f, θ, the set M^*.

LEMMA 6.1. *If $m \in M$, then $\mu m \mu \in M$, and $\mu m \in M^*$.*

Proof. From (6.3) we find that $\mu m \mu$ is given by

$$x' = x \cos\theta + y \sin\theta + e, \qquad y' = -x \sin\theta + y \cos\theta - f. \tag{6.4}$$

Hence $(\mu m)\mu \in M$, and therefore $\mu m \in M^*$.

THEOREM 6.1. *M^* is a group.*

Proof. An element of M^* which lies in M has an inverse in M (because M is a group), and it surely is contained in M^*. An element of M^* of the form $m\mu$, where $m \in M$, possesses an inverse μm^{-1} which, by Lemma 6.1, is in M^*. Hence every element in M^* possesses an inverse which lies in M^*. To prove that M^* satisfies the second requirement for a group, we need to consider separately the four types of products:

$$m_1 m_2, \qquad m_1(m_2 \mu), \qquad (m_1 \mu)m_2, \qquad (m_1 \mu)(m_2 \mu), \qquad m_1, m_2 \in M.$$

† The symbol $\cup$ is called the symbol of union. The union of two sets is the set consisting of those elements which belong to either set or to both.

The fourth of these is in M, and therefore in M^*, by virtue of the associative law and Lemma 6.1,

$$(m_1 \mu)(m_2 \mu) = m_1(\mu m_2 \mu).$$

The other three products can be analyzed similarly, and in all cases we can show that the product of two elements in M^* lies in M^*.

Although M^* was constructed by the adjunction of just one reflection, it will be seen later in this section that M^* contains all reflections.

It is the group M^* rather than M that we use in a formal definition of the Euclidean plane.

AXIOM 6.1. *There exists a set of objects in one-to-one correspondence with ordered pairs of real numbers.*

DEFINITION 6.1. We call these objects *points*. If P is a point, and if $(x(P), y(P))$ denotes the ordered pair of real numbers corresponding to P, we call $x = x(P)$, $y = y(P)$ the (Cartesian) coordinates of P. The correspondence between points and ordered pairs of real numbers is called the (postulated) *coordinate system.*

AXIOM 6.2. *There exists a group of one-to-one maps of the given set of points onto itself, and these maps can be represented, in terms of the postulated coordinate system, by equations* (2.13) *and* (6.3) *of* M^*:

$$(6.5) \qquad x' = x \cos \theta \pm y \sin \theta + e, \qquad y' = x \sin \theta \mp y \cos \theta + f.$$

DEFINITION 6.2. A set of points satisfying Axioms 6.1 and 6.2 is called a *Euclidean plane*; its invariant theory under the group of Axiom 6.2 is called *Euclidean metric geometry.*

Notation. We henceforth use E_2 and M^* to refer to the plane (and point set) and to the group of the axioms and definitions just stated; we use M to denote the subgroup of M^* that can be represented by (2.13).

DEFINITION 6.3. The maps of M^* are called *motions.* A motion given by (2.13) is called *direct*; otherwise it is called *opposite.*

THEOREM 6.2. *Let* $m_1, m_2, \ldots, m_n$ *be any* n *motions of which* k *are opposite and* $n-k$ *direct; the product motion* $m = m_1 m_2 \ldots m_n$ *is direct if* k *is an even integer, and opposite if* k *is an odd integer.*

Proof. The theorem is trivially true for $n = 1$, and is an immediate consequence of Lemma 6.1 for $n = 2$. We can now prove the theorem by induction by considering $m = (m_1 m_2 \ldots m_{n-1})m_n$. We leave the details to be filled in by the reader.

DEFINITION 6.4. Two point sets $\mathscr{C}$ and $\mathscr{D}$ are said to be *congruent* if there exists $m \in M^*$ such that $\mathscr{C} = m\mathscr{D}$; $\mathscr{C}$ and $\mathscr{D}$ are said to be *directly congruent* if there exists $m \in M$ such that $\mathscr{C} = m\mathscr{D}$.

The reader should note that the unsymmetrical form of these two definitions is justified by the group properties of M and M^*. Indeed, congruence is an equivalence relation.

We make the following observation: *The processes of algebra and analysis are completely independent of geometry.* The proof of this statement belongs to books on algebra and analysis. Let us note here that many definitions and theorems in elementary textbooks which make use of geometric ideas do so as a matter of convenience, and not of necessity. In particular, trigonometric functions can be defined by means of their power series, and their properties and relations derived from such definitions. The coefficients in (6.5) do not depend on the Euclidean concept of angle; (6.5) is simply an affine transformation (2.10) for which $a^2 + c^2 = 1, d = \pm a$, $b = \mp c$.

In Section 3, we proved several theorems concerning invariants and invariant properties and relations. These theorems were generally stated in geometrical language, but the proofs involved only algebraic processes, so that the relevant theorems are valid in the present context. Let us note also that M^* is a subgroup of the affine group, so that any invariants under G_6 are invariants under M^*. It is a simple matter to verify that the set of two transformations μ and I is a group. For simplicity, we shall refer to invariants under this group as invariants under μ. We note also that this group is a subgroup of L and of G_6, so that invariants under these groups are invariants under μ.

Since the geometry of Definition 6.2 is the invariant theory of E_2 under M^*, we can formulate geometric concepts only in terms of definitions that employ the various types of invariants. One of the simplest of loci is a point set consisting of all points whose coordinates satisfy a linear equation. The class of all such loci is an invariant space under M^* (see Theorems 3.3 and 3.5). We are therefore justified in making the following definition.

DEFINITION 6.5. A *line* is the set of points whose coordinates satisfy a linear equation

$$Ax + By + C = 0, \tag{6.6}$$

where A, B, C are any real numbers such that A and B are not both zero.

Clearly the locus of (6.6) coincides with that of the equation $\rho Ax + \rho By + \rho C = 0$ $(\rho \neq 0)$; from the properties of linear equations, it follows that if two lines coincide, the coefficients in their equations are proportional.

THEOREM 6.3. *Any two lines are directly congruent.*

Proof. If $Ax + By + C = 0$ is the equation of a given line, the transformation

$$x' = \frac{B}{\sqrt{A^2 + B^2}} x - \frac{A}{\sqrt{A^2 + B^2}} y + \frac{C}{\sqrt{A^2 + B^2}},$$

$$y' = \frac{A}{\sqrt{A^2 + B^2}} x + \frac{B}{\sqrt{A^2 + B^2}} y + \frac{C}{\sqrt{A^2 + B^2}}$$

belongs to M; it maps the given line onto the line $y = 0$. If p_1 and p_2 are any two lines, and if m_1 and m_2 are direct motions which map p_1 and p_2, respectively, onto the line $y = 0$, the transformation $m_2^{-1}m_1$ exists and is a direct motion; clearly it maps p_1 onto p_2.

In the context of Axioms 6.1 and 6.2 and Definition 6.5, equations (3.6) and (3.19) can be regarded as defining *distance between points* and *distance between a point and a line*; to justify these definitions, it suffices, in view of Theorems 3.2 and 3.6, to show that $d(P, Q) = d(\mu P, \mu Q)$, and $D(P, p) = D(\mu P, \mu p)$. We leave the proof to the reader.

THEOREM 6.4. *Let p_1 and p_2 be two arbitrary lines with equations given by*

$$p_1\colon \quad A_1 x + B_1 y + C_1 = 0,$$
$$p_2\colon \quad A_2 x + B_2 y + C_2 = 0.$$

Then

(a) *the vanishing of $A_1 B_2 - A_2 B_1$, and*

(b) *the vanishing of $A_1 A_2 + B_1 B_2$*

are invariant properties, and

(c) $\left| \dfrac{A_1 B_2 - A_2 B_1}{A_1 A_2 + B_1 B_2} \right|$

is an invariant of the two lines under the group M^*.

The proof of (a) is contained in the proof of Theorem 3.7; that of (b) is similar, but (b) does not hold for the affine group. To prove (c), we take note of equations (3.17). We leave the details to the reader.

By means of Theorem 6.4, we can define parallel and perpendicular lines and derive their familiar properties. The invariant of part (c) of Theorem 6.4 could be used to define the (acute) angle between two lines. But neither such a definition of angle, nor our definition of D is satisfactory for the study of Euclidean geometry. Such intuitive concepts as a directed line, directed angle, directed distance, the two senses of rotation of the plane, and many others need careful logical analysis and precise mathematical formulation. In the main, we shall do this in Chapter V, where we relate these problems to similar problems in the projective plane. But the logical existence of the

Euclidean plane is independent of that of other planes, and it is worthwhile to develop the concept of a directed line with our present tools.

If $P_0:(x_0, y_0)$ is a point on the line p with equation (6.6), then

$$Ax_0 + By_0 + C = 0,$$

and by subtraction from (6.6) we obtain that

$$A(x - x_0) + B(y - y_0) = 0. \tag{6.7}$$

The conditions

$$\sin \omega = \frac{A}{\sqrt{A^2 + B^2}}, \qquad \cos \omega = \frac{-B}{\sqrt{A^2 + B^2}}, \qquad 0 \leqq \omega < 2\pi,$$

determine uniquely a real number ω, and it follows that the equations

$$x = x_0 + s \cos \omega, \qquad y = y_0 + s \sin \omega \tag{6.8a}$$

constitute *parametric equations* of the given line p. A line possesses infinitely many parametrizations of the type (6.8a) which can be obtained either by replacing (x_0, y_0) by some other point of the line, or by replacing the coefficients A, B, C of (6.6) by ρA, ρB, ρC (we need consider only the possibility that $\rho < 0$, for $\rho > 0$ effects no change in (6.8a)). We can form two classes of parametrizations; one class consists of the parametrizations with the same ω but with all possible choices of (x_0, y_0). The second class consists of the parametrization

$$x = x_0 + s \cos \omega^*, \qquad y = y_0 + s \sin \omega^*, \tag{6.8b}$$

where

$$\omega^* = \omega + \pi \pmod{2\pi}, \tag{6.9}$$

together with the parametrizations obtained from (6.8b) by taking all possible choices for (x_0, y_0). We note that either class of parametrizations is determined by any one of its constituent members, so that (6.8a) can be regarded as representing an arbitrary one of the classes; then (6.8b) and (6.9) represent the other class. Note that $\omega = \omega^* + \pi \pmod{2\pi}$.

We find by direct substitution that an arbitrary motion $m \in M^*$ carries the parametrization (6.8a) into

$$x = x_0' + s \cos \omega', \qquad y = y_0' + s \sin \omega', \tag{6.10}$$

where $P_0':(x_0', y_0')$ is the map of $P_0:(x_0, y_0)$ under m, and where

$$\omega' = \omega + \theta \pmod{2\pi}, \quad \text{or} \quad \omega' = -\omega + \theta \pmod{2\pi}, \tag{6.11}$$

according as $m \in M$ or $m \notin M$. If (6.8a) is replaced by the other parametrizations of its class, (6.10) will run through *one* class of parametrizations of the transformed line. Hence a class of parametrizations is transformed by M^* into an object of the same kind. Thus the set of all classes of parametrizations of all lines is an invariant space under M^*.

DEFINITION 6.6. The class of parametrizations determined by (6.8a) is a *directed line.* We say that the directed line is *carried* by the given (undirected) line. We call ω the *direction angle* of the directed line.†

THEOREM 6.5. *An arbitrary line carries two directed lines; if a line p carries a directed line $\vec{p}$, mp carries $m(\vec{p})$ for all $m \in M^*$.*

The proof follows at once from the preceding discussion.

The reader should note that if a line p carries a directed line $\vec{p}$, and if $mp = p$ for some $m \in M$, it does not follow that $m(\vec{p}) = \vec{p}$, since m may interchange the two directed lines carried by p. For example, the rotation $x' = -x$, $y' = -y$ maps the x-axis directed "positively" onto the x-axis directed "negatively."

Each of the parametrizations (6.8a, b) establishes a one-to-one map from the points of the line p onto the field of real numbers. We call the variable s a *metric coordinate* on p, and the map from $P \in p$ to $s = s(P)$ a *metric coordinatization* of p. A metric coordinatization of a given line is determined by choice of origin (that is, of the point $P_0 \in p$ which corresponds to $s = 0$) and a choice of one of the two directed lines carried by the given line. If $s = s(P)$ and $s' = s'(P)$ are any two metric coordinates on p, there exist a real number k and a multiplier ε equal either to 1 or -1 such that

$$s'(P) = \varepsilon s(P) + k \qquad \text{for all } P \in p.$$

If s is the metric coordinate on p determined by origin P_0 and directed line $\vec{p}$, and if $\bar{s}$ is the metric coordinate on mp determined by mP_0 and $m\vec{p}$, it follows from (6.10) that $\bar{s}(mP) = s(P)$ for all $P \in p$, $m \in M^*$. Thus we have proved the following theorem:

THEOREM 6.6. *Metric coordinatizations of a line are preserved by all motions.*

DEFINITION 6.7. If s is a metric coordinate on a line p, and if $s_1 = s(P_1)$, $s_2 = s(P_2)$ for $P_1, P_2 \in p$, the difference $s_2 - s_1$ is called the *directed distance* from P_1 to P_2, for the chosen directed line.

Clearly the directed distance is independent of the choice of origin, it is an invariant under M^*, and $|s_2 - s_1| = d(P_1, P_2)$.

A definition of directed angle would lead us far afield. We note from (6.11) that $\omega_2 - \omega_1 \pmod{2\pi}$ is invariant under M, but not under M^*. In

† Each class of parametrizations determines an order relation on the points of the line: if $s(P) < s(Q)$ for one parametrization, the same inequality holds for all parametrizations of its class, and we can say that, by definition, P precedes Q on the directed line.

fact, the directed angle from one line to another is dependent on the orientability of E_2, and we shall discuss this in Chapter V.

In Axioms 6.1 and 6.2, we postulated one definite coordinate system in the plane. We would expect to show the existence of others that could have served equally in our axioms and in Definitions 6.1 and 6.2. This is indeed the case; we could derive the expected geometric characterization of our postulated coordinate system, and show that we can introduce others with analogous properties. But again, a careful analysis involves the two orientations of the plane, and at the present time we state the conclusion without proof.

THEOREM 6.7. *The transformations from one Cartesian coordinate system to another are given by equations* (6.5).

The remainder of this section will be devoted to a study of the transformations (6.5) themselves.

DEFINITION 6.8. A point is a *fixed point* of a transformation if it coincides with its transform.

Let us determine the fixed points of a direct motion m. From (2.13), $P:(x, y)$ is a fixed point of $m \in M$ if and only if x, y satisfy the equations

$$(6.12) \qquad \begin{aligned} (1 - \cos \theta)x + (\sin \theta)y &= e, \\ -(\sin \theta)x + (1 - \cos \theta)y &= f. \end{aligned}$$

There are two cases to be considered, according as the determinant

$$(6.13) \qquad \Delta = \begin{vmatrix} 1 - \cos \theta & \sin \theta \\ -\sin \theta & 1 - \cos \theta \end{vmatrix}$$

does or does not vanish.

Case I. $\Delta = 0$. From (6.13) we must have that

$$(1 - \cos \theta)^2 + \sin^2 \theta = 0,$$

or

$$(6.14) \qquad \cos \theta = 1.$$

In this case, equations (6.12) either possess no solution, or every pair (x, y) is a solution, that is, the transformation either has no fixed point, or every point is fixed, and the transformation is the identity. By means of (6.14), the equations of m become

$$(6.15) \qquad x' = x + e, \qquad y' = y + f.$$

We saw at the beginning of Section 2 that as e and f take on all real values, these transformations form a group, the group of translations.

Case II. $\Delta \neq 0$. Equations (6.12) possess a single solution. If we denote the solution by (x_1, y_1), we have that

$$x_1 = x_1 \cos\theta - y_1 \sin\theta + e,$$
$$y_1 = x_1 \sin\theta + y_1 \cos\theta + f. \tag{6.16}$$

Subtracting each of these equations from the corresponding equation of (2.13), we obtain

$$x' - x_1 = (x - x_1)\cos\theta - (y - y_1)\sin\theta,$$
$$y' - y_1 = (x - x_1)\sin\theta + (y - y_1)\cos\theta. \tag{6.17}$$

If we allow θ to take on all real values, including zero, while holding (x_1, y_1) fixed, the transformations (6.17) form an Abelian group, called the group of rotations about (x_1, y_1). Any directed line through (x_1, y_1) is transformed by a transformation of the group into a new directed line through (x_1, y_1), and one angle from the given directed line to its transform is the value of θ (mod 2π).

THEOREM 6.8. *Every direct motion is either a translation or a rotation about some point, and only the identity is both.*

The proof follows at once from the preceding discussion.

DEFINITION 6.9. If a given direct motion is a rotation, we call its fixed point the *center*, and the value of θ (mod 2π) its *angle*. A translation has no center; its angle is defined to be zero.

THEOREM 6.9. *The product of two direct motions is a direct motion whose angle is the sum* (mod 2π) *of the angles of the given motions.*

We leave the proof to the reader (Exercise 4 below).

THEOREM 6.10. *Every translation is expressible as the product of two rotations, one of which is arbitrary* (*but not the identity*).

Proof. Let τ be the given translation, and let σ be a given rotation, not the identity. Then the transformation m defined by

$$m = \sigma^{-1}\tau \tag{6.18}$$

is a direct motion. If we multiply (6.18) on the left by σ and remember that $\sigma(\sigma^{-1}\tau) = (\sigma\sigma^{-1})\,\tau = I\tau = \tau$, we obtain

$$\sigma m = \tau. \tag{6.19}$$

To complete the argument, we need only show that m is a rotation. From (6.19) and Theorem 6.9, the sum of the angles of σ and m is zero. Since σ is a rotation and $\sigma \neq I$, the angle of m is not zero. Hence m is a rotation, and (6.19) is one of the required factorizations. To show that the right factor can be preassigned, we write $m = \tau\sigma^{-1}$ in place of (6.18) and proceed similarly.

THEOREM 6.11. *If the transform of a single point P_0 under the product $m_1 m_2$ of two direct motions coincides with the transform of P_0 under $m_2 m_1$, then $m_1 m_2 = m_2 m_1$.*

Proof. Let $m = m_1 m_2$ and $m^* = m_2 m_1$; then by hypothesis

$$mP_0 = m^* P_0 .$$

We obtain by multiplying on the left by m^{*-1} that

$$m^{*-1} m P_0 = P_0, \tag{6.20}$$

so that $m^{*-1}m$ leaves P_0 fixed. Hence $m^{*-1}m$ is a rotation; if we call this rotation σ, we can write

$$\sigma = m^{*-1} m. \tag{6.21}$$

If the angles of m_1, m_2 are denoted by θ_1, θ_2, respectively, that of m (and m^*) is, by Theorem 6.9, $\theta_1 + \theta_2 \pmod{2\pi}$, and therefore that of σ is $0 \pmod{2\pi}$. But a rotation of angle zero is the identity, so that (6.21) becomes $m = m^*$, and the theorem is proved.

THEOREM 6.12. *The product of two direct motions (neither of which is the identity) is commutative if and only if either they are both translations or they are both rotations with the same center.*

Proof. We have already seen (I, 2, Exercise 2) that the product of two translations is commutative, and since (6.17) is an Abelian group, the product of two rotations with the same center is commutative. Conversely, let m_1, m_2 be two motions such that $m_1 m_2 = m_2 m_1$. If neither has a center, then m_1 and m_2 are both translations, and the theorem is true. If one of them, say m_1, possesses a center, A_1, then

$$m_1 A_1 = A_1, \qquad A_1 \in E_2 . \tag{6.22}$$

Let A_2 be the transform of A_1 under m_2, that is,

$$A_2 = m_2 A_1 . \tag{6.23}$$

Then

$$\begin{aligned} m_1 A_2 &= m_1 m_2 A_1 && \text{(from (6.23))} \\ &= m_2 m_1 A_1 && \text{(since } m_1 m_2 = m_2 m_1\text{)} \\ &= m_2 A_1 && \text{(from (6.22))} \\ &= A_2 && \text{(from (6.23)).} \end{aligned}$$

This says that A_2 is a fixed point of m_1. But m_1 has only one fixed point, A_1. Therefore $A_2 = A_1$, and from (6.23) it follows that m_2 leaves A_1 fixed; hence m_2 possesses a center which coincides with that of m_1.

If m is an opposite motion, its fixed points, if any, satisfy the equations

$$\begin{aligned}(1 - \cos\theta)x - (\sin\theta)y &= e,\\ -(\sin\theta)x + (1 + \cos\theta)y &= f.\end{aligned} \tag{6.24}$$

Since these equations are equivalent to

$$\begin{aligned}2(\sin\theta/2)(x\sin\theta/2 - y\cos\theta/2) &= e,\\ 2(\cos\theta/2)(x\sin\theta/2 - y\cos\theta/2) &= -f,\end{aligned} \tag{6.25}$$

they possess a solution if and only if

$$e\cos\theta/2 + f\sin\theta/2 = 0. \tag{6.26}$$

Conversely, if (6.26) holds, equations (6.25) are consistent, and determine a line all of whose points are fixed.

DEFINITION 6.10. An opposite motion possessing a line of fixed points is called a *line reflection*, or a reflection in that line. The line is called the *axis* of the reflection.

We can see quite readily that this concept of a line reflection agrees with our intuitive ideas. For if we write the equation of the axis in the form

$$x\sin\theta/2 - y\cos\theta/2 = r,$$

the coordinates (x, y) and (x', y') of points P and P' which are mirror images of each other in the axis satisfy

$$x'\sin\theta/2 - y'\cos\theta/2 - r = -(x\sin\theta/2 - y\cos\theta/2 - r) \tag{6.27a}$$

and

$$x'\cos\theta/2 + y'\sin\theta/2 = x\cos\theta/2 + y\sin\theta/2. \tag{6.27b}$$

These two equations determine a point transformation given by

$$\begin{aligned}x' &= x\cos\theta + y\sin\theta + 2r\sin\theta/2,\\ y' &= x\sin\theta - y\cos\theta - 2r\cos\theta/2;\end{aligned}$$

these equations are equivalent to (6.3) and (6.26), and thus (6.3) and (6.26) together are equivalent to (6.27a, b).

If (6.26) is not satisfied, (6.24) are inconsistent, and m possesses no fixed points. We have thus proved the following theorem.

THEOREM 6.13. *An opposite motion either has no fixed point, or it possesses a line of fixed points and is a reflection in that line.*

Let σ be any rotation, and let μ_1 be a reflection in a line through the center of σ. Then $\sigma\mu_1$ is an opposite motion that leaves the center of σ fixed, and by Theorem 6.13, $\sigma\mu_1$ is itself a line reflection, say μ_2. Consequently $\sigma = \mu_1 \mu_2$, and every rotation is the product of two reflections in lines through the center.

Conversely, the product of two line reflections is necessarily a direct motion; if the axes intersect, the point of intersection is a fixed point of the product. Hence the product of any two line reflections with nonparallel axes is a rotation with center at the intersection.

Translations too can be factored, in many ways, into the product of two line reflections. Let $\tau \in T$, let $P_1 \in E_2$, and let μ_1 be the reflection whose axis is the perpendicular bisector of the segment with endpoints P_1 and τP_1. Then $\mu_1 P_1 = \tau P_1$, and $\mu_1 \tau P_1 = P_1$. Hence $\mu_1\tau$ possesses a fixed point P_1. But $\mu_1\tau$ is opposite, and by Theorem 6.13 is a line reflection, say μ_2. Hence $\mu_1\tau = \mu_2$, or $\tau = \mu_1 \mu_2$. The axis of μ_2 must be parallel to that of μ_1: If it were not, $\mu_1 \mu_2$ would be a rotation. Conversely, if μ_1 and μ_2 are line reflections with parallel axes, we can show that $\mu_1 \mu_2$ is a translation: Let P_0 be a fixed point of $\mu_1 \mu_2$, so that $P_0 \in E_2$, $\mu_1 \mu_2 P_0 = P_0$. Then if p is the line through P_0 perpendicular to the axis of μ_1 (and of μ_2), $\mu_1 \mu_2 p = p$, and $\mu_1 \mu_2$ is a rotation of angle 0 or π. But a rotation of angle π would not leave fixed a line parallel to and distinct from p, whereas $\mu_1 \mu_2$ leaves every such line fixed. Hence if $\mu_1 \mu_2$ possesses a fixed point, it is the identity, and by Theorem 6.8, $\mu_1 \mu_2$ must be a translation.

We close this section with the following theorem.

THEOREM 6.14. *A motion is one and just one of the following transformations:*

(i) *a line reflection,*
(ii) *the product of two line reflections,*
(iii) *the product of three line reflections with three distinct axes that are neither concurrent nor parallel.*

The essential step in the proof is to show that the product of three line reflections with concurrent (or parallel) axes is a single line reflection. We leave the proof to the reader.

EXERCISES

1. Let m be a given direct motion, and σ the rotation with center O and angle equal to that of m. Prove that there exist translations τ and τ^* such that $m = \sigma\tau = \tau^*\sigma$.

2. Show that a translation $\tau \in T$ leaves fixed each of the directed lines carried by the lines of a parallel pencil. If τ is given by (1.7) and $\tau \neq I$, the pencil is given by $fx - ey = \text{const.}$

3. Prove that a direct motion $\neq I$ is a translation only if it leaves fixed at least one directed line.

4. Prove Theorem 6.9 by using the results of (I, 5, Exercise 22).

5. Prove that any two directed lines are directly congruent.

6. Prove Theorem 6.2.

7. Prove the following: If $\vec{p}$ is a directed line, $m_1, m_2 \in M$ and $m_1 \vec{p} = m_2 \vec{p}$, then there exists $\tau \in T$ such that $m_1 = m_2 \tau$.

8. Prove the following: If $m_1, m_2 \in M$, there exists at least one line p such that $m_1 m_2 p = m_2 m_1 p$.

#***9.** Prove the following one-dimensional analogue of Theorem 6.7: Let p be a given line, and let M_1 be the subgroup of M^* consisting of motions m for which $mp = p$. The map from $P \in p$ to mP, for $m \in M_1$, has the same algebraic form, when expressed in terms of a metric coordinate on p, as does the equation expressing the relationship between two metric coordinates.

10. Prove that the product of three line reflections with concurrent (or parallel) axes is a line reflection.

11. Prove Theorem 6.14 by using Exercise 10.

7 Projections

Let us consider, in E_2, two distinct lines p and p' and a point C not on either. The point transformation between p and p' determined by requiring corresponding points to be collinear with C is called a *central projection*, and

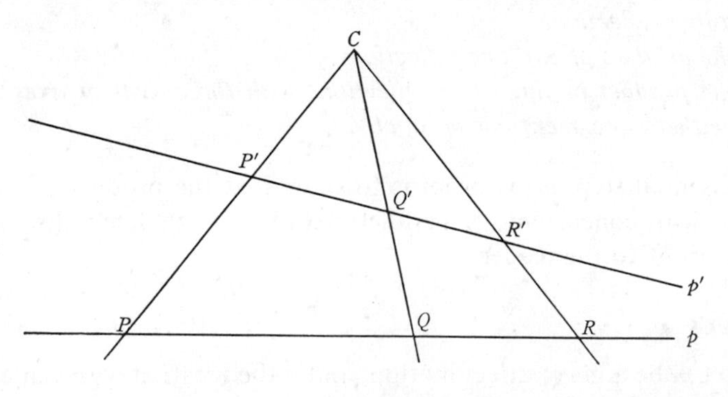

FIGURE 7.1

the point C its center (Figure 7.1). Similarly, if the lines joining pairs of corresponding points are parallel, the transformation is called a *parallel projection* (Figure 7.2). We can find the equations of a central projection in terms of metric coordinates on p and p' as follows: We establish Cartesian coordinates in E_2 with x axis on p and y axis through C. We can choose metric coordinates s and s' on p and p' respectively so that (see (6.8))

$$x = s, \qquad y = 0$$

represents p, and

$$x' = x_0 + s' \cos \omega, \qquad y' = y_0 + s' \sin \omega$$

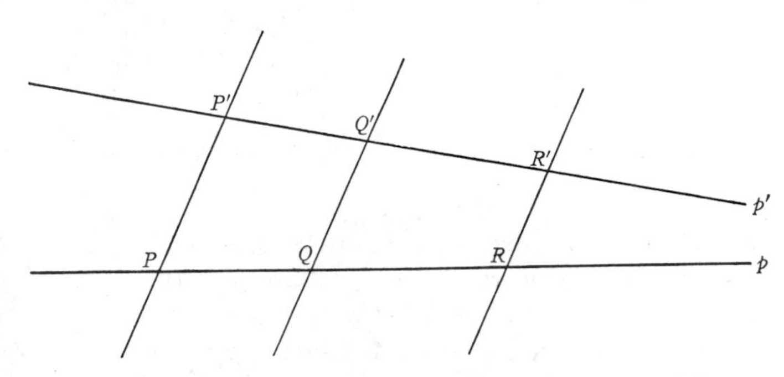

FIGURE 7.2

represents p'. If P':(x', y') is the projection of P:$(x, 0)$ from C:$(0, c)$, the three points are collinear and

$$\begin{vmatrix} 0 & s & x_0 + s' \cos \omega \\ c & 0 & y_0 + s' \sin \omega \\ 1 & 1 & 1 \end{vmatrix} = 0.$$

If we solve this equation for s', we find that corresponding points under the projection have metric coordinates related by

$$s' = \frac{s(c - y_0) - cx_0}{s \sin \omega + c \cos \omega}. \tag{7.1}$$

Our hypothesis that C does not lie on either p or p' implies that

$$(c - y_0)c \cos \omega + cx_0 \sin \omega \neq 0.$$

We can carry out a similar computation for parallel projections; we have then the following theorem:

THEOREM 7.1. *Every central or parallel projection between two lines in E_2 is given by a nonsingular linear fractional transformation*

$$s' = \frac{as + b}{cs + d}, \qquad \begin{vmatrix} a & b \\ c & d \end{vmatrix} \neq 0, \tag{7.2}$$

where s and s' are metric coordinates on the two lines.

Similarly in three-space, a projection between two planes is a correspondence between their points under which lines joining corresponding points are concurrent or parallel (according as the projection is central or parallel).

THEOREM 7.2. *Every central or parallel projection between two Euclidean planes is given by a nonsingular linear fractional transformation*

$$(7.3)\qquad x' = \frac{a_1 x + b_1 y + c_1}{a_3 x + b_3 y + c_3}, \quad y' = \frac{a_2 x + b_2 y + c_2}{a_3 x + b_3 y + c_3}, \qquad \begin{vmatrix} a_1 & b_1 & c_1 \\ a_2 & b_2 & c_2 \\ a_3 & b_3 & c_3 \end{vmatrix} \neq 0,$$

where (x, y), (x', y') *are rectangular Cartesian coordinates in the respective planes.*

We leave the proof to the reader (Exercise 1 below).

The converses of Theorems 7.1 and 7.2 are not true. Equations (7.2) and (7.3) do not necessarily represent projections. But we shall see later that (7.2) is either a projection or the product of at most three projections. Similarly (7.3) is the product of at most four projections.†

The set of transformations (7.2) obtained by varying the coefficients over all real values for which the determinant is not zero, and the analogous set (7.3) play a central role throughout this book. Written in a different form and interpreted more broadly, they serve as the starting point for our definitions, in Chapters II and III, of projective geometries of the line and of the plane.

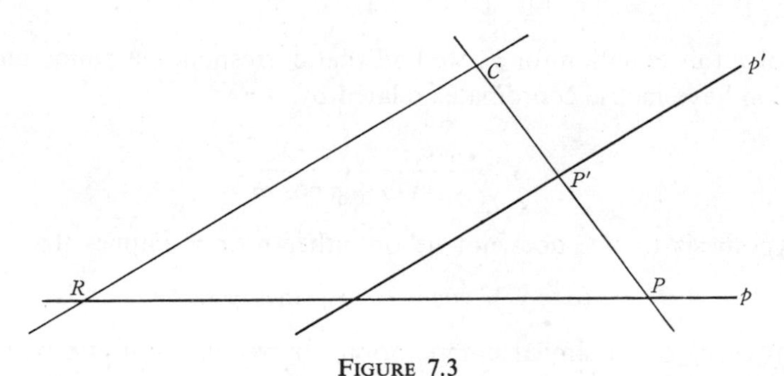

FIGURE 7.3

It is worthwhile, however, to examine the central projection (7.1) somewhat more closely in the present setting.

Referring to Figure 7.3, we see that the point R of p for which CR is parallel to p' has no transform; as a variable point P approaches R, its

†The linear fractional transformation between two distinct lines is the product of at most two projections, and that between distinct planes of at most three.

transform P' moves off indefinitely far. Equation (7.1) represents this limiting situation, for as $s \to -c \cot \omega$, $s' \to \infty$. If we interchange the roles of p and p', it follows similarly that if p and p' are not parallel there is a unique point of p' which has no transform on p. Unlike Euclidean motions, projections are therefore not one-to-one over the Euclidean line or plane. In order to create a one-to-one correspondence we adjoin to each line a "point at infinity," which can then be regarded as the transform of the exceptional point of the other. The adjunction of such a point thus gives us the point set which constitutes the projective line, but its structure is hardly clarified by such a process. Nevertheless we shall see that we can obtain Euclidean theorems from projective theorems by deleting any one point of the projective line.

Referring to Figure 7.4, let us label the points on p with integral coordinates, $s = \ldots, -1, 0, 1, 2, \ldots$. If we assign to each point of p' the coordinate of its image on p, we establish a coordinate system on p'; the points with coordinates $s = \ldots, -1, 0, 1, 2, \ldots$ are no longer equally spaced, and

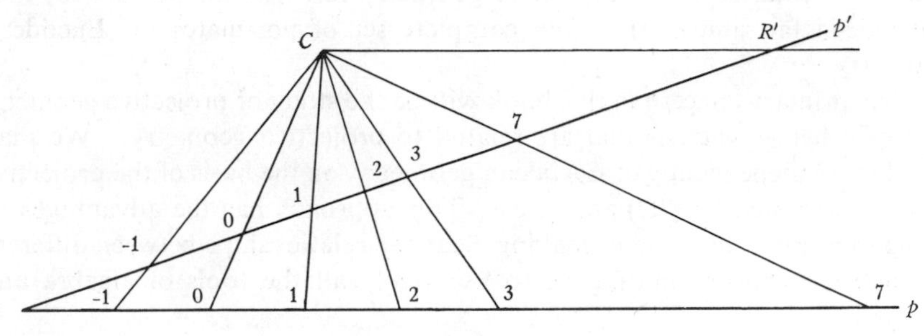

FIGURE 7.4

$s = \infty$ represents the very ordinary point R' determined by the condition that CR' is parallel to p. Equation (7.1) can be interpreted as representing this coordinate transformation on p', from the metric coordinate s' to a nonmetric coordinate s. We shall introduce projective coordinates in the next chapter, and we shall see that s, as a coordinate on p', is closely allied to such coordinates. It will turn out that, on p', s has a simple interpretation as a ratio of ratios of directed distances,

$$s = \frac{R'Q'}{R'P'} \div \frac{O'Q'}{O'P'},$$

where P' is a variable point with coordinate s, and O', Q' are the points for which $s = 0, 1$, respectively.

We can get some idea of the nature of projective geometry by considering properties which are left unchanged by a projection. For example, any two nondegenerate conics are congruent to two sections of the same cone of revolution, so that any nondegenerate conic can be transformed by central projections (and a motion) into any other such conic. Thus the projective geometry of conics yields the Euclidean properties which are common to all conics. The reader's geometric intuition will suggest that such properties as distance and angle are not preserved by projections, while properties such as intersections of curves and tangency are preserved.

Historically, projective geometry was developed on the basis of Euclidean geometry. Since the set of transformations (7.3) contains the Euclidean group of motions, Theorems 3.4, 3.5, and 3.11 suggest that every projective property is also a Euclidean property. Thus in the beginning, projective geometry was regarded as a selection of the more general properties of Euclidean figures.

Based as it was on Euclidean geometry, the historical development of projective geometry was often tortuous and the logical foundations were shaky. Actually the projective line and the projective plane have an abstract (that is, mathematical) existence which is completely independent of their Euclidean counterparts. Projective geometry has its own postulates; they are indeed far simpler than any complete set of postulates for Euclidean geometry.

Our primary concern in this book will be the study of projective geometry and of other geometries that are related to projective geometry. We shall develop it independently of Euclidean geometry, on the basis of the projective groups suggested by (7.2) and (7.3). This approach has the advantages of being logically sound and of making clear the relationships between different geometries, while permitting us to use freely all the tools of algebra and analysis.

EXERCISES

1. Carry out the proof of Theorem 7.2. Suggestion: Choose the x_1x_2-plane as one plane and C on the x_3-axis. Then let (r_1, r_2, r_3) be an arbitrary point of the second plane, and let $(\alpha_1, \alpha_2, \alpha_3)$ and $(\beta_1, \beta_2, \beta_3)$ be direction cosines of two mutually perpendicular lines through (r_1, r_2, r_3) in the second plane. Then if (x', y') are Cartesian coordinates in the second plane referred to these two lines as axes, the space coordinates of any point in the plane are $r_i + \alpha_i x' + \beta_i y'$ $(i = 1, 2, 3)$.

2. A metric coordinate x on a line is replaced by $x' = \dfrac{2x+1}{x+1}$. Mark the points $x' = 0, 3, -2, \infty$. Determine the points for which $x' > 0$; $x' < 0$.

3. Repeat Exercise 2 for the coordinate transformation $x' = \dfrac{1-x}{1+x}$.

4. If a central projection carries points A, B, into A', B', respectively, and if P lies between A and B, does P' necessarily lie between A' and B'?

#**5.** Verify that the transformation $x' = x/(x + y + 1)$, $y' = y/(x + y + 1)$ transforms any two lines which intersect on $x + y + 1 = 0$ into two parallel lines, and that it transforms the circles $x^2 + y^2 = 1$, and $x^2 + y^2 = \frac{1}{2}$ into a hyperbola and parabola, respectively, using methods which avoid lengthy numerical computation.

#**6.** Interpreting the transformation of Exercise 5 as a coordinate transformation from rectangular Cartesian coordinates (x, y) to new coordinates (x', y'), draw the new coordinate curves $x' = -1, 0, 3$, $y' = -3, 0, 5$. Describe the division of the plane into regions determined by the signs of x' and y'.

#**7.** Repeat Exercise 6 for the transformation

$$x' = \frac{x+1}{x}, \qquad y' = \frac{y}{x}.$$

***8.** Let σ be a rotation, and W the set of lines of E_2 through the center of σ, so that $p \in W$ implies that $\sigma p \in W$. Let $x(p)$ be the slope of p, referred to some specific initial line. Note that $x(p)$ fails to exist for one line, say p_0. Show that the map from p to σp is represented for $p \neq p_0$ by $x' = (x + a)/(1 - ax)$ where $x = x(p)$, $x' = x(\sigma p)$, and a is a real number determined by σ.

Discuss the inadequacies of the coordinate x and of this representation of the map, induced by σ, from W onto itself. Note both the similarities and differences between this situation and that discussed in the text for central projections.

***9.** Consider a circular cone and the sections by two planes, one perpendicular to the axis and one parallel to a generator. The one section is a circle, the other a parabola; the central projection with center at the vertex of the cone maps the points of the circle, with one exception, onto the points of the parabola. Describe the exception geometrically, and discuss the analogous problem for a circle and a hyperbola.

10. Verify geometrically (and analytically from Theorem 7.2) that in a central projection between two nonparallel planes, there exists in each plane a line that has no map in the other.

CHAPTER II

Projective Spaces of Dimension One

1 Homogeneous Classes

Spaces which share with E_2 or with higher-dimensional Euclidean space the property of possessing a one-to-one continuous map onto ordered sets of two or more real numbers are the exception rather than the rule. It is true, but not easily proved, that even such simple spaces as spheres, circular cylinders, and tori do not admit such coordinatizations. We begin this section by introducing the classes in terms of which we shall formulate our coordinatization of projective spaces.

We shall be dealing with ordered sets of numbers, mostly real numbers, sometimes complex numbers; we can cover all possibilities by requiring that our "numbers" be elements of an arbitrary but fixed field F, not of characteristic two. Let $(x_1, x_2, \ldots, x_n)$ be an ordered set of elements of F; this set determines a class of sets, the class of all nonzero multiples of the given set. We shall denote this class by means of square brackets, so that $[x_1, x_2, \ldots, x_n]$ denotes the collection of ordered sets $(\rho x_1, \rho x_2, \ldots, \rho x_n)$ obtained by varying ρ over all nonzero values in F. Thus $[1, 2]$ consists of all nonzero multiples of $(1, 2)$, so that $(2, 4)$ and $(-1, -2)$ are elements of $[1, 2]$; clearly $[2, 4] = [1, 2] = [-1, -2]$. More generally, if $(y_1, \ldots, y_n) \in [x_1, \ldots, x_n]$, there exists ρ in F such that

$$(1.1) \qquad \rho \neq 0 \quad \text{and} \quad y_i = \rho x_i, \qquad i = 1, 2, \ldots, n.$$

Then any multiple of $(y_1, \ldots, y_n)$ is a multiple of $(x_1, \ldots, x_n)$, so that $[y_1, \ldots, y_n] \subset [x_1, \ldots, x_n]$. Since $\rho \neq 0$, we have $x_i = (1/\rho)y_i$; the relation between $(x_1, \ldots, x_n)$ and $(y_1, \ldots, y_n)$ is symmetric, and $[y_1, \ldots, y_n] = [x_1, \ldots, x_n]$. Thus the class $[x_1, \ldots, x_n]$ is determined by any one of its members, and two classes that have a member in common coincide.

DEFINITION 1.1. The class $[x_1, \ldots, x_n]$ is called a *homogeneous class*, and any member of the class is called a *representative*. The class $[0, 0, \ldots, 0]$ is called the *zero class*; it contains only one member, consisting of zeros exclusively.

THEOREM 1.1. *If two nonzero classes* $[x_1, \ldots, x_n]$, $[y_1, \ldots, y_n]$ *are equal, the rank of the matrix*

$$\begin{pmatrix} x_1 & \cdots & x_n \\ y_1 & \cdots & y_n \end{pmatrix} \tag{1.2}$$

is 1; *conversely if the rank of* (1.2) *is* 1, *either the two classes are equal, or one of them is the zero class.*

We leave the details of the proof to the reader.

We shall use the square bracket in the above sense throughout this book, and the reader should not fail to distinguish the two conditions

$$(x_1, x_2, \ldots, x_n) = (y_1, y_2, \ldots, y_n)$$

and

$$[x_1, x_2, \ldots, x_n] = [y_1, y_2, \ldots, y_n].$$

In a great deal of our subsequent development we shall write an ordered set as a column matrix, as we did in considering solutions of homogeneous linear equations. If

$$\mathbf{X} = \begin{pmatrix} x_1 \\ x_2 \\ \vdots \\ x_n \end{pmatrix} = (x_1, x_2, \ldots, x_n)^T,$$

we shall denote by $[\mathbf{X}]$ the set of column matrices $\mathbf{Y}$ where $\mathbf{Y} = \rho\mathbf{X}$ with ρ varying over F and $\rho \neq 0$. We shall find it convenient to have a symbol for the aggregate of all such objects $[\mathbf{X}] \neq [\mathbf{0}]$.

DEFINITION 1.2. We denote by Ω_n the set of all $[\mathbf{X}]$, where $\mathbf{X}$ is an $n \times 1$ matrix over a given field F, and where

$$[\mathbf{X}] = \{\mathbf{Y} \mid \mathbf{Y} = \rho\mathbf{X}, \quad \rho \in F, \quad \rho \neq 0, \quad \mathbf{X} \neq \mathbf{0}\}.$$

We shall be concerned only with Ω_2 and Ω_3. Thus, for example, an element of Ω_2 is itself a set, the set of all nonzero scalar multiples of a nonzero matrix, over F, of order 2×1. We do not indicate that Ω_n depends on F because the choice of F will be clear from the context.

We next give some illustrations from Euclidean geometry of spaces which possess coordinatizations in terms of homogeneous classes.

Illustration 1. Let W be the space of lines, in E_2, that contain a given point. In terms of a Cartesian coordinate system with the point as origin, an element of W has an equation $Ax + By = 0$, and therefore can be represented by an ordered pair (A, B) of real numbers. But the equation is not unique, and the elements of W are in one-to-one correspondence with nonzero homogeneous classes $[A, B]$, not with ordered pairs (A, B).

We cannot coordinatize the lines of a pencil by means of a slope-variable, for then we have no coordinate for the line perpendicular to the initial line. Nor can we extend the real field R by adjoining an infinite element, for then our algebra ceases to be self-consistent.

Illustration 2. A line in E_3 has two sets of direction cosines, say (a, b, c) and $(-a, -b, -c)$ and infinitely many sets of direction numbers, so that lines through a given point in E_3 can be put in one-to-one correspondence with nonzero homogeneous classes $[a, b, c]$.

Illustration 3. A central projection (I, (7.2)) determines not the ordered set (a, b, c, d), but the homogeneous class $[a, b, c, d]$.

Illustration 4. If z is a complex variable, we can represent $z = x + iy$ $(i^2 = -1)$ by the point of E_2 with Cartesian coordinates (x, y). However, in the study of functions of a complex variable it turns out useful (and necessary) to talk about $z = \infty$. But the complex field C, like R, possesses no infinite element. Homogeneous classes gives us the kind of object needed; we represent an ordinary complex number z by the homogeneous pair $[z, 1]$, or equivalently $[z_1, z_2]$ where $z = z_1/z_2$ and $z_2 \neq 0$, and we let $[1, 0] = [z_1, 0]$ $(z_1 \neq 0)$ represent "infinity". Then every homogeneous class $[z_1, z_2]$ (with elements complex numbers) represents a unique "value" of the complex variable, and every value (infinity being allowed) is represented by a unique class.

Illustration 5. The reader is familiar with the coordinatization of a sphere in E_3 in terms of latitude and longitude. The disadvantages of this coordinatization are numerous. The poles have infinitely many coordinates, all values of the longitude being admissible. The meridian, corresponding roughly to the international date line on the surface of the earth, has ambiguous coordinates, and two points on either side of this meridian, no matter how close together, will have longitudes differing by more than 6 (in radians). We can eliminate these disadvantages by coordinatizing the sphere in terms of the homogeneous classes $[z_1, z_2]$ introduced in the preceding illustration. Let N be an arbitrary point of a sphere $\mathscr{W}$ (which point we call, for convenience, the north pole), and let p be a plane tangent to $\mathscr{W}$ at S, the south pole, that is, the point antipodal to N. Each point $P \in p$ determines uniquely a point $\pi P \in \mathscr{W}$, collinear with N and P, and the range of the map π is $\mathscr{W} - N$ (that is, $\mathscr{W}$ with N excepted). If we coordinatize the plane by means of a complex variable z, and if we assign to πP the coordinate z of P, we use up all complex numbers z without having a coordinate for N. The introduction of homogeneous classes, as in Illustration 4, yields a coordinatization of the sphere which has proved eminently satisfactory.

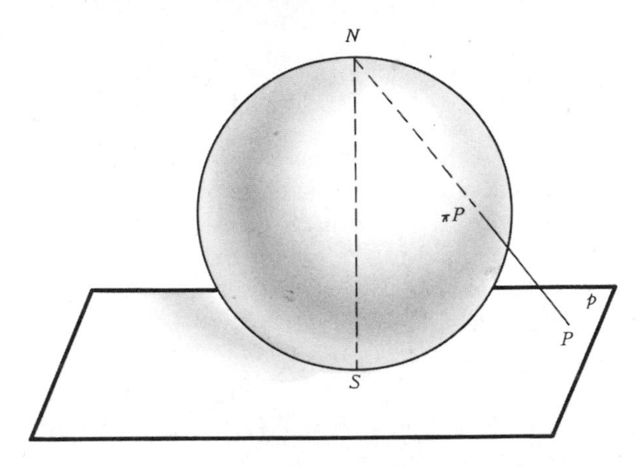

FIGURE 1.1

The map π (or its inverse) is called a *stereographic* projection.

Illustration 6. This illustration is more relevant to our immediate purposes. The group L (see I, (2.3)) maps the set of lines through the origin onto itself. If $P \in E_2$ is not the origin then $P:(x, y)$ and $Q:(\rho x, \rho y)$ for $\rho \neq 0$, lie on, and thereby determine, the same line through the origin; thus the space W of Illustration 1 can be coordinatized by means of the nonzero homogeneous classes $[x, y]$.† If $\sigma \in L$, σP and σQ are collinear with the origin, so that σ maps the homogeneous class $[x, y]$ onto a definite homogeneous class, say $[x', y']$, where

$$[x', y'] = [ax + by, cx + dy], \qquad \Delta \neq 0. \tag{1.3}$$

Thus (1.3) can be interpreted as representing the map, induced by L, on the lines through the origin. We can use matrix notation; let us replace

$$\begin{pmatrix} a & b \\ c & d \end{pmatrix} \text{ by } \begin{pmatrix} a_{11} & a_{12} \\ a_{21} & a_{22} \end{pmatrix} = \mathbf{A}, \quad \text{and} \quad \begin{pmatrix} x \\ y \end{pmatrix} \text{ by } \begin{pmatrix} x_1 \\ x_2 \end{pmatrix} = \mathbf{X},$$

and let us use a square bracket enclosing a matrix to represent the class of nonzero scalar multiples of the given matrix. Then (1.3) can be written

$$[\mathbf{X}'] = [\mathbf{AX}], \qquad \det \mathbf{A} \neq 0. \tag{1.4}$$

† Clearly this coordinatization is not the one given in Illustration 1.

Since a homogeneous class is determined by any one of its members, (1.3) can be written equally well as

(1.5) $$[x', y'] = [\rho ax + \rho by, \rho cx + \rho dy], \qquad \rho \neq 0,$$

and therefore

(1.6) $$[\mathbf{X}'] = [\rho\mathbf{AX}], \qquad \rho \neq 0$$

is equivalent to (1.4). Thus the distinct linear transformations, $\mathbf{X}' = \rho\mathbf{AX}$, for all $\rho \neq 0$, induce the same map (1.4) on homogeneous classes. It is useful, and possible, to write (1.4) as a linear transformation, but it is necessary that proper attention be paid to the choice of representatives: If $[\mathbf{X}]$, $[\mathbf{X}']$, and $[\mathbf{A}]$ are given and satisfy (1.4), we can select representatives $\mathbf{X}$, $\mathbf{X}'$, and $\mathbf{A}$ such that

(1.7) $$\mathbf{X}' = \mathbf{AX};$$

but if the representatives are preassigned, (1.7) need not hold; in this situation we can only assert that there exists $\rho \neq 0$ such that

(1.8) $$\mathbf{X}' = \rho\mathbf{AX}.$$

In general, the scalar multiplier ρ in (1.8) will vary with $\mathbf{X}$ (see Exercise 8 below).

Is the set of transformations (1.4) obtained by varying $\mathbf{A}$ a group?† Clearly we need to restrict $\mathbf{A}$ to be nonsingular, that is, $\det \mathbf{A} \neq 0$. Then $\mathbf{A}^{-1}$ exists, and the inverses of (1.8) are

(1.9) $$\mathbf{X}' = (1/\rho)\mathbf{A}^{-1}\mathbf{X}.$$

As ρ in (1.8) varies over nonzero real values, $1/\rho$ does likewise; hence the inverse of (1.4) is

$$[\mathbf{X}'] = [\mathbf{A}^{-1}\mathbf{X}].$$

Similarly, the product of (1.4) by $[\mathbf{X}'] = [\mathbf{BX}]$ is

$$[\mathbf{X}'] = [\mathbf{ABX}]$$

because $(\rho_1 \mathbf{A})(\rho_2 \mathbf{B}) = \rho_1 \rho_2 \mathbf{AB}$, and $\rho_1 \rho_2$ takes on all nonzero real values as ρ_1 and ρ_2 vary.

We can generalize these results by replacing the group L (based on R) by the group $L(\mathsf{F}, 2)$, where F is a given field. The geometrical interpretation of (1.4) is no longer valid, but the algebraic analysis remains unchanged. Recalling Definition 1.2, we can state our preceding results as follows.

† Strictly speaking, we are now broadening our concept of a group. A set of transformations operating on the elements of any given space is a group if it possesses properties (a) and (b) of (I, Definition 2.1).

THEOREM 1.2. *A transformation* (1.4) *with det* $\mathbf{A} \neq 0$ *is a one-to-one map from* Ω_2 *onto itself. The set of all such transformations is a group.*†

We have already seen that two transformations of $L(\mathsf{F}, 2)$ with matrices $\mathbf{A}$ and $\rho\mathbf{A}$ induce the same map of Ω_2. Do there exist other linear transformations whose induced maps on Ω_2 coincide with (1.4)? We prove that there are no others in the following lemma and theorem.

LEMMA 1.1. *The map* (1.4) *is the identity if and only if* $[\mathbf{A}] = [\mathbf{I}]$, *that is,* $\mathbf{A}$ *is a nonzero scalar multiple of the unit matrix.*

Proof. We have proved the sufficiency earlier; to prove the necessity, we suppose that (1.4) is the identity map. Then there exist a matrix $\mathbf{A}$ and three nonzero elements of F, ρ_1, ρ_2, and ρ_3, such that the linear transformation $\mathbf{X}' = \mathbf{AX}$ maps $(1, 0)^T$, $(0, 1)^T$, and $(1, 1)^T$ onto $(\rho_1, 0)^T$, $(0, \rho_2)^T$, and $(\rho_3, \rho_3)^T$, respectively. Direct substitution yields the necessary conditions

$$\begin{aligned} \rho_1 &= a_{11}, & 0 &= a_{12}, & \rho_3 &= a_{11} + a_{12}, \\ 0 &= a_{21}, & \rho_2 &= a_{22}, & \rho_3 &= a_{21} + a_{22}; \end{aligned}$$

these six equations, in the seven unknowns, have solutions given by $\mathbf{A} = \rho\mathbf{I}$, where $\rho \in \mathsf{F}$.

THEOREM 1.3. *The maps* $[\mathbf{X}'] = [\mathbf{AX}]$, $[\mathbf{X}'] = [\mathbf{BX}]$ *coincide if and only if* $[\mathbf{B}] = [\mathbf{A}]$.

Proof. Only the necessity is at issue. If the two transformations coincide, $[\mathbf{X}'] = [\mathbf{A}^{-1}\mathbf{BX}]$ must be the identity; then $\mathbf{A}^{-1}\mathbf{B} = \rho\mathbf{I}$, or $\mathbf{B} = \rho\mathbf{A}$.

Our proofs of Theorems 1.2 and 1.3 involved matrix notation and clearly remain valid when we replace $L(\mathsf{F}, 2)$ by $L(\mathsf{F}, n)$ (and make the corresponding adjustments in the orders of $\mathbf{A}$, $\mathbf{B}$, and $\mathbf{X}$ and in the definition of Ω_2), provided that we can show that Lemma 1.1 is true for any n. We shall need these results for $n = 3$ in Chapter III, and the reader should prove Lemma 1.1 for $n = 3$. This can be done by determining the linear transformations (I, (4.12)) with $n = 3$ that map $(1, 0, 0)^T$, $(0, 1, 0)^T$, $(0, 0, 1)^T$, and $(1, 1, 1)^T$ onto $(\rho_1, 0, 0)^T$, $(0, \rho_2, 0)^T$, $(0, 0, \rho_3)^T$, and $(\rho_4, \rho_4, \rho_4)^T$ respectively.

EXERCISES

In the numerical exercises below it may be assumed that the ground field is R.

1. Show that any circle in E_2 can be coordinatized with homogeneous classes $[t_1, t_2]$, where (t_1, t_2) vary over all real pairs except $(0, 0)$, by describing the locus in E_2 given by $x = (t_1^2 - t_2^2)/(t_1^2 + t_2^2)$, $y = 2t_1 t_2/(t_1^2 + t_2^2)$ and interpreting t_1, t_2 geometrically.

† The reader familiar with group theory will recognize that this group is the quotient group $L(\mathsf{F}, 2)/L_0$, where L_0 is the subgroup of $L(\mathsf{F}, 2)$ given by $\mathbf{X}' = \rho\mathbf{X}$, $\rho \neq 0$.

2. Express a rotation of the circle $x^2 + y^2 = a^2$ about its center in terms of $[t_1, t_2]$ of Exercise 1.

3. Show that $x_1' = 2x_1 + x_2$, $x_2' = x_1 - x_2$ maps $[1, 4]$, $[0, -1]$, and $[1, 1]$ onto $[-2, 1]$, $[-1, 1]$, and $[1, 0]$, respectively.

4. Determine a so that the transformation $x_1' = x_1 - ax_2$, $x_2' = 2x_1 + x_2$ maps $[1, -4]$ onto $[2, 3]$. ANS. $a = -7/12$.

5. Find all linear transformations ($n = 2$) which leave $(1, 0)^T$ and $(0, 1)^T$ fixed.

6. Find all transformations $[\mathbf{X}'] = [\mathbf{AX}]$ ($n = 2$) which leave $[(1, 0)^T]$ and $[(0, 1)^T]$ fixed. Show that the set is a group.

7. Prove that if (1.7) is a representation of (1.4), $\mathbf{X}' = \mathbf{A}^a\mathbf{X}$ is a representation of the inverse map (see I, (5.16)).

8. Show that $[\mathbf{X}'] = [\mathbf{AX}]$, where $\mathbf{A} = \begin{pmatrix} 2 & 3 \\ 3 & 2 \end{pmatrix}$, leaves $[(1, 1)^T]$ and $[(1, -1)^T]$ fixed. Do $(1, 1)^T$ and $(1, -1)^T$ satisfy (1.7) with $\mathbf{X}' = \mathbf{X}$? Verify the remark following (1.8).

***9.** Prove Lemma 1.1 for $n = 3$, using the suggestion in the text.

2 Projective Spaces of Dimension One

In the rest of this chapter we shall be dealing with homogeneous classes; we use the notation of the preceding section with the understanding that $\mathbf{X}$, $\mathbf{Y}$, $\mathbf{Z}$ represent matrices of order 2×1, and $\mathbf{A}$, $\mathbf{B}$ those of order 2×2. Elements of matrices belong to F, a given field not of characteristic 2.

AXIOM 2.1. *There exists a set of objects which are in one-to-one correspondence with Ω_2, the set of all nonzero homogeneous classes* $[\mathbf{X}]$.

We shall denote the objects of the given set by capital italic letters, X, Y, Z, P, Q, and such others as we may require; we shall use the same letter, in bold face, to indicate an arbitrary representative of the corresponding element of Ω_2, so that, for example, $\mathbf{X}$ denotes a representative of $[\mathbf{X}]$, the element of Ω_2 which corresponds to X.

DEFINITION 2.1. We call the given objects *points.* We call the class $[\mathbf{X}]$ corresponding to the point X the *homogeneous projective coordinate* of X, and any representative $\mathbf{Y} \in [\mathbf{X}]$ a *representative coordinate*, or briefly, a *representative* of X. We call the given map between the set of points and Ω_2 the *postulated projective coordinatization*, or for euphony, the *postulated projective coordinate system.*

AXIOM 2.2. *There exists a group of point transformations from the given set of points onto itself which is represented, in terms of the coordinate system of Definition* 2.1 *by equations* (1.4).

DEFINITION 2.2. A set of points satisfying Axioms 2.1 and 2.2 is called a *projective space of dimension one over the field* F; its invariant theory under the group of Axiom 2.2 is called *one-dimensional projective geometry over* F.

In this book we shall be largely concerned with *real* projective geometry, that is, F will frequently be replaced by R. But many of our conclusions, particularly those that involve only linear operations, will turn out to be valid in an arbitrary field, and we shall then state the conclusion in the more general form. On the other hand, real projective geometry often lacks the unity possessed by complex projective geometry, and we shall often find it necessary to distinguish between these two. We shall, as previously noted, denote the real field by R, and the complex field by C.

We shall use $S_1(\mathsf{F})$ to denote the set of points of a projective space of dimension one, as well as the space itself. Thus $S_1(\mathsf{R})$ is a real projective space or its set of points, and $S_1(\mathsf{C})$ is a complex projective space or its set of points. Occasionally, when no ambiguity can arise, we shall write S_1 without explicit designation of the field.

DEFINITION 2.3. The group of Axiom 2.2 is called the *one-dimensional projective group over* F. It is denoted† by $G_3(\mathsf{F})$, or simply by G_3 whenever the choice of F is clear from the context. If $\pi \in G_3(\mathsf{F})$, π is called a *one-dimensional projective transformation*, or a *projectivity*. If π is given by (1.4), any $\mathbf{A} \in [\mathbf{A}]$ is called a *representative matrix* of π.

DEFINITION 2.4. Two point sets contained in $S_1(\mathsf{F})$ are *projectively equivalent* if there exists $\pi \in G_3$ which maps the one onto the other.

A collection of objects is not a space in the mathematical sense. To be a space, the set must in some manner be endowed with inner relations, which are said to constitute its structure. Frequently a structure is induced on a given collection by the structure of the space in which it is immersed. Here, however, it must be postulated, and this we have done by our axioms and definitions.

The reader will note that only minor modifications in what we have done are needed to formulate a definition of projective space of dimension n, for any integer $n > 1$.

As remarked earlier, it will be convenient to use the same letter to refer to a point, to its homogeneous coordinate, and to a representative coordinate. If X is a point, we shall write $X{:}\mathbf{X}$ to be read the point X with representative

† The subscript 3 is used because $G_3(\mathsf{R})$ can be regarded as a three-dimensional real space.

coordinate the column matrix $\mathbf{X}$. Similarly, $X:[\mathbf{X}]$ is to be read the point X with coordinate the class $[\mathbf{X}]$. When the elements of $\mathbf{X}$ are exhibited explicitly, we shall find it convenient to write $\mathbf{X} = (x_1, x_2)^T$ and to use $[x_1, x_2]^T$ for $[\mathbf{X}]$ in place of the more cumbersome $[(x_1, x_2)^T]$.

In the Euclidean plane we have infinitely many Cartesian coordinate systems at our disposal; in many instances we are able to choose a convenient one for the particular problem at hand. We proceed to show that the postulated coordinate system of $S_1(\mathsf{F})$ is one of a class of coordinate systems that play, in the geometry of $S_1(\mathsf{F})$, a role analogous to that played by metric coordinates in E_1 and by Cartesian coordinates in E_2.

We need the following lemma.

LEMMA 2.1. *If Y_1, Y_2, U are three distinct points of $S_1(\mathsf{F})$, $\mathbf{Y}_1$ and $\mathbf{Y}_2$ possess representatives $\mathbf{Y}_1$ and $\mathbf{Y}_2$ such that a given representative $\mathbf{U}$ of U satisfies*

$$\mathbf{U} = \mathbf{Y}_1 + \mathbf{Y}_2. \tag{2.1}$$

Proof. Let $\mathbf{Y}_1'$, $\mathbf{Y}_2'$, $\mathbf{U}$ be given representatives of Y_1, Y_2, U, respectively. By (I, 5, Exercise 4) there exist scalar multipliers ρ_1, ρ_2 such that

$$\mathbf{U} = \rho_1 \mathbf{Y}_1' + \rho_2 \mathbf{Y}_2'.$$

Since Y_1, Y_2, U are distinct, $\rho_1 \rho_2 \neq 0$; then $\mathbf{Y}_1 = \rho_1 \mathbf{Y}_1'$ and $\mathbf{Y}_2 = \rho_2 \mathbf{Y}_2'$ are representatives satisfying (2.1).

Note that if we replace $\mathbf{U}$ by $\rho\mathbf{U}$, the representatives $\mathbf{Y}_1$, $\mathbf{Y}_2$ of the lemma will need to be replaced by $\rho\mathbf{Y}_1$, $\rho\mathbf{Y}_2$ to retain (2.1). (See also Exercise 2 below.)

Each of the coordinate systems that we are about to establish is determined by an ordered set of three distinct points. Denote these by Y_1, Y_2, U, and let $\mathbf{Y}_1$, $\mathbf{Y}_2$, $\mathbf{U}$ be representatives that satisfy (2.1). If X is any point, and $\mathbf{X}$ a given representative, the matrix $\mathbf{X}$ is a unique linear combination of the two independent matrices $\mathbf{Y}_1$ and $\mathbf{Y}_2$; if we write

$$\mathbf{X} = x_1^*\mathbf{Y}_1 + x_2^*\mathbf{Y}_2, \tag{2.2}$$

the *matrix* $\mathbf{X}$ determines $\mathbf{X}^*$, where

$$\mathbf{X}^* = (x_1^*, x_2^*)^T.$$

We should like to show that the *point* X, together with the points Y_1, Y_2, U, determines the *class* $[\mathbf{X}^*]$ uniquely. If we used $\mathbf{U}' = \rho\mathbf{U}$ in place of $\mathbf{U}$ in (2.1), we would need to replace $\mathbf{Y}_1$, $\mathbf{Y}_2$ by $\rho\mathbf{Y}_1$, $\rho\mathbf{Y}_2$, and, from (2.2), $\mathbf{X}^*$ by $(1/\rho)\mathbf{X}^*$. Similarly, if we used $\mathbf{X}' = \sigma\mathbf{X}$ in place of $\mathbf{X}$, we would need to replace $\mathbf{X}^*$ by $\sigma\mathbf{X}^*$. Compounding these two changes results in replacing

$\mathbf{X}^*$ by $(\sigma/\rho)\mathbf{X}^*$, that is, in leaving $[\mathbf{X}^*]$ unchanged, as required.† If we let

$$\mathbf{Y}_1 = (y_{11}, y_{21})^T, \qquad \mathbf{Y}_2 = (y_{12}, y_{22})^T,$$

and

$$\mathbf{B} = (\mathbf{Y}_1 \quad \mathbf{Y}_2) = \begin{pmatrix} y_{11} & y_{12} \\ y_{21} & y_{22} \end{pmatrix}, \tag{2.3}$$

we can express the relation between the classes $[\mathbf{X}]$ and $[\mathbf{X}^*]$ by

$$[\mathbf{X}] = [\mathbf{B}\mathbf{X}^*], \qquad \det \mathbf{B} \neq 0. \tag{2.4}$$

Since the point X determines $[\mathbf{X}]$ uniquely, we can interpret (2.4) as a map from $S_1(\mathsf{F})$ onto Ω_2, where the point $X : [\mathbf{X}]$ maps onto $[\mathbf{X}^*] \in \Omega_2$. Therefore we can assert that a choice of three points determines a new one-to-one mapping from $S_1(\mathsf{F})$ onto Ω_2. We have thus a collection of different coordinatizations of $S_1(\mathsf{F})$, each determined by an ordered triple of distinct points.

If for Y, Y_2, U we choose the points with representatives $(1, 0)^T$, $(0, 1)^T$, $(1, 1)^T$, (2.2) becomes $\mathbf{X} = \mathbf{X}^*$, so that our collection of coordinatizations includes the postulated one.

DEFINITION 2.5. A *projective coordinate system* or a *projective coordinatization* in $S_1(\mathsf{F})$ is any one-to-one mapping of the points of S_1 onto Ω_2 which is related to the postulated one by equation (2.4) for some choice of $\mathbf{B}$ with $\det \mathbf{B} \neq 0$.

Clearly an arbitrary choice of $\mathbf{B}$ ($\det \mathbf{B} \neq 0$) in Definition 2.5 does not give us any more leeway than we already had from an arbitrary choice of the triad, $Y_1 Y_2 U$. For if $\mathbf{B} = (b_{ij})$ is given, we can choose distinct points Y_1, Y_2, U by letting

$$\mathbf{Y}_1 = \begin{pmatrix} b_{11} \\ b_{21} \end{pmatrix}, \qquad \mathbf{Y}_2 = \begin{pmatrix} b_{21} \\ b_{22} \end{pmatrix}, \qquad \mathbf{U} = \begin{pmatrix} b_{11} + b_{12} \\ b_{21} + b_{22} \end{pmatrix}.$$

DEFINITION 2.6. In any projective coordinate system, the ordered set of three points with representatives $(1, 0)^T$, $(0, 1)^T$, and $(1, 1)^T$, respectively, is called the *reference frame*. The first two points are called the *vertices* of the reference frame, and the third the *unit point*.

Thus the triad $Y_1 Y_2 U$ is the reference frame of the $[\mathbf{X}^*]$-coordinatization given by (2.4).

Illustrative Example. Find the relation between the postulated coordinate system and the one that has as its reference frame the points Y_1, Y_2, U with respective representatives $(2, 1)^T$, $(1, -1)^T$, $(7, -1)^T$ in the postulated system.

† In substance, we have been solving several systems of two nonhomogeneous linear equations in two unknowns, with nonvanishing determinant. Since such systems have unique solutions, those we found by inspection must be the only solutions.

Solution. To satisfy (2.1), we write $7 = 2h + k$, $-1 = h - k$, and we find $h = 2$, $k = 3$. Hence we must use as representatives of the vertices $2(2, 1)^T = (4, 2)^T$ and $3(1, -1)^T = (3, -3)^T$. Then (2.2) becomes

$$x_1 = 4x_1^* + 3x_2^*, \qquad x_2 = 2x_1^* - 3x_2^*. \tag{2.5}$$

How can we represent a projectivity π in an arbitrary projective coordinate system? If $\mathbf{A}$ is a given representative matrix of π in the postulated system, and if $\mathbf{X}$ is a given representative of $X \in S_1(\mathsf{F})$, we can represent π by

$$\pi\colon \quad \mathbf{X}' = \mathbf{AX} \tag{2.6}$$

and regard (2.6) as determining a particular representative of πX. For a given $\mathbf{B} \in [\mathbf{B}]$, we can choose $\mathbf{X}^*$ and $\mathbf{X}^{*\prime}$, representatives of X and πX in the $[\mathbf{X}^*]$-system given by (2.4) to satisfy

$$\mathbf{X} = \mathbf{BX}^*, \qquad \mathbf{X}' = \mathbf{BX}^{*\prime}. \tag{2.7}$$

Eliminating $\mathbf{X}$ and $\mathbf{X}'$ from (2.6) and (2.7) gives $\mathbf{BX}^{*\prime} = \mathbf{ABX}^*$, or

$$\mathbf{X}^{*\prime} = \mathbf{B}^{-1}\mathbf{ABX}^*. \tag{2.8}$$

Thus a projectivity π with representative matrix $\mathbf{A}$ in the $[\mathbf{X}]$-system has the form (1.4) in every projective coordinate system, and if the second system is related to the first by (2.4), $\mathbf{A}^* = \mathbf{B}^{-1}\mathbf{AB}$ is a representative matrix of π in the second system. Conversely, it readily follows that the point transformation in $S_1(\mathsf{F})$ defined by $[\mathbf{X}^{*\prime}] = [\mathbf{A}^*\mathbf{X}^*]$, where $\mathbf{A}^*$ is a 2×2 nonsingular matrix, is a projectivity.

From these results, it follows that the postulated coordinate system plays no special role. On replacing the words, *the postulated coordinate system* by *any projective coordinate system*, the statements obtained from Axioms 2.1 and 2.2 and Definitions 2.1, 2.2, and 2.3 become theorems whose proofs the reader will be able to supply. Thus we might have formulated our definition of $S_1(\mathsf{F})$ in terms of any one projective coordinate system, and that one would lead to the construction of all others. The group G_3 is represented by the totality (1.4) in any projective coordinate system; equation (2.4) represents, for a suitable choice of $\mathbf{B}$, the relation between any two given projective coordinate systems, and if $[\mathbf{X}]$ is a coordinate of X in any one system, the coordinatization defined by (2.4) is again a projective coordinatization (see Exercises 12, 13, 14 below).

Since the set of all mappings (1.4) is algebraically identical with the set (2.4), we have for a given $\mathbf{A}$, three interpretations for the equation

$$[\mathbf{X}'] = [\mathbf{AX}], \qquad \det \mathbf{A} \neq 0. \tag{2.9}$$

1. It represents a map from Ω_2 onto itself.

2. If points X, X' have coordinates $[\mathbf{X}]$ and $[\mathbf{X}']$ in some specified projective coordinate system, it represents the projectivity π, where $X' = \pi X$. We note that this projectivity maps the reference frame of the given coordinate system onto the three points with representatives the two columns of $\mathbf{A}$ and the sum of the two columns; thus

$$Y_1 : (1, 0)^T \quad \text{is mapped onto} \quad \pi Y_1 : (a_{11}, a_{21})^T.$$

3. It defines a new coordinatization in which $X : [\mathbf{X}]$ has the coordinate $[\mathbf{X}']$. The columns of $\mathbf{A}$ now represent the coordinates in the $[\mathbf{X}']$-system of the vertices of the $[\mathbf{X}]$-system, and the columns of $\mathbf{A}^{-1}$ or of $\mathbf{A}^a$ represent the coordinates, in the $[\mathbf{X}]$-system of the vertices of the $[\mathbf{X}']$-system.

The first interpretation involves no geometry, and as we interpret $[\mathbf{X}]$ and $[\mathbf{X}']$ one way or the other, we get different results. For example, the proof of Lemma 1.1 contains the proof of the assertion that if a map (2.9) of Ω_2 onto itself leaves $[1, 0]^T$, $[0, 1]^T$, and $[1, 1]^T$ fixed, it is the identity. Let us now suppose that π is a projectivity that leaves fixed each of three given distinct points; if we seek a representation of π in a coordinate system with the points as reference frame, we are led to the algebraic problem whose solution we have just described. Hence we have proved the following theorem.

THEOREM 2.1. *A projectivity in $S_1(\mathsf{F})$ that leaves fixed three distinct points must be the identity.*

The next theorem contains the preceding one as a special case.

THEOREM 2.2. *Let P_1, P_2, P_3 and P_1', P_2', P_3' be two triads of distinct points in $S_1(\mathsf{F})$. There exists one and only one projectivity which maps P_i onto P_i' for $i = 1, 2, 3$.*

Proof. Let us employ the coordinate system with reference frame P_1, P_2, P_3. By Lemma 2.1 we can choose a representative of P_1', say $(a_{11}, a_{21})^T$, and one of P_2', say $(a_{12}, a_{22})^T$, such that $(a_{11} + a_{12}, a_{21} + a_{22})^T$ is a representative of P_3'. Then $\mathbf{A} = (a_{ij})$ is a representative matrix of a projectivity π such that $\pi P_i = P_i'$ $(i = 1, 2, 3)$. To prove uniqueness, let π_1 be any projectivity such that $\pi_1 P_i = P_i'$. Then $\pi^{-1}\pi_1 P_i = P_i$; by Theorem 2.1, $\pi^{-1}\pi_1 = I$, so that $\pi_1 = \pi$.

THEOREM 2.3. *Let $[p_{1i}, p_{2i}]^T$ $(i = 1, 2, 3)$ be three distinct elements of Ω_2, and let $[p_{1i}', p_{2i}']^T$ be a second such triad. There exists one and only one map* (2.9), *of Ω_2 onto itself, that maps $[p_{1i}, p_{2i}]^T$ onto $[p_{1i}', p_{2i}']^T$ for $i = 1, 2, 3$.*

Proof. Every projectivity can be reinterpreted as a map (2.9) of Ω_2 onto itself, and every such map can be reinterpreted as a projectivity. Hence this theorem expresses the algebraic content of Theorem 2.2.

A direct algebraic proof of Theorem 2.3 would be rather involved.

EXERCISES

In the numerical exercises below it may be assumed that the ground field is R.

1. Find representatives of $Y_1:(1,2)^T$, $Y_2:(2,-3)^T$, $U:(0,1)^T$ that satisfy (2.1).

2. Prove that if $\mathbf{X}, \mathbf{Y}, \mathbf{Z}$, representatives of three distinct points, satisfy (2.1), and if $\rho_1 \mathbf{X}, \rho_2 \mathbf{Y}, \rho_3 \mathbf{Z}$ do likewise, then $\rho_1 = \rho_2 = \rho_3$.

3. Find coordinates of $X:(1,1)^T$ in the coordinate system with Y_1, Y_2, U of Exercise 1 as reference frame.

4. If X has coordinate $[\mathbf{X}]$ in a given system and $[\mathbf{X}^*]$ in the system with reference frame the points Y_1, Y_2, U of Exercise 1, find $\mathbf{A}$ such that $[\mathbf{X}] = [\mathbf{AX}^*]$. Compute $\mathbf{A}^a$ and determine a value of $\mathbf{X}^*$ for each point of the reference frame of the given system.

5. If the equations $x_1' = x_1 - 3x_2, x_2' = 2x_1 + x_2$ are interpreted as a coordinate transformation, find the coordinates in each system of the reference points of the other.

6. Two coordinate systems have the same vertices, and the unit point of the first system has the representative $\mathbf{X}^* = (3,2)^T$ in the second. Find equations of the coordinate transformation.

7. Find the projectivity that maps the points with coordinates $[1,0]^T$, $[0,1]^T$, and $[1,1]^T$ onto the points with coordinates $[2,3]^T$, $[-1,2]^T$, and $[3,1]^T$, respectively.

8. Find the projectivity that maps the points with representatives $(1,2)^T$, $(1,1)^T$, $(2,1)^T$ onto the points with representatives $(1,0)^T$, $(0,1)^T$, and $(1,1)^T$.

9. If $\begin{pmatrix} 1 & 1 \\ 2 & 1 \end{pmatrix}$ is a representative matrix of a projectivity π in a given coordinate system and if $\mathbf{X}^* = \mathbf{BX}$, where $\mathbf{B} = \begin{pmatrix} 1 & -1 \\ 1 & 2 \end{pmatrix}$, is a coordinate transformation with $\mathbf{X}$ a representative in the given system, find a representative matrix of π in the $[\mathbf{X}^*]$-coordinate system.

10. Find the relation between the two coordinatizations of the lines, in E_2, through a point that was described in Illustrations 1 and 6, of Section 1.

***11.** A projectivity π maps $X:[x,1]^T$ onto $\pi X:(x',1)^T$ where $x' = \dfrac{ax+b}{cx+d}$. Find πY and $\pi^{-1} Y$ for $Y:[1,0]^T$.

***12.** Prove the assertion in the text that the map given by $[\mathbf{X}^{*\prime}] = [\mathbf{AX}^*]$, $\det \mathbf{A} \neq 0$, is a projectivity.

***13.** Prove that if $[\mathbf{X}^*]$ and $[\mathbf{X}^{**}]$ are two given projective coordinatizations, they are related by (2.4), that is, there exists a nonsingular matrix $\mathbf{C}$ such that $[\mathbf{X}^{**}] = [\mathbf{CX}^*]$.

***14.** Prove that if $[\mathbf{X}^*]$ denotes a given projective coordinatization, and if another mapping from $S_1(\mathsf{F})$ onto Ω_2 is defined by $[\mathbf{X}^*] = [\mathbf{CX}^{**}]$, $\det \mathbf{C} \neq 0$, then $[\mathbf{X}^{**}]$ is a projective coordinatization.

3 Cross Ratio

If P_1 and P_2 are points of $S_1(\mathsf{F})$, we denote by $(\mathbf{P}_1 \quad \mathbf{P}_2)$ the 2×2 matrix whose columns are the representatives $\mathbf{P}_1$ and $\mathbf{P}_2$ of the respective points, and by $\det(\mathbf{P}_1 \quad \mathbf{P}_2)$ the determinant of this matrix. If $\pi \in G_3$ with representative matrix $\mathbf{A}$, and if for every $X \in S_1$ we choose representatives $\mathbf{X}$ of X and $\mathbf{X}'$ of $X' = \pi X$ satisfying

$$(3.1) \qquad \mathbf{X}' = \mathbf{A}\mathbf{X}, \qquad \det \mathbf{A} \neq 0,$$

we have by (I, (3.4)) that

$$(3.2) \qquad \det(\mathbf{P}_1' \quad \mathbf{P}_2') = (\det \mathbf{A}) \det(\mathbf{P}_1 \quad \mathbf{P}_2).$$

Since any two sets of two, or three, distinct points are projectively equivalent (Theorem 2.2), neither two nor three points possess any projective invariants except trivial ones that characterize distinctness conditions. Indeed, from (3.2) the condition $\det(\mathbf{P}_1 \quad \mathbf{P}_2) = 0$ characterizes pairs of points P_1, P_2 such that $P_1 = P_2$. Two quadruples of distinct points need not be projectively equivalent (see Theorem 2.2), and we seek to construct an invariant function (with range in F itself) defined for all quadruples of distinct points and possibly for some quadruples of nondistinct points. Besides (3.2), we need to consider the change in $\det(\mathbf{P}_1 \quad \mathbf{P}_2)$ when we replace the representatives $\mathbf{P}_i$ by $\mathbf{P}_i^* = \rho_i \mathbf{P}_i$; clearly

$$(3.3) \qquad \det(\mathbf{P}_1^* \quad \mathbf{P}_2^*) = \rho_1 \rho_2 \det(\mathbf{P}_1 \quad \mathbf{P}_2), \qquad \rho_1 \rho_2 \neq 0.$$

Let $P_i : \mathbf{P}_i$ $(i = 1, 2, 3, 4)$ be four points, and let $(P_1 P_2, P_3 P_4)$ be the ratio of ratios defined, for distinct points, by

$$(3.4) \qquad (P_1 P_2, P_3 P_4) = \frac{\det(\mathbf{P}_1 \quad \mathbf{P}_3)}{\det(\mathbf{P}_1 \quad \mathbf{P}_4)} \div \frac{\det(\mathbf{P}_2 \quad \mathbf{P}_3)}{\det(\mathbf{P}_2 \quad \mathbf{P}_4)}.$$

Our notation anticipates our conclusion that $(P_1 P_2, P_3 P_4)$ is determined when *points* P_i are specified, even though (3.4) expresses $(P_1 P_2, P_3 P_4)$ in terms of the representatives of a particular projective coordinate system. Since (3.4) can be written

$$(3.5) \qquad (P_1 P_2, P_3 P_4) = \frac{\det(\mathbf{P}_1 \quad \mathbf{P}_3)}{\det(\mathbf{P}_1 \quad \mathbf{P}_4)} \; \frac{\det(\mathbf{P}_2 \quad \mathbf{P}_4)}{\det(\mathbf{P}_2 \quad \mathbf{P}_3)},$$

a change of representatives would introduce the same factor in both numerator and denominator of the right side of (3.5), and thus the quotient would be unchanged. Similarly, a transformation of coordinates would, for representatives satisfying (3.1), introduce the factor $(\det \mathbf{A})^2$ in both numerator and denominator of (3.5) and would leave the fraction unchanged. Hence we have justified the following definition.

DEFINITION 3.1. The function $(P_1 P_2, P_3 P_4)$ of four ordered points (where $P_1 \neq P_4$ and $P_2 \neq P_3$) defined by (3.5) is called the *cross ratio* of the four points. When we speak of the cross ratio of four specific points, we shall always understand that the ordering is that given by their enumeration.

Our argument that the right side of (3.5) does not depend on the chosen projective coordinatization can be reinterpreted: If we interpet (3.1) as a projectivity π rather than a coordinate transformation, we conclude that

$$(P_1 P_2, P_3 P_4) = (\pi P_1 \, \pi P_2, \pi P_3 \, \pi P_4). \tag{3.6}$$

We can summarize these results in the following theorem.

THEOREM 3.1. *The cross ratio $(P_1 P_2, P_3 P_4)$ of four ordered points P_1, P_2, P_3, P_4 is given, in terms of any projective coordinate system by* (3.5), *and is undefined only if $P_1 = P_4$ or $P_2 = P_3$. The cross ratio is a projective invariant, that is, two quadruples that are projectively equivalent have equal cross ratios.*

Four distinct points P_1, P_2, P_3, P_4 possess twenty-four permutations. Since

$$\det(\mathbf{P}_i \quad \mathbf{P}_j) = -\det(\mathbf{P}_j \quad \mathbf{P}_i), \tag{3.7}$$

it follows from the definition of cross ratio that

$$(P_1 P_2, P_3 P_4) = (P_2 P_1, P_4 P_3) = (P_3 P_4, P_1 P_2) = (P_4 P_3, P_2 P_1). \tag{3.8}$$

Consequently four unordered points have at most six distinct cross ratios. How these six are related among themselves is described in the following theorem.

THEOREM 3.2. *Four unordered points have at most six distinct cross ratios. All can be obtained from a particular one by repeated applications of the following relations*:

$$(P_1 P_2, P_3 P_4) = (P_3 P_4, P_1 P_2), \tag{3.9}$$

$$(P_1 P_2, P_3 P_4) = 1/(P_1 P_2, P_4 P_3), \tag{3.10}$$

$$(P_1 P_2, P_3 P_4) = 1 - (P_1 P_3, P_2 P_4). \tag{3.11}$$

Proof. We first prove these relations. Equation (3.9) is contained in (3.8), and (3.10) is an immediate consequence of the definition of cross ratio. To prove (3.11), we shall use the following algebraic identity involving any four column matrices of order 2×1, the proof of which we leave to the reader (Exercise 8 below).

$$\det(\mathbf{P}_1 \quad \mathbf{P}_2)\det(\mathbf{P}_3 \quad \mathbf{P}_4) + \det(\mathbf{P}_1 \quad \mathbf{P}_3)\det(\mathbf{P}_4 \quad \mathbf{P}_2) + \det(\mathbf{P}_1 \quad \mathbf{P}_4)\det(\mathbf{P}_2 \quad \mathbf{P}_3) = 0. \tag{3.12}$$

We divide (3.12) by $\det(\mathbf{P}_1 \quad \mathbf{P}_4)\det(\mathbf{P}_2 \quad \mathbf{P}_3)$ and use (3.5) and (3.7) to prove (3.11).

We leave the rest of the proof to the reader (Exercise 6 below). He will find that if λ is one of the cross ratios, the others are $1/\lambda$, $1-\lambda$, $1/(1-\lambda)$, $\lambda/(\lambda-1)$, and $(\lambda-1)/\lambda$.

We shall use the following lemmas frequently.

LEMMA 3.1. *If P_1, P_2, P_3, P_4 are four points in $S_1(\mathsf{F})$ with representatives $(w, 1)^T$, $(x, 1)^T$, $(y, 1)^T$, $(z, 1)^T$, respectively,*

$$(P_1 P_2, P_3 P_4) = (w-y)(x-z)/(w-z)(x-y).$$

LEMMA 3.2. *If Y_1, P_2, P_3, P_4 are four points in $S_1(\mathsf{F})$ with representatives $(1, 0)^T$, $(x, 1)^T$, $(y, 1)^T$, $(z, 1)^T$,*

$$(Y_1 P_2, P_3 P_4) = (x-z)/(x-y).$$

The reader can supply the proofs using the definition of cross ratio. He should note that the hypotheses require that the points P_i be distinct from the point Y_1. He should also observe that the *formal* operation of taking the limit of the first cross ratio as w becomes infinite gives the second cross ratio.

THEOREM 3.3. If *$Y_1 Y_2 U$ is the reference frame, and $X: (x_1, x_2)^T$ is any point except Y_1,*

$$(Y_1 Y_2, U X) = x_1/x_2. \tag{3.13}$$

Equation (3.13) is an immediate consequence of (3.5). We note that $(Y_1 Y_2, U X)$ fails to exist if and only if $X = Y_1$, and that

$$(Y_1 Y_2, U Y_2) = 0, \qquad (Y_1 Y_2, U U) = 1. \tag{3.14}$$

Let P_1, P_2, P_3 be any three distinct points; Theorems 3.1 and 3.3 assert that

$$\begin{aligned} &\text{(a)} \quad (P_1 P_2, P_3 X) = 0 && \text{if and only if} \quad X = P_2, \\ &\text{(b)} \quad (P_1 P_2, P_3 X) = 1 && \text{if and only if} \quad X = P_3, \\ &\text{(c)} \quad (P_1 P_2, P_3 X) \text{ does not exist} && \text{if and only if} \quad X = P_1. \end{aligned} \tag{3.15}$$

COROLLARY 3.1. *Let P_1, P_2, P_3 be distinct points, and let X vary in $S_1(\mathsf{F})$, with P_1 excluded.* Then *$(P_1 P_2, P_3 X)$ varies over* F, *and the map from $S_1(\mathsf{F})$ (with P_1 excluded) to* F *is one-to-one and onto.*

We have already seen that every projectivity preserves cross ratio, that is, every quadruple of four ordered points that possesses cross ratio is transformed into a quadruple of equal cross ratio. The following theorem points up the basic role of cross ratio.

THEOREM 3.4. *Every point transformation of $S_1(\mathsf{F})$ into itself that preserves cross ratio is a projectivity.*

Instead of this theorem, we shall prove a stronger one.

THEOREM 3.5. *Let τ be a point transformation of $S_1(\mathsf{F})$ into itself, and let P_1, P_2, P_3 be three given distinct points. If $(P_1 P_2, P_3 X) = (\tau P_1\, \tau P_2, \tau P_3\, \tau X)$ for $X \in S_1(\mathsf{F})$, $X \neq P_1$, then τ is a projectivity.*

Proof. We first conclude that the three points τP_i are distinct: we have from (3.15b) that $(\tau P_1\, \tau P_2, \tau P_3\, \tau P_3) = 1$, and therefore (see Exercise 5 below) that τP_3 is distinct from τP_1 and τP_2; if $X = P_2$, $(\tau P_1\, \tau P_2, \tau P_3\, \tau P_2) = 0$, and therefore $\tau P_1 \neq \tau P_2$. We next find the equation of τ in the coordinate system with $\tau P_1, \tau P_2, \tau P_3$ as reference frame; we denote representatives of X and τX by $\mathbf{X} = (x_1, x_2)^T, \mathbf{X}' = (x_1', x_2')^T$, respectively; by Theorem 3.3

(3.16a) $$(\tau P_1\, \tau P_2, \tau P_3\, \tau X) = x_1'/x_2', \qquad X \neq P_1.$$

We let $\mathbf{X}^*$, where $\mathbf{X}^* = (x_1^*, x_2^*)^T$, be a representative of X in the coordinate system with $P_1 P_2 P_3$ as reference frame, so that

(3.16b) $$(P_1 P_2, P_3 X) = x_1^*/x_2^*, \qquad X \neq P_1.$$

Our hypothesis that τ preserves the specified cross ratios, together with (3.15c), implies that

(3.17) $$[\mathbf{X}'] = [\mathbf{X}^*], \qquad \text{for all } X \in S_1(\mathsf{F}).$$

But the two coordinatizations are related; there exists a nonsingular matrix $\mathbf{A}$ such that $[\mathbf{X}^*] = [\mathbf{AX}]$. Hence $[\mathbf{X}'] = [\mathbf{AX}]$, det $\mathbf{A} \neq 0$, and consequently τ is a projectivity.

Of special importance, throughout this book, are sets of four points, one of whose cross ratios is -1. From equations (3.9), (3.10), and (3.11), we see that the different cross ratios of such sets, corresponding to the different permutations of the four points have only the three distinct values -1, 2, and 1/2. We note further that if

(3.18) $$(P_1 P_2, P_3 P_4) = -1,$$

then we have from the above equations that also

$$(P_1 P_2, P_4 P_3) = -1, \qquad (P_3 P_4, P_1 P_2) = -1, \qquad (P_4 P_3, P_1 P_2) = -1.$$

We thus see that interchanging the elements of either pair independently of the other pair, as well as interchanging the pairs, leaves the value of the cross ratio (3.18) unchanged.

DEFINITION 3.2. If the cross ratio $(P_1 P_2, P_3 P_4)$ is equal to -1, we say that the one pair of points P_1, P_2 (or P_3, P_4) *separates* the other pair P_3, P_4 (or P_1, P_2) *harmonically*; the elements of either pair are *harmonic conjugates*, or briefly, conjugate, with respect to the other pair.

By Corollary 3.1 the harmonic conjugate of a given point with respect to a given pair of points (when the three given points are distinct) is unique.

We shall have frequent occasion to use the following particular harmonic sets.

LEMMA 3.3. *The following quadruples have cross ratio equal to* -1 *provided that* x, y *are any elements of* F *for which each quadruple consists of distinct points*:

(a) $Y_1:(1,0)^T$, $Y_2:(0,1)^T$, $X:(x,1)^T$, $X':(-x,1)^T$;
(b) $X:(x,1)^T$, $Y:(y,1)^T$, $Y_1:(1,0)^T$, $X'':(\frac{1}{2}(x+y),1)^T$;
(c) $X:(x,1)^T$, $X':(-x,1)^T$, $U:(1,1)^T$, $X''':(x^2,1)^T$.

To prove the lemma, it suffices to compute the cross ratios. A convenient way to express the substance of this lemma is to use the symbol ∞ in place of Y_1 and to represent the point $X:(x,1)$ by the mark x which also denotes an element of F. Then we can write

$$(\infty\ 0, x\ -x) = -1, \qquad x \neq 0; \tag{3.19}$$

$$(x\ y, \tfrac{1}{2}(x+y)\ \infty) = -1, \qquad x \neq y; \tag{3.20}$$

$$(x\ -x, 1\ x^2) = -1, \qquad x^2 \neq 1. \tag{3.21}$$

The next theorem plays a very basic role in real projective geometry.

THEOREM 3.6. *A map with domain* $S_1(\mathsf{R})$, *and range contained in* $S_1(\mathsf{R})$, *which preserves harmonic sets is a projectivity.*

Proof. We first show that the given map, say τ, is one-to-one. If distinct points Y,Z had coincident maps, $\tau Y = \tau Z$, we could select P,Q so that $(P\ Q, Y\ Z) = -1$. But $(\tau P\ \tau Q, \tau Y\ \tau Z) = -1$ for $\tau Y = \tau Z$ is impossible, so $\tau Y \neq \tau Z$.

Introduce a projective coordinate system, with reference frame say $Y_1\ Y_2\ U$, and let π be the projectivity which maps τY_1, τY_2, and τU onto Y_1, Y_2, and U, respectively. Then $\pi\tau$ leaves Y_1, Y_2, U fixed, and still preserves harmonic sets. For convenience, let $\sigma = \pi\tau$; we shall show that σ is the identity map, from which it follows that τ is the projectivity π^{-1}.

We let $(x,1)^T$ be a representative of $X \in S_1(\mathsf{R})$, $X \neq Y_1$, and $(\sigma x, 1)^T$ of σX. From (3.20), $(x\ 0, \frac{1}{2}x\ \infty) = -1$; since $\sigma 0 = 0$, $\sigma\infty = \infty$, and σ preserves harmonic sets,

$$(\sigma x\ 0, \sigma(\tfrac{1}{2}x)\ \infty) = -1.$$

But the "fourth" harmonic is unique, and from (3.20)

$$\sigma(\tfrac{1}{2}x) = \tfrac{1}{2}\sigma x. \tag{3.22}$$

Again, the maps of the four points in (3.20) form a harmonic set,

$$(\sigma x\ \sigma y, \sigma(\tfrac{1}{2}(x+y))\ \infty) = -1;$$

therefore by (3.20) and the uniqueness of the "fourth" harmonic,

$$\sigma(\tfrac{1}{2}(x+y)) = \tfrac{1}{2}(\sigma x + \sigma y),$$

or, by using (3.22),

$$\sigma(x+y) = \sigma x + \sigma y. \tag{3.23}$$

Letting $x+y=0$, we have $\sigma(-x) = -\sigma x$. From (3.23), for $y = x$, we obtain that $\sigma(2x) = 2\sigma x$; by induction it follows that $\sigma(nx) = n\sigma x$ for all integers n. Letting $x = 1$, we have $\sigma n = n$; letting $x = m/n$ (where m, n are integers) we have $\sigma m = n\sigma(m/n)$, or $\sigma(m/n) = (1/n)\sigma m = m/n$. Thus σ leaves fixed every point for which x is rational.

We do not need to require that τ be continuous† to finish the proof. Applying σ to the four points in (3.21), we obtain that $\sigma(x^2) = (\sigma x)^2$; since every positive real number is a square, it follows that $x > 0$ implies $\sigma x > 0$. Accordingly $x > y$, or its equivalent $x - y > 0$ implies that $\sigma(x-y) > 0$, or $\sigma x > \sigma y$. Thus σ preserves the order relation of the reals.

We are now ready to show that $\sigma x = x$ for all $x \in \mathsf{R}$. Let x be irrational, and suppose that $x < \sigma x$. Then we can choose a rational r so that $x < r < \sigma x$. Since σ preserves order and leaves all rationals fixed, $x < r$ implies $\sigma x < r$, and we have a contradiction. Similarly, $\sigma x < x$ is impossible, and we must have $\sigma x = x$.

EXERCISES

In the numerical exercises it may be assumed that the ground field is R.

1. Find the values of the cross ratio for each of the twenty-four permutations of the points $P_1 : (2,1)^T$, $P_2 : (1,2)^T$, $P_3 : (-1,1)^T$, and $P_4 : (1,0)^T$.

2. Find the cross ratios $(P_1 P_1, P_2 P_3)$, $(P_1 P_2, P_3 P_3)$, and $(P_1 P_2, P_1 P_3)$
(a) where P_1, P_2, P_3 have coordinates as in Exercise 1;
(b) where P_1, P_2, P_3 are any three distinct points.

3. Find X if $(P_1 P_2, P_3 X) = 2$ and P_1, P_2, P_3 are as given in Exercise 1.

***4.** Prove that $(P_1 P_2, P_3 P_4)(P_1 P_2, P_4 P_5)(P_1 P_2, P_5 P_3) = 1$, if each cross ratio is defined.

5. Prove that $(P_1 P_2, P_3 P_3) = 1$ implies that $P_3 \neq P_1$ and $P_3 \neq P_2$. What conclusion can you draw from $(P_1 P_2, P_3 P_2) = 0$?

6. Finish the proof of Theorem 3.2 by verifying the assertion in the text.

7. Identify all quadruples of distinct points in $S_1(\mathsf{R})$ that have less than six distinct cross ratios. Is the answer the same in $S_1(\mathsf{C})$?

***8.** Prove (3.12). Consider the three cases: (a) $\det(\mathbf{P}_3 \quad \mathbf{P}_4) \neq 0$; (b) $\det(\mathbf{P}_3 \quad \mathbf{P}_4) = 0$, $\mathbf{P}_4 \neq \mathbf{0}_{21}$; (c) $\mathbf{P}_4 = \mathbf{0}_{21}$. In (a) express the other two column matrices as linear combinations of $\mathbf{P}_3$ and $\mathbf{P}_4$. Can this be done in (b)?

† We have not even defined continuity in $S_1(\mathsf{R})$.

9. Let three points have representatives $(1,1)^T$, $(2,1)^T$, and $(3,1)^T$. Find the harmonic conjugate of each with respect to the other two.

***10.** Prove that in $S_1(\mathsf{R})$ the cross ratio given in Lemma 3.1 has a limit as w becomes infinite. What is the value of the limit? Can you conclude that $\lim_{w\to\infty} P_1 = Y_1:(1,0)$?

#***11.** Prove that if P_1, P_2, P_3 are three distinct points, there exists a nonsingular matrix **A** with elements a_{ij} such that

$$(P_1 P_2, P_3 X) = (a_{11}x_1 + a_{12}x_2)/(a_{21}x_1 + a_{22}x_2)$$

for all $X \in S_1(\mathsf{F})$, $X \neq P_1$. Describe $[\mathbf{X}'] = [\mathbf{AX}]$, (a) as a projectivity, and (b) as a coordinate transformation.

12. Find the projectivity that maps the points $P_1:(1,1)^T$, $P_1:(2,1)^T$, and $P_3:(3,4)^T$ onto $P_1':(1,2)^T$, $P_2':(5,3)^T$, and $P_3':(0,1)^T$, respectively.

$$\text{Ans. } \mathbf{A} = \begin{pmatrix} 4 & -3 \\ 1 & 1 \end{pmatrix}.$$

13. Find $x' \in \mathsf{F}$ as a function of $x \in \mathsf{F}$ if $(-1\,1, x\,x') = -1$.

#***14.** Let P_1, P_2, P_3, P_4 be four distinct points in $S_1(\mathsf{R})$. The pair P_1, P_2 is said to *separate* the pair P_3, P_4 (written $P_1P_2 \int P_3P_4$) whenever $(P_1P_2, P_3P_4) < 0$; P_1, P_2 *do not separate* P_3, P_4 (written $P_1P_2 \not\int P_3P_4$) whenever $(P_1P_2, P_3P_4) > 0$. Prove the following properties of separation:

(a) Separation is a projective property of four points.

(b) If $P_1P_2 \int P_3P_4$, then $P_1P_2 \int P_4P_3$ and $P_3P_4 \int P_1P_2$.

(c) If $P_1P_2 \int P_3P_4$, then $P_1P_3 \not\int P_2P_4$ and $P_1P_4 \not\int P_2P_3$.

(d) Four distinct points can be divided into two mutually separating pairs in one and only one way.

#***15.** Show that Theorem 3.5 does not hold in $S_1(\mathsf{C})$ by verifying that the map given by $x_1' = \bar{x}_1$, $x_2' = \bar{x}_2$, where $x_1, x_2 \in \mathsf{C}$ and $\bar{x}_i$ is the complex conjugate of x_i, preserves harmonic sets.

4 Real Projective Space and Euclidean Lines

Let s be a metric coordinate on a Euclidean line E_1, and let $[\mathbf{X}] = [x_1, x_2]^T$ be a projective coordinate on $S_1(\mathsf{R})$. Equations such as

$$s = x_1/x_2, \qquad s = x_1^3/x_2^3, \qquad s = (x_1^2 - x_2^2)/(x_1^2 + x_2^2)$$

define point transformations or maps of a set of points in the one space into the other. We regard such maps as geometric entities, so that their analytic representation by means of coordinates changes with coordinate transformations. We shall be concerned with a certain class of maps of E_1 into $S_1(\mathsf{R})$

that we call *embeddings* of E_1 in $S_1(\mathsf{R})$. It will suffice for our present purposes to say that a map of E_1 to $S_1(\mathsf{R})$ is an embedding if there exists a metric coordinatization of E_1 and a projective coordinatization of $S_1(\mathsf{R})$ in terms of which the map is given by†

$$s = x_1/x_2 . \tag{4.1}$$

Conversely, for given coordinatizations of E_1 and $S_1(\mathsf{R})$, (4.1) establishes a map of E_1 into $S_1(\mathsf{R})$, and hence we can associate a definite embedding (4.1) with the given coordinatizations. In discussing an embedding, we shall generally employ coordinatizations in which (4.1) represents the embedding.

Let $\mathscr{E}$ be a given embedding. From (4.1), the domain of definition of $\mathscr{E}$ is the entire Euclidean line, but the range is not $S_1(\mathsf{R})$, but $S_1(\mathsf{R})$ with one point excluded. We call this point the *absolute point*, or the *point at infinity*, of the embedding. We shall denote this point by $\infty(\mathscr{E})$. When we are considering only one embedding, it will generally suffice to write ∞ for $\infty(\mathscr{E})$. Thus $\infty \in S_1(\mathsf{R})$, and if P is a given point of $S_1(\mathsf{R})$, there exists an embedding $\mathscr{E}$ such that $\infty(\mathscr{E}) = P$.

Let P_1, P_2, P_3, P_4 be four points of E_1; we use temporarily the notation $P_i P_j$ to denote directed distance from P_i to P_j. We call the ratio of directed distances $P_1 P_3/P_1 P_4$ the ratio in which P_3 divides the ordered pair P_1, P_4. The Euclidean counterpart of (projective) cross ratio is the Euclidean *cross ratio of four points*, also denoted by $(P_1 P_2, P_3 P_4)$ where $P_i \in E_1$, and defined, for distinct points, as the ratio of the two ratios, $P_1 P_3/P_1 P_4$ divided by $P_2 P_3/P_2 P_4$. To include the possibility that $P_2 = P_4$, we let

$$(P_1 P_2, P_3 P_4) = \frac{P_1 P_3}{P_1 P_4} \cdot \frac{P_2 P_4}{P_2 P_3} . \tag{4.2}$$

If s is a metric coordinate on E_1, and if $s(P_i) = s_i$ $(i = 1, 2, 3, 4)$, we have $P_i P_j = s_j - s_i$ (I, Definition 6.7); hence

$$P_1 P_3/P_1 P_4 = (s_3 - s_1)/(s_4 - s_1), \tag{4.3}$$

and

$$(P_1 P_2, P_3 P_4) = (s_1 - s_3)(s_2 - s_4)/(s_1 - s_4)(s_2 - s_3). \tag{4.4}$$

THEOREM 4.1. *The cross ratio of four points of E_1 is equal to the cross ratio, in $S_1(\mathsf{R})$, of their maps under an embedding.*

Proof. We let $\mathscr{E}$ be any embedding, and we choose coordinatizations in which $\mathscr{E}$ is given by (4.1). Then $\infty(\mathscr{E}) = Y_1 : (1, 0)^T$, so that if $P_i \in E_1$ and $s(P_i) = s_i, \mathscr{E} P_i$ possesses a representative $(s_i, 1)^T$. By (4.4) and Lemma 3.1, the two quadruples have equal cross ratios.

† Our present definition of an embedding is incomplete; we give the complete definition in Chapter V. But our immediate objectives do not require an analysis of the relation between the group of motions on E_1 and the group G_3 of $S_1(\mathsf{R})$.

THEOREM 4.2. *The ratio, in E_1, in which a point P_4 divides the points P_2, P_3 is equal to the cross ratio in $S_1(\mathsf{R})$ of the four points: the absolute point of an embedding and the maps by the embedding of the three points, that is,*

$$P_2 P_4 / P_2 P_3 = (\infty(\mathscr{E})\ \mathscr{E}P_2, \mathscr{E}P_3\ \mathscr{E}P_4). \tag{4.5}$$

The proof follows from Lemma 3.2 and (4.3).

THEOREM 4.3. *A projection between any two Euclidean lines preserves cross ratio.*

Proof. Let the lines be denoted by E_1 and E_1', and the projection by τ. If s and s' are metric coordinates in E_1 and E_1', respectively, τ is given by (I, Theorem 7.1)

$$s' = (a_{11} s + a_{12})/(a_{21} s + a_{22}), \qquad \det(a_{ij}) \neq 0. \tag{4.6}$$

It would be a straightforward computation to evaluate the cross ratio of the transforms, by τ, of four arbitrary points of E_1 in terms of the cross ratio of the points themselves and thereby establish the theorem. But the computation would essentially duplicate earlier computations, and we prefer to present a type of argument which it is important to understand. In a given coordinatization of $S_1(\mathsf{R})$, the equations

$$s = x_1/x_2, \qquad s' = x_1/x_2 \tag{4.7}$$

establish embeddings $\mathscr{E}$ and $\mathscr{E}'$ of E_1 and E_1', respectively, in S_1. Let us indicate these maps, together with τ, schematically in the diagram below,

$$\begin{array}{ccc} P & \xrightarrow{\mathscr{E}} & X \\ \downarrow \tau & & \\ P' & \xrightarrow{\mathscr{E}'} & X' \end{array}$$

where $P \in E_1$, $P' = \tau P \in E_1'$, $X = \mathscr{E}P \in S_1(\mathsf{R})$, and $X' = \mathscr{E}'P' \in S_1(\mathsf{R})$. The map, in S_1, from X to X' is the product map $\mathscr{E}'\tau\mathscr{E}^{-1}$. Let $\sigma = \mathscr{E}'\tau\mathscr{E}^{-1}$, so that $\tau = \mathscr{E}'^{-1}\sigma\mathscr{E}$. By Theorem 4.1, under $\mathscr{E}$ and $\mathscr{E}'^{-1}$, Euclidean and projective cross ratios of corresponding quadruples of points are equal, so that to prove the theorem, it suffices to show that σ preserves projective cross ratios. We find an equation of σ from (4.6) and (4.7) by the usual procedure for finding products. We find that σ coincides with the projectivity

$$\pi\colon\ [\mathbf{X}'] = [\mathbf{AX}], \qquad (\mathbf{A})_{ij} = a_{ij},$$

at all points of $X \in S_1(\mathsf{R})$ for which σ is defined.† Hence σ preserves the cross ratio of all quadruples that are relevant for our purposes, and the theorem is proved.

† We note that $\sigma = \mathscr{E}'\tau\mathscr{E}^{-1}$ is not defined at $\infty(\mathscr{E})$, whereas π is; if τ is a central projection between nonparallel lines, there exists $Q \in E_1$ such that τQ is not defined, so that σ is not defined at $\mathscr{E}Q$.

We note further that if there exists $P_1 \in E_1$ at which the projection τ is not defined, and if P_2, P_3, P_4 are three other points of E_1, and $P'_i = \tau P_i$ $(i = 2, 3, 4)$, then

$$(4.8) \qquad (P_1 P_2, P_3 P_4) = P'_2 P'_4 / P'_2 P'_3 .$$

If p_1, p_2, p_3, p_4 are four concurrent lines of E_2, and if a line p (not through their common point) intersects p_i in a point P_i, the cross ratio $(P_1 P_2, P_3 P_4)$ does not vary with p: If P'_1, P'_2, P'_3, P'_4 is a second set of intersections (Figure 4.1), there exists a projection τ that maps P_i onto P'_i, and by Theorem

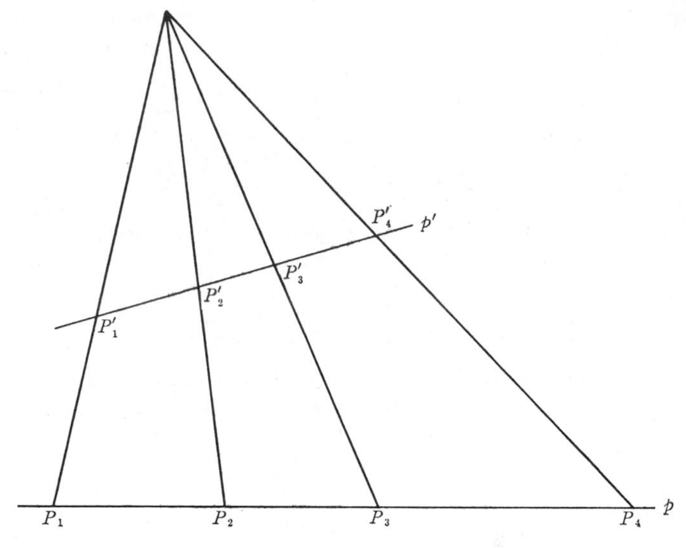

FIGURE 4.1

4.3, $(P_1 P_2, P_3 P_4) = (P'_1 P'_2, P'_3 P'_4)$. We can thereby define the Euclidean *cross ratio of four concurrent lines* to be the cross ratio of their intersections with an arbitrary line not through the common point of the four lines. (4.8) permits us to choose the transversal p to be parallel to one of the lines p_i.

Let W be any Euclidean pencil of concurrent lines, and let W be coordinatized in the manner described in Illustration 6, Section 1, so that if $[\mathbf{p}] = [p_1, p_2]^T \in \Omega_2$ (over R), the line $p : [\mathbf{p}]$ has the equation (in a suitable Cartesian system)

$$(4.9) \qquad p_2 x - p_1 y = 0.$$

Let $[\mathbf{X}] = [x_1, x_2]^T$ be projective coordinates in $S_1(\mathrm{R})$. We define an *embedding* of W in $S_1(\mathrm{R})$ to be any map from W to $S_1(\mathrm{R})$ which can be represented, for suitable choices of the $[\mathbf{p}]$- and $[\mathbf{X}]$-coordinatizations, by the equations

$$(4.10) \qquad [\mathbf{p}] = [\mathbf{X}].$$

We note that an embedding $\mathscr{E}$ of E_1 in $S_1(\mathsf{R})$ is into $S_1(\mathsf{R})$, with range consisting of $S_1(\mathsf{R}) - \infty(\mathscr{E})$. On the other hand, the embedding (4.10) is one-to-one from W onto $S_1(\mathsf{R})$. In the first case the space embedded in $S_1(\mathsf{R})$ possesses a metric coordinate (distance) which corresponds to a nonhomogeneous projective coordinate in $S_1(\mathsf{R})$. In the second case, the space embedded in $S_1(\mathsf{R})$ possesses a metric invariant (angle) whose tangent (that is, slope) corresponds to a nonhomogeneous projective coordinate in $S_1(\mathsf{R})$. We shall occasionally refer to these embeddings as *embeddings of the first* and *second kinds*, respectively.

THEOREM 4.4. *The Euclidean cross ratio of four concurrent lines is equal to the cross ratio in* $S_1(\mathsf{R})$ *of their maps under an embedding* (4.10).

Proof. Let us first suppose that for each of the lines $p_i : \mathbf{p}_i = (p_{1i}, p_{2i})^T$ we have $p_{2i} \neq 0$ for $i = 1, 2, 3, 4$. Then, from (4.9), the lines p_i are not parallel to the line $y = 1$, and $x = p_1/p_2$ is a metric coordinate on $y = 1$. Therefore the cross ratio of the four points of intersection of the lines p_i with $y = 1$ is given by (4.4) with $s_i = p_{1i}/p_{2i}$. But the cross ratio of the maps of p_i under the embedding (4.10) has, by Lemma 3.1, the same value.

If one of the lines, say p_1, is parallel to $y = 1$, $p_{12} = 0$, and the map of p_1 by the embedding (4.10) is the point $Y_1 : (1, 0)^T$. Then the cross ratio of the four lines is given by the ratio (4.8); by Lemma 3.2 and equation (4.3), the two cross ratios are equal.

COROLLARY 4.1. *A point* $P \in E_1$ *is the midpoint of two points* P_1, P_2 *if and only if an embedding* $\mathscr{E}$ *maps* P *onto the harmonic conjugate of the absolute point with respect to the pair* $\mathscr{E}P_1, \mathscr{E}P_2$, *that is,*

$$P_1 P / P_1 P_2 = 1/2 \quad \textit{if and only if} \quad (\mathscr{E}P_1 \, \mathscr{E}P_2, \mathscr{E}P \, \infty) = -1.$$

The proof follows from (3.19).

COROLLARY 4.2. *The bisectors of the angles between two lines of* E_2 *separate the lines harmonically.*

Proof. We can suppose that the lines have the equations $y = \lambda x$ and $y = -\lambda x$, so that their bisectors are the lines $x = 0$ and $y = 0$. By (3.19), $(\infty \, 0, \lambda \, -\lambda) = -1$, and the corollary is proved.

CONSTRUCTION PROBLEM 4.1. Let P_1, P_2, P_3 be three distinct collinear points of E_2. Construct P_4 so that $(P_1 P_2, P_3 P_4) = -1$.

Solution. Let $Q \in E_2$ not collinear with P_1, P_2, and let Q' be the midpoint of $P_1 Q$ (Figure 4.2). Draw the lines QP_2 and $Q'P_3$, and suppose they intersect in Q''. The line through Q'' parallel to $P_1 Q$ will intersect $P_1 P_2$ in the required point. Why?

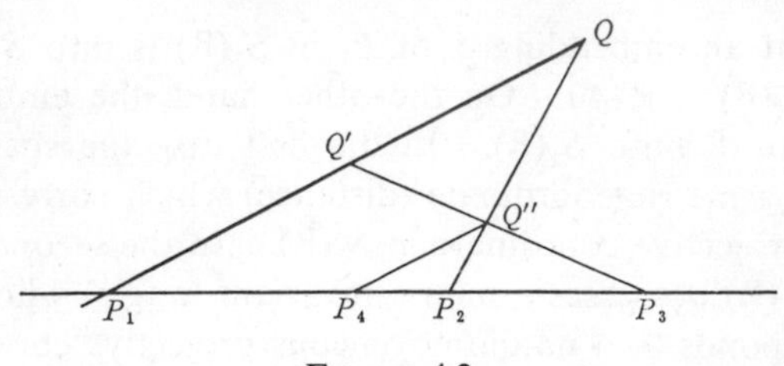

FIGURE 4.2

EXERCISES

1. The points in E_2 with Cartesian coordinates $(1,2)$, $(3,6)$, $(-1,-2)$, and $(0,0)$ lie on the line $y = 2x$. Find their cross ratio (a) by taking projections on the coordinate axes, (b) by introducing a metric coordinatization on the line.

2. Let s be a metric coordinate on a Euclidean line, and let $s' = (s+1)/(2s-2)$ define a coordinate transformation. Interpret the s' coordinate as a cross ratio, and discuss the variation of s' on the line. Is the set of points for which s' satisfies $0 \leqq s' \leqq 2$ a segment?

3. Determine the Euclidean cross ratio of four lines of a pencil in terms of the coordinatization described in Illustration 1, Section 1.

4. Prove that in any (nonisosceles) triangle in E_2, the two angle bisectors at one vertex intersect the opposite side in points that separate the two vertices harmonically, by using the results of this section.

5. Prove that under an embedding (4.10) of a Euclidean pencil of lines in $S_1(\mathsf{R})$, a rotation in the pencil corresponds to a projectivity.

#6. Prove that an order-preserving point transformation of the Euclidean line onto itself which leaves two points fixed and which preserves midpoints must leave all points fixed.

5 Fixed Points of Projectivities

In this section we classify projectivities in terms of their fixed points. We shall see that the fixed points can be determined by the solutions of a quadratic equation, and therefore our conclusions will depend on the choice of the field F. We shall emphasize the two special cases: the real field R and the complex field C.

We represent a projectivity π by

$$\text{(5.1)} \qquad \mathbf{X}' = \mathbf{A}\mathbf{X}, \qquad \det \mathbf{A} \neq 0,$$

and a point $X:\mathbf{X}$ coincides with its map $\pi X:\mathbf{X}'$ if and only if $\det(\mathbf{X} \quad \mathbf{X}') = 0$. Applying this criterion when $\mathbf{X}' = \mathbf{A}\mathbf{X} = (a_{11}x_1 + a_{12}x_2,\ a_{21}x_1 + a_{22}x_2)^T$

and expanding the determinant, we find that the point $X:(x_1, x_2)^T$ is a fixed point if and only if

$$a_{21}x_1^2 + (a_{22} - a_{11})x_1x_2 - a_{12}x_2^2 = 0. \tag{5.2}$$

It will be convenient to let $Q(\mathbf{A})$ denote the quadratic form† in (5.2):

$$Q(\mathbf{A}) = a_{21}x_1^2 + (a_{22} - a_{11})x_1x_2 - a_{12}x_2^2. \tag{5.3}$$

We note that a given binary quadratic form,

$$Q = b_{11}x_1^2 + 2b_{12}x_1x_2 + b_{22}x_2^2, \qquad b_{ij} \in \mathsf{F}, \tag{5.4}$$

is $Q(\mathbf{A})$ for suitable choices of $\mathbf{A}$, so that (5.2), as $\mathbf{A}$ varies, represents all homogeneous quadratic equations in x_1, x_2.

We digress briefly to consider binary quadratic forms (5.4). If Q has the value zero at a point of $S_1(\mathsf{F})$ with coordinate $[r_1, r_2]^T$, then

$$0 = b_{11}r_1^2 + 2b_{12}r_1r_2 + b_{22}r_2^2. \tag{5.5}$$

If we multiply (5.4) by r_2^2 and (5.5) by x_2^2 and subtract, we find that Q can be factored and that $r_2x_1 - r_1x_2$ is one factor. The other factor is of course linear, and we can choose s_1, s_2 so that

$$Q = (r_2x_1 - r_1x_2)(s_2x_1 - s_1x_2). \tag{5.6a}$$

Conversely, if Q vanishes at two points, we can choose representatives $(r_1, r_2)^T$, $(s_1, s_2)^T$ so that (5.6a) holds; if $(r_1, r_2)^T$, $(s_1, s_2)^T$ denote given representatives of points at which $Q = 0$, there exists $\rho \in \mathsf{F}$ such that

$$Q = \rho(r_2x_1 - r_1x_2)(s_2x_1 - s_1x_2), \qquad \rho \neq 0. \tag{5.6b}$$

Expanding the right side of (5.6b) and comparing coefficients with those in (5.4), we find that

$$(r_2s_2, -r_1s_2 - r_2s_1, r_1s_1) \in [b_{11}, 2b_{12}, b_{22}]. \tag{5.7}$$

This relation is the analogue, for binary quadratic forms, of the familiar relation between the coefficients of a real quadratic polynomial and its zeros.

There need not exist points in $S_1(\mathsf{F})$ at which $Q = 0$: Thus $x_1^2 + x_2^2$ does not vanish in $S_1(\mathsf{R})$, and $x_1^2 - 2x_2^2$ does not vanish in projective space over the rational field.

Returning to (5.2), we see that it is quadratic except if $\pi = I$, the identity projectivity, and we have the following theorem.

THEOREM 5.1. *In $S_1(\mathsf{C})$, a projectivity, other than the identity I, has either two distinct fixed points or one (double-counting) fixed point. In $S_1(\mathsf{R})$, a given projectivity, not I, has no fixed point, one (double-counting) fixed point, or two distinct fixed points.*

† A *form* is a homogeneous polynomial in a given number of variables; binary and ternary forms are forms in two and three variables, respectively.

For a given F, $S_1(\mathsf{F})$ may, with respect to existence of fixed points, follow the pattern of either $S_1(\mathsf{C})$ or $S_1(\mathsf{R})$.

DEFINITION 5.1. A projectivity in $S_1(\mathsf{F})$ is *parabolic* if it possesses exactly one fixed point; it is *nonparabolic* if it is not the identity and not parabolic.

DEFINITION 5.2. In $S_1(\mathsf{R})$, a (nonparabolic) projectivity that possesses no fixed points is *elliptic*, and one that possesses two fixed points is *hyperbolic*.

Thus the identity is neither parabolic nor nonparabolic, neither elliptic nor hyperbolic.

Whenever π possesses a fixed point, we can select a coordinate system in $S_1(\mathsf{F})$ whose reference frame is simply related to the fixed points and thereby obtain canonical representations of different types of projectivities. Suppose first that π is parabolic; if we choose a coordinate system whose vertex $Y_1:(1,0)^T$ is the fixed point of π, (5.2) is equivalent to the equation $x_2^2=0$. Hence in any such coordinate system, we must have $a_{21}=0$, $a_{11}=a_{22}$, and $a_{12}\neq 0$. Conversely, the map $x_1'=a_{11}x_1+a_{12}x_2$, $x_2'=a_{11}x_2$ is a projectivity if $a_{11}\neq 0$; it is parabolic if $a_{11}a_{12}\neq 0$; and it is the identity if $a_{11}\neq 0$, $a_{12}=0$. We can choose a representation for which $a_{11}=1$, and we have the following theorem.

THEOREM 5.2. *In $S_1(\mathsf{F})$, a parabolic projectivity has the canonical representation*

$$x_1'=x_1+ax_2,\qquad x_2'=x_2,\qquad a\neq 0. \tag{5.8}$$

The value of a in (5.8) is not significant; our coordinatization has not been uniquely defined, and if we choose the unit point to be the transform of $Y_2:(0,1)$, we have $a=1$.

If π possesses two fixed points, and if these are taken as the vertices of the reference frame, (5.2) is equivalent to $x_1x_2=0$; then $a_{21}=a_{12}=0$, $a_{11}\neq a_{22}$, and π is given by $x_1'=a_{11}x_1$, $x_2'=a_{22}x_2$. Another canonical representation of π can be obtained by choosing the unit point as one of the fixed points, and the vertices as any pair that separate the fixed points harmonically. Then the other fixed point has a representative $(1,-1)^T$, and (5.2) is equivalent to $x_1^2-x_2^2=0$; hence $a_{11}=a_{22}$, and $a_{12}=a_{21}\neq 0$.

THEOREM 5.3. *In $S_1(\mathsf{F})$, a projectivity with two distinct fixed points possesses the canonical representations*

$$x_1'=ax_1,\qquad x_2'=x_2,\qquad a\neq 0,1, \tag{5.9}$$

and

$$x_1'=ax_1+bx_2,\qquad x_2'=bx_1+ax_2,\qquad a^2-b^2\neq 0,\quad b\neq 0. \tag{5.10}$$

We note that the conditions $a\neq 0$ in (5.9) and $a^2-b^2\neq 0$ in (5.10) are equivalent to $\det\mathbf{A}\neq 0$; the other condition, $a\neq 1$ or $b\neq 0$, excludes the identity.

Theorem 5.3 asserts that in $S_1(\mathsf{R})$ a given hyperbolic projectivity can be represented, in a suitably selected coordinate system and for a suitable value of a, by (5.9); or, equally well, by (5.10) in a different coordinate system with suitable values for a, b. There remain to be considered projectivities without fixed points. For this purpose we complete the square in (5.4) and write

$$b_{11}Q = (b_{11}x_1 + b_{12}x_2)^2 + (b_{11}b_{22} - b_{12}^2)x_2^2.$$

If the equation $Q = 0$ has no solution in the real field, we must have $b_{11} \neq 0$ and $b_{11}b_{22} - b_{12}^2 > 0$. Hence in $S_1(\mathsf{R})$ we can introduce a coordinatization given by

$$[x_1^*, x_2^*]^T = [b_{11}x_1 + b_{12}x_2, \sqrt{b_{11}b_{22} - b_{12}^2}\,x_2]^T, \tag{5.11}$$

and in this coordinate system, the quadratic form Q becomes a constant multiple of $x_1^{*2} + x_2^{*2}$. Thus if π is an elliptic projectivity in $S_1(\mathsf{R})$, we can suppose coordinates chosen so that $Q(\mathbf{A}) = \rho(x_1^2 + x_2^2)$. Then $a_{11} = a_{22}$, and $a_{21} = -a_{12}$. The transformation is not a projectivity unless $\det \mathbf{A} = a_{11}^2 + a_{12}^2 \neq 0$, and it is the identity if $a_{21} = 0$. We thus have the following theorem.

THEOREM 5.4. *In $S_1(\mathsf{R})$, an elliptic projectivity possesses the canonical representation*

$$x_1' = ax_1 - bx_2, \qquad x_2' = bx_1 + ax_2, \qquad b \neq 0. \tag{5.12}$$

From (5.3) we see that $Q(\rho\mathbf{A}) = \rho Q(\mathbf{A})$, so that, in a given coordinatization, a projectivity π determines not the form $Q(\mathbf{A})$, but rather the class of forms $[Q(\mathbf{A})]$ consisting of all nonzero scalar multiples of $Q(\mathbf{A})$. For this and other reasons, we might expect that $[Q]$, rather than Q, has geometric significance. Indeed, if Q is an arbitrary form (5.4), we cannot even define the transform of Q by a projectivity; but variations in the choice of representative coordinates or matrices do not affect $[Q]$; a given projectivity (5.1) transforms a class $[Q]$ into a class $[Q']$ of the same character. Our preceding discussion contains the proof of the following theorem.

THEOREM 5.5. *In $S_1(\mathsf{R})$, a class $[Q]$, where Q is given by* (5.4), *is projectively equivalent to one and just one of the three following classes:*

$$\text{(a)}\ [x_1^2], \qquad \text{(b)}\ [x_1^2 - x_2^2], \qquad \text{(c)}\ [x_1^2 + x_2^2].$$

The three cases occur according as, in (5.4),

$$\det(b_{ij}) = 0, \qquad \det(b_{ij}) < 0, \qquad \det(b_{ij}) > 0.$$

In $S_1(\mathsf{C})$, the two forms (b) and (c) of Theorem 5.5 are projectively equivalent, and $[Q]$ is necessarily equivalent to one of two canonical forms. In any field F, we can write, if Q is given by (5.4) with $b_{11} \neq 0$,

$$[Q] = [(b_{11}x_1 + b_{12}x_2)^2 + (b_{11}b_{22} - b_{12}^2)x_2^2].$$

If $b_{11}b_{22} - b_{12}^2$ is a square in F, $[Q]$ is reducible to $[x_1^2 + x_2^2]$; if $b_{11}b_{22} - b_{12}^2$ is the additive inverse in F of a square, $[Q]$ is reducible to $[x_1^2 - x_2^2]$. But F may possess elements that are neither squares nor negatives of squares, for instance, 2 in the field F_5 and 5 in F_{13}. Hence $S_1(F)$ may possess more than three canonical quadratic forms.

We call the class of forms $[Q(\mathbf{A})]$, represented by (5.3) for the projectivity (5.1), the *invariant quadratic form* of the projectivity.

For many purposes it is convenient to express a projectivity π in terms of representatives $(x, 1)^T$ and $(x', 1)^T$ of points $X \neq Y_1 : (1, 0)^T$ and $\pi X \neq Y_1$. We then have for the four canonical representations

$$x' = x + a; \tag{5.13}$$

$$x' = ax, \qquad a \neq 0; \tag{5.14}$$

$$x' = (ax + b)/(bx + a), \qquad a^2 - b^2 \neq 0; \tag{5.15}$$

$$x' = (ax - b)/(bx + a), \qquad a^2 + b^2 \neq 0; \tag{5.16}$$

we have included the identity projectivity, which is given, in the four cases, by $a = 0$, $a = 1$, $b = 0$, and $b = 0$, respectively. Since $Y_1 : (1, 0)^T$ possesses no representative $(x, 1)^T$, it is a valid objection to these equations that they do not describe the projectivity in question completely. But the formal operation of letting x (or x') become infinite yields valid results, and with this extension of meaning, the linear fractional form itself defines the map, or the inverse map, of $Y_1 : (1, 0)^T$. In this connection the reader should also refer to (II, 3, Exercise 10) and to (II, 2, Exercise 11).

We close this section with a geometric characterization of projectivities with fixed points.

THEOREM 5.6. *If P_1 and P_2 are distinct fixed points of a projectivity π, not I, and if X is a variable point (not P_1, P_2) of $S_1(F)$, the cross ratio $(P_1 P_2, X\, \pi X)$ is constant.*

Proof. We can use the canonical representation (5.14); from Lemma 3.2, $(\infty\, 0, x\, x') = x'/x = a$.

THEOREM 5.7. *Let $a \in F$ distinct from 0 and 1, and let P_1, P_2 be two distinct points of $S_1(F)$. The point transformation π in $S_1(F)$ defined by*

$$\pi X = X' \quad \textit{for} \quad X \neq P_i, \qquad \pi P_i = P_i, \qquad i = 1, 2,$$

where X' is determined by

$$(P_1 P_2, X X') = a, \tag{5.17}$$

is a projectivity.

Proof. Choose coordinates with P_1, P_2 as vertices of the reference frame. Then π is given by (5.14), and the theorem is proved.

DEFINITION 5.3. The constant $(P_1 P_2, X X')$ of Theorems 5.6 and 5.7 is called the *characteristic* of π, corresponding to the ordering P_1, P_2 of its fixed points.

Clearly if k is one characteristic of π, $1/k$ is the other. From (5.17) we have the following theorem.

THEOREM 5.8. *A projectivity is determined by its ordered fixed points and the corresponding characteristic.*

In the canonical form (5.12) (or (5.16)) of an elliptic projectivity in $S_1(\mathsf{R})$, the coefficients belong to the real field. Since every real number can be regarded as a complex number, it follows that in $S_1(\mathsf{C})$, (5.12) (with real coefficients) represents a projectivity with fixed points; these are found to be given by $x = \pm\sqrt{-1}$, and the characteristic can be shown to be a complex constant, not 0 or 1, with absolute value 1. Conversely, the projectivity (5.17) in $S_1(\mathsf{C})$ turns out to possess a real representation if it is expressed in a coordinate system in which the fixed points P_1 and P_2 have representative coordinates which are conjugate complex and if its characteristic is a complex constant with absolute value 1.

EXERCISES

In the numerical exercises it may be assumed that the ground field is R.

1. Find a coordinate transformation which reduces the projectivity $x_1' = x_1 + 5x_2, x_2' = 3x_1 - x_2$ to one of the canonical forms.

2. Show that the projectivity $x_1' = x_1 - 4x_2, x_2' = 3x_1 + 2x_2$ is elliptic. Find its characteristic in $S_1(\mathsf{C})$.

3. Show that the projectivity $x_1' = 6x_1 - 4x_2, x_2' = x_1 + x_2$ is hyperbolic, and find a coordinate transformation which reduces it to the canonical form (5.14).

4. Find all thc projcctivities which leave fixed the points with representatives $(3, 1)^T$ and $(5, 1)^T$.

5. Show that the set of all projectivities with the same fixed points (including the identity) is a group. Is the set of all hyperbolic projectivities and the identity a group?

6. Is the invariant quadratic form of a projectivity an invariant in any of the meanings of Section 3, Chapter I.

7. Prove that the set of projectivities which possess a given invariant quadratic form, together with the identity, is a group.

8. Let **A** and **B** be matrix representations of two projectivities with the same invariant quadratic form. Show that there exist $\rho, \rho' \in \mathsf{F}$ such that $\rho\mathbf{A} - \rho'\mathbf{B} = \mathbf{I}$.

#9. Prove the following theorem: If P_0 is the fixed point of a parabolic projectivity π, then for every point $X \neq P_0, (P_0 X, \pi X\, \pi^{-1}X) = -1$; conversely, if a projectivity leaves P_0 fixed, and if there exists a single point P_1 such that $(P_0 P_1, \pi P_1\ \pi^{-1} P_1) = -1$, then the projectivity is parabolic.

10. Prove that under an embedding (4.10) of a Euclidean pencil of lines in $S_1(\mathsf{R})$, a rotation in the pencil corresponds to an elliptic projectivity.

11. Show that a projectivity π which maps the points A, B, C onto B, C, A respectively, satisfies $\pi^3 = I$, and find the characteristic of π as an element of $G_3(\mathsf{C})$.

6 Involutions

A transformation is said to *interchange* two points P and P' if each is the map of the other.

DEFINITION 6.1. An *involution* is a projectivity that interchanges two distinct points. We say that the two points are a *pair* in the involution.

THEOREM 6.1. *A coordinatization exists in which a given involution in* $S_1(\mathsf{F})$ *has the representation*

$$x_1' = cx_2, \qquad x_2' = x_1, \qquad c \in \mathsf{F}, \quad c \neq 0 \tag{6.1}$$

Proof. Let us choose as the vertices of the reference frame the pair of points that are interchanged. Then $\mathbf{A}(1,0)^T = (0,\rho)^T$, and $\mathbf{A}(0,1)^T = (\rho',0)^T$, so that $a_{11} = a_{22} = 0$. Det $\mathbf{A} \neq 0$ implies that $a_{12}a_{21} \neq 0$, and therefore $x_1' = a_{12}x_2, x_2' = a_{21}x_1$ is an equivalent representation of (6.1).

THEOREM 6.2. *An involution interchanges every point and its transform.*

Proof. The map of $[cx_2, x_1]^T$, by (6.1), is $[cx_1, cx_2]^T = [x_1, x_2]^T$.

The following are immediate consequences of the preceding.

COROLLARY 6.1. *An involution coincides with its inverse, and a projectivity that coincides with its inverse is either the identity or an involution.*

COROLLARY 6.2. *The square of an involution is the identity; a projectivity whose square is the identity is either the identity or an involution.*

THEOREM 6.3. *The projectivity* $[\mathbf{X}'] = [\mathbf{AX}]$, det $\mathbf{A} \neq 0$ *is an involution if and only if*

$$a_{11} + a_{22} = 0. \tag{6.2}$$

Proof. Let us recall the definition of $\mathbf{A}^a$ (I, (5.16)):

$$\mathbf{A} = \begin{pmatrix} a_{11} & a_{12} \\ a_{21} & a_{22} \end{pmatrix}, \qquad \mathbf{A}^a = \begin{pmatrix} a_{22} & -a_{12} \\ -a_{21} & a_{11} \end{pmatrix}.$$

If (6.2) holds, $\mathbf{A}^a = -\mathbf{A}$, so that $\mathbf{A}^a \in [\mathbf{A}]$. But $\mathbf{A}^{-1} \in [\mathbf{A}^a]$, and therefore $\mathbf{A}^{-1} \in [\mathbf{A}]$; since $\mathbf{A} \neq \rho\mathbf{I}$, $\mathbf{X}' = \mathbf{AX}$ is an involution by Corollary 6.1. Conversely, if $\mathbf{X}' = \mathbf{AX}$ is an involution, $\mathbf{A}^{-1} \in [\mathbf{A}]$, and therefore $\mathbf{A}^a \in [\mathbf{A}]$. Hence $\rho \in \mathsf{F}$ exists such that $\mathbf{A}^a = \rho\mathbf{A}$, that is,

$$(6.3) \qquad a_{22} = \rho a_{11}, \qquad -a_{12} = \rho a_{12}, \qquad -a_{21} = \rho a_{21}, \qquad a_{11} = \rho a_{22}.$$

From the first and last of these four equations, we find that $a_{11} + a_{22} = \rho(a_{11} + a_{22})$. We must have $a_{11} + a_{22} = 0$ because $\rho = 1$ implies by (6.3) that $\mathbf{A} \in [\mathbf{I}]$, contrary to our hypothesis that $\mathbf{X}' = \mathbf{AX}$ is an involution.

THEOREM 6.4. *If P_1, P_1' and P_2, P_2' are two pairs of distinct points that have no common member, there exists a unique involution σ such that $\sigma P_1 = P_1'$, $\sigma P_2 = P_2'$.*

Proof. Under the hypothesis, P_1, P_1', P_2 and P_1', P_1, P_2' are two triads of distinct points; by Theorem 2.2 there exists a unique projectivity mapping P_1, P_1', P_2 onto P_1', P_1, P_2', respectively. This projectivity interchanges P_1 and P_1', and, by Definition 6.1, it is an involution. The uniqueness of the involution is a consequence of the uniqueness of the projectivity.

We shall see that the hypotheses $P_1 \neq P_1', P_2 \neq P_2'$ are not essential to the conclusion.

THEOREM 6.5. *In $S_1(\mathsf{R})$, $x' = -x$ and $x' = -1/x$ are canonical representations of hyperbolic and elliptic involutions, respectively.*

Proof. The hyperbolic projectivity (5.14) is an involution if and only if $a = -1$; the elliptic projectivity (5.16) is an involution if and only if $a = 0$.

The embeddings that we defined in Section 4 yield projective interpretations of certain Euclidean relations; we shall leave to the reader the proofs of the two corollaries that follow.

COROLLARY 6.3. *The embedding* (4.10), *of a Euclidean pencil of concurrent lines in $S_1(\mathsf{R})$, maps pairs of perpendicular lines onto pairs in an elliptic involution.*

COROLLARY 6.4. *Let σ be a point reflection on a Euclidean line E_1, and let τ be a hyperbolic involution on $S_1(\mathsf{R})$. There exists an embedding $\mathscr{E}$ of E_1 in $S_1(\mathsf{R})$ that maps points of E_1 that correspond under σ onto points of $S_1(\mathsf{R})$ that correspond under τ.*

Returning to the involution (6.1), we see that its fixed points are determined by the equation

$$(6.4) \qquad x_1^2 - cx_2^2 = 0.$$

Since $c \neq 0$, every involution is nonparabolic. In $S_1(\mathsf{R})$, (6.1) is elliptic or hyperbolic according as $c < 0$ or $c > 0$. In $S_1(\mathsf{C})$, every involution possesses fixed points, and therefore, a characteristic. If P_1, P_2 are fixed points, and k the characteristic, of an involution in $S_1(\mathsf{F})$, we have by Definition 5.2 that

(6.5) $$(P_1 P_2, X X') = k;$$

since the involution maps X onto X', and X' onto X, we must also have

$$(P_1 P_2, X' X) = k.$$

From (3.10), the two cross ratios are reciprocals; hence $k = 1/k$, and $k = \pm 1$. The projectivity with $k = 1$ is the identity, and therefore the characteristic of an involution, whenever it exists, has the value -1. Consequently an involution is determined uniquely by specifying its fixed points, and *pairs in an involution are harmonic conjugates with respect to its fixed points* (when these exist).

The dichotomy that exists in $S_1(\mathsf{R})$ between hyperbolic and elliptic involutions can be avoided by relating the theory of involutions to that of quadratic forms. A nonsingular quadratic form

(6.6) $$Q = b_{11} x_1^2 + 2b_{12} x_1 x_2 + b_{22} x_2^2, \qquad \det(b_{ij}) \neq 0,$$

determines the mapping from $X:(x_1, x_2)^T$ to $X':(x_1', x_2')^T$ given by

(6.7a) $$b_{11} x_1 x_1' + b_{12}(x_1 x_2' + x_2 x_1') + b_{22} x_2 x_2' = 0.\dagger$$

This map is seen to be an involution by virtue of the linearity and symmetry of (6.7a). Alternatively, we can write (6.7a) as

(6.7b) $$[x_1', x_2']^T = [b_{12} x_1 + b_{22} x_2, -b_{11} x_1 - b_{12} x_2]^T,$$

and we note that the determinant of any matrix representative of (6.7) is different from zero, and (6.2) holds. Conversely, only a change of notation is involved in replacing an involution $[\mathbf{X}'] = [\mathbf{AX}]$ (where $a_{11} + a_{22} = 0$) by (6.7b), or its equivalent (6.7a). Hence if $Q = 0$ has solutions, they are coordinates of the fixed points of the involution (6.7), and any pair of points (other than the fixed points) whose coordinates satisfy (6.7) separate the fixed points harmonically. Whether or not $Q = 0$ has solutions, we speak of (6.7) as the involution of (or determined by) the class $[Q]$, and pairs of points in the involution are said to be *conjugate with respect to* $[Q]$, or with respect to any representative $Q \in [Q]$.

A pair of points $X:\mathbf{X}$ and $X':\mathbf{X}'$ are solutions of the equation $Q_1 = 0$, where

(6.8) $$Q_1 = c_{11} x_1^2 + 2c_{12} x_1 x_2 + c_{22} x_2^2,$$

† The process of obtaining (6.7a) from (6.6) is one that the reader may have met previously, in writing the equation of the tangent to a conic in E_2.

if and only if (see (5.7))

$$(x_1 x_1', x_1 x_2' + x_2 x_1', x_2 x_2') \in [c_{22}, -2c_{12}, c_{11}]. \tag{6.9}$$

If the points X, X' are a pair in the involution (6.7) as well as solutions of $Q_1 = 0$, we have from (6.9) and (6.7) that

$$b_{11} c_{22} - 2b_{12} c_{12} + b_{22} c_{11} = 0. \tag{6.10}$$

Conversely, if (6.8) vanishes for a pair of points, and if (6.10) holds, the solutions of (6.8) satisfy (6.7). But the criterion (6.10) does not require that $Q_1 = 0$ have solutions.

DEFINITION 6.2. In $S_1(\mathsf{F})$, two binary quadratic forms Q and Q_1 are *apolar* if their coefficients satisfy (6.10).

In $S_1(\mathsf{C})$, we have nothing new; if two nonsingular forms Q, Q_1 are apolar, the points at which one form vanishes separate harmonically the points at which the other form vanishes. But in $S_1(\mathsf{R})$, we have a generalization which contains the special case of harmonic separation.

Since (6.10) is linear in the coefficients of either form, it follows (I, 5, Exercises 11, 18) that the forms apolar to two independent forms constitute a class $[Q]$, and those apolar to one form constitute a *pencil* of forms, $\lambda Q_1 + \mu Q_2$, where $\lambda, \mu \in \mathsf{F}$. Thus the forms apolar to $x_1^2 - x_2^2$ and $x_1 x_2$ constitute the class $[x_1^2 + x_2^2]$, which determines the involution given by $x_1 x_1' + x_2 x_2' = 0$. The two pairs of points determined by $x_1^2 - x_2^2 = 0$ and $x_1 x_2 = 0$ are two pairs in the involution, and every pair in the involution (including the fixed points, if any) determines $[\lambda, \mu]$ so that their representatives are the solutions of $\lambda(x_1^2 - x_2^2) + \mu x_1 x_2 = 0$. We say that the pencil of quadratic forms $\lambda(x_1^2 - x_2^2) + \mu x_1 x_2$ *cuts out* the involution. Conversely, it can be shown that if two given independent quadratic forms possess no common zero, their common apolar forms are nonsingular, so that the pencil determined by the two forms cuts out an involution. For later reference, we state our conclusions in the following form.

THEOREM 6.6. *Every involution in $S_1(\mathsf{F})$ is cut out by a pencil of quadratic forms; conversely the pencil determined by two independent forms that have no common zero cuts out an involution.*

An important property of apolar forms is related to products of involutions. If σ is the involution (6.7b), and τ the involution determined by the quadratic form (6.8), the product $\sigma\tau$ is the projectivity with representative matrix the product

$$\begin{pmatrix} b_{12} & b_{22} \\ -b_{11} & -b_{12} \end{pmatrix} \begin{pmatrix} c_{12} & c_{22} \\ -c_{11} & -c_{12} \end{pmatrix}$$

The diagonal elements of this product are seen to be $b_{12} c_{12} - b_{22} c_{11}$ and

$-b_{11}c_{22} + b_{12}c_{12}$, and their sum is the left side of (6.10), to within the factor -1. Recalling Theorem 6.3, we have proved the following.

THEOREM 6.7. *The product of two involutions in* $S_1(\mathsf{F})$ *is an involution if and only if their quadratic forms are apolar.*

Thus the quadratic forms of involutions τ such that $\sigma\tau$ is an involution belong to a pencil of quadratic forms, and their representative matrices belong to a pencil of matrices. We note however that the condition that $\lambda Q_1 + \mu Q_2$ be a singular form is quadratic in λ, μ, and therefore the pencil may contain two forms which possess no involution. Corresponding to these singular forms, the maps (6.7b) are singular, mapping all points onto a single point. For convenience, we shall call these singular maps *singular involutions*. Thus we can say that the set of all involutions τ such that $\sigma\tau$ is either an involution or a singular involution is a pencil of involutions.

EXERCISES

In the numerical exercises it may be assumed that the ground field is R.

1. Find the equations of the involution with fixed points $P_1:(2, -1)^T$ and $P_2:(1, 3)^T$.

2. Find the equations of the involution in which $P_1:(3, 1)^T$ and $P_1':(0, 1)^T$ are a pair and $P_2:(1, 2)^T$ and $P_2':(1, 1)^T$ are another pair.

3. Write the equation of the involution whose fixed points are represented by $x_1^2 - 2x_1x_2 + 3x_2^2 = 0$.

4. Find the harmonic conjugate of $Y:(y_1, y_2)^T$ with respect to the pair represented by $a_{11}x_1^2 + 2a_{12}x_1x_2 + a_{22}x_2^2 = 0$.

5. Find the fixed points of the involution cut out by the pencil

$$\lambda(x_1^2 - 3x_1x_2) + \mu(2x_1^2 - 3x_1x_2 + x_2^2).$$

6. Find a pair of points which separates harmonically each of the pairs $x_1^2 + 4x_2^2 = 0$ and $2x_1^2 - 3x_1x_2 - x_2^2 = 0$.

7. Without finding the equations of the involution, find the transform of the point $P_1:(2, -1)^T$ under the involution which interchanges the pair of points with representatives $(1, -2)^T$ and $(1, 1)^T$ and also the pair $(2, -3)^T$ and $(-1, 1)^T$.

8. Consider the transformation cut out by the pencil

$$\lambda(x_1^2 - x_2^2) + \mu(x_1^2 + 4x_1x_2 + 3x_2^2) = 0.$$

Does Theorem 6.6 apply? What can you say about the transformation?

\#**9.** Prove that in $S_1(\mathsf{R})$ there exists a pair of points which separate each of two given pairs harmonically if and only if the one given pair does not separate the other pair (see II, 3, Exercise 14).

##**10.** Prove that if σ is an elliptic involution in $S_1(\mathsf{R})$ and τ is any other involution, there exist just two points which are a pair in both involutions.

##**11.** Prove that every projectivity in $S_1(\mathsf{F})$ can be expressed as the product of two involutions. *Suggestion*: If the projectivity π maps P_1 onto $P_2 \neq P_1$ and P_2 onto P_3, let σ be the involution which leaves P_2 fixed and maps P_1 onto P_3, and consider the product transformation $\sigma\pi$.

12. Show that if Q_1 and Q_2 are two quadratic forms with no common zero, the fixed points of the involution cut out by their pencil are given by $J = 0$, where J is the Jacobian determinant

$$J = \begin{vmatrix} \partial Q_1/\partial x_1 & \partial Q_1/\partial x_2 \\ \partial Q_2/\partial x_1 & \partial Q_2/\partial x_2 \end{vmatrix}.$$

What does $J = 0$ represent if Q_1 and Q_2 have a common zero?

13. Find a transformation on the lines of a Euclidean pencil which yields an analogue of Corollary 6.3 for hyperbolic involutions.

14. Show that every form apolar to the singular nonhomogeneous form $x^2 - 2rx + r^2$ vanishes for $x = \mathrm{r}$.

15. Find the forms apolar to $(x - r)(x - s)$ and $(x - r)(x - t)$ for $s \neq t$.

16. Prove the assertion preceding Theorem 6.6 that the forms apolar to two given independent forms with no common zero are nonsingular.

17. Does (6.10) determine invariantly related pairs of forms?

##**18.** Let σ be an involution in $S_1(\mathsf{R})$, and A, B two points. Show that A and σA separate B and σB if and only if σ is elliptic.

***19.** Show that two distinct involutions, σ and τ, satisfy $\sigma\tau = \tau\sigma$ if and only if $\sigma\tau$ is an involution.

***20.** Prove that two involutions commute if and only if their quadratic forms are apolar.

21. Prove that three distinct involutions which commute with a given involution possess representative matrices $\mathbf{A}, \mathbf{A}', \mathbf{A}''$ such that $\mathbf{A}'' = \mathbf{A} + \mathbf{A}'$.

CHAPTER III

Projective Spaces of Dimension Two

1 Projective Coordinatizations

In this chapter we shall be concerned with linear properties of projective spaces of dimension two. Except when a contrary assertion is made, $\mathbf{X}$, $\mathbf{Y}$, $\mathbf{Z}$, etc., denote column matrices with row order three, and $\mathbf{A}$, $\mathbf{B}$, $\mathbf{C}$, etc., square matrices of order 3. We shall denote the elements of $\mathbf{X}$, $\mathbf{Y}$, $\mathbf{A}$, etc., by x_i, y_i, a_{ij}, etc. $(i, j = 1, 2, 3)$. As in Chapter II, we use the square bracket to denote homogeneous classes: $[\mathbf{X}]$ denotes the class of matrices $\rho\mathbf{X}$ obtained by varying ρ over all nonzero values. We shall use Ω_3 to represent the set of all classes $[\mathbf{X}]$ of 3×1 matrices for which $\mathbf{X} \neq \mathbf{0}$. Although our primary concern is with *real* projective geometry, the major results of this chapter hold in projective spaces over F, a commutative field not of characteristic two. We shall therefore continue to require that elements of matrices and scalar multipliers belong to such a field, F.

Our definitions follow the pattern used earlier for $S_1(\mathsf{F})$ (II, 2).

AXIOM 1.1. *There exists a set of objects which are mapped one-to-one onto* Ω_3.

DEFINITION 1.1. We call the objects of Axiom 1.1 *points*. If X is a point, we denote the corresponding element of Ω_3 by $[\mathbf{X}]$. We call the class $[\mathbf{X}]$ *the postulated homogeneous projective coordinate* of the point X, and any representative $\mathbf{Y} \in [\mathbf{X}]$ a *representative coordinate*, or briefly a *representative* of X. We call the given map between the set of points and Ω_3 *the postulated projective coordinatization*, or *the postulated projective coordinate system.*

The notation $X : \mathbf{X}$ and $X : [\mathbf{X}]$ is to be read as in S_1, (II, 2). It will be convenient at times to refer to the elements of $\mathbf{X}$ as the three coordinates of X.

AXIOM 1.2. *There exists a group of point transformations from the given set of points onto itself which can be represented, in terms of the postulated coordinatization, by the equation*

$$[\mathbf{X}'] = [\mathbf{AX}], \qquad \det \mathbf{A} \neq 0. \tag{1.1}$$

DEFINITION 1.2. A set of points satisfying Axioms 1.1 and 1.2 is called a *projective space of dimension two*, or *a projective plane, over* F; its invariant theory under the group of Axiom 1.2 is called two-dimensional *projective geometry over* F.

We denote a projective plane (or its set of points) by $S_2(\mathsf{F})$, or, when no ambiguity can arise, by S_2. Real and complex projective planes will be denoted by $S_2(\mathsf{R})$ and $S_2(\mathsf{C})$, respectively.

DEFINITION 1.3. The group of Axiom 1.2 is called the *two-dimensional projective group.* We denote it by $G_8(\mathsf{F})$, or, frequently, by G_8.† If $g \in G_8(\mathsf{F})$, we call g a (two-dimensional) *projective transformation* or a (plane) *collineation.* If g is given by (1.1), and $\mathbf{B} \in [\mathbf{A}]$, we call $\mathbf{B}$ a *representative matrix* of g.

DEFINITION 1.4. Two point sets in $S_2(\mathsf{F})$ are *projectively equivalent* if there exists $g \in G_8$ which maps one onto the other.

It will be useful to have before us concrete representations of the point set of $S_2(\mathsf{R})$. We already have one (II, 1, Illustration 2) as the set of lines in E_3 through a given point. Since each line of the set intersects a sphere with center at the point in two antipodal‡ points, we obtain a two-to-one map from the sphere onto $S_2(\mathsf{R})$. Analytically, this amounts to normalizing a representative $\mathbf{X}$ by requiring that§

$$\mathbf{X}^T\mathbf{X} = x_1^2 + x_2^2 + x_3^2 = 1.$$

This can be done in two ways, and if $\mathbf{X}$ is one such normalized representative, $-\mathbf{X}$ is another. We can obtain a one-to-one representation of $S_2(\mathsf{R})$ on part of the sphere by requiring, for example, that $x_3 > 0$, or for $x_3 = 0$, that $x_2 > 0$, or for $x_2 = x_3 = 0$, that $x_1 = 1$. Geometrically, this set consists of an open hemisphere, an open semicircle on the boundary of the hemisphere, and one of the endpoints of the semicircle. By projecting this set orthogonally into the plane of the bounding semicircle, we map S_2 (R) onto

† The subscript 8 probably seems to the reader to be artificial. Actually, the group $G_8(\mathsf{R})$ is a space that possesses dimension, and this dimension is 8. At a later stage, the reader might study Hurewicz and Wallman, *Dimension Theory*, Princeton, N.J., Princeton University Press, 1941.

‡ Antipodal points (on a sphere, or circle) are endpoints of a diameter.

§ We could equally conveniently use a normalization for which $\mathbf{X}^T\mathbf{X}$ is equal to a given positive constant.

the Euclidean disc $x^2 + y^2 \leqq 1$ with identification of antipodal points on the boundary. Thus, in Figure 1.1, the points A and A' represent the same point of $S_2(\mathsf{R})$. However we must be careful not to base any of our conclusions on Euclidean properties that have no validity in $S_2(\mathsf{R})$, nor should we hesitate to accept conclusions that are not in accord with our intuitive ideas. We shall see, for example, that the diameter AA' (Figure 1.1) represents a simple

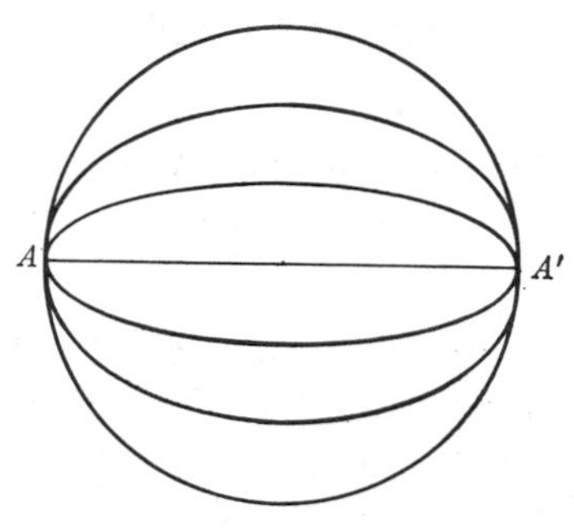

FIGURE 1.1

closed curve in $S_2(\mathsf{R})$, and that the two ellipses of the figure, tangent to the circle at A and A', represent four distinct lines through A.

As in $S_1(\mathsf{F})$, our postulated coordinate system is but one of many that play equivalent roles in projective geometry. To introduce this class of coordinate systems, we shall need the analogue of (II, Lemma 2.1) and the appropriate substitute for the distinctness hypothesis of that lemma.

Let Y_1, Y_2, Y_3 be three points with respective representatives $\mathbf{Y}_1, \mathbf{Y}_2, \mathbf{Y}_3$; we can form the square matrix $(\mathbf{Y}_1 \quad \mathbf{Y}_2 \quad \mathbf{Y}_3)$ and its determinant, $\det(\mathbf{Y}_1 \quad \mathbf{Y}_2 \quad \mathbf{Y}_3)$. If $\det(\mathbf{Y}_1 \quad \mathbf{Y}_2 \quad \mathbf{Y}_3) = 0$, the determinants formed by any representatives of the three points Y_1, Y_2, Y_3 also vanish. If $g \in G_8$ with representative matrix $\mathbf{A}$, the points Y_i map onto the points gY_i with representatives $\mathbf{Y}'_i = \mathbf{A}\,\mathbf{Y}_i$ $(i = 1, 2, 3)$. By (I, Theorem 4.2) we have

$$\det(\mathbf{Y}'_1 \quad \mathbf{Y}'_2 \quad \mathbf{Y}'_3) = (\det \mathbf{A}) \det(\mathbf{Y}_1 \quad \mathbf{Y}_2 \quad \mathbf{Y}_3). \tag{1.2}$$

Hence the vanishing or nonvanishing of $\det(\mathbf{Y}_1 \quad \mathbf{Y}_2 \quad \mathbf{Y}_3)$ is a projective property of the three points Y_1, Y_2, Y_3.

It is natural to say that a set of k points $Y_1, Y_2, \ldots, Y_k$ is *independent* or *dependent* according as the rank of $(\mathbf{Y}_1 \quad \mathbf{Y}_2 \quad \ldots \quad \mathbf{Y}_k)$ is k or less than k (see I, 5). When $k = 3$, we shall, for reasons which will appear in the next section, use *collinear* synonymously with dependent, and *noncollinear* synonymously with independent.

We can now state the two-dimensional analogue of Lemma 2.1 of Chapter II.

LEMMA 1.1. *Let Y_1, Y_2, Y_3, U be four points no three of which are collinear, and let* **U** *be a given representative of U. There exist representatives* $\mathbf{Y}_i$ *of* Y_i $(i = 1, 2, 3)$ *such that*

$$\mathbf{U} = \mathbf{Y}_1 + \mathbf{Y}_2 + \mathbf{Y}_3. \tag{1.3}$$

Proof. Let $\mathbf{Y}_i'$ and $\mathbf{U}$ be given representatives of the points Y_i and U; our hypothesis asserts that

$$\det(\mathbf{Y}_1' \quad \mathbf{Y}_2' \quad \mathbf{Y}_3') \neq 0, \qquad \det(\mathbf{Y}_i' \quad \mathbf{Y}_j' \quad \mathbf{U}) \neq 0, \qquad i,j = 1,2,3; \quad i \neq j. \tag{1.4}$$

We claim that there exist ρ_1, ρ_2, ρ_3 in F such that

$$\mathbf{U} = \rho_1 \mathbf{Y}_1' + \rho_2 \mathbf{Y}_2' + \rho_3 \mathbf{Y}_3'. \tag{1.5}$$

For this matrix equation is a system of three scalar equations in the three unknowns ρ_1, ρ_2, ρ_3. The hypothesis (1.4) guarantees that the solution is unique, and, moreover, that none of the ρ's is zero. Therefore the matrices $\mathbf{Y}_i = \rho_i \mathbf{Y}_i'$ are representatives of the points Y_i, and they indeed satisfy (1.3).

As in S_1, if we replace $\mathbf{U}$ by $\rho\mathbf{U}$, the representatives of Y_i that satisfy (1.3) are $\rho\mathbf{Y}_i$.

Each of the coordinate systems that we are about to establish is determined by an ordered set of four points no three of which are collinear. We denote these by Y_1, Y_2, Y_3, and U, and we let $\mathbf{Y}_1, \mathbf{Y}_2, \mathbf{Y}_3$, and $\mathbf{U}$ be representatives satisfying (1.3) (and (1.4)). If X is any point of the plane, and $\mathbf{X}$ a given representative, the matrix $\mathbf{X}$ is a unique linear combination of the three matrices $\mathbf{Y}_i$. Denoting the coefficients of dependence by x_1^*, x_2^*, and x_3^*, we can write

$$\mathbf{X} = x_1^*\mathbf{Y}_1 + x_2^*\mathbf{Y}_2 + x_3^*\mathbf{Y}_3. \tag{1.6}$$

We can repeat the argument used earlier for $S_1(\mathsf{F})$ and thereby conclude that each point X determines the class $[\mathbf{X}^*] = [x_1^*, x_2^*, x_3^*]^T$ uniquely, and, conversely, each $[\mathbf{X}^*]$ in Ω_3 determines, by (1.6), a unique point X.

We can therefore assert that each choice of an ordered quadruple of points, no three of which are collinear, determines a one-to-one mapping from $S_2(\mathsf{F})$ onto Ω_3. From (1.6), it follows that this mapping can be expressed in terms of our postulated coordinate system by the equation

$$[\mathbf{X}] = [\mathbf{B}\mathbf{X}^*], \qquad \det \mathbf{B} \neq 0, \tag{1.7}$$

where the three columns of $\mathbf{B}$ are $\mathbf{Y}_1$, $\mathbf{Y}_2$, and $\mathbf{Y}_3$, respectively. Conversely, if $\mathbf{B}$ with $\det \mathbf{B} \neq 0$ is given, the map from a point X to the class $[\mathbf{X}^*]$ determined by (1.7) is the map obtained by choosing points Y_i with representatives the three columns of $\mathbf{B}$. The point U is then determined by (1.3). We thus have a collection of different coordinatizations of $S_2(\mathsf{F})$, each determined from (1.6) by an ordered quadruple of points no three of which are collinear, or, equivalently, each determined from (1.7) by the choice of [**B**]. For later reference, we note that (1.7) is equivalent to either of the following

$$[\mathbf{X}^*] = [\mathbf{B}^{-1}\mathbf{X}], \quad \text{or} \quad [\mathbf{X}^*] = [\mathbf{B}^a\mathbf{X}]. \tag{1.8}$$

DEFINITION 1.5. A *projective coordinate system* or a *projective coordinatization* of $S_2(\mathsf{F})$ is any one-to-one mapping of the points of $S_2(\mathsf{F})$ onto Ω_3 which is related to the postulated one by equation (1.7), for some choice of $\mathbf{B}$ with $\det \mathbf{B} \neq 0$.

DEFINITION 1.6. In any projective coordinate system the ordered set of four points with representatives $(1,0,0)^T$, $(0,1,0)^T$, $(0,0,1)^T$, $(1,1,1)^T$ respectively is called the *reference frame*. The first three points determine the *reference triangle* and the fourth is the *unit point*.

Thus the quadruple $Y_1\, Y_2\, Y_3\, U$ is the reference frame of the [**X***]-coordinatization given by (1.6).

The reader should now rewrite the discussion of projective coordinates in $S_1(\mathsf{F})$, beginning with the paragraph below (II, (2.5)), adapting it to $S_2(\mathsf{F})$. He should include proofs for $n = 3$ of Theorems 1.2 and 1.3 and Lemma 1.1 of Chapter II, and the material suggested by Exercises 8, 9, 10 below, and he should prove the following three theorems, the two-dimensional analogues of (II, Theorems 2.1, 2.2, and 2.3).

THEOREM 1.1. *A collineation in $S_2(\mathsf{F})$ that leaves fixed four points, no three of which are collinear, must be the identity.*

THEOREM 1.2. *Let P_1, P_2, P_3, P_4 be any four points no three of which are collinear, and let P_1', P_2', P_3', P_4' be another such quadruple. There exists one and only one collineation which maps P_i onto P_i' for $i = 1, 2, 3, 4$.*

THEOREM 1.3. *Let $\mathbf{P}_i = [p_{1i}, p_{2i}, p_{3i}]^T$ $(i = 1, 2, 3, 4)$ be four elements of Ω_3, each three independent, and let $\mathbf{P}_i' = [p_{1i}', p_{2i}', p_{3i}']^T$ be a second such quadruple. There exists one and only one map* (1.1) *of Ω_3 onto itself that maps $\mathbf{P}_i$ onto $\mathbf{P}_i'$ for $i = 1, 2, 3, 4$.*

Remark. Whenever we are working in a fixed coordinate system, we shall find it convenient to denote by $A_1\, A_2\, A_3\, D$ the reference frame of that coordinate system, so that representatives of A_1, A_2, A_3, D in the given coordinate system are $(1,0,0)^T$, $(0,1,0)^T$, $(0,0,1)^T$, and $(1,1,1)^T$ respectively.

EXERCISES

In the numerical exercises, it may be assumed that the ground field F *is the real field* R.

1. Find representatives of Y_1: $(1, 1, 1)^T$, Y_2: $(1, 0, 1)^T$, Y_3: $(0, 1, 1)^T$. which with $\mathbf{U} = (2, 1, -1)^T$ satisfy (1.3). ANS. $\mathbf{Y}_1 = (4, 4, 4)^T$.

2. Let the reference frame of an **X***-system be the points of Exercise 1. Find **B**, so that $[\mathbf{X}] = [\mathbf{BX}^*]$.

3. In Exercise 2, find **X***-representatives of the reference frame of the **X**-system.

4. Find the collineation that maps the points Y_1, Y_2, Y_3, U of Exercise 1 onto the points A_1, A_2, A_3, D, respectively (see *Remark* above).

5. Let $[\mathbf{X}] = [\mathbf{BX}^*]$, where **B** is given in (I, 5, Exercise 5), define a coordinate transformation. Find the **X**-representatives of the reference frame of the **X***-system.

6. Find the coordinate transformation that preserves the reference triangle if the new unit point has the representative $(2, 3, -1)^T$.

7. Find the collineation that maps A_1, A_2, A_3, D onto A_2, A_3, D, A_1 respectively.

***8.** Prove the theorem: A collineation in $S_2(\mathsf{F})$ possesses a representation (1.1) in every projective coordinate system; conversely, whenever $[\mathbf{X}]$ denotes a projective coordinatization, the point transformation (1.1) is a collineation.

***9.** State and prove the theorems which generalize to $S_2(\mathsf{F})$ the theorems in $S_1(\mathsf{F})$ given in (II, 2, Exercises 12, 13, 14).

***10.** Adapt the three interpretations of the map (II, (2.9)) to $S_2(\mathsf{F})$.

11.** Let a collineation g have representative matrices **A** and **A in **X**- and **X***-coordinate systems, respectively, and let these coordinate systems be related (see Exercise 9) by $[\mathbf{X}] = [\mathbf{BX}^*]$. Prove that $[\mathbf{A}^*] = [\mathbf{B}^{-1}\mathbf{AB}]$.

2 Lines and Line Coordinates

By an *algebraic curve* in $S_2(\mathsf{F})$, we mean the set of points whose three coordinates satisfy an equation $F(x_1, x_2, x_3) = 0$, where F is a *homogeneous* polynomial in x_1, x_2, x_3 and the x's denote any fixed projective coordinate system. Clearly, an algebraic curve remains an algebraic curve under all transformations of G_8, that is, the space of algebraic curves is an invariant space under G_8. Furthermore it can easily be shown that the degree of F, which we call the *order* of the curve, is an invariant under G_8 (see I, Theorem 3.3). Equivalently, an algebraic curve of order n has an equation $F(x_1, x_2, x_3) = 0$, where $F(x_1, x_2, x_3)$ is of degree n, in all projective coordinate systems.

DEFINITION 2.1. An algebraic curve of order one, that is, the set of points whose coordinates satisfy a linear equation

(2.1a) $$v_1 x_1 + v_2 x_2 + v_3 x_3 = 0,$$

where the v's are not all zero, is called a *straight line*, or for brevity, a *line*.

We shall regard the set of coefficients of (2.1a) as a row matrix, so that (2.1a) can be written

$$\mathbf{VX} = \mathbf{0}. \tag{2.1b}$$

Since two linear equations have the same locus if and only if their coefficients are proportional, a given line determines, with reference to a chosen coordinatization of $S_2(\mathsf{F})$, a homogeneous class $[\mathbf{V}]$, rather than the row matrix $\mathbf{V}$ itself.

DEFINITION 2.2. If V is the line with an equation (2.1), we call the mapping from V to $[\mathbf{V}]$ the *projective line-coordinatization* associated with the given (that is, the $\mathbf{X}$-) coordinatization of $S_2(\mathsf{F})$. We call $[\mathbf{V}]$ the *line coordinate* of V, and $\mathbf{V}$ a *representative line coordinate*, or briefly a *representative* of V.

We adopt the notation used for points: If V is a line, we read $V\colon\mathbf{V}$ as the line V with representative (the row matrix) $\mathbf{V}$. We read $V\colon[\mathbf{V}]$ and $V\colon\mathbf{VX} = \mathbf{0}$ as the line V with coordinate the class of matrices $[\mathbf{V}]$ and the line V with equation $\mathbf{VX} = \mathbf{0}$.

When we are concerned with several lines, for example, with V_1, V_2, V_3 with representatives $\mathbf{V}_i = (v_{i1}, v_{i2}, v_{i3})$ $(i = 1, 2, 3)$, we shall write $(\mathbf{V}_1 \quad \mathbf{V}_2 \quad \mathbf{V}_3)^T$ for the following matrix:†

$$(\mathbf{V}_1 \quad \mathbf{V}_2 \quad \mathbf{V}_3)^T = \begin{pmatrix} \mathbf{V}_1 \\ \mathbf{V}_2 \\ \mathbf{V}_3 \end{pmatrix} = \begin{pmatrix} v_{11} & v_{12} & v_{13} \\ v_{21} & v_{22} & v_{23} \\ v_{31} & v_{32} & v_{33} \end{pmatrix}. \tag{2.2}$$

Note that in the expanded matrix the *first* index specifies the line, while in a matrix determined by points, the *second* index specifies the point (see II, (2.3)).

Remark. The *reference triangle* of an associated line coordinate system, that is, the triangle whose three sides have representatives $(1, 0, 0)$, $(0, 1, 0)$, and $(0, 0, 1)$ respectively, coincides with the reference triangle of the point coordinate system; the unit line, that is the line $(1, 1, 1)$, will be seen to be related geometrically to the reference triangle and to the unit point (see III, 3, Exercises 14, 15).

DEFINITION 2.3. A line $V\colon\mathbf{V}$ and a point $Y\colon\mathbf{Y}$ are said to be *incident* if Y belongs to the point set V, that is, if $\mathbf{VY} = \mathbf{0}$.

DEFINITION 2.4. The set of lines incident to a point Y is called the *pencil* with *vertex* Y, or briefly, the *pencil* Y.

† Strict conformity to custom would require the cumbersome notation $q(\mathbf{V}_1^T \quad \mathbf{V}_2^T \quad \mathbf{V}_3^T)^T$.

We naturally say that a line V and a pencil Y are incident if the line V belongs to the pencil Y. It therefore follows that a line V and a pencil Y are incident if and only if the line V and the point Y are incident.

THEOREM 2.1. *The equation* $\mathbf{UY} = \mathbf{0}$, *where* $\mathbf{Y}$ *is fixed and* $\mathbf{U}$ *varies, represents the pencil with vertex* $Y:\mathbf{Y}$.

We leave the proof to the reader.

THEOREM 2.2. *There exists one and just one line incident to two distinct points; there exists one and just one point incident to two distinct lines.*

This theorem is a restatement in geometric language of the results obtained in (I, 5, Exercises 11, 12). From the remarks following Definition 2.4, it follows that we obtain a new theorem from Theorem 2.2 by replacing *point* by *pencil.*

We shall call the line containing two points their *join*, and the common point of two lines their *intersection.* Points incident to some one line are said to be *collinear*, and lines incident to some one point are *concurrent.* We shall denote the join of points Y, Z by $Y \oplus Z$, and the intersection† of lines V, W by $V \cap W$.

THEOREM 2.3. *If* $Y:\mathbf{Y} = (y_1, y_2, y_3)^T$ *and* $Z:\mathbf{Z} = (z_1, z_2, z_3)^T$ *are two distinct points of a line* V,

(a) *every point* X *of* V *has representatives that are linearly dependent on* $\mathbf{Y}, \mathbf{Z}$; *that is, there exist* $\lambda, \mu \in \mathsf{F}, (\lambda, \mu) \neq (0, 0)$, *such that*

$$\mathbf{X} = \lambda\mathbf{Y} + \mu\mathbf{Z}; \tag{2.3}$$

(b) *the equation of* V, $\mathbf{VX} = \mathbf{0}$, *is equivalent to the equation*

$$\det(\mathbf{X} \quad \mathbf{Y} \quad \mathbf{Z}) = 0; \tag{2.4}$$

(c) *a representative of* V *is the set of cofactors of the elements in the first column of* $(\mathbf{X} \quad \mathbf{Y} \quad \mathbf{Z})$:

$$\mathbf{V} = (y_2 z_3 - y_3 z_2, \quad y_3 z_1 - y_1 z_3, \quad y_1 z_2 - y_2 z_1). \tag{2.5}$$

Proof. Since the points Y and Z are distinct, their representatives are two *independent* solutions of the equation $\mathbf{VX} = \mathbf{0}$. Then any other solution is a linear combination of these two. Parts (b) and (c) of the theorem are consequences of the properties of linear equations cited in (I, 5, Exercises 11, 12, 13).

† The symbols $\cap$ and $\cup$ are used extensively in mathematics. If $\mathscr{C}$ and $\mathscr{D}$ are any two sets (of points, or of any other kind of objects), the intersection of $\mathscr{C}$ and $\mathscr{D}$, written $\mathscr{C} \cap \mathscr{D}$, is the set of elements that belong to both $\mathscr{C}$ and $\mathscr{D}$. The union of $\mathscr{C}$ and $\mathscr{D}$, written $\mathscr{C} \cup \mathscr{D}$, is the set of elements that belong to at least one, $\mathscr{C}$ or $\mathscr{D}$.

THEOREM 2.4. *If V and W are two distinct lines of the pencil Y,*

(a) *every line U of the pencil Y is linearly dependent on V, W; that is, there exist* $\lambda, \mu \in \mathsf{F}$, $(\lambda, \mu) \neq (0, 0)$, *such that*

$$\mathbf{U} = \lambda\mathbf{V} + \mu\mathbf{W}; \tag{2.6}$$

(b) *the equation* $\mathbf{UY} = \mathbf{0}$ *of the pencil Y is equivalent to the equation*

$$\det(\mathbf{U} \quad \mathbf{V} \quad \mathbf{W})^T = \mathbf{0}; \tag{2.7}$$

(c) *a representative of the point Y is the set of cofactors of the elements in the first row of* $(\mathbf{U} \quad \mathbf{V} \quad \mathbf{W})^T$:

$$\mathbf{Y} = (v_2 w_3 - v_3 w_2, \quad v_3 w_1 - v_1 w_3, \quad v_1 w_2 - v_2 w_1)^T. \tag{2.8}$$

Proof. Since V and W are distinct lines, their representatives are independent solutions of the equation $\mathbf{UY} = \mathbf{0}$. The proof is then algebraically identical with that of Theorem 2.3.

It follows from Theorems 2.3 and 2.4 that the representatives of three collinear points (concurrent lines) are linearly dependent matrices, and conversely. We shall therefore refer to three collinear points or three concurrent lines as dependent; three noncollinear points (or three nonconcurrent lines) are independent.

ILLUSTRATION 2.1. In $S_2(\mathsf{R})$, the line V with representative $(2, 3, -1)$ and the point Y with representative $(1, 2, 4)^T$ are not incident since

$$\mathbf{VY} = (2, 3, -1)(1, 2, 4)^T = (4) \neq \mathbf{0}.$$

The lines incident to Y satisfy $(u_1, u_2, u_3)(1, 2, 4)^T = (u_1 + 2u_2 + 4u_3) = \mathbf{0}$. The lines with representatives $(4, 0, -1)$ and $(0, 2, -1)$ are two such lines. The set of lines incident to Y (the pencil Y) is therefore represented by $\mathbf{U} = \lambda(4, 0, -1) + \mu(0, 2, -1)$ where $\lambda, \mu \in \mathsf{R}$, $(\lambda, \mu) \neq (0, 0)$. The equations of the lines $(4, 0, -1)$ and $(0, 2, -1)$ are $4x_1 - x_3 = 0$ and $2x_2 - x_3 = 0$, respectively. The equation $\lambda(4x_1 - x_3) + \mu(2x_2 - x_3) = 0$ for each $(\lambda, \mu) \neq (0, 0)$ represents a line of the pencil Y.

Similarly the points incident to V satisfy

$$(2, 3, -1)(x_1, x_2, x_3)^T = 2x_1 + 3x_2 - x_3 = 0;\dagger$$

the points with representatives $(1, 0, 2)^T$ and $(0, 1, 3)^T$ are two such points, so that the set of points of the line V is given by $\mathbf{X} = \lambda(1, 0, 2)^T + \mu(0, 1, 3)^T$.

† The first term of this continued equation is a matrix of order 1×1. For 1×1 matrices, the matrix equation $(a) = (b)$ is equivalent to the scalar equation $a = b$ $(a, b \in \mathsf{F})$. The running equality in the text can here be regarded as a convenient contraction of the two equivalent equations $(2, 3, -1)(x_1, x_2, x_3)^T = \mathbf{0}_{11}$ and $2x_1 + 3x_2 - x_3 = 0$. We shall frequently identify a 1×1 matrix with its one element, and understand by $\mathbf{VX}$ the element of F given by $v_1 x_1 + v_2 x_2 + v_3 x_3$.

The equation $u_1 + 2u_3 = 0$ is that of the pencil with vertex $(1, 0, 2)^T$, and $u_2 + 3u_3 = 0$ is the equation of the pencil with vertex $(0, 1, 3)^T$. The equation $\lambda(u_1 + 2u_3) + \mu(u_2 + 3u_3) = 0$ represents, for each $(\lambda, \mu) \neq (0, 0)$ a pencil with vertex at the point X.

We close this section with a brief discussion of the effect on the associated line coordinatization when we change from one projective coordinatization of $S_2(\mathsf{F})$ to another. Let $\mathbf{X}$- and $\mathbf{X}^*$-coordinatizations be related by

$$[\mathbf{X}^*] = [\mathbf{AX}]. \tag{2.9}$$

(Here $\mathbf{A}$ could be $\mathbf{B}^{-1}$ of (1.8)). Then, for representatives satisfying $\mathbf{X}^* = \mathbf{AX}$, we have

$$\mathbf{U}^*\mathbf{X}^* = \mathbf{U}^*\mathbf{AX},$$

so that $\mathbf{U} = \mathbf{U}^*\mathbf{A}$ is a representative, in the $\mathbf{X}$-system, of the line with equation $\mathbf{U}^*\mathbf{X}^* = \mathbf{0}$ in the $\mathbf{X}^*$-system. From $\mathbf{U} = \mathbf{U}^*\mathbf{A}$, it follows that

$$[\mathbf{U}^*] = [\mathbf{UA}^{-1}]. \tag{2.10}$$

We have thus proved the following theorem.

THEOREM 2.5. *If two coordinatizations of $S_2(\mathsf{F})$ are related by* (2.9), *their associated line coordinatizations are related by* (2.10).

From our earlier comments, the columns of $\mathbf{A}^{-1}$ are the $\mathbf{X}$-representatives of the vertices of the reference triangle of the $\mathbf{X}^*$-system; from $\mathbf{U} = \mathbf{U}^*\mathbf{A}$ and Exercise 1 below, we see that the rows of $\mathbf{A}$ are the $\mathbf{X}$-representatives of the sides of the reference triangle of the $\mathbf{X}^*$-system.

EXERCISES

In the numerical exercises, it may be assumed that the ground field F *is the real field* R.

1. Find the coordinates of the sides of the reference triangle and the equations of the pencils A_i ($i = 1, 2, 3$) (see *Remark* at end of Section 1).

2. Let $D_i = (A_i \oplus D) \cap (A_j \oplus A_k)$, where ijk is a permutation of 123, and $A_1 A_2 A_3 D$ is the reference frame. Find the coordinates of D_i, and the equation of the pencil D_i.

3. Given the lines $2x_1 + 3x_2 - 4x_3 = 0$ and $x_1 + x_2 - x_3 = 0$, find the intersections of each of these lines with the sides of the coordinate triangle, and the join of the intersection of the two lines with each of the vertices of the coordinate triangle.

4. Find the coordinates and equation of the line common to the two pencils $u_1 + u_2 + u_3 = 0$, and $2u_1 - 2u_2 - u_3 = 0$.

5. Find the point of intersection of the line $(1, 2, 4)$ with the line joining the points $(1, 2, 1)^T$ and $(2, 1, 3)^T$ without writing the equation of any of these lines. ANS. $(2, -23, 11)$.

6. Find the coordinates of the point in which the line common to the pencils $2u_1 + 3u_2 - u_3 = 0$, $u_1 + u_2 = 0$, intersects the line $(2, 1, 4)$.

ANS. $(1, 2, -1)$.

7. Prove: The line U: (u_1, u_2, u_3) is incident to the vertex A_i if and only if $u_i = 0$.

8. Find the points of the curve (of order two) with equation $x_1^2 - x_2 x_3 = 0$ that lie on the line joining the points $(3, 2, 5)^T$ and $(1, 0, 3)^T$.

ANS. $(2, 1, 4)$, $(1, 1, 1)$.

9. Show algebraically that incidence is an invariant relation under the group of collineations in $S_2(\mathsf{F})$.

***10.** Find a representative of the point of intersection of the line V and the line joining the points Y, Z. ANS. $(\mathbf{VZ})\mathbf{Y} - (\mathbf{VY})\mathbf{Z}$.†

#**11.** Let V, W be distinct lines, and Y a point not incident to both lines. Show that the points X whose representatives satisfy

$$(\mathbf{WY})(\mathbf{VX}) - (\mathbf{VY})(\mathbf{WX}) = \mathbf{0}$$

constitute the line joining Y to the point of intersection of V and W.

#**12.** Let Y_i $(i = 1, 2, 3, 4, 5)$ be five points. Show that

$$\det(\mathbf{Y}_1 \quad \mathbf{Y}_2 \quad \mathbf{Y}_3)\det(\mathbf{X} \quad \mathbf{Y}_4 \quad \mathbf{Y}_5) - \det(\mathbf{Y}_1 \quad \mathbf{Y}_4 \quad \mathbf{Y}_5)\det(\mathbf{X} \quad \mathbf{Y}_2 \quad \mathbf{Y}_3) = 0$$

is the equation of the line V, where $V = Y_1 \oplus \{(Y_2 \oplus Y_3) \cap (Y_4 \oplus Y_5)\}$, provided that the five points satisfy certain independence conditions. Find these conditions, and determine whether the geometric and algebraic conditions are compatible.

#**13.** If X, Y in Exercise 11 are given points, and W is a given line, what does the equation of Exercise 11 represent?

#**14.** Determine the point of intersection of the line V with the line joining the intersection of the lines V_1, V_2 to the intersection of the lines W_1, W_2 by finding the equation of the pencil with that point as vertex (see Exercise 12).

***15.** A collineation g has a representation (1.1), and maps a line U:$\mathbf{U}$ onto gU:$\mathbf{U}'$. Find $[\mathbf{U}']$.

***16.** Express, in terms of $a_{ij} = (\mathbf{A})_{ij}$ and $A_{ij} = (\mathbf{A}^a)_{ij}$ (see I, (5.2) and (5.16)), representatives

(i) of the points and lines onto which the vertices and sides of the reference triangle are mapped by the collineation g:$[\mathbf{X}'] = [\mathbf{AX}]$;

(ii) of the points and lines which are mapped by g onto the vertices and sides of the reference triangle.

17. The lines: $x_1 - x_2 + x_3 = 0$, $2x_1 + x_2 = 0$, $x_2 - x_3 = 0$ are taken as the sides of the reference triangle, and the point: $(3, 1, 2)^T$ as the unit point. Find representatives in the new coordinatization of the point $(2, 3, 4)^T$ and of the line $(2, 3, 4)$. ANS. $(3, 4, 4)^T$ and $(-48, 49, 16)$.

†See footnote, page 104.

3 The Principle of Duality

The reader has doubtless observed the striking parallel between Theorems 2.3 and 2.4 of the preceding section. In this section we shall see that this is no isolated instance: every theorem in projective plane geometry is paralleled by its *dual.* The first step in the proof of this remarkable property is given in the following theorem.

THEOREM 3.1. *The lines of $S_2(\mathsf{F})$ constitute a projective space of dimension two over* F.

Proof. We have already represented the lines of $S_2(\mathsf{F})$ by means of the classes $[u_1, u_2, u_3]$. Since the map from $[u_1, u_2, u_3]$ to $[u_1, u_2, u_3]^T$ is one-to-one and onto, the set of all lines of S_2 constitute a set of "objects" in one-to-one correspondence with Ω_3. It remains to show that the transformations induced on these objects, by virtue of their being lines of $S_2(\mathsf{F})$, constitute the group of Definition 1.3. Let $g \in G_8$ possess a representation

$$\mathbf{X}' = \mathbf{A}\mathbf{X}, \qquad \det \mathbf{A} \neq 0. \tag{3.1}$$

We have seen (Theorem 2.5, or Exercise 15 above) that if $U{:}\mathbf{U}$ is a line of $S_2(\mathsf{F})$, $U' = gU$ possesses a representative given by

$$\mathbf{U}' = \mathbf{U}\mathbf{A}^{-1}, \tag{3.2}$$

or that

$$[\mathbf{U}'] = [\mathbf{U}\mathbf{A}^{-1}]. \tag{3.3}$$

This equation is equivalent to

$$[\mathbf{U}'^T] = [\mathbf{A}^{-T}\mathbf{U}^T]. \tag{3.4}$$

Thus the induced transformation on the lines of $S_2(\mathsf{F})$ is indeed a nonsingular homogeneous linear transformation; as $\mathbf{A}$ varies over all nonsingular matrices† (to give G_8), so does $\mathbf{A}^{-T}$. Hence (3.4) represents the full group of nonsingular homogeneous linear transformations. The lines of S_2 thus satisfy all the requirements of Definition 1.2, and therefore constitute a projective space of two dimensions.

We shall denote by $\Sigma_2(\mathsf{F})$ the projective space of all lines of $S_2(\mathsf{F})$. In the terminology of Definition 1.1 the *points* of Σ_2—the objects which constitute Σ_2—are the lines of S_2. What are the *lines* of Σ_2? By Definition 2.1, a

† The exponent $-T$ in $\mathbf{A}^{-T}$ can be regarded as determining a mapping from the space of nonsingular matrices onto itself. This mapping is one-to-one.

line of Σ_2 is the set of lines U whose coordinates satisfy a linear equation. We can write this equation†

$$\mathbf{UY} = u_1 y_1 + u_2 y_2 + u_3 y_3 = 0.$$

By Theorem 2.1 this is the equation of the pencil Y. The column matrix of coefficients of the u's in this equation is by Definition 2.2 a representative coordinate of our *line* in Σ_2. It is also a representative coordinate of the point Y, the vertex of the pencil Y. We have thus the following theorem.

THEOREM 3.2. *The lines of Σ_2 are the pencils of lines of S_2; their coordinates are the coordinates in S_2 of the vertices of the pencils.*

Theorems 3.1 and 3.2 together make up the *Principle of Duality* in the projective plane. From Theorem 3.1 it follows that every property of a projective space of two dimensions holds in particular for Σ_2. That is, a theorem regarding points and lines (or other sets of points defined in terms of points and lines) of $S_2(\mathsf{F})$ will hold automatically for the *points* and *lines* of $\Sigma_2(\mathsf{F})$. If we now take into account that the *points* and *lines* of Σ_2 are the lines and pencils of S_2, we obtain a new theorem in S_2. A theorem in S_2 in a sense does double duty: first it appears as a theorem in S_2; when applied to Σ_2, it yields a new theorem in S_2. This new theorem is called the *dual* of the original theorem. Thus the second statement in Theorem 2.2 is the dual of the first. Theorem 2.4 is the dual of Theorem 2.3 and vice versa.

In the proof of Theorem 3.1 we noted that the group of transformation (3.4) is the group G_8 (with the x's replaced by u's). Nevertheless, for a particular $\mathbf{A}$, the transformation (3.4) (with the u's replaced by x's) need not represent the transformation (3.1). We therefore cannot set up a correspondence between the individual points and lines of S_2 that is invariant under the group of collineations. We can however set up a correspondence between classes of point sets. Thus the class of all points corresponds by duality to the class of all lines. We shall often describe this correspondence briefly by saying the dual of a point is a line.‡

In order to obtain the dual of a theorem, we must replace *point*, wherever the *idea* occurs, by *line*. In the proof of Theorem 3.2 we saw that this entails replacing *line* by *pencil of lines*. Suppose we carry this process of dualizing one step further: We started with S_2 and obtained Σ_2 in which the fundamental objects were lines of S_2. Let us now start with Σ_2 and obtain a new projective space in which the fundamental objects are the lines of Σ_2, that is, the pencils of S_2. Since a pencil of lines is uniquely determined by its vertex and vice versa, and since by Theorem 3.2 the coordinate of the pencil regarded as a line of Σ_2 is precisely the coordinate of its vertex as a point of S_2, and since the point Y and the pencil Y are transformed, under a trans-

† See footnote, page 104.

‡ But the expression "the dual of the point $(1, 2, 3)^T$" is meaningless.

formation of G_8 in exactly the same way, this new space, the dual of Σ_2 is, for all practical purposes, simply S_2 itself. We now see the significance of the term *duality*. If we obtain the dual of a given theorem or of a class of figures, its dual in turn will be the original theorem or class of figures. Therefore the dual of the class of all lines is the class of all points, and for brevity we speak of a point and a line as being each the dual of the other.

As we develop the geometry of a projective space of two dimensions, we shall constantly keep in mind the principle of duality. For the present, let us consider several examples of duality.

If a theorem says that a set of points constructed in some definite manner are collinear, that is, belong to a line, the dual theorem says that the set of lines constructed in the dual manner belong to a pencil of lines, that is, they are concurrent. Similarly, if a theorem says that a set of lines are concurrent (that is, contain a common point), the dual theorem says that a set of pencils contain a common line, or that the vertices of these pencils are collinear. Thus collinear points and concurrent lines are dual concepts. We leave to the reader to show that incidence is a self-dual concept.

We define the dual of any class of point sets to be the same class of line sets. Thus a triangle is an (unordered) set of three independent points. The dual configuration is a set of three independent (that is, nonconcurrent) lines. We say that the class of triangles is self-dual since the three independent points determine three lines and vice versa, so that it is immaterial whether we start with the three points or the three lines.

A (complete) *quadrangle* is a set of four points, no three of which are collinear; we call these points the *vertices*. The six lines obtained by joining pairs of vertices are called the *sides*; two sides that have no vertex in common are called *opposite*, and their point of intersection is called a *diagonal point*. We leave to the reader to prove that under our hypotheses on F the three diagonal points are not collinear (see Exercise 6 below); their triangle is called the *diagonal triangle*.

The dual of the class of (complete) quadrangles is the class of (complete) *quadrilaterals*. The four given lines (each three independent) of a quadrilateral are its *sides*; it has six *vertices* which fall into three pairs of *opposite* vertices; each pair of opposite vertices determines a *diagonal line*, and the three diagonal lines form the *diagonal triangle*. Consequently, we obtain the dual of a theorem concerning quadrangles by replacing quadrangles, vertices, sides, and diagonal points by quadrilaterals, sides, vertices, and diagonal lines, respectively.

A curve that possesses tangent lines can be regarded either as the locus of its points or the envelope of its tangents. We can clarify the meaning of this statement by an illustration from Euclidean geometry. The equation

$$y^2 = 4x \tag{3.5}$$

represents a parabola. The tangent to this parabola at (x_1, y_1) has the equation $y_1 y = 2(x + x_1)$. This is the line $u_1 x + u_2 y + u_3 = 0$, where

$$[u_1, u_2, u_3] = [2, -y_1, 2x_1];$$

therefore

$$y_1 = -2u_2/u_1, \qquad x_1 = u_3/u_1.$$

Since (x_1, y_1) is by hypothesis a point of the parabola, we must have that $y_1^2 = 4x_1$, so that every tangent line U to the parabola has coordinates which satisfy

$$u_2^2 = u_1 u_3, \qquad u_1 \neq 0. \tag{3.6}$$

Conversely, the reader can verify that every line U whose coordinates satisfy (3.6) is a tangent line of the parabola (3.5). Hence this parabola can be regarded either as the point set with the equation (3.5) or as the set of lines given by (3.6).

We shall see that the situation for curves in the real projective plane is entirely similar to this illustration, and that in $S_2(\mathsf{R})$, algebraic curves are, as a class, self-dual. However other more limited classes of curves are not necessarily self-dual. We shall return to this subject in Chapter IV.

EXERCISES

1. Find the vertices of the diagonal triangle of the quadrangle whose vertices are A_1, A_2, A_3, D.

2. Find the diagonal lines of the quadrilateral with sides $A_1 \oplus A_2$, $A_2 \oplus A_3, A_3 \oplus A_1$, and the line $x_1 + x_2 + x_3 = 0$.

3. What is the dual in S_2 of the group of collineations?

4. Show that incidence is a self-dual relation.

5. Show that the correspondence by which the point with coordinate $[x_1, x_2, x_3]^T$ corresponds to the line with the coordinate $[x_1, x_2, x_3]$ is not invariant under the group of collineations.

6. Prove that in $S_2(\mathsf{F})$ the diagonal points of a complete quadrangle are not collinear. Is the hypothesis that the ground field is not of characteristic two essential to the conclusion? What is the dual of this theorem?

#**7.** Prove: If A, B, C are three given points, the points P, Q, R, where $\mathbf{P} = \mu\mathbf{B} - \nu\mathbf{C}$, $\mathbf{Q} = \nu\mathbf{C} - \lambda\mathbf{A}$, $\mathbf{R} = \lambda\mathbf{A} - \mu\mathbf{B}$ are collinear for all values of λ, μ, ν. Conversely if A, B, and C are independent, and if P, Q, R are any three collinear points on the lines $B \oplus C$, $C \oplus A$, $A \oplus B$, respectively, representative coordinates of P, Q, and R can be put in the above form.

#**8.** State the duals of the two theorems of Exercise 7.

9. In the Euclidean plane, find the line equation of the curve $y = x^3$.

ANS. $4u_1^3 + 27u_2 u_3^2 = 0$.

***10.** Let V_1, V_2, V_3, and W be four lines, no three of which are concurrent, and $\mathbf{W}$ a given representative of W. Prove that the lines V_i $(i = 1, 2, 3)$ possess representatives $\mathbf{V}_i$ such that $\mathbf{W} = \mathbf{V}_1 + \mathbf{V}_2 + \mathbf{V}_3$.

11. In $S_2(\mathsf{R})$, find the representatives $\mathbf{V}_i$ of Exercise 10 if the lines V_i have equations $x_1 - x_2 = 0$, $x_2 - x_3 = 0$, $x_1 + x_3 = 0$ respectively, and if $\mathbf{WX} = x_1 - 2x_2 + 2x_3$.

12. Find the coordinate transformation $[\mathbf{X}^*] = [\mathbf{AX}]$ if the sides of the reference triangle are the lines V_i of Exercise 11, and the unit line is W (see Exercise 16 below).

***13.** State the dual of Theorems 1.1 and 1.2.

14. Using the notation of (III, 2, Exercise 2) and letting $E_i = (D_j \oplus D_k) \cap (A_j \oplus A_k)$ $(i, j, k$ unequal), show that the three points E_1, E_2, E_3 are collinear. State your conclusion geometrically. (This is a special case of Desargues' triangle theorem which we shall consider in Section 8.)

***15.** The preceding exercise shows that the *unit line*, that is, the line with equation $x_1 + x_2 + x_3 = 0$, can be described geometrically in terms of the reference frame. Show that conversely the unit point is determined by the reference triangle and the unit line, and state your conclusion geometrically.

#***16.** All projective line coordinatizations can be obtained from a given one by an algebraic development analogous to that followed in Section 1. Starting with an appropriate substitute for Lemma 1.1, carry out this development, and determine how four points and four lines must be related if the point and line coordinatizations they determine are associated (see Exercises 14, 15).

4 Cross Ratio

Let L be a given line, and let $\mathbf{Y}_1, \mathbf{Y}_2$ be given representatives of two distinct points Y_1, Y_2 of L. By Theorem 2.3, the points of L can be represented uniquely by the classes $[\lambda, \mu]^T$ where a representative $(\lambda, \mu)^T \in [\lambda, \mu]^T$ is determined for a given representative $\mathbf{X}$ of $X \in L$ by†

$$\mathbf{X} = \lambda\mathbf{Y}_1 + \mu\mathbf{Y}_2. \tag{4.1}$$

Thus Y_1 itself is represented by the class $[1, 0]^T$, and Y_2 by $[0, 1]^T$. The class $[1, 1]^T$ determines the point with coordinate $[\mathbf{Y}_1 + \mathbf{Y}_2]$. Thus the choice of representatives $\mathbf{Y}_1$ and $\mathbf{Y}_2$ determines a one-to-one map from L onto Ω_2. Although it might seem that we need only two points to determine this map, actually we need three. For if Y_1, Y_2, Z are any three distinct points of L, we can assert (see II, Lemma 2.1 and III, Lemma 1.1) that there exist

† The right side of (4.1) can be written as the product of the matrices $(\mathbf{Y}_1 \;\; \mathbf{Y}_2)$ and $(\lambda, \mu)^T$.

representatives of Y_1, Y_2 whose sum is a given representative of Z. Thus any three distinct points of L serve as the reference frame of a representation (4.1).

The existence of this map suggests, but does not guarantee, that the line L is a projective space of dimension one. To determine whether it is, we must investigate the structure induced on the points of L by those collineations that leave L fixed.

For this purpose we suppose that the collineation g, with representation $\mathbf{X}' = \mathbf{AX}$, leaves L fixed so that $X \in L$ implies that $X' = gX \in L$. Let us denote by $[\lambda', \mu']^T$ the element of Ω_2 which, by (4.1), corresponds to X', that is,

$$\mathbf{X}' = \lambda' \mathbf{Y}_1 + \mu' \mathbf{Y}_2. \tag{4.2}$$

We have two maps, g and (4.1), which we can portray in the diagram below:

$$\begin{array}{ccc} X & \xrightarrow{\quad g \quad} & X' \\ {\scriptstyle (4.1)}\big\downarrow & & \big\downarrow{\scriptstyle (4.1)} \\ [\lambda, \mu]^T & & [\lambda', \mu']^T \end{array}$$

Since these maps are one-to-one, we can conclude that g induces a one-to-one map of Ω_2 onto itself under which $[\lambda, \mu]^T$ is mapped onto $[\lambda', \mu']^T$. In finding a representation of this map, we must bear in mind that $[\lambda, \mu]^T, [\lambda', \mu']^T, \mathbf{X}, \mathbf{X}'$ are variables, whereas $\mathbf{Y}_i, \mathbf{A}$ are constant. Choosing $\mathbf{Y}_i' = \mathbf{AY}_i$, we can find $b_{ij} \in \mathsf{F}$ such that

$$\begin{aligned} \mathbf{Y}_1' &= b_{11}\mathbf{Y}_1 + b_{21}\mathbf{Y}_2, \\ \mathbf{Y}_2' &= b_{12}\mathbf{Y}_1 + b_{22}\mathbf{Y}_2, \end{aligned} \qquad b_{11}b_{22} - b_{12}b_{21} \neq 0. \tag{4.3}$$

Then we have for all $X \in L$

$$\begin{aligned} \mathbf{X}' = \mathbf{AX} &= \mathbf{A}(\lambda \mathbf{Y}_1) + \mathbf{A}(\mu \mathbf{Y}_2) \\ &= \lambda \mathbf{Y}_1' + \mu \mathbf{Y}_2' \\ &= (b_{11}\lambda + b_{12}\mu)\mathbf{Y}_1 + (b_{21}\lambda + b_{22}\mu)\mathbf{Y}_2. \end{aligned}$$

Since the representative $(\lambda', \mu')^T$ in (4.2) is unique, we have

$$\lambda' = b_{11}\lambda + b_{12}\mu, \qquad \mu' = b_{21}\lambda + b_{22}\mu. \tag{4.4}$$

If we introduce the 2×1 matrices

$$\mathbf{\Lambda} = (\lambda, \mu)^T, \qquad \mathbf{\Lambda}' = (\lambda', \mu')^T,$$

we can write (4.4) as

$$[\mathbf{\Lambda}'] = [\mathbf{B\Lambda}], \qquad (\mathbf{B})_{ij} = b_{ij}, \quad \det \mathbf{B} \neq 0. \tag{4.5}$$

Thus the mapping induced by g on the points of L satisfies (II, Axiom 2.2) and belongs to the group G_3 of that axiom. Moreover, it can be seen that as

g runs through all elements of G_8 for which $gL = L$, the maps (4.5) traverse G_3. We have therefore the following theorem.

THEOREM 4.1a. *The points of a line of* $S_2(\mathsf{F})$ *constitute a projective space of dimension one over* F. *If the line is represented by equation* (4.1), *the coordinates* $[\lambda, \mu]^T$ *are projective coordinates on the line.*

By duality, we have the following theorem.

THEOREM 4.1b. *The lines through a point of* $S_2(\mathsf{F})$ *constitute a projective space of dimension one. If the pencil is represented by* $\mathbf{U} = \lambda\mathbf{V} + \mu\mathbf{W}$, $[\lambda, \mu]$ *are projective coordinates in the pencil.*

We have previously defined cross ratio of four points in a projective space of dimension one. Theorems 4.1a and 4.1b enable us to introduce the concept of cross ratio on the lines and in the pencils of $S_2(\mathsf{F})$, and to apply to both the theory of cross ratio developed in Chapter II. But we can expect

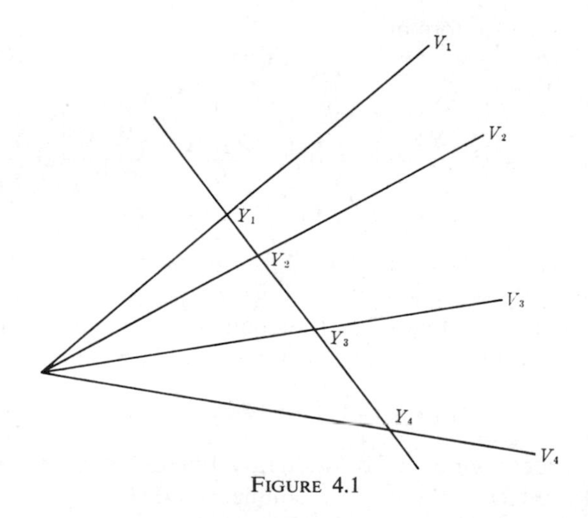

FIGURE 4.1

further development, and our earlier conclusions for the Euclidean plane (see II, Theorem 4.3) suggest the direction of attack. We let V_i $(i = 1, 2, 3, 4)$ be four distinct concurrent lines which intersect a line not in their pencil in the points Y_i respectively (Figure 4.1). By (III, 2, Exercise 10) we have†

$$\mathbf{Y}_1 = (\mathbf{V}_1\,\mathbf{Y}_4)\mathbf{Y}_3 - (\mathbf{V}_1\,\mathbf{Y}_3)\mathbf{Y}_4,$$
$$\mathbf{Y}_2 = (\mathbf{V}_2\,\mathbf{Y}_4)\mathbf{Y}_3 - (\mathbf{V}_2\,\mathbf{Y}_3)\mathbf{Y}_4.$$

In this representation, the points Y_i as points of a projective space of dimension one, have representatives

† See footnote, page 104.

$$(\mathbf{V}_1 \mathbf{Y}_4, -\mathbf{V}_1 \mathbf{Y}_3)^T, \qquad (\mathbf{V}_2 \mathbf{Y}_4, -\mathbf{V}_2 \mathbf{Y}_3)^T, \qquad (1,0)^T, \qquad (0,1)^T,$$

respectively. We therefore have (see II, (3.5))

$$(4.6) \qquad (Y_1 Y_2, Y_3 Y_4) = \frac{\begin{vmatrix} \mathbf{V}_1 \mathbf{Y}_4 & 1 \\ -\mathbf{V}_1 \mathbf{Y}_3 & 0 \end{vmatrix}}{\begin{vmatrix} \mathbf{V}_1 \mathbf{Y}_4 & 0 \\ -\mathbf{V}_1 \mathbf{Y}_3 & 1 \end{vmatrix}} \frac{\begin{vmatrix} \mathbf{V}_2 \mathbf{Y}_4 & 0 \\ -\mathbf{V}_2 \mathbf{Y}_3 & 1 \end{vmatrix}}{\begin{vmatrix} \mathbf{V}_2 \mathbf{Y}_4 & 1 \\ -\mathbf{V}_2 \mathbf{Y}_3 & 0 \end{vmatrix}} = \frac{\mathbf{V}_1 \mathbf{Y}_3}{\mathbf{V}_1 \mathbf{Y}_4} \frac{\mathbf{V}_2 \mathbf{Y}_4}{\mathbf{V}_2 \mathbf{Y}_3}.$$

Dually, we have (see III, 2, Exercise 11)

$$\mathbf{V}_3 = (\mathbf{V}_2 \mathbf{Y}_3)\mathbf{V}_1 - (\mathbf{V}_1 \mathbf{Y}_3)\mathbf{V}_2,$$
$$\mathbf{V}_4 = (\mathbf{V}_2 \mathbf{Y}_4)\mathbf{V}_1 - (\mathbf{V}_1 \mathbf{Y}_4)\mathbf{V}_2,$$

and by Theorem 4.1b, the lines V_1, V_2, V_3, V_4, as lines of a projective space of dimension one, have representative coordinates

$$(1,0), \qquad (0,1), \qquad (\mathbf{V}_2 \mathbf{Y}_3, -\mathbf{V}_1 \mathbf{Y}_3), \qquad (\mathbf{V}_2 \mathbf{Y}_4, -\mathbf{V}_1 \mathbf{Y}_4),$$

respectively. We therefore obtain

$$(4.7) \qquad (V_1 V_2, V_3 V_4) = \frac{\begin{vmatrix} 1 & 0 \\ \mathbf{V}_2 \mathbf{Y}_3 & -\mathbf{V}_1 \mathbf{Y}_3 \end{vmatrix}}{\begin{vmatrix} 1 & 0 \\ \mathbf{V}_2 \mathbf{Y}_4 & -\mathbf{V}_1 \mathbf{Y}_4 \end{vmatrix}} \frac{\begin{vmatrix} 0 & 1 \\ \mathbf{V}_2 \mathbf{Y}_4 & -\mathbf{V}_1 \mathbf{Y}_4 \end{vmatrix}}{\begin{vmatrix} 0 & 1 \\ \mathbf{V}_2 \mathbf{Y}_3 & -\mathbf{V}_1 \mathbf{Y}_3 \end{vmatrix}} = \frac{\mathbf{V}_1 \mathbf{Y}_3}{\mathbf{V}_1 \mathbf{Y}_4} \frac{\mathbf{V}_2 \mathbf{Y}_4}{\mathbf{V}_2 \mathbf{Y}_3}.$$

Equation (4.6) gives us the cross ratio of four points on a line of S_2, and equation (4.7) gives us the cross ratio of four lines of a pencil of S_2. By comparing their values we discover that if the four points of the line and the four lines of the pencil are related as in Figure 4.1, the two cross ratios are equal:

$$(4.8) \qquad (V_1 V_2, V_3 V_4) = (Y_1 Y_2, Y_3 Y_4).$$

Let us now consider Figure 4.1 from a slightly different point of view. We can regard Y_1, Y_2, Y_3, Y_4 as four given collinear points, and V_1, V_2, V_3, V_4 as the lines joining them to a fifth point. If this latter point is allowed to vary, it follows from (4.8) that the cross ratio of the four variable lines is equal to the cross ratio of the given points, in the corresponding order. This very important relationship gives us the following theorem and its dual.

THEOREM 4.2a. *Four collinear points determine with a variable fifth point (not on their line) four lines whose cross ratio is constant and equal to that of the four given points, in the corresponding order.*

THEOREM 4.2b. *Four concurrent lines are cut by a variable line (not in their pencil) in four points whose cross ratio is constant and equal to that of the four given lines, in the corresponding order.*

We can obtain a self-dual form of the cross ratios (4.6) and (4.7) by regarding V_1, V_2, Y_3, Y_4 as the independent variables, with V_3, V_4, Y_1, Y_2 determined as the appropriate joins and intersections.

DEFINITION 4.1. If V_1, V_2 are any two lines, and Y_3, Y_4 any two points, we denote by $(V_1\,V_2, Y_3\,Y_4)$ the common value of the cross ratios (4.6) and (4.7), whenever the latter exist.

We can then write, for lines V, W and points Y, Z,

$$(4.9) \qquad (V\,W, Y\,Z) = \frac{\mathbf{VY}}{\mathbf{VZ}}\,\frac{\mathbf{WZ}}{\mathbf{WY}}.$$

We note that equation (4.9) enables us to express cross ratio of four collinear points, or of four concurrent lines, in terms of coordinates in $S_2(\mathsf{F})$. The reader will find this formula easy to remember, but he should bear in mind that the quantities appearing on the right side are matrix products and not determinants as was the case in $S_1(\mathsf{F})$ (see II, (3.5)).

We know that cross ratio is an invariant of $S_1(\mathsf{F})$ under the group $G_3(\mathsf{F})$ and therefore, by the discussion at the beginning of this section, under those transformations of G_8 that leave S_1 fixed. How is cross ratio affected by an arbitrary collineation? We have the answer in the following theorem.

THEOREM 4.3. *Cross ratio is invariant under the group* $G_8(\mathsf{F})$.

Proof. It will be sufficient to prove that the function $(V\,W, Y Z)$ given by (4.9) is invariant under G_8. We see that $(V\,W, Y Z)$ is a homogeneous function of degree zero of the elements of each of the matrices $\mathbf{V}$, $\mathbf{W}$, $\mathbf{Y}$, $\mathbf{Z}$. Hence $(V\,W, Y Z)$ is independent of the choice of representatives of V, W, Y, Z. If a collineation (3.1) maps V, W, Y, Z onto V', W', Y', Z', respectively, we can select representatives which satisfy (see (1.1) and (3.2) above)

$$\mathbf{V}' = \mathbf{VA}^{-1}, \qquad \mathbf{W}' = \mathbf{WA}^{-1}, \qquad \mathbf{Y}' = \mathbf{AY}, \qquad \mathbf{Z}' = \mathbf{AZ}.$$

Consequently we have

$$\mathbf{V}'\mathbf{Y}' = \mathbf{VA}^{-1}\mathbf{AY} = \mathbf{V}(\mathbf{A}^{-1}\mathbf{A})\mathbf{Y} = \mathbf{VIY} = \mathbf{VY},$$

with a similar result for each of the other matrix products appearing in (4.9). The theorem now follows immediately.

We shall need the following theorem.

THEOREM 4.4. *If Y and Z are two points, and U, V, and W three lines, the product of the three cross ratios, $(U\,V, Y Z)(V\,W, Y Z)(W\,U, Y Z)$, when it exists, is one.*

This theorem can be proved easily by direct calculation, making use of equation (4.9).

We can now obtain a geometric interpretation of projective coordinates in terms of cross ratio, analogous to that found in $S_1(\mathsf{F})$ (see II, Theorem 3.3).

THEOREM 4.5. *Let* $\alpha_1, \alpha_2, \alpha_3$ *be the sides of the reference triangle opposite the respective vertices* A_1, A_2, A_3, *and let* i, j, k *be any permutation of* 1, 2, 3. *Then for any point* $X:(x_1, x_2, x_3)^T$

$$(4.10) \qquad (\alpha_j \alpha_k, D\,X) = x_k/x_j$$

whenever either ratio exists. Let D_i *and* X_i *be the projections, from* A_i *on* α_i, *of* D *and* $X \neq A_i$, *respectively; then*

$$(4.11) \qquad (A_k A_j, D_i X_i) = x_k/x_j.$$

Proof. Because of (4.8), it suffices to prove (4.10). Since an equation of α_j is $x_j = 0$, we can choose a representative of α_j whose j^{th} element is 1, the other two being zero. The matrix product of such a representative with $(1, 1, 1)^T$ is 1, and with $(x_1, x_2, x_3)^T$ is x_j. Hence

$$(4.12) \qquad \boldsymbol{\alpha}_j \mathbf{D} = 1, \qquad \boldsymbol{\alpha}_k \mathbf{D} = 1, \qquad \boldsymbol{\alpha}_j \mathbf{X} = x_j, \qquad \boldsymbol{\alpha}_k \mathbf{X} = x_k,$$

and (4.10) follows from (4.9) and (4.12).

Conversely, we can show that the geometric interpretation of projective coordinates, in terms of cross ratios, expressed by Theorem 4.5, characterizes these coordinates. For if we choose a triangle with sides V_1, V_2, V_3, and a point Y not incident to any V_i $(i = 1, 2, 3)$, we can define coordinates $[\mathbf{X}^*]$ in terms of cross ratio as follows: If X is not incident to V_1, the two equations

$$(4.13) \qquad x_2^*/x_1^* = (V_1 V_2, Y X), \qquad x_3^*/x_1^* = (V_1 V_3, Y X)$$

determine the class $[\mathbf{X}^*] = [x_1^*, x_2^*, x_3^*]^T$ uniquely; by (4.9), we can suppose that a representative $(x_1^*, x_2^*, x_3^*]^T$ is given by

$$(4.14) \qquad x_1^* = \frac{\mathbf{V}_1 \mathbf{X}}{\mathbf{V}_1 \mathbf{Y}}, \qquad x_2^* = \frac{\mathbf{V}_2 \mathbf{X}}{\mathbf{V}_2 \mathbf{Y}}, \qquad x_3^* = \frac{\mathbf{V}_3 X}{\mathbf{V}_3 \mathbf{Y}}.$$

By Theorem 4.4 and (II, (3.10)), we can conclude that whichever of the six cross ratios $(V_i V_j, Y X)$ $(i, j = 1, 2, 3;\ i \neq j)$ exist satisfy

$$(4.15) \qquad (V_i V_j, Y X) = x_j^*/x_i^*.$$

If X is incident to V_1, $\mathbf{V}_1 \mathbf{X} = 0$, and the right members of (4.13) do not exist. In this case we can select a different pair of equations (4.15) to determine $[\mathbf{X}^*]$, but again (4.14) holds for particular representatives of X and X^*, and (4.15) holds for all i, j $(i \neq j)$ for which either ratio is defined.

Since V_1, V_2, V_3 are independent lines, the matrix of (4.14) has a non-vanishing determinant, and (4.14) coincides with the transformation (1.8) for a suitable choice of **B**. Thus [**X***] is indeed a projective coordinatization; we note that the lines V_i are the sides of the reference triangle and that Y is the unit point.

We have suggested (Exercise 16 above) that we can obtain all projective line coordinate systems from a given one by the algebraic process used in Section 1 to obtain all point coordinate systems. Alternatively, we can use the dual of (4.10) and show that projective line coordinates are characterized by the property that

$$(\delta U, A_i A_j) = u_j/u_i, \qquad i \neq j, \tag{4.16}$$

where δ is the unit line and U has the representative (u_1, u_2, u_3) (see Exercise 15 below).

We shall sometimes find it convenient to use nonhomogeneous projective coordinates in $S_2(\mathsf{F})$. If $[x_1, x_2, x_3]^T$ are homogeneous projective coordinates, the coordinates (x, y) defined by any one of the three following pairs of equations:

$$\text{(4.17)} \qquad \text{(a)} \begin{cases} x = x_1/x_3, \\ y = x_2/x_3, \end{cases} \qquad \text{(b)} \begin{cases} x = x_1/x_2, \\ y = x_3/x_2, \end{cases} \qquad \text{(c)} \begin{cases} x = x_2/x_1, \\ y = x_3/x_1, \end{cases}$$

are called *nonhomogeneous* projective coordinates. In the first case the points of the line $x_3 = 0$, and no other points, fail to possess nonhomogeneous coordinates, and similarly in every nonhomogenous projective coordinate system, there exists one and just one line whose points have no coordinates. We call that line the *exceptional* line or the *line at infinity* of the (given) nonhomogeneous coordinate system. Clearly, any line of $S_2(\mathsf{F})$ can be selected to be the line at infinity of some nonhomogeneous coordinate system.

Similarly, if we replace line coordinates $[u_1, u_2, u_3]$ by (u, v) defined by one of the following pairs of equations:

$$\text{(4.18)} \qquad \text{(a)} \begin{cases} u = u_1/u_3, \\ v = u_2/u_3, \end{cases} \qquad \text{(b)} \begin{cases} u = u_1/u_2, \\ v = u_3/u_2, \end{cases} \qquad \text{(c)} \begin{cases} u = u_2/u_1, \\ v = u_3/u_1, \end{cases}$$

the resulting nonhomogeneous line coordinatization (u, v) possesses an exceptional point; the lines incident to this point have no nonhomogeneous coordinates. If the nonhomogeneous point and line coordinates are related to the homogeneous point and line coordinates by (3.16a) and (3.17a) (or by (3.16b) and (3.17b) or by (3.16c) and (3.17c)) it follows that the incidence condition is

$$ux + vy + 1 = 0.$$

Nonhomogeneous coordinates may be used especially when the conditions of a problem permit one to disregard the points of a given line or the lines of a given pencil. When that is the case, the procedures involved in finding equations or coordinates of points or lines from incidence conditions become identical with the corresponding procedures in elementary analytic geometry in terms of rectangular Cartesian coordinates.

EXERCISES

In the numerical exercises, it may be assumed that the ground field F *is the real field* R.

1. Let L be the join of $(1, 1, 2)^T$ and $(3, 1, 2)^T$. Show that $Y_1:(2, 1, 2)^T$, $Z_1:(1, 0, 0)^T$, $Y_2:(3, -1, -2)^T$, and $Z_2:(1, 2, 4)^T$ are points of L. Express a variable point X of L (a) as $\lambda\mathbf{Y}_1 + \mu\mathbf{Z}_1$, and (b) as $\lambda'\mathbf{Y}_2 + \mu'\mathbf{Z}_2$, and find the relation between $[\lambda, \mu]^T$ and $[\lambda', \mu']^T$.

2. How is the representation $\mathbf{X} = \lambda\mathbf{Y} + \mu\mathbf{Z}$ of the points of the line $Y \oplus Z$ affected if the representatives $\mathbf{Y}$ and $\mathbf{Z}$ of Y and Z are replaced by $\mathbf{Y}' = \rho\mathbf{Y}$ and $\mathbf{Z}' = \sigma\mathbf{Z}$, respectively $(\rho, \sigma \in \mathsf{F})$.

3. Find values of λ, μ for the point $(2, 1, 2)^T$ of the line L of Exercise 1, if $\lambda = 1, \mu = 0$ is the point $(1, 1, 2)^T$, $\lambda = 0, \mu = 1$ is the point $(3, 1, 2)^T$, and if $\lambda = 1, \mu = 1$ is $(3, -1, -2)^T$. ANS. $(-2, 3)$.

4. Find the cross ratio formed by the points $(1, 1, 2)^T$, $(2, 3, 4)^T$, and the points in which their line intersects the lines $x_1 + x_2 + x_3 = 0$, $2x_1 + x_3 = 0$. ANS. $8/9$.

5. Find the cross ratio of the four lines:

(a) $x_1 - x_2 + x_3 = 0$,
(b) $x_1 + 2x_2 + x_3 = 0$,
(c) the line joining the intersection of (a) and (b) to $(1, 2, 3)^T$,
(d) the line joining the intersection of (a) and (b) to $(2, 1, 1)^T$.

ANS. $5/8$.

6. Show that the points $(1, -1, 1)^T$, $(1, 2, 1)^T$, $(2, 1, 2)^T$, and $(1, -4, 1)^T$ are collinear, and find their cross ratio. ANS. -2.

7. Show that $x_1 - x_2 + x_3 = 0$, $x_1 + 2x_2 + x_3 = 0$, $2x_1 + x_2 + 2x_3 = 0$, $x_1 - 4x_2 + x_3 = 0$ are concurrent lines. Find their cross ratio (see Exercise 6).

8. Find the cross ratio of the lines joining the point $(1, 2, -3)^T$ to the four points $(1, 0, 1)^T$, $(1, 1, 0)^T$, $(0, 1, 1)^T$, and $(1, 1, 1)^T$.

***9.** Express the cross ratio of the lines joining the point $R:(r_1, r_2, r_3)^T$ to the four points $(a_1, a_2, a_3)^T$, $(b_1, b_2, b_3)^T$, $(c_1, c_2, c_3)^T$, and $(d_1, d_2, d_3)^T$ in terms of determinants.

ANS. $\det(\mathbf{R}\ \ \mathbf{A}\ \ \mathbf{C}) \det(\mathbf{R}\ \ \mathbf{B}\ \ \mathbf{D})/\det(\mathbf{R}\ \ \mathbf{A}\ \ \mathbf{D}) \det(\mathbf{R}\ \ \mathbf{B}\ \ \mathbf{C})$.

10. State the dual of Theorem 4.3.

11. State the dual of Theorem 4.4.

12. Let the points $(1, 1, 0)^T$, $(1, 0, 1)^T$, $(0, 1, 1)^T$, and $(1, 1, 1)^T$ be chosen as the reference frame of a new coordinate system; find the relation between the two systems by using Theorem 4.5 and Exercise 9.

***13.** Let L be a line not incident to A_1, and let $X:(x_1, x_2, x_3)^T$ be any point of L. Show that the classes $[x_2, x_3]^T$ constitute a projective coordinatization of L, and then work Exercise 6 by using (II, (3.5)) for this coordinatization. Observe that this procedure for finding cross ratio can be interpreted as finding the cross ratio of the projections, from A_1 onto the line $x_1 = 0$, of the given points.

#**14.** Prove Theorem 1.1 (or its dual) geometrically by using known properties of projectivities together with the conclusion that a collineation establishes a projectivity on any line that it leaves fixed (or the dual of this conclusion).

15. Prove (4.16).

16. State and prove the dual of (4.11) independently.

17. Show that the collineation with representative matrix

$$\mathbf{A} = \begin{pmatrix} 1 & 1 & 1 \\ 1 & -1 & -2 \\ 0 & 0 & 2 \end{pmatrix}$$

leaves fixed the line $x_3 = 0$, and determine the fixed points of the projectivity established thereon.

*__18.__ Find a necessary and sufficient condition that the two lines with equations $ax + by + c = 0$, $a'x + b'y + c' = 0$, intersect on the line at infinity of the nonhomogeneous coordinate system.

*__19.__ Find, in terms of nonhomogeneous coordinates, the harmonic conjugate, with respect to two given points, of the point in which their line intersects the line at infinity of the nonhomogeneous coordinate system.

5 Drawing Figures

From his earliest contact with geometry, the reader has been accustomed to drawing figures, that is, to representing the objects he has been discussing by marks made on paper with the aid of certain instruments. For example, he has used a sharp pencil—pressed lightly—to produce a "point," and has drawn the pencil along a straight edge to produce a "line." Such material representations of mathematical concepts should not be confused with the concepts themselves, and a representation that reflects closely some aspects of a given mathematical structure may depart widely in other respects. Putting his faith in figures may easily lead the student astray. Figures, however, are indispensable in focusing ideas and in clarifying complex situations. We must therefore learn to use them properly.

Before deciding what representation will be most useful for lines in $S_2(\mathsf{F})$ we shall need to consider more carefully some of their properties. Actually the ground field plays an important role. If F is finite, $S_1(\mathsf{F})$ possesses only a finite number of points; $S_1(\mathsf{R})$ and $S_1(\mathsf{C})$ have many properties that are very different from each other and from those of a finite S_1. However, in the first part of this section we shall be discussing *real* spaces only.

One important property of a line in $S_2(\mathsf{R})$ is that it is a *simple closed* curve; by this we mean that there exist maps of the line onto a circle in E_2 which are one-to-one and continuous both ways. Even though we are not yet prepared to prove this (we shall do so in Section 7, after defining limit operations and continuity in projective spaces), this property appears completely natural when we recall (Theorem 4.1) that a line in $S_2(\mathsf{R})$ and a pencil of lines in E_2 possess the same coordinatization; it is intuitively clear that a variable line of the pencil can traverse the pencil continuously, returning to its initial line.

Meanwhile, let us prove that no one-to-one bicontinuous map of the Euclidean line onto a circle can exist. Suppose one did; let us denote it by f, so that $f(P)$ is the point of the circle onto which a point P of the line is mapped. Let us now select an infinite sequence of points P_n ($n = 1, 2, 3, \ldots$) on the line, chosen so that the directed distance from P_n to P_{n+1} is 1, for all n

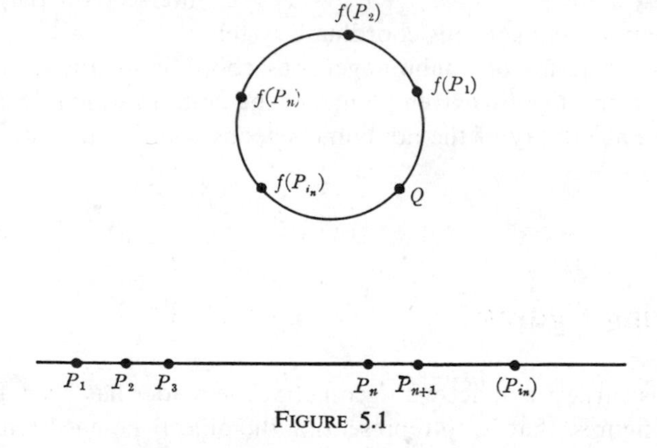

FIGURE 5.1

(Figure 5.1). Then the images on the circle, that is, the points $f(P_n)$, constitute a bounded infinite sequence, and in E_2, as in E_1, every such sequence contains a convergent subsequence.† Denote a convergent subsequence of $f(P_n)$ by $f(P_{i_n})$ ($0 < i_n < i_{n+1}$ for all n), and let $Q = \lim_{n\to\infty} f(P_{i_n})$. Then Q lies on the circle, and $f^{-1}(Q)$ lies on the line. Continuity of f^{-1} implies that it and the limit operator commute,

$$\lim_{n\to\infty} f^{-1}(f(P_{i_n})) = f^{-1}(\lim_{n\to\infty} f(P_{i_n})).$$

Since $f^{-1}(f(P_{i_n})) = P_{i_n}$, the continuity of f^{-1} asserts that the sequence of points P_{i_n} on the line converges to $f^{-1}(Q)$. This is false, and the map f cannot exist.

† This is the classical Bolzano-Weierstrass theorem; see Tom M. Apostol, *Mathematical Analysis*, Reading, Mass., Addison-Wesley Publishing Co., 1957, p. 43.

In many respects the real projective line, or an $S_1(\mathsf{R})$ bears a closer resemblance to a circle than to a Euclidean line. In fact such phrases as "betweeen P and Q," "the segment PQ," and "the (infinite) ray PQ," which have meanings on the Euclidean line, have no meaning on a projective line. But on a circle two points do determine *two* segments. We shall see in the following discussion that such is also the case on the projective line, or indeed in any $S_1(\mathsf{R})$.

DEFINITION 5.1. Let A, B, C, D be four distinct points of $S_1(\mathsf{R})$; the pair A, B is said to *separate* the pair C, D (written $AB \int CD$) if $(A\,B, C\,D) < 0$; the pair A, B *does not separate* C, D (written $AB \not\int CD$) if $(A\,B, C\,D) > 0$.

The property of separation is clearly projectively invariant; it is symmetric both in the pairs and in the elements of each pair, that is, if $AB \int CD$, then $CD \int AB$, and $AB \int DC$ (see II, 3, Exercise 14).

THEOREM 5.1. *Two distinct points A, B, of $S_1(\mathsf{R})$ partition the remaining points into two mutually exclusive sets; two points belonging to different sets separate A, B, while two points belonging to the same set do not separate A, B.*

Proof. Let C be any chosen point of $S_1(\mathsf{R})$ distinct from A and B. Then for any point X, distinct from A and B, one and just one of the following statements is true:

(1) $(A\,B, C\,X) < 0$,
(2) $(A\,B, C\,X) > 0$.

Let points X which satisfy the first inequality belong to one set, and points X which satisfy the second inequality belong to the other set. We recall that (see II, 3, Exercise 4)

$$(A\,B, C\,X)(A\,B, X\,Y)(A\,B, Y\,C) = 1.$$

If X and Y belong to the same set, the first and third factors of the left side have the same sign and $(A\,B, X\,Y) > 0$, that is, X, Y do not separate A, B. If X and Y belong to different sets, the first and third factors have opposite signs, and $(A\,B, X\,Y) < 0$, that is, X, Y separate A, B.

DEFINITION 5.2. Each of the two sets determined in Theorem 5.1 is called an (open) *segment* with *end points* A and B. The segment containing a point C is written seg ACB, and the one not containing C is written seg* ACB. An open segment together with its end points is called a *closed* segment, and we write the closed segment ACB as $\overline{\text{seg}}\,ACB$.

THEOREM 5.2. *If Y and Z are any two distinct points in $S_2(\mathsf{R})$, the locus of the points $\mathbf{X} = \lambda\mathbf{Y} + \mu\mathbf{Z}$, where $\lambda\mu > 0$, is one open segment with Y and Z as end points, and the locus of the points X for which $\lambda\mu < 0$ is the other.*

We leave the proof to the reader (see Exercise 7 below).

We next define order on a projective line. As in the case of segments, we shall see that projective order is similar to order on a circle.

DEFINITION 5.3. A finite set of four or more distinct points of $S_1(\mathsf{R})$: $A_1, A_2, \ldots, A_n$, is said to be in the *projective order* $\langle A_1 A_2 \ldots A_n \rangle$ if two consecutive points do not separate any other two points of the set and if A_n, A_1 do not separate any other two points of the set.

This definition is clearly projectively invariant, since separation is, but it is not immediately obvious whether there exist sets of points that satisfy the conditions of the definition. The following theorem shows that every finite set possesses a projective order.

THEOREM 5.3. *A finite number n $(n \geqq 4)$ of distinct points of $S_1(\mathsf{R})$ can always be so labeled that they are in the projective order $\langle A_1 A_2 \ldots A_n \rangle$.*

Proof. Let us establish in $S_1(\mathsf{R})$ a coordinate system whose reference elements do not belong to the set. Then all of the given points will have nonhomogeneous coordinates that are real numbers. Let us designate these coordinates by λ_i $(i = 1, 2, \ldots, n)$ in such a manner that

$$\lambda_1 < \lambda_2 < \lambda_3 < \cdots < \lambda_n, \tag{5.1}$$

and attach the label A_i to the point with nonhomogeneous coordinate λ_i. Let us consider the cross ratio

$$(A_i A_{i+1}, A_j A_k) = \frac{\lambda_i - \lambda_j}{\lambda_{i+1} - \lambda_j} \frac{\lambda_{i+1} - \lambda_k}{\lambda_i - \lambda_k}, \tag{5.2}$$

where i takes on values from 1 to $n - 1$, and A_j and A_k are any points of the given set distinct from A_i and A_{i+1}. Since λ_j (or λ_k) is either greater or less than both λ_i and λ_{i+1}, each of the fractions on the right side is positive, and the cross ratio is positive; hence A_i, A_{i+1} do not separate A_j, A_k. From the inequalities (5.1), it follows that the cross ratio

$$(A_n A_1, A_j A_k) = \frac{\lambda_n - \lambda_j}{\lambda_n - \lambda_k} \frac{\lambda_1 - \lambda_k}{\lambda_1 - \lambda_j},$$

where A_j and A_k are any two points distinct from A_n and A_1, is also positive; hence A_n, A_1 do not separate A_j, A_k. By Definition 5.3, the n points are in the projective order $\langle A_1 A_2 \ldots A_n \rangle$.

COROLLARY 5.1. *If n points are in the projective order $\langle A_1 A_2 \ldots A_n \rangle$ and if $h < i < j < k$, then $A_h A_j \mathrel{\int} A_i A_k$.*

We leave the proof to the reader.

From Definitions 5.3 and 5.1, it can easily be shown that if n points are in the projective order $\langle A_1 A_2 \ldots A_n \rangle$, they are also in the projective orders $\langle A_i A_{i+1} \ldots A_n A_1 \ldots A_{i-1} \rangle$, and $\langle A_n A_{n-1} \ldots A_1 \rangle$.

We thus see that projective order can be represented by order on a circle. Just as on a circle, we can start at any point and go around in either direction (Figure 5.2). It remains, however, to show that a finite set of points

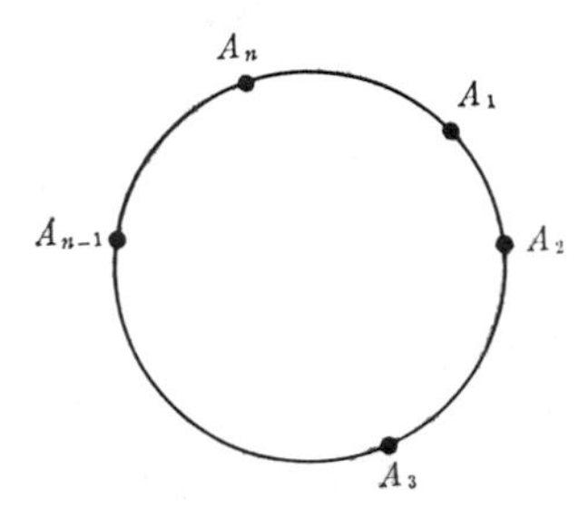

FIGURE 5.2

does not possess any other projective orders than the ones obtained from a given one in this manner. We can prove this as follows: Let n given points be in the projective order $\langle A_1 A_2 \ldots A_n \rangle$, and let $B_1, B_2, \ldots, B_n$ be any permutation of $A_1, A_2, \ldots, A_n$ such that the points are in the projective order $\langle B_1 B_2 \ldots B_n \rangle$. Since we can start at any point, we can assume that $B_1 = A_1$. Suppose $B_2 = A_i \, (i \neq 1, 2, n)$. Since the points are in the projective order $\langle B_1 B_2 \ldots B_n \rangle$, the points B_1, B_2 (that is, A_1, A_i) do not separate any other two points of the set, and in particular $A_1 A_i \int A_2 A_{i+1}$. But this contradicts the corollary to Theorem 5.3. Therefore B_2 is either A_2 or A_n. An identical type of argument suffices to show that in the first case $B_3 = A_3$ and in the second $B_3 = A_{n-1}$. After $n - 2$ applications of the argument, we find that either $B_1, B_2, \ldots, B_n = A_1, A_2, \ldots, A_n$, respectively, or $B_1, B_2, \ldots, B_n = A_1, A_n, A_{n-1}, \ldots, A_2$, respectively.

If we were concerned only with order relations in $S_1(R)$, we would find a circle a good representation of a projective line. Indeed we used a circle in Figure 5.2. Usually, however, we are concerned with other properties, for example, incidence relations, and circles would be most unsatisfactory for exhibiting these relations. We shall therefore in our figures usually represent a projective line by a mark drawn along a straightedge. We must constantly keep in mind, however, that a projective line is a closed curve.

Even though $S_2(R)$ cannot be represented consistently by marks made on a sheet of paper (indeed no mathematical structure can be represented exactly by objects possessing physical reality), we do want to keep the inconsistencies to a minimum. In particular, we can learn to locate points, when their coordinates are given, with a reasonable degree of consistency by means of the two constructions which follow.

Construction Problem 5.1. Given two points on a line L, find the point on L whose nonhomogeneous projective coordinate with respect to a given reference frame is the sum of the nonhomogeneous coordinates of the given points.

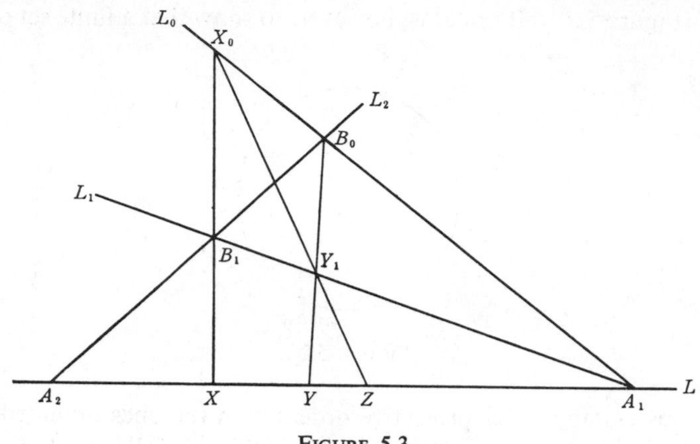

Figure 5.3

Procedure. Let $A_1 A_2 D_3$ (Figure 5.3) be the reference frame of the coordinate system on L, with A_1 as the exceptional point of the nonhomogeneous system, and let X and Y be the given points. (It is implicit in the statement of the problem that both X and Y possess a nonhomogeneous coordinate and therefore that neither is the exceptional point A_1.) Choose two distinct lines ($\neq L$) through A_1, and label them L_0 and L_1. Choose any line ($\neq L$) through A_2 and label it L_2. We let

$$B_0 = L_0 \cap L_2, \qquad B_1 = L_1 \cap L_2,$$
$$X_0 = L_0 \cap (X \oplus B_1), \qquad Y_1 = L_1 \cap (Y \oplus B_0).$$

Then the required point Z is $L \cap (X_0 \oplus Y_1)$.

Proof. Let us establish a coordinate system in the plane with reference triangle $A_1 A_2 B_0$, and unit point D on $B_0 \oplus D_3$. Since $B_1 \neq B_0$, we can suppose $\mathbf{B}_1 = (0, 1, b)^T$, $(b \neq 0)$. Then the several points of Figure 5.3 have representatives as follows:

$$A_1:(1,0,0)^T, \qquad A_2:(0,1,0)^T, \qquad B_0:(0,0,1)^T,$$
$$B_1:(0,1,b)^T, \qquad X:(x,1,0)^T, \qquad Y:(y,1,0)^T.$$

We can compute a representative of Z by following through the construction, finding representatives of each line and point until we arrive at Z.

Those of $X \oplus B_1$ are the three two-rowed determinants from the matrix of coordinates of X and B_1,

$$\begin{pmatrix} x & 0 \\ 1 & 1 \\ 0 & b \end{pmatrix},$$

that is, $(b, -bx, x)$. The point X_0, the intersection of this line with L_0, has coordinates that are the three two-rowed determinants from the matrix of coordinates of these lines,

$$\begin{pmatrix} b & -bx & x \\ 0 & 1 & 0 \end{pmatrix},$$

that is, $\mathbf{X}_0 = (-x, 0, b)^T$. Similarly, we find that $Y \oplus B_0$ has coordinates $(1, -y, 0)$, and L_1, which is $A_1 \oplus B_1$, has coordinates $(0, -b, 1)$; Y_1, the intersection of these lines, has coordinates $(y, 1, b)^T$. $X_0 \oplus Y_1$ has coordinates $(-b, bx + by, -x)$; its intersection with L:$(0, 0, 1)$ is Z:$(x + y, 1, 0)^T$. The nonhomogeneous coordinate of Z as a point of L is therefore $x + y$, as required.

Since the nonhomogeneous coordinate of Z as a point of L is uniquely determined by the coordinates of the points X and Y and the reference frame $A_1 A_2 D_3$, it follows that the point Z is uniquely determined by these points and is independent of the choice of L_0, L_1, L_2. The choice of these lines affects the point B_0, and therefore the coordinate system in S_2, but not the coordinates of points on L.

CONSTRUCTION PROBLEM 5.2. Given two points on a line L, find the point on L whose nonhomogeneous projective coordinate with respect to a given reference frame is the product of the nonhomogeneous coordinates of the two given points.

Procedure. Let $A_1 A_2 D_3$ (Figure 5.4) be the reference frame of the coordinate system on L, with A_1 as the exceptional point of the nonhomogeneous

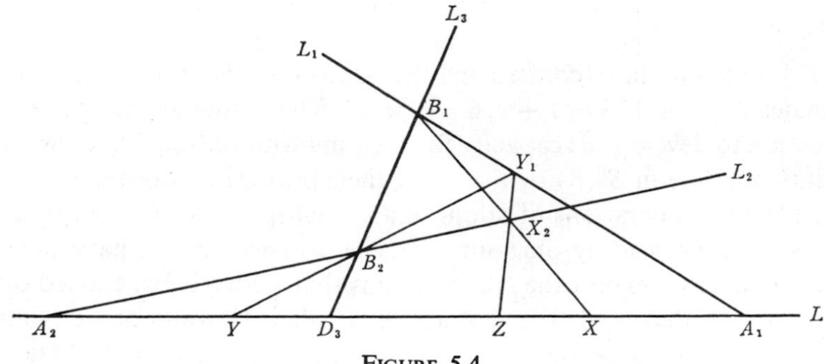

FIGURE 5.4

system, and let X and Y be the given points. (Again, neither X nor Y is A_1.) Choose any three nonconcurrent lines ($\neq L$), one through each of the points A_1, A_2, D_3, and label them L_1, L_2, L_3, respectively. We let

$$B_1 = L_1 \cap L_3, \qquad B_2 = L_2 \cap L_3,$$
$$X_2 = L_2 \cap (X \oplus B_1), \qquad Y_1 = L_1 \cap (Y \oplus B_2).$$

Then the required point is $Z = L \cap (X_2 \oplus Y_1)$.

Proof. We establish a coordinate system in the plane with $A_1 A_2 B_1 B_2$ as reference frame. Then representatives of the several points of the construction are as follows:

$$A_1:(1,0,0)^T, \qquad A_2:(0,1,0)^T, \qquad B_1:(0,0,1)^T,$$
$$B_2:(1,1,1)^T, \qquad D_3:(1,1,0)^T,$$
$$X:(x,1,0)^T, \qquad Y:(y,1,0)^T.$$

As in the proof of the previous construction problem, we compute representatives of the other points of the construction; we find

$$\mathbf{X}_2 = (x,1,x)^T, \qquad \mathbf{Y}_1 = (1-y,0,1)^T, \qquad \mathbf{Z} = (xy,1,0)^T.$$

The nonhomogeneous coordinate of Z as a point of L is therefore xy, as required. By an argument identical to that used above, the point Z is independent of the choice of the lines L_1, L_2, L_3.

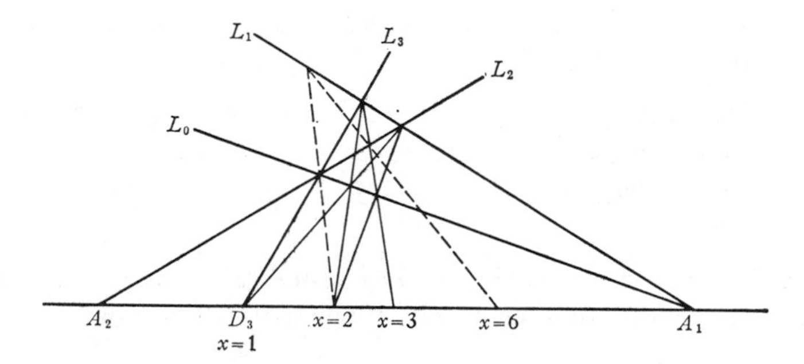

FIGURE 5.5

In Figure 5.5 we have constructed the points on L with nonhomogeneous coordinates $2 = 1 + 1$, $3 = 1 + 2$, $6 = 3 \times 2$. The reader should extend this construction to develop his capacity for locating with reasonable consistency the points of a line in $S_2(\mathsf{R})$ by means of their projective coordinates.

The algebraic operations of addition and multiplication (except by zero), which we have been using on nonhomogeneous coordinates, have inverses. We would therefore expect the constructions that we have just carried out to to be reversible, that is, if X and Z are given, that Y would be determined. This is easily seen to be the case. In the first construction, for example,

B_0, B_1 are determined by the choice of L_0, L_1, L_2; X then determines X_0; $X_0 \oplus Z$ determines Y_1 on L_1; and $Y = L \cap (B_0 \oplus Y_1)$. In this manner we can construct points whose coordinates are differences. Similarly, from the second construction we can derive one for points whose coordinates are quotients. Thus we can describe the points of a line that have rational coordinates in a given reference frame by a sequence of joins and intersections.†

To locate a point $X:(x, 1)$, where x is irrational, we note that for all rational numbers r, s, t such that $r < s < x < t$, $X \in \text{seg } RST$.

In passing from projective coordinates in one dimension to those in two, it suffices to observe that the projection of $X:(x_1, x_2, x_3)^T$ from A_i on the side of the reference triangle opposite A_i is the point whose i^{th} coordinate is zero, and whose other two coordinates are equal to the corresponding coordinates of X. Hence if we locate the projection of a point on two sides of the coordinate triangle, we can locate the point itself.

So far in this section we have assumed that we were dealing with real spaces. It is worthwhile, however, to consider which, if any, of our results are valid in space over other fields. In our definition of separation and in the theorems and definitions that followed, we made use of the fact that among the real numbers there are numbers, called positive, with the following properties:

(1) For any given number a, one and only one of the following alternatives holds: a is a positive number, or $a = 0$, or there exists a positive number x such that $x + a = 0$.
(2) The sum and product of two positive numbers are positive.

A field is said to be *ordered* if it possesses these properties. It then follows that Definitions 5.1 to 5.3 and Theorems 5.1 to 5.3 are valid in a projective space whose ground field is ordered. This is a considerable restriction, for many fields are not ordered, for example, the complex field, and the modular field described below.

Thc situation is quite different in the case of Construction Problems 5.1 and 5.2. In these, the procedures—that is, the verbal descriptions—and the proofs are valid in any field, for we made use only of incidence relations and the field properties of coordinates. To what extent do the accompanying figures portray the situation for an arbitrary ground field? Not too well, as we shall see! One difficulty is that in many S_2's the straightedge representation is not possible for all of the lines. This is clearly the case for $S_2(\mathsf{C})$ in which a line is a two-dimensional real continuum. It is also the case in many other projective planes. Let us examine in detail one such case: the plane whose ground field is F_3, the modular field of characteristic 3. This field possesses but three elements: 0, 1, 2. Addition and multiplication are defined as the remainders when the ordinary sums and products are divided

† In $S_2(\mathsf{F})$, such a set of points is called a net of rationality on the line; see Veblen and Young, *Projective Geometry*, Boston, Ginn and Co., 1910, pp. 84–86.

by 3. $S_1(\mathsf{F}_3)$ has but four points: $(0,1)^T$, $(1,0)^T$, $(1,1)^T$, and $(1,2)^T \in [2,1]^T$. The reader can verify that $S_2(\mathsf{F}_3)$ has the following thirteen points and no others:

$$\begin{array}{llll} A_1:(1,0,0)^T & D_1:(0,1,1)^T & E_1:(2,1,1)^T & F_1:(0,1,2)^T \\ A_2:(0,1,0)^T & D_2:(1,0,1)^T & E_2:(1,2,1)^T & F_2:(2,0,1)^T \\ A_3:(0,0,1)^T & D_3:(1,1,0)^T & E_3:(1,1,2)^T & F_3:(1,2,0)^T \end{array}$$
$$D:(1,1,1)^T$$

By duality, there are thirteen lines with representatives these same triples of values. Let us construct such a plane by first marking four points A_1, A_2, A_3, D to serve as the reference frame. The line $A_i \oplus A_j$ intersects $D \oplus A_k$ in D_k (i, j, k is any permutation of 1, 2, 3). Let us mark these points as the intersection of two straightedges laid along A_i, A_j and along D, A_k. Now each two of the D's determine a line, and from their equations we note that these three lines are distinct from each other and from each of the six lines already considered. We can find, by solving their equations, that $D_i \oplus D_j$ intersects $A_i \oplus A_j$ in F_k, and $A_k \oplus D_k$ in E_k. We have by now Figure 5.6.

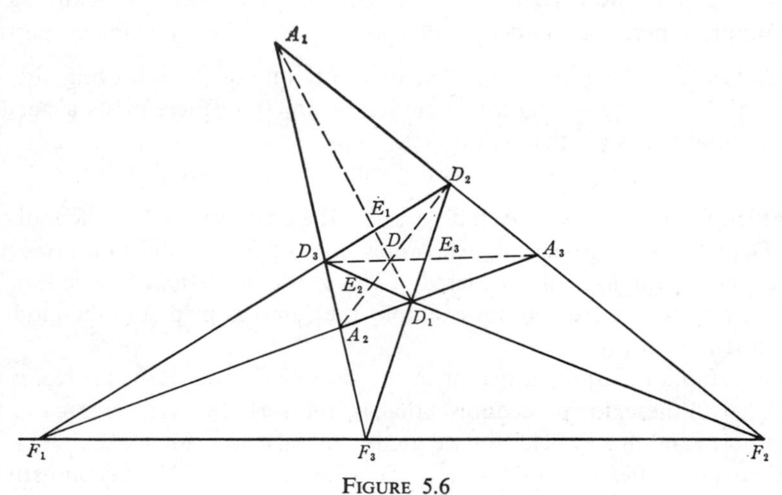

FIGURE 5.6

We have accounted for all thirteen points, but only nine lines. There are four additional lines. We find that $E_1 \oplus E_2$ is distinct from the nine lines already mentioned; it must intersect each of them, but the points of intersection must be included in the thirteen points already marked. In all, we find that the thirteen lines consist of the following quadruples of points:

$$\begin{array}{llll} A_1 A_2 D_3 F_3, & A_1 D_1 D E_1, & D_1 D_2 E_3 F_3, & E_1 E_2 A_3 F_3, \\ A_2 A_3 D_1 F_1, & A_2 D_2 D E_2, & D_2 D_3 E_1 F_1, & E_2 E_3 A_1 F_1, \\ A_3 A_1 D_2 F_2, & A_3 D_3 D E_3, & D_3 D_1 E_2 F_2, & E_3 E_1 A_2 F_2, \end{array}$$
$$F_1 F_2 F_3 D.$$

If Figure 5.6 is then to represent $S_2(\mathsf{F}_3)$, we must regard as collinear, not only the points that lie along a straightedge in the figure, but also the four sets that do not. Thus four lines of the thirteen in $S_2(\mathsf{F}_3)$ have no straightedge representation.

The situation in this projective plane is typical. It is not generally possible to represent all lines by a physical image of the edge of a ruler. Nevertheless Constructions 5.1 and 5.2 are always valid. To carry them out in a figure we would have to know what points in the figure comprise the line joining a chosen pair.

EXERCISES

Prove the following ten theorems on segments and projective order in $S_1(\mathsf{R})$:

1. If seg $ACB =$ seg ADB, seg $CAD =$ seg CBD.

2. If $C \in$ seg ADB, then either $C \in$ seg BAD, or $C \in$ seg ABD.

3. If A, B, C are distinct points, seg* $ABC \subset$ seg ACB.

4. If C lies in one of the segments with A and B as end points and D lies in the other, then A and C lie in the same segment with end points B and D, and A and D lie in the same segment with end points B and C.

5. If C and D both lie in one of the segments with A, B as end points and E lies in the other, then A and B both lie in seg CED.

***6.** If $D \in$ seg ACB, one of the segments with C, D as end points contains A and B, the other is contained in seg ACB.

7. Theorem 5.2.

8. If n points are in the projective order $\langle A_1 A_2 \ldots A_n \rangle$, then any subset of four or more points is in the projective order $\langle A_i A_j \ldots A_k \rangle$, where $i < j < \cdots < k$.

9. If n points are in the projective order $\langle A_1 A_2 \ldots A_n \rangle$, the segments $A_1 A_i A_n$ for $i = 2, \ldots, n-1$ coincide and contain seg $A_i A_j A_k$ for $i < j < k$.

10. If n points are in the projective order $\langle A_1 A_2 \ldots A_n \rangle$, and if m additional points together with A_1, A_2, A_n are in the projective order $\langle A_1 A_2 A_n A_{n+1} \ldots A_{n+m} \rangle$, then the $n+m$ points are in the projective order $\langle A_1 A_2 \ldots A_{n+m} \rangle$.

11. Construction problem: Given two points X and Y on a line L, find the point on L whose nonhomogeneous projective coordinate with respect to a given reference frame is the nonhomogeneous coordinate of X divided by the coordinate of Y.

12. Choose a reference frame $A_1 A_2 D_3$ on a line, and construct the points with the following nonhomogeneous coordinates: $2, 3, 4, 5, -2, -2/5, 12, 25$.

13. Select a reference frame in $S_2(\mathsf{R})$, and estimate the location of each of the following points: $(6, 3, 1)$, $(2, 1, -2)$, $(-1, 9, 1)$. Check one estimate by a straightedge construction.

6 Separation Theorems in $S_2(\mathsf{R})$

We shall see that the one-dimensional concepts of separation and of segments introduced in the preceding section play an essential role in the development of the theorems of this section. We might therefore expect that the results of this section are valid in a projective plane over any ordered field, and such is indeed the case. There is, however, some slight gain in simplicity if we concern ourselves solely with $S_2(\mathsf{R})$. We shall find that its topological structure is quite different from that of either a Euclidean plane or a sphere. For example, a straight line in the Euclidean plane (or a great circle on the sphere) separates the remaining points of the plane (or sphere) into two mutually exclusive sets such that every segment of a straight line (or of a great circle) with end points in different sets intersects the given line (or great circle). Such is not the case in $S_2(\mathsf{R})$. The following theorem shows that two points are always on the same "side" of a given projective line.

THEOREM 6.1. *If A and B are any two distinct points of $S_2(\mathsf{R})$, and L is any line not incident to A or B, there exists a closed segment with A, B as end points that has no point in common with L.*

Proof. Let C be the point of intersection of L and $A \oplus B$, and let D be any point such that $AB \int CD$. Then $\overline{\text{seg}}\, ADB$ does not contain C, and therefore has no intersection with L.

THEOREM 6.2. *Two distinct lines separate the remaining points of $S_2(\mathsf{R})$ into two mutually exclusive sets with the following properties:*

(1) *Two points in the same set determine two segments one of which has no intersection with the given lines, and the other of which intersects both.*

(2) *Two points in different sets determine two segments each of which intersects one and just one of the given lines.*

Proof. Let the lines be V_1 and V_2. The pencil determined by these lines is a projective space of dimension one which, by Theorem 5.1, is separated into two mutually exclusive classes by V_1 and V_2. Then we define one set in $S_2(\mathsf{R})$ to consist of the points (not $V_1 \cap V_2$) on the lines of one class, and the other set to consist of the points (not $V_1 \cap V_2$) on the lines of the other class. We thus have two mutually exclusive sets, and it remains to show that they have the properties described in the theorem. Let Y_3 and Y_4 be any two points not incident to V_1, V_2. If $Y_3 \oplus Y_4$ is a line of the pencil, by definition they belong to the same set, and their two segments obviously have property (1). If $Y_3 \oplus Y_4$ does not belong to the pencil, we denote by Y_1, Y_2 its intersections with V_1, V_2 respectively, and by V_3, V_4 the lines of the pencil incident to Y_3, Y_4 respectively (see Figure 6.1). By (4.8)

$$(V_1 V_2, V_3 V_4) = (Y_1 Y_2, Y_3 Y_4).$$

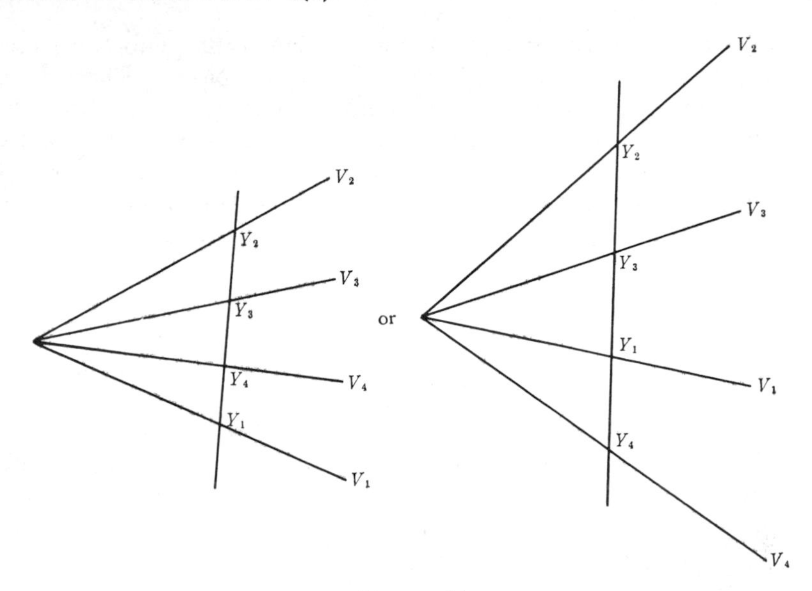

FIGURE 6.1

If Y_3, Y_4 belong to the same set, it follows from Theorem 5.1, applied to the pencil determined by V_1 and V_2, that $(V_1 V_2, V_3 V_4) > 0$. But then $(Y_1 Y_2, Y_3 Y_4) > 0$, and again from Theorem 5.1, applied now to $Y_3 \oplus Y_4$, we have that Y_1, Y_2 lie in the same segment, so that seg $Y_3 Y_1 Y_4$ contains both points of intersection, and the other segment contains no intersection. On the other hand, if Y_3, Y_4 belong to different sets, it follows by a similar argument that the intersections belong to different segments.

DEFINITION 6.1. The two sets of Theorem 6.2 are called (open) *sectors*, and the lines that determine them their *bounding lines*. We denote the sector with bounding lines V, W and containing a point Y by sec VYW, and the complementary sector (not containing Y) by sec* VYW.†

The reader should now prove the following three statements.

COROLLARY 6.1. *Any two points of a sector can be joined by a segment all of whose points are contained in the sector.*

COROLLARY 6.2. *A line U not concurrent with lines V, W intersects either one of the sectors whose bounding lines are V, W in a segment whose endpoints are $U \cap V$, $U \cap W$.*

COROLLARY 6.3. *Let V, W be two distinct lines, and Y, Z two points not incident to either line. Then $Z \in$ sec VYW if and only if $(VW, YZ) > 0$, and $Z \in$ sec* VYW if and only if $(VW, YZ) < 0$.*

† We shall not have occasion to use the symbol sec in its usual sense, as denoting the secant function.

In E_2, the deletion of one line causes the plane to fall into two pieces, and the deletion of two intersecting lines, into four pieces. These pieces are *disjoint* (no two have a point in common), and each is *connected* (any two of its points can be joined by a continuous arc). Not so with the projective plane! The deletion of one line leaves $S_2(\mathsf{R})$ connected, and each of the regions of Theorem 6.2 (indicated by I and II in Figure 6.2) is connected.

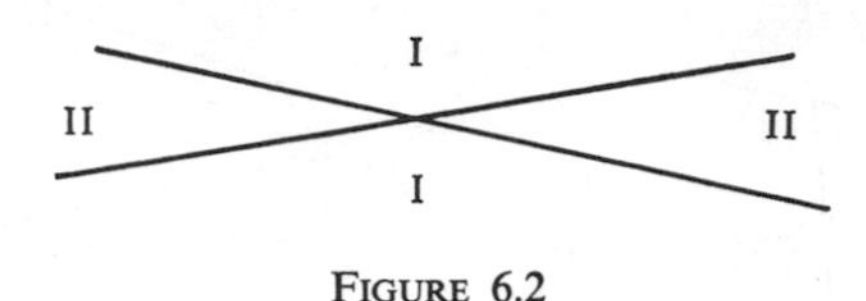

FIGURE 6.2

We consider next the separation relations induced in the plane by three independent lines. Let us denote these by U, V, W, and let Y be a point not incident to any of the lines. The three pairs of lines determine three sectors, each containing Y,

$$(6.1) \qquad \sec UYV, \qquad \sec VYW, \qquad \sec WYU,$$

and the respective complementary sectors, not containing Y,

$$(6.2) \qquad \sec^* UYV, \qquad \sec^* VYW, \qquad \sec^* WYU.$$

A point X (not incident to U, V, W) lies in those of the sectors (6.1) for which the corresponding cross ratios

$$(6.3) \qquad (UV, YX), \qquad (VW, YX), \qquad (WU, YX)$$

are positive, and in those of the sectors (6.2) for which the cross ratios (6.3) are negative. Since the product of the three cross ratios is 1 (see III, Theorem 4.4), the signs of two of them determine that of the third. By Corollary 6.3, the point X lies in exactly three of the six sectors (6.1), (6.2), and any two of the three determine the third. Conversely, the intersection of each two noncomplementary sectors (6.1), (6.2) coincides with the intersection of either one of the two and a uniquely determined third sector. Thus, in Figure 6.3 we have shaded sec UYV and sec* VYW; the doubly shaded region represents their intersection. We have

$$\sec UYV \cap \sec^* VYW = \sec UYV \cap \sec^* WYU = \sec^* VYW \cap \sec^* WYU.$$

Since there are just four admissible triples of sectors, the lines U, V, W determine four sets,† which we can write symmetrically, although redundantly, as follows:

† The argument that each of the four sets can be represented, in three ways, as the intersection of two sectors is slightly subtle. The reader will find it useful first to work Exercise 3 below.

$$
\begin{aligned}
\Delta^{+++} &= \sec UYV \cap \sec VYW \cap \sec WYU, \\
\Delta^{+--} &= \sec UYV \cap \sec^* VYW \cap \sec^* WYU, \\
\Delta^{-+-} &= \sec^* UYV \cap \sec VYW \cap \sec^* WYU, \\
\Delta^{--+} &= \sec^* UYV \cap \sec^* VYW \cap \sec WYU.
\end{aligned} \tag{6.4}
$$

Here the superscripts on Δ denote the signs of the cross ratios (6.3) for any point X in that set. Thus, $Y \in \Delta^{+++}$, and the doubly shaded region of Figure 6.3 is Δ^{+--}.

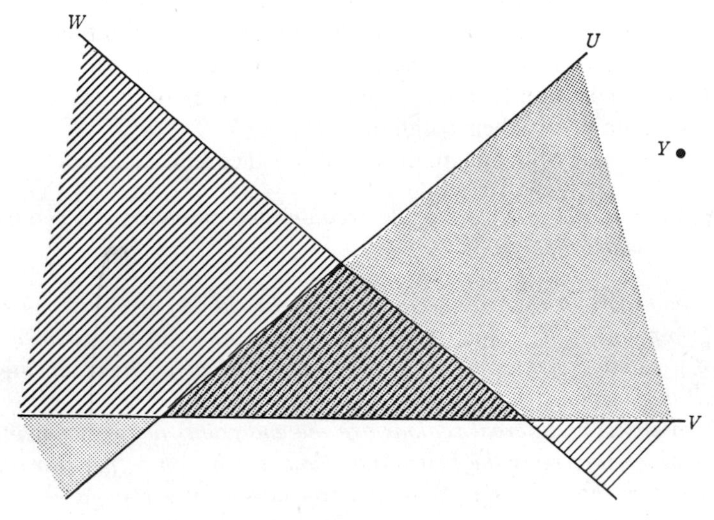

FIGURE 6.3

DEFINITION 6.2. We call each of the four sets (6.4) a *triangular region* with *bounding lines* U, V, W and with *vertices* the vertices of the triangle UVW.

THEOREM 6.3. *If two points lie in a given triangular region, their projections (from any vertex to the opposite bounding side) lie on the same one of the two segments whose end points are the vertices on that side.*

Proof. We can use our preceding notation, and suppose that we are considering projections on W. For all points X in a given region, the sign of (UV, YX) is constant; that is, for any two points X_1, X_2 in a given region, $(UV, YX_1)(UV, YX_2) > 0$. By the dual of Theorem 4.4, we have

$$(UV, YX_1)(UV, X_1X_2)(UV, X_2Y) = 1,$$

so that the middle cross ratio is necessarily positive. Our conclusion now follows from Definitions 4.1 and (5.2).

We can now define the boundary of a triangular region.

DEFINITION 6.3. If Y is a point of a triangular region with vertices A_1, A_2, A_3, and if Y_i $(i = 1, 2, 3)$ is the projection of Y from A_i to the opposite side, the three closed segments $\overline{\text{seg}}\, A_1 Y_3 A_2$, $\overline{\text{seg}}\, A_2 Y_1 A_3$, $\overline{\text{seg}}\, A_3 Y_2 A_1$ are called the *bounding segments* of the region, and their union the *boundary* of the region.

Of the four triangular regions determined by three independent lines (or points), each two have exactly one bounding segment in common: the superscripts of each two Δ's of (6.4) have one sign in common, and these signs, as remarked earlier, agree with the signs of the corresponding cross ratios. It follows that the common bounding segment of two regions is (except for the end points) contained in their common sector.

We are now ready for our main separation theorem.

THEOREM 6.4. *The four triangular regions determined by a given triangle have the following properties*:

(a) *A point not on the sides of the triangle lies in one and only one region.*
(b) *Two points in the same region are the end points of two segments, one of which does not intersect the sides of the triangle; the other intersects all three sides.*
(c) *Two points in different regions are the end points of two segments, one of which intersects the bounding segment common to the two regions; the other intersects the remaining two sides of the triangle.*

Proof. The first two statements are obvious conclusions from Definition 6.3 and Theorem 6.2. To prove (c), we let the point Y used in (6.4) to distinguish the four regions be one of the given points, and we let Z denote the second point. Let us suppose, for definiteness, that $Z \in \Delta^{+--}$; from (6.4), $Y, Z \in \sec UYV$. By Theorem 6.2, one segment, say seg YRZ, does not intersect either U or V, and the other, seg* YRZ, intersects both U and V. On the other hand, $Z \in \sec^* VYW$, and $Y \notin \sec^* VYW$; by applying Theorem 6.2 to V, W, it follows that seg YRZ (which does not intersect V) must intersect W. It remains to show that this intersection lies on the common bounding segment of Δ^{+++} and Δ^{+--}. This segment is contained in sec UYV; the hypothesis that $(W \cap \text{seg}\, YRZ) \notin \sec UYV$ leads to the contradictory conclusion that seg YRZ intersects one of the lines U or V. Finally, we note that if Z is contained in one of the remaining regions (6.4), the argument can be repeated with only minor modifications.

We leave to the reader to show that in the regions established by the reference triangle, products of two of the three coordinates have signs given in the following table:

(6.5)

	x_2x_3	x_3x_1	x_1x_2
I	+	+	+
II	+	−	−
III	−	+	−
IV	−	−	+

These regions can be identified with (6.4) if we take U, V, W as the lines $x_1 = 0$, $x_2 = 0$, $x_3 = 0$ respectively, and Y as the unit point. We portray them twice in Figure 6.4. Note that D_1, D_2, D_3 (the projections of D from

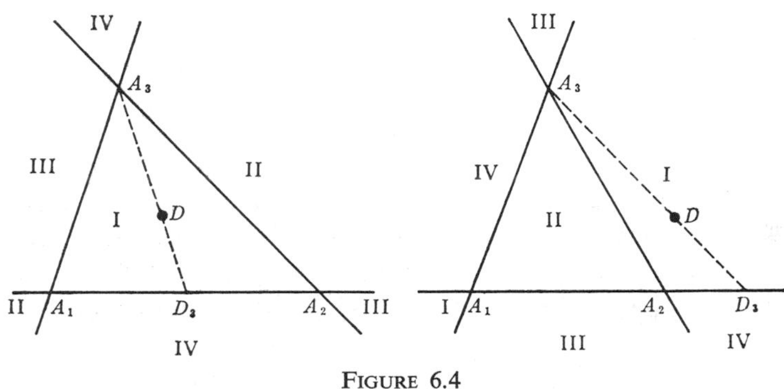

FIGURE 6.4

A_1, A_2, A_3 respectively) lie on the common bounding segments of I and II, I and III, I and IV, respectively, and that I is the region containing D.

The collineation $x_1' = x_1, x_2' = x_2, x_3' = -x_3$ interchanges regions I and IV; furthermore there exists a collineation that carries any one region into any other (see Exercise 7 below). The four regions determined by a triangle are therefore projectively equivalent.

Theorem 6.4 exhibits further differences between the structures of the Euclidean plane, the sphere, and the real projective plane. Three independent lines determine in the Euclidean plane seven regions with the property that a segment joining points in different regions intersects at least one of the lines, whereas three nonconcurrent great circles on the sphere divide the sphere into eight regions with the corresponding property.

Theorem 6.1 and 6.4 show that there exist in $S_2(\mathsf{R})$ (at least) two types of simple closed curves. One, exemplified by the projective line, is a *nonbounding* curve, and removal of its points leaves the plane *connected.* An example of the other type is furnished by the boundary of a triangular region; see Figure 6.5, where the shaded portion portrays region II of (6.5). We leave to the reader to show that if Δ is a triangular region, and if $Y \in \Delta$, $Z \notin \Delta$, then both closed segments with end points Y, Z have a nonempty intersection with the boundary of Δ. Thus the boundary of Δ is a *bounding* curve in that removal of its points disconnects the plane.

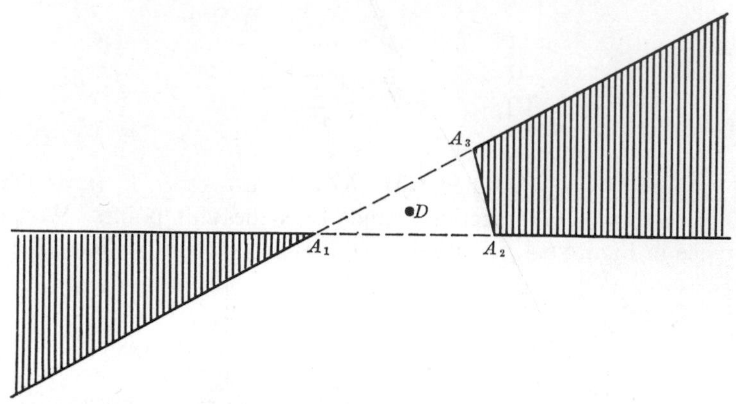

FIGURE 6.5

In E_2, every simple closed curve is a bounding curve.† One of the simplest geometrical structures in E_3 that fails to possess this property is the torus. If we remove from the torus a longitudinal circle (e.g., $ABCD$, Figure 6.6), or a latitudinal circle (e.g., $AFA'F'$), or both, the torus remains connected.

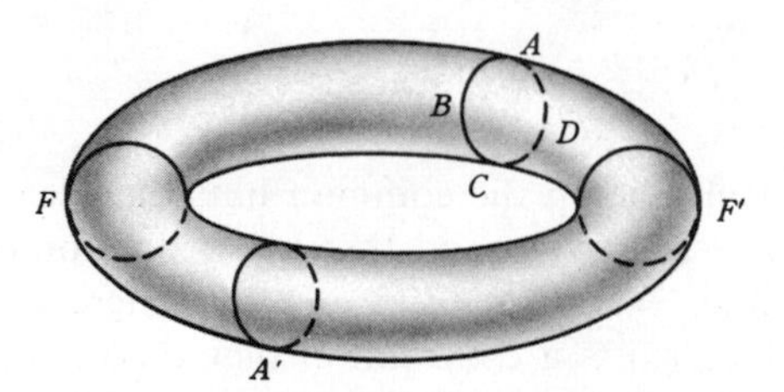

FIGURE 6.6

Another structure that possesses nonbounding simple closed curves is the Möbius strip. To construct it, we take a rectangular strip $ABCD$ in the Euclidean plane and bring C, D into coincidence with A, B, respectively, by twisting the strip (Figure 6.7). The strip remains connected when it is cut along the closed curve represented by P_1QP_2. The Möbius strip is also the simplest example of a nonorientable structure: if the center of a directed circle traces the curve P_1QP_2, the initial and final circles are directed oppositely.

We note without proof that in E_4 (four-dimensional Euclidean space), we can bring into coincidence the edges BRC and DSA of the Möbius strip, and that the resulting structure possesses the separation properties of $S_2(\mathsf{R})$ and, like $S_2(\mathsf{R})$, is nonorientable. Indeed this model would portray the

† This is the classical Jordan theorem; for a proof, see S. S. Cairns, "An Elementary Proof of the Jordon–Schoenflies Theorem," *Proceedings of the American Mathematical Society* 1951, 860–867.

topological properties of $S_2(R)$ completely. There does not exist any subset of E_3 that does so. An analytical example of a surface in E_4 free of self-intersections and singularities which is topologically equivalent to $S_2(R)$ is given by the equations†

$$y(z^2 - t^2) = xzt, \qquad y^2z^2 + t^2y^2 + z^2t^2 = yzt,$$

where x, y, z, t are rectangular Cartesian coordinates in E_4.

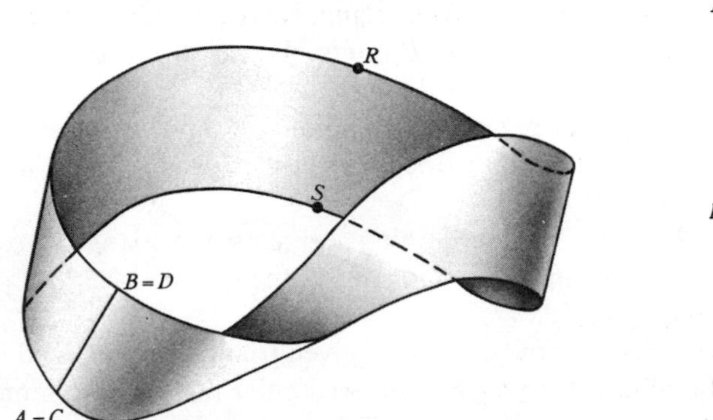

FIGURE 6.7

EXERCISES

1. Choose a reference frame, and number the regions according to (6.5). In what region is each of the following points: $(2, 3, 1)^T$, $(-2, 3, -1)^T$, $(1, -2, 3)^T$, $(1, -1, 3)^T$, $(-2, 1, 3)^T$, $(-4, -1, -1)^T$, $(-3, 2, 1)^T$, $(4, 1, -2)^T$. Now introduce coordinates with the same reference frame, and with $(1, -2, 3)^T$ as the new unit point, and relabel the regions accordingly.

2. Let $B_1:(b_{11}, b_{12}, b_{13})^T$, $B_2:(b_{21}, b_{22}, b_{23})^T$, and $B_3:(b_{31}, b_{32}, b_{33})^T$ be the vertices of a triangle, and let

$$\mathbf{X} = \lambda_1 \mathbf{B}_1 + \lambda_2 \mathbf{B}_2 + \lambda_3 \mathbf{B}_3,$$
$$\mathbf{Y} = \mu_1 \mathbf{B}_1 + \mu_2 \mathbf{B}_2 + \mu_3 \mathbf{B}_3.$$

Determine a necessary and sufficient condition on the λ's and μ's, that X and Y be in the same one of the four regions determined by the given triangle.

3. Prove that if $\mathscr{C}_1, \mathscr{C}_2, \mathscr{C}_3$ are any three sets of points such that the intersection of each two sets is contained in the third, then the three intersection sets, $\mathscr{C}_1 \cap \mathscr{C}_2$, $\mathscr{C}_2 \cap \mathscr{C}_3$, $\mathscr{C}_3 \cap \mathscr{C}_1$ coincide.

Prove the following eight theorems on sectors and triangular regions in $S_2(R)$.

4. Segments whose end points lie on (distinct) bounding lines of a sector are contained in one sector.

† See Hilbert and Cohn-Vossen, *Geometry and the Imagination*, New York, Chelsea Publishing Co., 1956, pp. 340–341, 313–321.

5. If two points lie in a closed triangular region, so does every point of one of their closed segments.

6. A closed segment one and only one of whose end points lies in a given triangular region must intersect the boundary of the region. Is *closed* necessary?

7. Let Δ_1 and Δ_2 be two triangular regions; there exists a collineation g such that $g\Delta_1 = \Delta_2$.

8. Let A, B be two points in a given triangular region, not collinear with a vertex of the triangle. The line $A \oplus B$ intersects just two of the bounding segments of the region.

9. Let R be a triangular region, T its boundary, and S the remaining points of the plane; a segment with one end point in R and the other in S necessarily contains a point of T.

#**10.** Let T_1, T_2, T_3 be the three bounding segments of a triangular region, and let T_3^* be the complementary segment of T_3; the closure of $T_1 \cup T_2 \cup T_3^*$ is a closed nonbounding curve.

11. A line not incident to any vertex of a given triangle is contained in the closure of the union of just three of the four triangular regions determined by the triangle.

7 Limits and Continuity in $S_2(\mathsf{R})$

We turn our attention to the limit concept. Let $t(n)$ be a real-valued function defined over the positive integers; we denote the infinite sequence of real numbers $t(1), t(2), t(3), \ldots$ by $\{t(n)\}$. We suppose the reader is familiar with the *arithmetical* nature of the assertion, $\lim_{n\to\infty} t(n) = t$, even though his first contact with such an assertion has been within the framework of Euclidean geometry. The words *approaches*, *near*, and others used in the theory of limits, need not involve any metric properties of Euclidean geometry. Now consider in $S_2(\mathsf{R})$ for example, the sequence of points $\{Y_n\}$ where $\mathbf{Y}_n = (1, n, n^2)^T$ $(n = 1, 2, 3, \ldots)$. Since $(1/n^2, 1/n, 1)^T$ are equivalent representatives of Y_n, and since $1/n$ and $1/n^2$ converge to 0 as n increases without limit, we would like to define the limit of a sequence of points in such a way that the particular sequence $\{Y_n\}$ converges to A_3:$(0, 0, 1)^T$. The following definition will prove to be satisfactory.

DEFINITION 7.1. In $S_2(\mathsf{R})$, a point Y is the *limit* of a sequence of points $\{Y_n\}$ if there exist representatives $\mathbf{Y}_n = (y_1(n), y_2(n), y_3(n))^T$ of Y_n and $\mathbf{Y} = (y_1, y_2, y_3)^T$ of Y such that

$$y_i = \lim_{n\to\infty} y_i(n), \qquad i = 1, 2, 3.$$

We say that the sequence $\{Y_n\}$ *converges* to Y, and that the sequence of representatives $\{\mathbf{Y}_n\}$ converges to $\mathbf{Y}$, and we write

$$Y = \lim_{n\to\infty} Y_n \quad \text{or} \quad Y_n \to Y,$$

with a similar notation for representatives.

If a sequence of points converges, the limit is unique, for if two sequences of representatives $\{\mathbf{Y}_n\}$ and $\{\mathbf{Y}_n^*\}$, where $\mathbf{Y}_n^* = \rho(n)\mathbf{Y}_n$, converge (neither to $\mathbf{0}$), it follows that $\lim \rho(n)$ exists and is different from 0, and that $\lim \mathbf{Y}_n^* = \lim \rho(n) \lim \mathbf{Y}_n$.

We can see that the limit relation is projectively invariant by considering an arbitrary collineation with representation $\mathbf{X}' = \mathbf{AX}$; if $\mathbf{Y}_n \to \mathbf{Y}$, then $\mathbf{AY}_n \to \mathbf{AY}$.

We leave to the reader to rephrase Definition 7.1 to give a definition of convergence in $S_1(\mathsf{R})$, and to show that a sequence of collinear points in $S_2(\mathsf{R})$ converges according to Definition 7.1 if and only if it converges as a sequence in $S_1(\mathsf{R})$ (see Exercise 2 below).

Many theorems on limits can be stated in terms of geometric properties of the projective line or plane. For example, a bounded infinite sequence of increasing real numbers $\{a_n\}$ ($a_m < a_n < a$ for all $m < n$) possesses a limit less than or equal to the bound a. We leave to the reader to show that this is equivalent to the theorem that if $\{A_n\}$ is a sequence of points in $S_1(\mathsf{R})$ such that A_1, A_2, A_n, A_{n+1} are in the projective order $\langle A_1 A_2 A_n A_{n+1}\rangle$ for all $n \geqq 3$, then $A = \lim A_n$ exists, and either $A = A_1$ or A_1, A_2, A_n, A are for $n \geqq 3$ in the projective order $\langle A_1 A_2 A_n A\rangle$.

If a given irrational number is expressed as a limit of a monotonic sequence of rationals, it follows from the remarks above that the corresponding points in $S_1(\mathsf{R})$ with rational representatives can be ordered projectively to correspond, and this sequence of points will converge.

Continuity in Euclidean spaces can be defined solely in terms of convergence of sequences,† and we shall define continuity in real projective spaces in such terms.

DEFINITION 7.2. If $f(X)$ is a real-valued function whose domain is $S_1(\mathsf{R})$ or $S_2(\mathsf{R})$, $f(X)$ is *continuous* at Y if $\{f(Y_n)\}$ converges to $f(Y)$ for every sequence $\{Y_n\}$ which converges to Y. More generally, if ϕ is a map whose domain is contained in $S_2(\mathsf{R})$ and whose range is contained in E_2, ϕ is *continuous* at Y if the sequence of points $\{\phi(Y_n)\}$ converges in E_2 to $\phi(Y)$, for every sequence $\{Y_n\}$ which converges to Y.

These definitions can be extended to include maps between any two spaces in each of which convergence has been defined.

† See Apostol, *op. cit.*, p. 65.

Our earlier assertion that a line is a simple closed curve is now easily verified. We first map the circle $(x-1)^2+y^2=1$ in E_2 onto the pencil of lines in E_2 with vertex $(0,0)$ by mapping the point $(0,0)$ onto the line $x=0$ (the tangent to the circle), and any other point of the circle onto its join to $(0,0)$. If $[x_1, x_2]$ represents the line $x_2 x - x_1 y = 0$ (see II, 1, Illustration 6), the map is given by

$$(7.1) \qquad \begin{aligned} [x_1, x_2] &= [x, y] \quad \text{for} \quad (x, y) \neq (0,0), \\ [x_1, x_2] &= [0, 1] \quad \text{for} \quad (x, y) = (0,0); \end{aligned}$$

the inverse map is found to be

$$(7.2) \qquad x = 2x_1^2/(x_1^2+x_2^2), \qquad y = 2x_1 x_2/(x_1^2+x_2^2).$$

We can now interpret these equations as those of a one-to-one map of $S_1(\mathsf{R})$ onto the circle; it remains to show that this map is continuous both ways. If a sequence of points of $S_1(\mathsf{R})$ converges, they possess representatives which converge to, say, $\mathbf{Y} \neq \mathbf{0}$; for such representatives the denominators in (7.2) will not approach zero, and the map from $S_1(\mathsf{R})$ onto the circle is continuous. The continuity the other way is in question only for a sequence of points, on the circle, that converges to $(0,0)$. But if (x,y) satisfies $x^2+y^2-2x=0$ and $xy \neq 0$, $[x,y]=[y,2-x]$; if (x,y) converges to $(0,0)$, $[y,2-x]$ converges to $[0,1]$, as required for continuity.

Since the totality of lines of $S_2(\mathsf{R})$ is itself a projective space, Definition 7.1 provides us with a definition of a convergent sequence of lines. The reader should relate convergence of lines to that of points. Exercises 4–7 below suggest some questions that need to be answered.

It would have been possible to formulate the limit concept in real projective spaces geometrically rather than analytically. To do this, we would define a *neighborhood of a point*, in $S_1(\mathsf{R})$, to be any (open) segment containing the point, and, in $S_2(\mathsf{R})$, to be any (open) triangular region containing the point. In terms of neighborhoods, $\lim Y_n = Y$ is equivalent to the requirement that every neighborhood of Y contain all but a finite number of points Y_n.† Although such a geometrical formulation of the limit concept is more elegant than our analytical one, a full development would take more time than we have available. One advantage of the analytical formulation is that it is immediately clear that the embeddings considered in Section 4, Chapter II, preserve the limit operation, except for sequences of points in $S_1(\mathsf{R})$ which converge to $\infty(\mathscr{E})$.

Real projective spaces possess an important limit property that is not shared by Euclidean spaces.

† The reader familiar with the elements of topology may recognize that, with the above definitions of neighborhoods, real projective spaces are Hausdorff spaces. For the defining axioms of such a space and the limit concept therein, see Hall and Spencer, *Elementary Topology*, New York, John Wiley and Sons, 1959.

THEOREM 7.1. *Every infinite set of points in a real projective space contains a sequence that converges.*

Proof. In $S_1(R)$, the map (7.2) maps the set onto a set of points on the circle in E_2. This set is bounded, and, as noted in Section 5, it contains a convergent sequence. Since the inverse map (7.1) is continuous, the convergent sequence on the circle maps back into a convergent sequence in $S_1(R)$.

To prove the theorem in $S_2(R)$, we can suppose that no line contains infinitely many points of the set. (If one did, the theorem in $S_1(R)$ would apply.)

We now choose $A_1 \in S_2(R)$ at pleasure, and consider the joins of A_1 and points of the set; this infinite set of lines can be regarded as contained in a projective space of dimension one, namely in the pencil A_1, and, by our theorem for $S_1(R)$, it contains a convergent sequence of lines. We can denote this sequence (not necessarily uniquely) by $\{A_1 \oplus Y_n\}$, where $\{Y_n\}$ is a sequence of points contained in the given set of points. Next we select $A_2 \in S_2(R)$, $A_2 \notin \lim \{A_1 \oplus Y_n\}$, and consider the sequence $\{A_2 \oplus Y_n\}$. Applying the theorem for $S_1(R)$ again, we see that $\{A_2 \oplus Y_n\}$ contains a convergent sequence; we can denote it by $\{A_2 \oplus Y_{i_n}\}$, where $\{i_n\}$ is an increasing sequence of positive integers.

We note that $\{A_1 \oplus Y_{i_n}\}$ converges because it is a subsequence of the convergent sequence $\{A_1 \oplus Y_n\}$, and that (by the choice of A_2) $\lim (A_1 \oplus Y_{i_n}) \neq \lim (A_2 \oplus Y_{i_n})$. Since $Y_{i_n} = (A_1 \oplus Y_{i_n}) \cap (A_2 \oplus Y_{i_n})$, the convergence of $\{Y_{i_n}\}$ follows by the dual of Exercise 6 below, the proof of which we leave to the reader.

Theorem 7.1 is frequently stated in the form: *Real projective spaces are compact.*

EXERCISES

1. Does the sequence of points $\{Y_n\}$ where $\mathbf{Y}_n = (n, n^2 \sin 1/n, \cos n)^T$ converge?

***2.** Modify Definition 7.1 to yield a definition of convergence in $S_1(R)$, and show that a sequence of collinear points in $S_2(R)$ converges if and only if it converges as a sequence in $S_1(R)$.

3. Let Y_0, Y_1, Y_2 be three given points in $S_1(R)$; a sequence of points $\{Y_n\}$ is defined recursively by $(Y_0\, Y_n, Y_{n+1}\, Y_{n+2}) = -1$ $(n = 1, 2, 3, \ldots)$. Prove that $\lim Y_n = Y_0$. (*Hint*: introduce coordinates with $Y_0\, Y_1\, Y_2$ as the reference frame, and use (II, Lemma 3.3).

***4.** Let $\{V_n\}$ be a convergent sequence of lines, and let W be a given line distinct from $\lim V_n$. Prove that the sequence of points $\{Y_n\}$, where $Y_n = V_n \cap W$, converges.

***5.** State the dual of the theorem of Exercise 4.

***6.** Let $\{Y_n\}$ and $\{Z_n\}$ be two convergent sequences of points, with distinct limits. Prove that the sequence of lines $\{Y_n \oplus Z_n\}$ converges to $(\lim Y_n) \oplus (\lim Z_n)$, and state the dual.

#****7.** If the sequence of lines $\{V_n\}$ converges to V, prove that for every point $X \in V$, we can find points $X_n \in V_n$ such that $\{X_n\}$ converges to X. Show further that it is possible to introduce projective coordinates $[\lambda, \mu]^T$ simultaneously on the lines V_n and V so that, for suitably chosen representatives, $\mathbf{X}_n = \lambda\mathbf{Y}_n + \mu\mathbf{Z}_n$ for $X_n \in V_n$, and $\{\mathbf{X}_n\}$ converges to $\mathbf{X} = \lambda\mathbf{Y} + \mu\mathbf{Z}$, for all $[\lambda, \mu]^T \in \Omega_2$.

***8.** The map of $S_2(\mathsf{R})$ into a closed disc in E_2 given in Section 1 can be made one-to-one by taking as the range the half-open disc

$$\{(x, y) \mid x^2 + y^2 < 1\} \cup \{(x, y) \mid x^2 + y^2 = 1, y > 0\} \cup \{(x, y) \mid x = 1, y = 0\},$$

where (x, y) denotes the point in E_2 with Cartesian coordinates (x, y). Show that this map is not topological (that is, not continuous both ways).

#**9.** We remarked above that when convergence in a space is defined in terms of neighborhoods, a sequence of points $\{Y_n\}$ converges to Y if and only if every neighborhood of Y contains all but a finite number of points of the sequence. In E_2, it is possible to take as neighborhoods of a point open circular discs with center at the point. How could we define neighborhoods in the Euclidean representation of $S_2(\mathsf{R})$ given in Exercise 8 if the resulting convergence is to coincide with convergence as defined in $S_2(\mathsf{R})$?

8 Triangles, Quadrangles, and Quadrilaterals

In the first four sections of this chapter we developed machinery for proving theorems involving linear relations (for example, incidence relations of points and lines, cross ratio, etc.) in a projective space of two dimensions. In this section we shall show how this machinery works by proving some basic properties of triples and quadruples of points and lines. We shall draw figures for $S_2(\mathsf{R})$, and this will be very helpful in keeping our thoughts straight, but the proofs naturally will be independent of the figures. Except for the last theorem of this section we shall use only field properties so that our conclusions are valid in $S_2(\mathsf{F})$, where F, as usual, is a commutative field not of characteristic 2.

We introduce the terminology *triangles perspective from a point*: The triangles $A_1 A_2 A_3$ and $B_1 B_2 B_3$ (here A_1, A_2, A_3 and B_1, B_2, B_3 are two ordered triples of independent points) are *perspective from a point D* if the points of each of the three sets A_1, B_1, D; A_2, B_2, D; and A_3, B_3, D are collinear.† Dually, two triangles with sides a_1, a_2, a_3, and b_1, b_2, b_3 are *perspective from a line d* if each of the sets a_1, b_1, d; a_2, b_2, d; and a_3, b_3, d_3 consists of concurrent lines. If each pair of corresponding vertices, A_i and B_i $(i = 1, 2, 3)$, are distinct, the assertion that the triangles $A_1 A_2 A_3$ and $B_1 B_2 B_3$ are perspective from a point is equivalent to the assertion that $A_i \oplus B_i$ $(i = 1, 2, 3)$ is a set of concurrent lines.

THEOREM 8.1a. DESARGUES' TRIANGLE THEOREM. *If two (ordered) triangles in $S_2(\mathsf{F})$ are perspective from a point, they are perspective from a line.*

Proof. We let A_1, A_2, A_3 be the vertices of one triangle, and B_1, B_2, B_3 the corresponding vertices of the other. We consider first the possibility of coincidences among corresponding vertices.

Three coincidences. If $A_i = B_i$, the theorem is trivially true, although neither the point nor the line of the theorem is unique.

Two coincidences. We can suppose $A_1 = B_1$ and $A_2 = B_2$. Clearly the two triangles $A_1 A_2 A_3$ and $A_1 A_2 B_3$ are perspective from any point on $A_3 \oplus B_3$, and from the line $A_1 \oplus A_2$.‡

One coincidence. We can suppose $A_1 = B_1$; two possibilities occur, according as $A_2 \oplus B_2$ and $A_3 \oplus B_3$ are distinct or coincident lines. In the first case (Figure 8.1) the triangles are perspective from the point

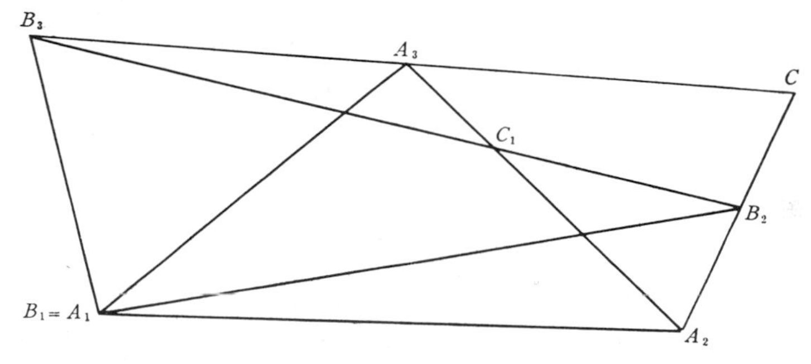

FIGURE 8.1

$(A_2 \oplus B_2) \cap (A_3 \oplus B_3)$, and from the line,§ $A_1 \oplus ((A_2 \oplus A_3) \cap (B_2 \oplus B_3))$. When $A_2 \oplus B_2 = A_3 \oplus B_3$, the two triangles are perspective from any point on $A_2 \oplus B_2$ and from any line of the pencil A_1.

† We should recall that the statement A_1, B_1, D are collinear points means only that there exists (at least) one line incident to A_1, B_1, and D. A similar remark holds for a set of concurrent lines.

‡ If $B_3 \in A_1 \oplus A_3$ (or $A_2 \oplus A_3$), the two triangles are perspective from any line incident to A_2 (or A_1).

§ If $B_2 \in A_1 \oplus A_2$, $B_3 \in A_1 \oplus A_3$, the two triangles are perspective from any line incident to $C = (A_2 \oplus B_2) \cap (A_3 \oplus B_3)$.

No coincidences. The hypothesis of the theorem implies the existence of a point D (Figure 8.2) common to the lines $A_i \oplus B_i$ $(i = 1, 2, 3)$. Whether or not these lines are distinct, we can choose representatives and coefficients of dependence so that

$$\mathbf{D} = \lambda_1 \mathbf{A}_1 + \mu_1 \mathbf{B}_1 = \lambda_2 \mathbf{A}_2 + \mu_2 \mathbf{B}_2 = \lambda_3 \mathbf{A}_3 + \mu_3 \mathbf{B}_3 . \tag{8.1}$$

From these equations we can define points C_1, C_2, C_3 given by

$$\begin{aligned} \mathbf{C}_1 &= \lambda_2 \mathbf{A}_2 - \lambda_3 \mathbf{A}_3 = -\mu_2 \mathbf{B}_2 + \mu_3 \mathbf{B}_3 , \\ \mathbf{C}_2 &= \lambda_3 \mathbf{A}_3 - \lambda_1 \mathbf{A}_1 = -\mu_3 \mathbf{B}_3 + \mu_1 \mathbf{B}_1 , \\ \mathbf{C}_3 &= \lambda_1 \mathbf{A}_1 - \lambda_2 \mathbf{A}_2 = -\mu_1 \mathbf{B}_1 + \mu_2 \mathbf{B}_2 . \end{aligned} \tag{8.2}$$

Since A_1, A_2 are distinct points, C_3 must lie on the line $A_1 \oplus A_2$. But we

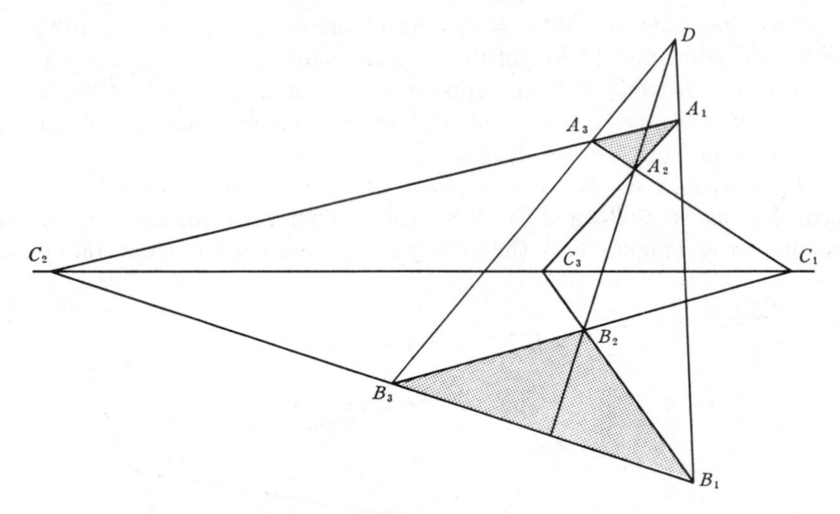

FIGURE 8.2

also have $C_3 \in (B_1 \oplus B_2)$; therefore $C_3 \in (A_1 \oplus A_2) \cap (B_1 \oplus B_2)$ (even if the sides coincide). Similarly we obtain $C_1 \in (A_2 \oplus A_3) \cap (B_2 \oplus B_3)$, and $C_2 \in (A_1 \oplus A_3) \cap (B_1 \oplus B_3)$.

With this analytic representation, the proof of the theorem is immediate. We need only observe that from (8.2)

$$\mathbf{C}_1 + \mathbf{C}_2 + \mathbf{C}_3 = \mathbf{0},$$

and therefore the points C_1, C_2, and C_3 are collinear.

Theorem 8.1b. *If two ordered triangles are perspective from a line, they are perspective from a point.*

This is the converse of Theorem 8.1a. But it is also the dual, and it is therefore a consequence of Theorem 8.1a and the Principle of Duality.

We shall call two ordered triangles that satisfy the conditions of Theorems 8.1a, b *Desarguean*.†

A very useful corollary to Desargues' Theorem asserts that if two ordered quadrangles, $P_1P_2P_3P_4$ and $P_1'P_2'P_3'P_4'$, have distinct pairs of vertices ($P_i \neq P_i'$), and if five pairs of corresponding sides intersect in collinear points, their line contains the intersection of the sixth pair. This corollary need not be valid when coincidences exist among the pairs of vertices, and to retain the conclusion we state the corollary as follows.

THEOREM 8.2. *Let $P_{12}, P_{13}, P_{14}, P_{34}, P_{42}$ be collinear points in $S_2(\mathsf{F})$, satisfying one of the following conditions:*

(a) *all five are distinct;*

(b) *four are distinct, with $P_{34} = P_{12}$ or $P_{42} = P_{13}$;*

(c) *three are distinct, with $P_{34} = P_{12}$ and $P_{42} = P_{13}$.*

Then there exists a unique point P_{23} such that every quadrangle $P_1P_2P_3P_4$ satisfying five of the six equations

$$P_{ij} = L \cap (P_i \oplus P_j), \qquad ij = 12, 13, 14, 34, 42, 23, \tag{8.3}$$

where L is the line of the given points, satisfies the sixth.

Proof. We can find one quadrangle as follows: Choose $P_1 \notin L$, and $P_2 \in (P_1 \oplus P_{12})$, $P_2 \neq P_1, P_2 \neq P_{12}$; now define successively (Figure 8.3)

$$P_4 = (P_1 \oplus P_{14}) \cap (P_2 \oplus P_{42}),$$
$$P_3 = (P_1 \oplus P_{13}) \cap (P_4 \oplus P_{34}),$$
$$P_{23} = L \cap (P_2 \oplus P_3).$$

Clearly (8.3) are satisfied.

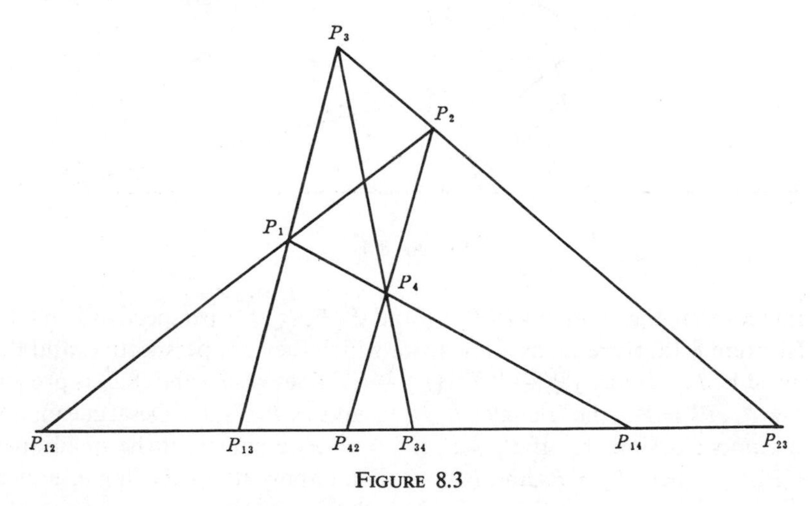

FIGURE 8.3

† There exist more general classes of projective planes than those that we are considering, in which Desargues' Theorem need not be valid; see L. M. Blumenthal, *A Modern View of Geometry*, San Francisco, W. H. Freeman & Co., 1961.

To prove that P_{23} is determined uniquely by the given points, we can suppose that $P_1' P_2' P_3' P_4'$ is a quadrangle satisfying the first five of equations (8.3),

$$P_{ij} = L \cap (P_i' \oplus P_j'), \qquad ij = 12, 13, 14, 34, 42; \tag{8.4}$$

then it suffices to show that the sixth equation

$$P_{23} = L \cap (P_2' \oplus P_3') \tag{8.5}$$

is also satisfied. Coincidences among the given points P_{ij} do not affect our argument, but we need to distinguish three cases:

(i) $P_1' = P_1, \quad P_2' = P_2$;
(ii) $P_1' \oplus P_2' = P_1 \oplus P_2$;
(iii) $P_1' \oplus P_2' \neq P_1 \oplus P_2$.

In (i), the two quadrangles coincide vertex for vertex, and (8.5) holds.

In (ii), we first suppose (Figure 8.4) $P_1' = P_1, P_2' \neq P_2$. Then (8.4)

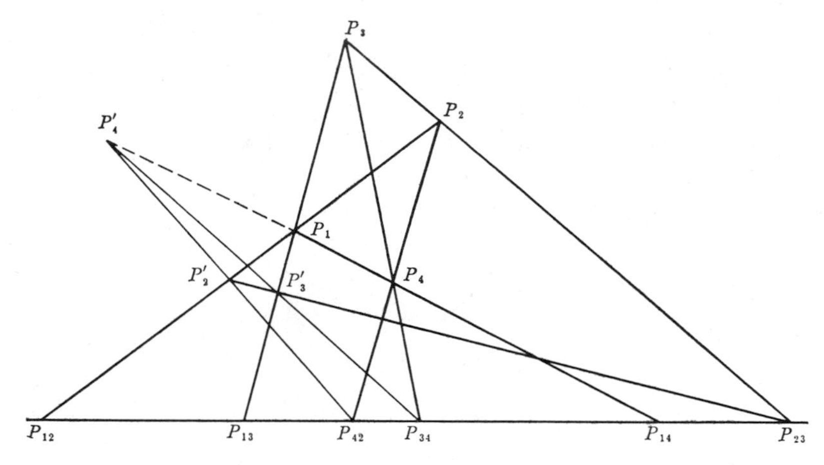

FIGURE 8.4

guarantees that the triangles $P_2' P_3' P_4'$ and $P_2 P_3 P_4$ are perspective from P_1; by Theorem 8.1a, there exists a line from which they are perspective, and this line must be L. Hence $(P_2' \oplus P_3') \cap (P_2 \oplus P_3)$ lines on L, and (8.5) is proved. If $P_1' \neq P_1, P_2' = P_2$, the triangles $P_1' P_3' P_4'$ and $P_1 P_3 P_4$ are Desarguean, and the argument is similar. If $P_1' \neq P_1, P_2' \neq P_2$, we construct the quadrangle $P_1'' P_2'' P_3'' P_4''$, where $P_1'' = P_1$ and $P_2'' = P_2'$, and apply the preceding argument twice.

In (iii), we have necessarily $P_1' \neq P_1, P_2' \neq P_2$, but one pair P_3', P_3 or P_4', P_4 may coincide. The triangles $P_1' P_2' P_4'$ and $P_1 P_2 P_4$ are by (8.4) perspective from L; by Theorem 8.1b, they are perspective from the point $D = (P_1 \oplus P_1') \cap (P_2 \oplus P_2')$. The triangles $P_1' P_3' P_4'$ and $P_1 P_3 P_4$ are perspective from L, so there exists a point D^* from which they are perspective. If $P_4' \neq P_4$, we have $D^* = D$; if $P_4' = P_4$, we must have $P_1' \in (P_1 \oplus P_4)$, $P_2' \in (P_2 \oplus P_4)$, $P_3' \neq P_3$, $D = P_4 \in P_3' \oplus P_3$, so again $D^* = D$. Therefore the triangles $P_2' P_3' P_4'$ and $P_2 P_3 P_4$ are perspective from D; by Theorem 8.1a, they are perspective from a line. This line must be L, and (8.5) follows.

Note the order of the points P_{ij}; the first three, P_{12}, P_{13}, P_{14}, represent intersections of L with a triple of *concurrent* sides of a quadrangle, and the remaining three are the intersections with the respective opposite sides. Nevertheless, any one of the points P_{jk} can play the role of P_{23} in the above argument, for if $ijkl$ is a permutation of 1234 we can enumerate the six points in the order $P_{ij} P_{ik} P_{il} P_{kl} P_{lj} P_{jk}$.

COROLLARY 8.1. *Five of the points of intersection of the sides of an unknown quadrangle with a line not through a vertex determine the intersection of the line with the sixth side.*

Theorem 8.2 enables us to prove synthetically that the point Z of Construction Problems 5.1 and 5.2 is independent of the construction lines L_1, L_2, L_0 (or L_3). For in Problem 5.1, Z is the intersection with the sixth side of the quadrangle $B_1 Y_1 X_0 B_0$, where A_1, X, A_2, A_1, Y are the other five intersections; in Problem 5.2, the quadrangle is $B_1 Y_1 X_2 B_2$, and A_1, X, D_3, A_2, Y are the five intersections.

Fundamental to the development of projective plane gometry are the harmonic properties of quadrangles and quadrilaterals. In many axiomatic developments these properties are used to define harmonic sets.

THEOREM 8.3a. *Any two vertices of a quadrangle in $S_2(\mathsf{F})$ separate harmonically the diagonal point on their side and the point of intersection of their side and the line joining the other two diagonal points.*

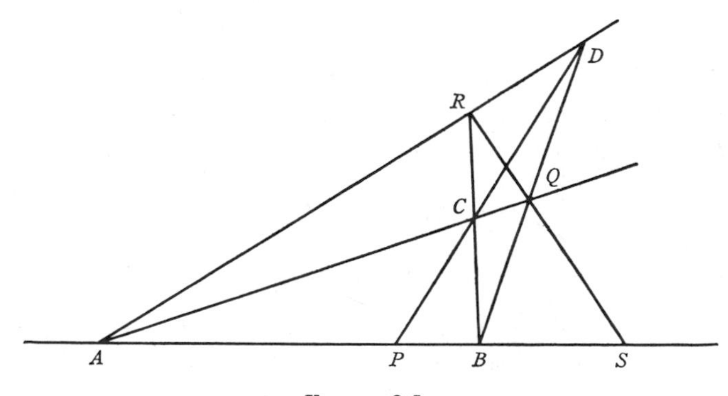

FIGURE 8.5

Proof. Let the given vertices of the quadrangle be A, B, and let C, D be the other two. We label the diagonal points as suggested by Figure 8.5, and we let $S = (A \oplus B) \cap (Q \oplus R)$. Then the theorem asserts that $(A\,B, P\,S) = -1$. We establish any convenient coordinate system, and we can choose representatives that satisfy (see Lemma 1.1)

$$\mathbf{D} = \mathbf{A} + \mathbf{B} + \mathbf{C}, \tag{8.6}$$

so that

$$\mathbf{A} + \mathbf{B} = \mathbf{D} - \mathbf{C}, \qquad \mathbf{A} + \mathbf{C} = \mathbf{D} - \mathbf{B}, \qquad \mathbf{B} + \mathbf{C} = \mathbf{D} - \mathbf{A}. \tag{8.7}$$

The first of these three pairs of matrices must represent a point that lies on both $A \oplus B$ and $C \oplus D$; this point is P. A similar result holds for the other two pairs, so that we can write

$$\mathbf{P} = \mathbf{A} + \mathbf{B}, \qquad \mathbf{Q} = \mathbf{A} + \mathbf{C}, \qquad \mathbf{R} = \mathbf{B} + \mathbf{C}. \tag{8.8}$$

Then $\mathbf{Q} - \mathbf{R} = \mathbf{A} - \mathbf{B}$, so that

$$\mathbf{S} = \mathbf{A} - \mathbf{B}. \tag{8.9}$$

Since the cross ratio of points $\mathbf{A}$, $\mathbf{B}$, $\mathbf{A} + \mathbf{B}$, $\mathbf{A} - \mathbf{B}$ is -1 (see III, Theorem 4.1a and II, Lemma 3.3), the theorem is proved.

Since the cross ratio $(A\,B, P\,S)$ is equal to that of their joins to R, we have the following alternative form of Theorem 8.3a.

COROLLARY 8.2a. *Two sides of the diagonal triangle of a quadrangle separate harmonically the two sides of the quadrangle through their intersection.*

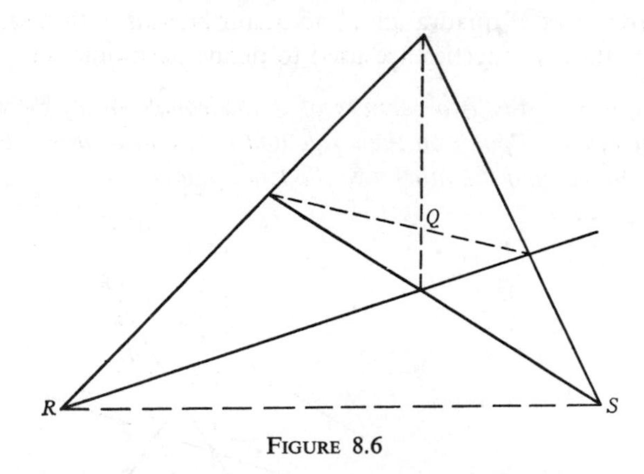

FIGURE 8.6

The dual of Theorem 8.3a is the following:

THEOREM 8.3b. *Any two sides of a quadrilateral separate harmonically the diagonal line through their common vertex and the line joining this vertex to the intersection of the other two diagonal lines.*

In Figure 8.6 the four solid lines are the sides, and the three dotted lines the diagonals of the quadrilateral. R and S are a pair of opposite vertices, and Q is the point of intersection of the two diagonal lines not through R or S. The two sides through R separate the lines $R \oplus Q$, $R \oplus S$ harmonically.

Corresponding to Corollary 8.2a, we have the following.

COROLLARY 8.2b. *Two vertices of the diagonal triangle of a quadrilateral separate harmonically the two vertices of the quadrilateral that lie on their line.*

It is apparent that the diagonal triangle of a quadrangle and any three vertices are perspective from the fourth vertex; by Theorem 8.3a the two triangles are perspective from a line. We leave to the reader to show that the four axes (one for each choice of the *fourth* vertex) are the sides of a quadrilateral whose diagonal triangle is that of the given quadrangle.

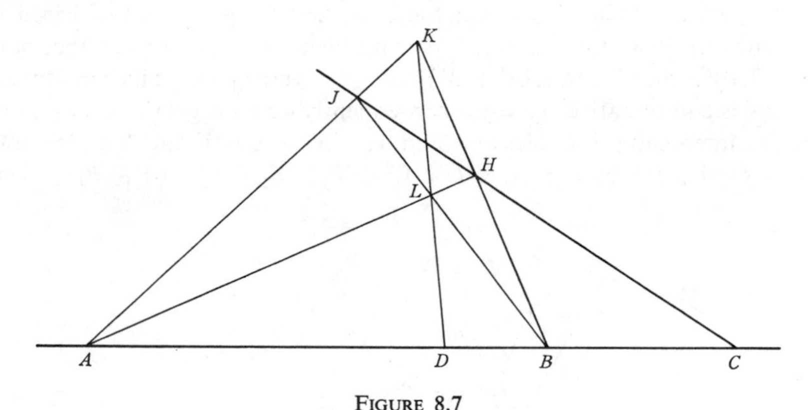

FIGURE 8.7

CONSTRUCTION PROBLEM 8.1. Given three distinct collinear points A, B, C, construct the harmonic conjugate of C with respect to A and B.

Procedure. Let H, J (Figure 8.7) be any two distinct points collinear with C but not on $A \oplus B$. Let $K = (A \oplus J) \cap (B \oplus H)$, and let $L = (B \oplus J) \cap (A \oplus H)$. Then the required point is $D = (K \oplus L) \cap (A \oplus B)$.

Proof. A, B, J, H is a quadrangle, C is the diagonal point on $A \oplus B$, and K and L the other two diagonal points. By Theorem 8.3a, D is the harmonic conjugate of C with respect to A and B.

This problem is a special case of Construction Problem 5.1. We have only to choose A and B as the zero and exceptional point, and C as the point with nonhomogeneous coordinate x. Then the point with coordinate $0 - x$ is the harmonic conjugate of C with respect to A and B. The lines drawn to construct this point are identical with those of Figure 8.7.

We leave as an exercise for the reader the dual construction (see Exercise 3 below).

Remark. In $S_2(\mathsf{F})$, *construct* means determine in terms of a finite sequence of joins and intersections.

THEOREM 8.4. THEOREM OF PAPPUS. *If ABC and $A'B'C'$ are two ordered triples of distinct collinear points lying on distinct lines, and if at most one of the six points is the point of intersection of the lines, then the points of intersection of crosswise joins, that is, the three points*

$$(A \oplus B') \cap (A' \oplus B), \quad (A \oplus C') \cap (A' \oplus C), \quad (B \oplus C') \cap (B' \oplus C),$$

are collinear.

Proof. If a point of one triple lies on both lines, the theorem is trivial. We suppose then that this is not the case, and we give a proof based on Construction Problem 5.2. In that problem we constructed the point $Z:(xy, 1, 0)^T$, when $X:(x, 1, 0)^T$ and $Y:(y, 1, 0)^T$ were given. Since multiplication in F is commutative, $xy = yx$; consequently we must get the same point Z when we interchange the roles of X and Y. Let us use (Figure 8.8), the notation of Figure 5.4, and let $X_1 = L_1 \cap (X \oplus B_2)$, $Y_2 = L_2 \cap (Y \oplus B_1)$. Then

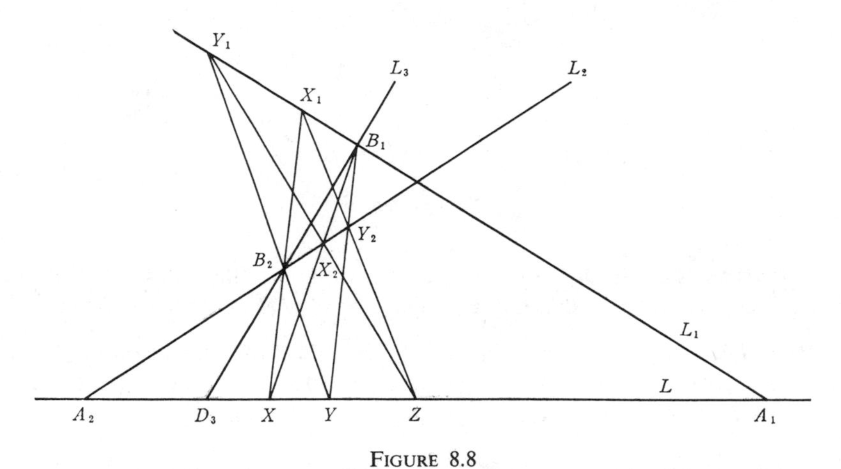

FIGURE 8.8

Z, X_1, and Y_2 must be collinear. But this says that for the two ordered triples of points

$$X_1\, Y_1\, B_1 \quad \text{and} \quad X_2\, Y_2\, B_2 \tag{8.10}$$

the Theorem of Pappus is true. It remains to show that these two triples are in no way special, that is, that if two triples (8.10) of collinear points are given, we can construct the remaining points of Figure 8.8 from these two triples. This is easily done:

$$X = (X_1 \oplus B_2) \cap (X_2 \oplus B_1), \quad Y = (Y_1 \oplus B_2) \cap (Y_2 \oplus B_1),$$
$$L = X \oplus Y, \quad L_1 = X_1 \oplus B_1, \quad L_2 = Y_2 \oplus B_2, \quad L_3 = B_1 \oplus B_2,$$

and we let A_1, A_2, D_3 be the intersections with L of the lines L_1, L_2, and L_3, respectively. It therefore follows that the Theorem of Pappus is valid for the two given triples.

The line of Theorem 8.4 containing the points of intersection of crosswise joins is called the *Pappus line* of the two triples of points.

This proof exhibits the equivalence of the Theorem of Pappus and the commutativity of multiplication. Clearly if in Definition 1.2 we had required multiplication to be noncommutative,† it would follow, by the preceding argument, that the Theorem of Pappus would not hold.

At this stage, it might occur to the enterprising reader that an alternative proof of the Theorem of Pappus might be constructed by repeated applications of Desargues' Theorem, somewhat along the lines of the proof of Theorem 8.2. This is not possible; by discarding the requirement that multiplication in the ground field F be commutative, we can construct more general classes of projective planes in which Desargues' Theorem is valid, and Pappus' is not. One such plane is obtained by using coordinates which are quaternions.

THEOREM 8.5. *Let there be given on each side of a triangle a pair of points that separate the vertices on that side harmonically. Three points, one from each of the three pairs, are collinear if and only if the three lines each joining one of the remaining points to the opposite vertex are concurrent.*

Proof. (1) The condition is sufficient. Let the vertices be A_1, A_2, A_3, and let B_i and C_i be the given points (Figure 8.9) on the side opposite $A_i\,(i = 1, 2, 3)$. By hypothesis the lines $A_i \oplus B_i$ are concurrent; let us denote the point of concurrency by D. We establish coordinates by choosing A_1, A_2, A_3 as the triangle of reference and D as the unit point. Then a representative of B_1 is $(0, 1, 1)^T$, of B_2 is $(1, 0, 1)^T$, and of B_3 is $(1, 1, 0)^T$. Their harmonic conjugates, C_1, C_2, C_3, have the respective representatives $(0, 1, -1)^T$, $(1, 0, -1)^T$ and $(1, -1, 0)^T$. Clearly these points lie on the unit line, that is, on $x_1 + x_2 + x_3 = 0$.

(2) The condition is necessary. This follows from the dual of the sufficiency condition when we note that at the ith vertex the two sides separate

† The reader interested in a discussion of geometric axioms for $S_2(\mathsf{R})$ and $S_2(\mathsf{F})$ could consult Chapter 10 of W. T. Fishback, *Projective and Euclidean Geometry*, New York and London, John Wiley and Sons, 1962 and A. Seidenberg, *Lectures in Projective Geometry*, Princeton, N. J., D. Van Nostrand Company, 1962.

harmonically the lines joining that vertex to the points B_i and C_i on the opposite side.

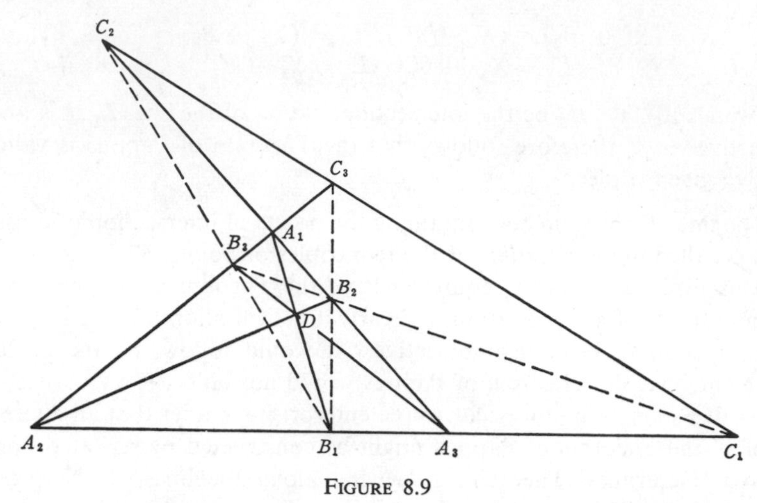

FIGURE 8.9

We could at this stage proceed with the development of incidence theorems for a variety of sets of points and lines. This would not involve the introduction of new principles or of new methods. We could employ analytic methods using an arbitrary coordinate system as we did in the proofs of Theorems 8.1a and 8.3a, or using a special coordinate system as we did in the sufficiency proof of Theorem 8.5. Or we could synthesize known results as we did in the proofs of Theorems 8.1b, 8.2, 8.4, and the necessity proof of Theorem 8.5. In the exercises that follow the reader will find some additional theorems that can be proved by one or several of these methods.

We close this section with a theorem which is of fundamental importance in real projective geometry.

THEOREM 8.6. *A one-to-one map of $S_2(\mathsf{R})$ onto itself that maps collinear points onto collinear points is a collineation, that is, it belongs to $G_8(\mathsf{R})$.*

Proof. We let γ be a map that satisfies the hypothesis of the theorem; we first show that γ preserves harmonic sets. If A, B, C, D are collinear points with $(A\,B, C\,D) = -1$, we can construct a quadrangle $ABJH$ (see Figure 8.7) with C as one diagonal point and with D as the intersection of $A \oplus B$ and the join of the other two diagonal points. γ maps a quadrangle and its diagonal points onto a quadrangle and its diagonal points; by Theorem 8.3a, we must have $(\gamma A \;\gamma B, \gamma C \;\gamma D) = -1$.

We next let $ABJH$ be any quadrangle, and we let g be the unique collineation determined by (see Theorem 1.2)

$$g\gamma A = A, \qquad g\gamma B = B, \qquad g\gamma J = J, \qquad g\gamma H = H.$$

Then $g\gamma$ is a map that satisfies the hypothesis of the theorem; it preserves harmonic sets, and leaves fixed the four points A, B, J, H. We shall complete the proof by showing that $g\gamma$ is the identity map so that $\gamma = g^{-1}$.

Consider $A \oplus B$; $g\gamma$ maps this line onto itself, and leaves fixed the three points A, B, and $(A \oplus B) \cap (J \oplus H)$. By (II, Theorem 3.6) $g\gamma$ restricted to $A \oplus B$ is a projectivity, and by (II, Theorem 2.1) the identity projectivity. Thus $g\gamma$ leaves fixed every point of $A \oplus B$. Similarly, $g\gamma$ leaves fixed every point of $J \oplus H$. Now let P be any point of the plane not on these two lines, and choose two lines through P intersecting $A \oplus B$ and $J \oplus H$ in the four distinct points P_i $(i = 1, 2, 3, 4)$ (Figure 8.10). Then $g\gamma P_i = P_i$, and hence $g\gamma$

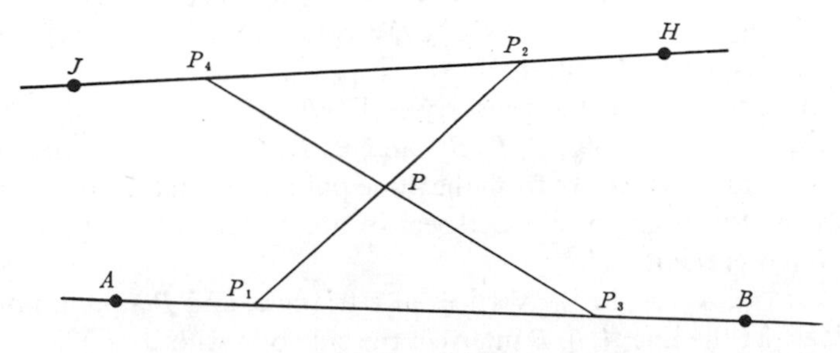

FIGURE 8.10

maps these two lines onto themselves. Since the map is one-to-one, the map of P (the intersection of these two lines) is P itself. Thus $g\gamma$ leaves every point fixed, and our proof is complete.

Theorem 8.6 does not hold in $S_2(\mathsf{C})$. Although the map $x_i = \bar{x}_i$ (where the bar denotes the complex conjugate) is one-to-one and preserves collinearity, it is not in $G_8(\mathsf{C})$. More generally, it can be shown that Theorem 8.6 does not hold in $S_2(\mathsf{F})$ whenever F possesses a nontrivial automorphism.†

EXERCISES

1. Prove the harmonic properties of the quadrilateral directly from those of the quadrangle.

2. Prove: In the configuration of Pappus, the lines $A \oplus A'$, $B \oplus B'$, and $C \oplus C'$ are concurrent if and only if the Pappus line is concurrent with the given lines.

3. Construction Problem: Given three concurrent lines, construct the harmonic conjugate of one with respect to the other two.

4. Construction Problem: Construct the line through a given point and through the intersection of two lines, without using their point of intersection.

† An automorphism of F is a one-to-one map f of F onto itself satisfying $f(a+b) = f(a) + f(b), f(ab) = f(a)f(b)$, for all $a, b \in \mathsf{F}$.

5. State the dual of the Theorem of Pappus and the dual of Theorem 8.2.

6. Let PQR be the diagonal triangle of a quadrangle, and let an arbitrary line through P intersect a pair of opposite sides not through P, in M, N. Prove that the harmonic conjugate of P with respect to M, N is collinear with Q, R.

7. Let $APQR$ be a quadrangle. Show that there exists a unique quadrangle with PQR as its diagonal triangle and with A as one of its vertices.

#**8.** Prove the assertion in the text just preceding Construction Problem 8.1.

#**9.** Let A_1, A_2, A_3 be the vertices of a triangle inscribed in a triangle with side β_i, where A_i and β_i are incident ($i = 1, 2, 3$). Denote by γ_i the harmonic conjugate of β_i with respect to the two sides of the first triangle that intersect on β_i. Prove that the lines $\gamma_1, \gamma_2, \gamma_3$ are concurrent if and only if the two given triangles are Desarguean.

#**10.** State the dual of the property of Exercise 9.

11. Prove: If $A_1 A_2 A_3$, $B_1 B_2 B_3$, and $C_1 C_2 C_3$ are three triangles each two of which are perspective from the same point O, then the lines from which each two of the triangles are perspective are concurrent. Is the converse true? What is the dual?

12. Let A_1, A_2, A_3 be the vertices of a triangle, and B a point not on any of its sides, let the line $A_i \oplus B$ intersect the side opposite A_i in C_i ($i = 1, 2, 3$), and let D_i be the harmonic conjugate of B with respect to A_i and C_i. Prove that the line $D_i \oplus D_j$ contains A_k, where i, j, k are unequal.

#**13.** Prove analytically and geometrically that an arbitrary line not through a vertex intersects the three pairs of opposite sides of a quadrangle in points that are pairs in an involution.

#**14.** Use the theorem of Exercise 13 to construct the transform of any point P of a given line in the involution that transforms two given points A, B into A', B', respectively. What theorem guarantees the uniqueness of the point P' of your construction? Is your construction valid for $A = A'$?

#**15.** Let there be given an involution on a line L, and let $A_1 A_2 A_3$ be a triangle with no vertices on L. Join each vertex to the point of L that is the transform under the given involution of the point in which the side of the triangle opposite that vertex intersects L. Prove that the three lines so obtained are concurrent.

#**16.** State the dual of the theorem of Exercise 15.

9 Projectivities and Perspectivities

In this section we continue our study of $S_2(\mathsf{F})$ with particular reference to the maps induced by its collineations on its lines (as sets of points) and its pencils (as sets of lines). If $g \in G_8(\mathsf{F})$ (the group of collineations), and if L

denotes either of these projective spaces of dimension one (a line of points, or a pencil of lines), gL is a one-dimensional space of the same type as L, and the map from L to $L' = gL$ preserves cross ratio (see Theorem 4.3).

If we now introduce projective coordinates $[x_1, x_2]^T$ in L, and $[x'_1, x'_2]^T$ in L', it follows by an argument identical with that used in the proof of (II, Theorem 3.5) that the map from L to L' expressed in terms of these one-dimensional projective coordinates, must be a nonsingular homogeneous linear transformation, that is,

$$[\mathbf{X}'] = [\mathbf{AX}], \qquad \det \mathbf{A} \neq 0, \tag{9.1a}$$

where

$$\mathbf{X} = \begin{pmatrix} x_1 \\ x_2 \end{pmatrix}, \qquad \mathbf{X}' = \begin{pmatrix} x'_1 \\ x'_2 \end{pmatrix}, \qquad \mathbf{A} = \begin{pmatrix} a_{11} & a_{12} \\ a_{21} & a_{22} \end{pmatrix}. \tag{9.1b}$$

Conversely, let π be the transformation (9.1) from L, a space of dimension one in $S_2(\mathsf{F})$, onto L', a second space of the same type. Since the transformations (9.1) are algebraically identical with the transformations of $G_3(\mathsf{F})$, the proofs of (II, Theorems 3.1 and 2.2) permit us to conclude that π preserves cross ratio, and that π is determined when the transforms of three elements of L are given. Let these be A, B, C (points or lines, according as L is a line or a pencil), and let $A' = \pi A$, $B' = \pi B$, $C' = \pi C$. Choose any two elements D, E (points or lines according as A, B, C are points or lines) that are distinct, not incident with L, and such that C, D, E are dependent. Let D' and E' be similarly chosen with respect to L' (Figure 9.1). Then there exists a collineation (see Theorem 1.2) of $S_2(\mathsf{F})$ that maps A, B, D, E onto A', B', D',

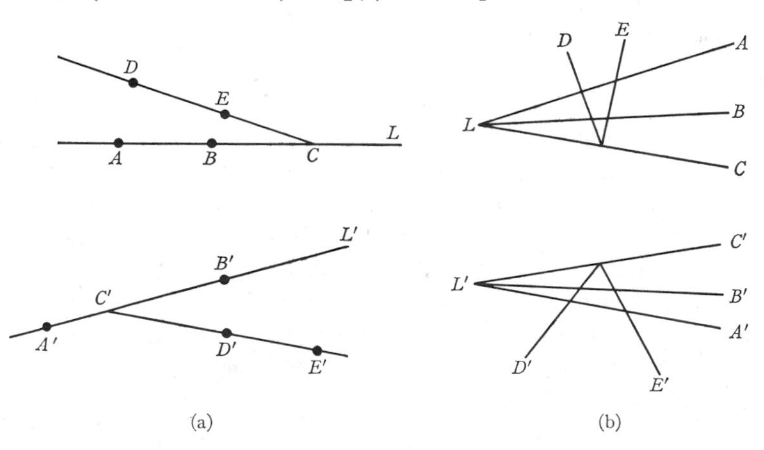

FIGURE 9.1

E', respectively; this collineation maps C onto C', and therefore on L it coincides with π. Thus π can necessarily be effected by some collineation. We say that the collineation *induces* π, or that π is the *restriction* of the collineation to L.

In our earlier definition of a projectivity we required that the range coincide with the domain. We now extend the usage of this term.

DEFINITION 9.1. If L and L' are any two lines (or two pencils) of $S_2(\mathsf{F})$, and $[x_1, x_2]^T$ and $[x'_1, x'_2)^T$ are projective coordinates of the points (lines) of L and L', respectively, a transformation (9.1) is called a *projectivity* of L onto L'.

The remarks preceding Definition (9.1) are summarized in the following theorem.

THEOREM 9.1. *A collineation of $G_8(\mathsf{F})$ that maps a line (pencil) L onto a line (pencil) L' induces a projectivity of L onto L', and a given projectivity of L onto L' can be induced by some collineation of $G_8(\mathsf{F})$.*

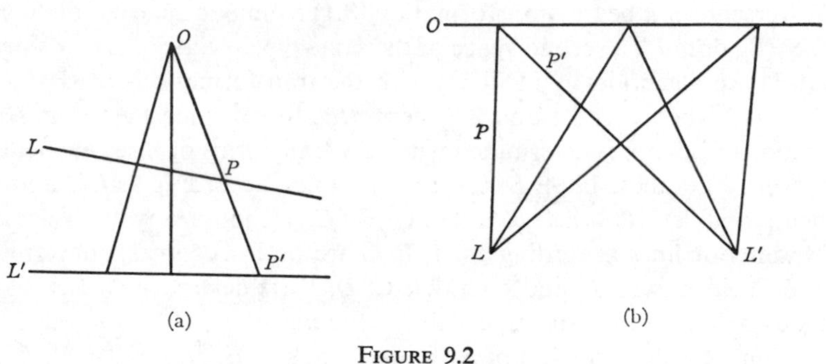

FIGURE 9.2

We note that (9.1) also establishes a map of L' onto L, given by

$$[\mathbf{X}] = [\mathbf{A}^{-1}\mathbf{X}']. \tag{9.2}$$

We naturally call this the inverse of (9.1). However we cannot necessarily speak of the product of two transformations (9.1). But if we have three like one-dimensional spaces L, L', L'' and two transformations (9.1), one of L onto L', and the second of L' onto L'', then we form the product in the usual manner to obtain a transformation of the set (9.1) of L onto L''. Thus we see that although with our present interpretation the set of transformations (9.1) does not form a group, the group property of linear transformations appears in a modified form in the following theorem.

THEOREM 9.2. *If the product of two projectivities is defined, it is a projectivity.*

DEFINITION 9.2. Let L, L' be two lines in S_2, and O a point on neither. Let τ be the transformation that maps a point P of L onto the point P' of L' that is collinear with P and O (Figure 9.2). Any such transformation τ, or the dual transformation between pencils, is called a *perspectivity*. The point

O (or in the dual case, the line O) is called the *center* (or in the dual case, the *central line* or *axis*), and we say that the lines L, L' (or the pencils L, L') are *perspective* from O.

By Theorem 4.2b, it follows that every perspectivity is a projectivity, and therefore our earlier remarks regarding the existence of a product apply here. We then have the following theorem.

THEOREM 9.3. *The product of a finite number of perspectivities (when i exists) is a projectivity.*

We remarked earlier (page 56), that a linear fractional transformation (expressed in terms of Euclidean distance) between two lines of the Euclidean plane is the product of central projections. This remark is related to the following theorem for the projective plane.

THEOREM 9.4. *A projectivity in $S_2(\mathsf{F})$ between the points of distinct lines (or between the lines of distinct pencils) is the product of two perspectivities.*

Proof. We shall prove the theorem for a projectivity between two lines; the theorem for a projectivity between two pencils follows by duality. Let the projectivity map the points D, E, F of the line L onto the points D', E', F' of L', where D, D', and $L \cap L'$ are distinct points (Figure 9.3). Let $E^* = (D' \oplus E) \cap (E' \oplus D)$, $F^* = (D' \oplus F) \cap (F' \oplus D)$, and $L^* = E^* \oplus F^*$. The perspectivity of L onto L^* with center D', followed by the perspectivity of

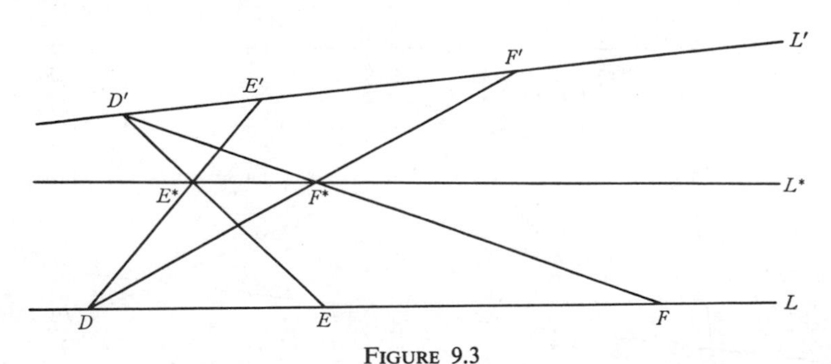

FIGURE 9.3

L^* onto L' with center D clearly maps D, E, and F onto D', E', and F', respectively; this product must be the given projectivity since a projectivity is determined when the maps of three elements are given (see II, Theorem 2.2).

The factorization of a projectivity into the product of two perspectivities is not unique: D and D', the centers of the perspectivities may be any two corresponding points distinct from $L \cap L'$. We have however even greater freedom; we can select as centers any two distinct points that are collinear with such a pair of corresponding points. We take O, O' (Figure 9.4) collinear with D, D' ($O \neq D, O' \neq D'$), and we let $E'' = (O \oplus E) \cap (O' \oplus E')$, and $F'' = (O \oplus F) \cap (O' \oplus F')$. The given projectivity is equal to the product: the perspectivity of L onto L'' with center O, followed by the perspectivity of L'' onto L' with center O'.

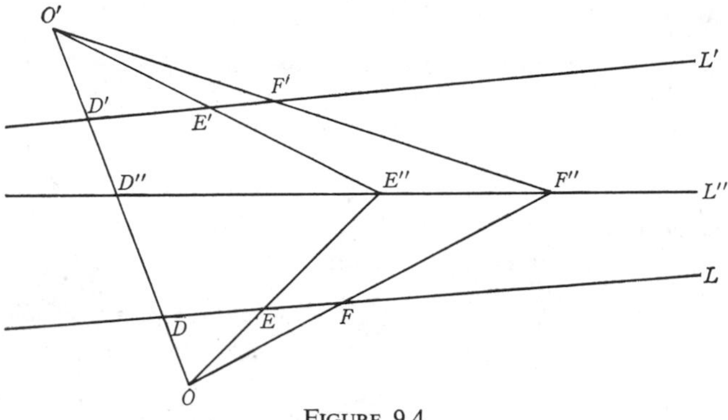

FIGURE 9.4

The line L'' of Figure 9.4 is determined by the choice of centers O, O'. Suppose however that L'' is given. Do there exist perspectivities of L onto L'' and of L'' onto L' whose product is a given projectivity? Let us denote

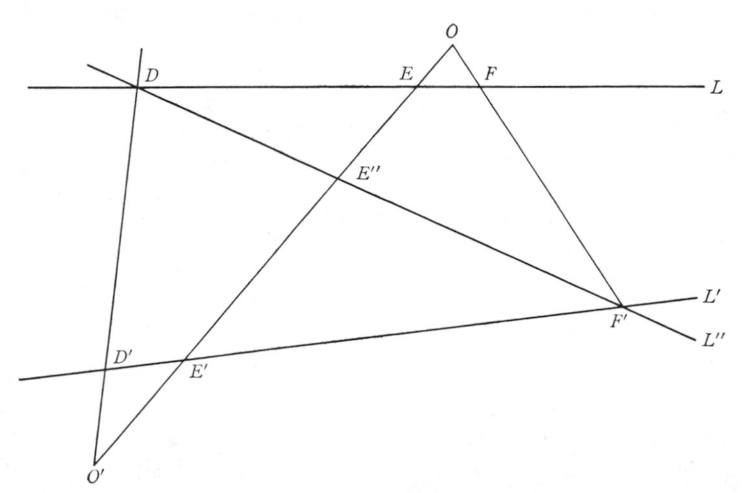

FIGURE 9.5

(Figure 9.5) the intersection of L'' with L and L' by D and F', respectively; let D' be the map of D, and F the point whose map is F', let E, E' be any pair of distinct corresponding points, and let $O = (E \oplus E') \cap (F \oplus F')$, $O' = (E \oplus E') \cap (D \oplus D')$. Then if $F' \neq D'$, the given projectivity is the product of the two perspectivities with centers O and O' and with L'' the middle line. It is thus possible to find perspectivities from L to L'' and from L'' to L' whose product is a given projectivity from L to L' provided that L, L', L'' are independent and that the intersections of L'' with L and L' are not corresponding points under the given projectivity.

Suppose now that we choose our centers of perspectivity as in Figure 9.3, that is, as corresponding points under the given projectivity; does the line L^* depend upon the choice of D? If the points $L \cap L', L \cap L^*, L' \cap L^*$ are denoted by Q, R, S, respectively (Figure 9.6), it follows that the given pro-

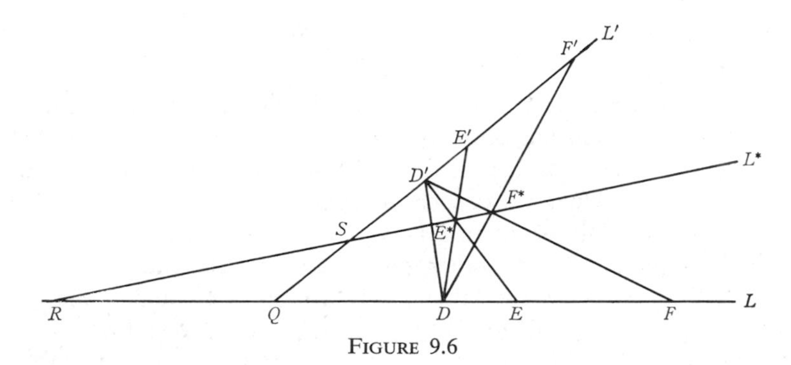

FIGURE 9.6

jectivity maps Q, as a point of L onto S, and R onto Q. Hence the line L^* contains the map of $L \cap L'$, as well as the point that maps onto this intersection. L^* is therefore surely independent of the choice of D whenever R, S are distinct. The following theorem shows that L^* is independent of the choice of D even if $R = S$.

THEOREM 9.5a. *If distinct lines L, L' are projective,† and if X, Y of L map onto X', Y', respectively, of L', the locus of the point $(X \oplus Y') \cap (X' \oplus Y)$, as X, Y $(X \neq Y)$ vary independently over L, is a line.*

Proof. Let the given projectivity map D onto D' where D, D', and $L \cap L'$ are distinct; if the projectivity is factored into two perspectivities from D and D' as in Figure 9.3, it follows that $(D \oplus X') \cap (D' \oplus X) \in L^*$, and $(D \oplus Y') \cap (D' \oplus Y) \in L^*$. By the Theorem of Pappus it follows that $X \oplus Y'$ and $X' \oplus Y$ also intersect on L^*.

By duality, we have the following theorem.

THEOREM 9.5b. *If two pencils are projective, and if the lines U, V of one pencil map onto U', V' of the second, the locus of lines $(U \cap V') \oplus (U' \cap V)$ $(U \neq V)$ is, as U and V vary, a pencil of lines.*

† The expression, "two lines (or two pencils) are projective," appears frequently in the literature; it means that a given map from the one space onto the other is a projectivity.

We shall call the line of Theorem 9.5a the *axis* of the projectivity, and the vertex of the pencil of Theorem 9.5b the *axial point.*

The distinctness condition of Theorem 9.4 is essential. For if a projectivity of a line L onto itself can be factored into the product of τ_1 and τ_2, where τ_1 is a perspectivity of L onto a line L' with center O, and τ_2 a perspectivity of L' onto L with center O', it follows that the point $(O \oplus O') \cap L$ and the point $L \cap L'$ are fixed under the given projectivity. But a projectivity of a line onto itself need not possess fixed points.

THEOREM 9.6. *A projectivity of a line onto itself is always expressible as the product of three perspectivities. If the projectivity possesses fixed points, it is expressible as the product of two perspectivities.*

Proof. To prove the first part of the theorem, we introduce a perspectivity τ from the given line onto some other line. If π is the given projectivity, $\tau\pi$ is a projectivity between two distinct lines, and by Theorem 9.4, there exist perspectivities τ_1, τ_2 such that $\tau\pi = \tau_1 \tau_2$. Then $\pi = \tau^{-1}\tau_1 \tau_2$, and the first part of the theorem follows. For the second part, we let A, B be the fixed points, C any other point, and C' its transform. Select any two points O and O' such that O, O', B are distinct and collinear, and let $L' = A \oplus (O \oplus C) \cap (O' \oplus C')$ (Figure 9.7). It follows that the given projectivity is the product: the perspectivity from L onto L' with center O, followed by the perspectivity from L' onto L with center O'.

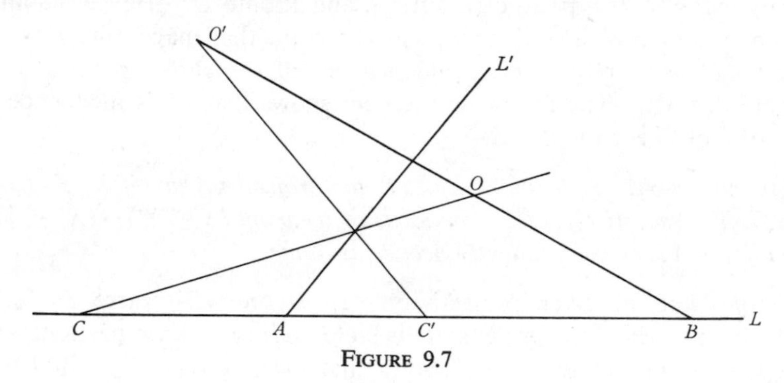

FIGURE 9.7

The reader should note that we did not in the above proof require that A and B be distinct. Since the existence of fixed points depends upon the existence of solutions of a quadratic equation, we can restate the second part of the theorem as follows:

COROLLARY 9.1. *A necessary and sufficient condition that every projectivity of a line in $S_2(\mathsf{F})$ onto itself be the product of two perspectivities is that every element in* F *be a square.*†

† The complex field is such a field; the real field is not.

We leave to the reader to state the duals of Theorem 9.6 and Corollary 9.1.

In a projectivity of a line L onto a line L', the point $L \cap L'$, as a point of L, may map onto itself, as a point of L'. We say then that the point is *self-corresponding*.

THEOREM 9.7. *A projectivity between distinct lines is a perspectivity if and only if their point of intersection is self-corresponding.*

Proof. If the projectivity is a perspectivity, the common point is clearly self-corresponding. Conversely, let the common point be self-corresponding. With the notation of Figure 9.6, it follows that $D \oplus Q$ and $D' \oplus Q$ must intersect on L^*, that is, that L, L', L^* are concurrent. Then the triangles $EE'E^*$ and $FF'F^*$ are Desarguean, so that the points D, D', and $(E \oplus E') \cap (F \oplus F')$ are collinear. If we let $O = (D \oplus D') \cap (E \oplus E')$, it follows that O, F, F' are collinear for every F and its transform F'. Hence the given projectivity is a perspectivity with center O.

COROLLARY 9.2. *A projectivity between two lines is a perspectivity if and only if the axis is concurrent with the two lines.*

We leave the proof to the reader.

THEOREM 9.8. *The center of a perspectivity between two distinct lines lies on the harmonic conjugate of the axis, with respect to the given lines.*

This theorem is an immediate consequence of the harmonic properties of a quadrangle (see Corollary 8.2).

EXERCISES

1. Show that the collineation represented by $x_1' = x_1 + x_2 + x_3, x_2' = x_2 + x_3, x_3' = x_3$ maps the line $x_3 = 0$ onto itself and induces thereon a parabolic projectivity.

2. Show that the collineation $\mathbf{U}' = \mathbf{A}\mathbf{U}$, where $\mathbf{A}$ is given in (III, 4, Exercise 17), leaves $A_3 : (0, 0, 1)^T$ fixed. Are any lines through A_3 fixed?

3. Find a collineation that induces on the line $x_1 = 0$ an elliptic projectivity.

4. Find all collineations that induce on the line $x_2 = 0$ the identity projectivity.

5. Prove that a one-to-one correspondence between two distinct lines is a projectivity if and only if the intersections of the lines joining crosswise corresponding pairs are collinear.

6. Prove: If a projectivity π between distinct lines L and L' maps $D \in L$ onto $D' \in L'$, and if τ is a perspectivity from L' onto a line L'' through D, with center on the line $D \oplus D'$, the product $\tau\pi$ is a perspectivity.

7. State the dual of each of the following: Theorem 9.7, Corollary 9.2, and Theorem 9.8.

8. Let τ_1 be a perspectivity from a line L onto a line L'', and let τ_2 be a perspectivity from L'' onto a third line L'. Prove that if L, L', L'' are concurrent, the product $\tau_2\,\tau_1$ is a perspectivity, and that its center is collinear with the centers of τ_1 and τ_2.

9. Can the product of two perspectivities from L to L', and from L' to L'' where L, L', L'' are independent, be a perspectivity?

10. Construction Problem: Let A, B, C, D be four lines of one pencil, and A', B', C' three lines of a different pencil. Construct the line D' of the second pencil that is the transform of D under the projectivity that maps A, B, C onto A', B', C', respectively.

11. PQR is a variable triangle whose vertices P, Q, R lie on three given independent lines, L, L', L'', respectively. The sides $P \oplus R$, $R \oplus Q$ pass through given points A, B, respectively, that are collinear with $L \cap L'$ Prove that the side $Q \oplus P$ passes through a fixed point.

12. Let A, B, C be three collinear points, and L_1, L_2 two lines not containing A, B, or C. Let a map be established between the lines of the pencils A and B by requiring that corresponding lines of A and B intersect L_1 and L_2, respectively, in points collinear with C. Prove that this map is projective, and find the locus of the points of intersection of corresponding lines of the two pencils.

13. Let $ABCD$ be a quadrangle, and let $R = (A \oplus C) \cap (B \oplus D)$. A map between the points of $A \oplus B$ and those of $C \oplus D$ is established as follows: P on $A \oplus B$ corresponds to P' on $C \oplus D$ if the harmonic conjugate of P with respect to A and B, and the harmonic conjugate of P' with respect to C and D are collinear with R. Prove that the map is a perspectivity.

14. Let τ be a perspectivity from a line L onto a line L', and g an involution on the line L'. Prove that the map $\tau^{-1}g\tau$ is an involution on L.

\#**15.** Let F, A, A' be three points on a line; construct the map of a point P of the line under the parabolic projectivity that leaves F fixed and maps A onto A'. By means of this construction prove the first part of (II, 6, Exercise 9) geometrically.

16. Construction Problem: Given a projectivity that leaves fixed a given point F of a line, and maps two other points A, B onto A', B', respectively, construct the other fixed point.

\#**17.** Let τ be an involution on a line L, and let A, B, $A' = \tau A$, $B' = \tau B$ be four given distinct points on L. Construct τP, where $P \in L$.

18. Let A, B be the vertices of two projective pencils of lines, and let L be a line of neither pencil. Let π be the map of L onto itself determined by the condition that the map of a point P of L is the intersection with L of that line of the pencil B that corresponds to the line $A \oplus P$ of the pencil A. Prove that π is a projectivity.

#**19.** Show that the map π of Exercise 18 is an involution if and only if L contains the axial point of the projectivity between the pencils A, B.

#**20.** State the duals of Exercises 18 and 19.

#**21.** Let a projectivity with fixed elements F_1, F_2 transform A, B into A', B', respectively. Prove that the three pairs F_1, F_2; A, B'; A', B are pairs in an involution.

10 Projective Properties of the Euclidean Plane

In this section we develop the two-dimensional analogue of the ideas introduced in Section 4, Chapter II. It suffices for our present purposes to say† that a map $\mathscr{E}$ of E_2 into $S_2(\mathsf{R})$ is an embedding of E_2 in $S_2(\mathsf{R})$ if there exists a Cartesian coordinatization (x, y) of E_2 and a projective coordinatization $[\mathbf{X}] = [x_1, x_2, x_3]^T$ of $S_2(\mathsf{R})$ in terms of which $\mathscr{E}$ is given by

$$x = x_1/x_3, \qquad y = x_2/x_3. \tag{10.1}$$

Conversely, for given coordinatizations of E_2 and $S_2(\mathsf{R})$, (10.1) establishes a map, and hence we can associate with given coordinatizations the embedding $\mathscr{E}$ given by (10.1).

Let $\mathscr{E}$ be an arbitrary embedding. Then we see from (10.1) that its domain of definition is E_2, and that its range is $S_2(\mathsf{R})$ with one line excluded. We call this line the *absolute line*, or the *line at infinity* of the embedding. We let $l(\mathscr{E})$ denote the absolute line of an embedding $\mathscr{E}$, and $S_2 - l$ the set of points of $S_2(\mathsf{R})$ that do not lie on the line l. We note that $\mathscr{E}$ is one-to-one from E_2 onto $S_2 - l(\mathscr{E})$. Since we can introduce in $S_2(\mathsf{R})$ projective coordinates with a given line as the line $x_3 = 0$, $l(\mathscr{E})$ is otherwise indistinguishable from the other lines of $S_2(\mathsf{R})$; if a line $l \subset S_2(\mathsf{R})$ is given, there exist (infinitely many) embeddings $\mathscr{E}$ such that $l = l(\mathscr{E})$.

Let L be an arbitrary line in E_2,

$$L\colon x \cos \omega + y \sin \omega - p = 0. \tag{10.2}$$

Then $\mathscr{E}L$ is contained in the projective line

$$L'\colon x_1 \cos \omega + x_2 \sin \omega - px_3 = 0. \tag{10.3}$$

We shall show that the map from L into L' is an embedding in the sense of our earlier definition. We can define a point function s on L by (10.2) and

$$s = -x \sin \omega + y \cos \omega; \tag{10.4}$$

s, so defined, is a metric coordinate on L; we can define projective coordinates $[\lambda, \mu]^T$ on L' by noting that $(-\sin \omega, \cos \omega, 0)^T$ and $(p \cos \omega, p \sin \omega, 1)^T$ are

† See footnote, page 80.

independent solutions of (10.3), and by writing

$$\mathbf{X} = \lambda(-\sin \omega, \cos \omega, 0)^T + \mu(p \cos \omega, p \sin \omega, 1)^T. \tag{10.5}$$

Then $[\lambda, \mu]^T$ is given on L' by (10.3) and

$$[\lambda, \mu]^T = [-x_1 \sin \omega + x_2 \cos \omega, x_3]^T. \tag{10.6}$$

Comparing with (10.4), we see that, on L, $\mathscr{E}$ coincides with the map $s = \lambda/\mu$. Thus $\mathscr{E}$ induces an embedding of a line $L \subset E_2$ in the projective line L' that contains $\mathscr{E}L$.

We note further that (10.2), with p variable, represents a pencil of parallel lines, and then (10.3) consists of the lines (exclusive of $x_3 = 0$) of the pencil with vertex $[-\sin \omega, \cos \omega, 0]^T$ on $x_3 = 0$. In the pencil in E_2, p is a metric coordinate; it is the directed distance from a fixed line of the pencil to a variable one. From (10.3), we see that, in the pencil in S_2, p is a nonhomogeneous projective coordinate.

If (10.2) represents a pencil W of concurrent lines with vertex (a, b), we can rewrite it as

$$(x - a) \cos \omega + (y - b) \sin \omega = 0, \tag{10.7}$$

where ω varies. Then, from (10.7) and (10.1), L' is given by

$$(x_1 - ax_3) \cos \omega + (x_2 - bx_3) \sin \omega = 0; \tag{10.8}$$

letting ω vary we see that $\mathscr{E}$ maps the pencil W (as a set of lines) one-to-one onto a pencil in S_2. This map is an embedding of the second kind (see page 83). We note that $[\cos \omega, \sin \omega]^T$ is a projective coordinatization of the lines of $\mathscr{E}W$; thus the metric coordinatization of W expressed by a slope variable ($m = \tan(\omega + \pi/2)$, or $m = \tan \omega$, or more generally $\tan(\omega + c)$, for c a constant) corresponds, under $\mathscr{E}$, to a nonhomogeneous projective coordinatization of $\mathscr{E}W$.

We summarize these conclusions in the following theorem.

THEOREM 10.1. *An embedding $\mathscr{E}$ of E_2 in $S_2(\mathsf{R})$ embeds the lines of E_2 in the lines of $S_2(\mathsf{R})$. A pencil of parallel lines is mapped into a pencil in $S_2(\mathsf{R})$ with vertex on $l(\mathscr{E})$, and these maps are one-dimensional embeddings of the first kind; a pencil of concurrent lines is mapped one-to-one onto a pencil of $S_2(\mathsf{R})$, and these maps are one-dimensional embeddings of the second kind.*

This theorem together with our earlier conclusions (see II, Theorems 4.1, 4.2, 4.4 and Corollaries 4.1, 4.2) yields the following.

THEOREM 10.2. *The cross ratio of four collinear points or concurrent lines in E_2 is equal to the cross ratio in S_2 of their maps under an embedding.*

If μ is a map of E_2 onto itself, $P \in E_2$ and μP are mapped by an embedding $\mathscr{E}$ onto the points $\mathscr{E}P$ and $\mathscr{E}\mu P$. Hence the map $\gamma = \mathscr{E}\mu\mathscr{E}^{-1}$ has domain and range $S_2(\mathsf{R}) - l(\mathscr{E})$, and maps $X = \mathscr{E}P$ onto $\gamma X = \mathscr{E}\mu P$. We call γ the image of μ, under $\mathscr{E}$, and we *complete* γ by finding a map, with domain $S_2(\mathsf{R})$, which coincides with γ on $S_2(\mathsf{R}) - l(\mathscr{E})$. The following theorem in $S_2(\mathsf{R})$ is a useful extension of Theorem 8.6.

THEOREM 10.3. *Let l be a line in $S_2(\mathsf{R})$, and let γ be a given one-to-one map of $S_2(\mathsf{R}) - l$ onto itself. If γ maps collinear points onto collinear points, there exists a unique $g \in G_8(\mathsf{R})$ which is a completion of γ.*

Proof. Since γ is one-to-one, it maps lines which intersect on l onto lines which intersect on l. If $X \in l$, there exists $X' \in l$ such that γ maps the pencil X (exclusive of l and X) into a pencil with vertex X'. We now define a map g of $S_2(\mathsf{R})$ onto itself,

$$\begin{aligned} gX &= \gamma X \quad \text{if} \quad X \in S_2(\mathsf{R}) - l, \\ gX &= X' \quad \text{if} \quad X \in l. \end{aligned}$$

By Theorem 8.6, $g \in G_8(\mathsf{R})$; the uniqueness of g is established by showing that the contrary hypothesis leads to a contradiction.

We use this theorem in giving a geometric characterization of embeddings.

THEOREM 10.4. *If l is a line of $S_2(\mathsf{R})$. and if g is a map from E_2 onto $S_2(\mathsf{R}) - l$ which is one-to-one and which maps collinear points of E_2 onto collinear points of $S_2(\mathsf{R})$, g is an embedding of E_2 in $S_2(\mathsf{R})$.*

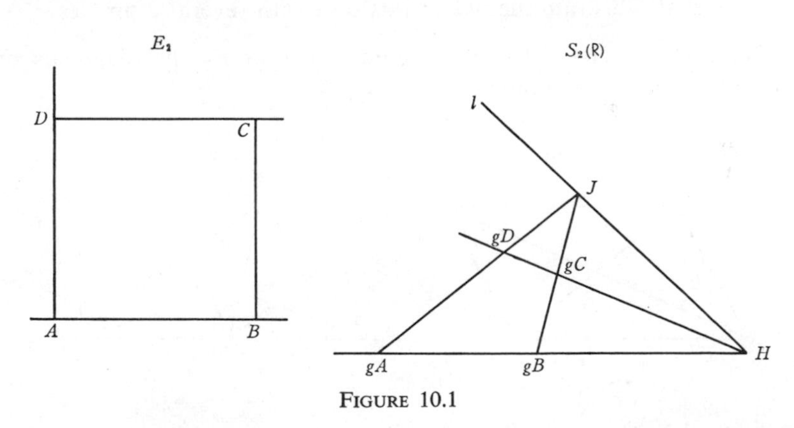

FIGURE 10.1

Proof. In E_2, let A, B, C, D be the vertices of a unit square (Figure 10.1). Since† $A \oplus B$ and $C \oplus D$ are parallel, $gA \oplus gB$ and $gC \oplus gD$ can have no intersection in $S_2(\mathsf{R}) - l$; consequently in $S_2(\mathsf{R})$ these lines‡ must intersect in a point of l, say H. Similarly we let $J = (gA \oplus gD) \cap (gB \oplus gC) \in l$. We

† As in S_2, we let $A \oplus B$ denote the line joining A and B.

‡ The reader should note that $gA \oplus gB = H \cup g(A \oplus B)$, and that the symbol $\oplus$ is used with two meanings.

now introduce Cartesian coordinates (x, y) in E_2 with $A:(0,0)$, $B:(1,0)$, $D:(0,1)$, and projective coordinates $[\mathbf{X}]$ in $S_2(\mathsf{R})$ with H, J, gA as the vertices of the reference triangle and gC as the unit point, and we let $\mathscr{E}$ be the embedding (10.1) for these coordinates. We then have

$$(10.9) \qquad \mathscr{E}A = gA, \qquad \mathscr{E}B = gB, \qquad \mathscr{E}C = gC, \qquad \mathscr{E}D = gD.$$

We shall show that $g = \mathscr{E}$. Clearly, $\mathscr{E}g^{-1}$ satisfies the hypothesis of Theorem 10.3, and therefore there exists a unique $g' \in G_8(\mathsf{R})$ which is the completion of $\mathscr{E}g^{-1}$. From (10.9) and Theorem 1.1, $g' = I$, so that for all $X \in S_2(\mathsf{R}) - l$, $g'X = \mathscr{E}g^{-1}X = X$. Letting $X = gP$ in the last equality, we find that $\mathscr{E}P = gP$ for all $P \in E_2$.

For logical completeness we need the following theorem.

THEOREM 10.5. *If $\mathscr{E}_1$ and $\mathscr{E}_2$ are two embeddings of E_2 in $S_2(\mathsf{R})$, there exists a unique $g \in G_8(\mathsf{R})$ which maps $\mathscr{E}_1 P$ onto $\mathscr{E}_2 P$ for all $P \in E_2$.*

Proof. If g is any collineation satisfying $gl(\mathscr{E}_1) = l(\mathscr{E}_2)$, the map $g\mathscr{E}_1 \mathscr{E}_2^{-1}$ (with $l(\mathscr{E}_2)$ playing the role of l) satisfies the hypotheses of Theorem 10.3. We leave the details to the reader.

Embeddings provide us with a powerful tool for the generalization of Euclidean theorems and the discovery of new ones. Theorem 10.5 insures that the projective generalization is independent of the choice of the embedding. We shall illustrate the use of this tool with several examples.

Illustration 1. Generalize the theorem that in E_2 the diagonals of a parallelogram bisect each other.

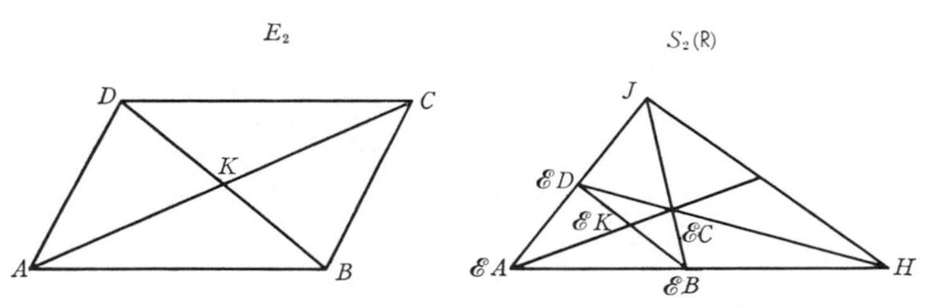

FIGURE 10.2

Solution. If we embed E_2 in $S_2(\mathsf{R})$, a parallelogram $ABCD$ (Figure 10.2) maps onto the quadrangle $\mathscr{E}A\,\mathscr{E}B\,\mathscr{E}C\,\mathscr{E}D$ two of whose diagonal points, H, J lie on the absolute line of the embedding. By (II, Corollary 4.1), $\mathscr{E}A$ and $\mathscr{E}C$ separate harmonically $\mathscr{E}K$ and the absolute point of their line. In $S_2(\mathsf{R})$ however, any two quadrangles are projectively equivalent, and therefore the harmonic properties of the quadrangle $\mathscr{E}A\,\mathscr{E}B\,\mathscr{E}C\,\mathscr{E}D$ hold for any quadrangle. We thus have another proof of Theorem 8.3a.

But this is not all. We can choose in $S_2(\mathsf{R})$ a quadrangle whose diagonal points do not lie on the absolute line; the inverse image under the embedding is a quadrangle in E_2 no two of whose sides are parallel; such a quadrangle must possess the harmonic properties of the quadrangle in S_2. Again, we can choose a quadrangle in S_2 with just one diagonal point on the absolute line and thereby prove that, in E_2, the line joining the point of intersection of the diagonals of a trapezoid to the point of intersection of the two opposite nonparallel sides bisects the two sides.

Illustration 2. Generalize the theorem that in E_2 the medians of a triangle are concurrent.

Solution. With the notation of Figure 10.3, P_3, the harmonic conjugate

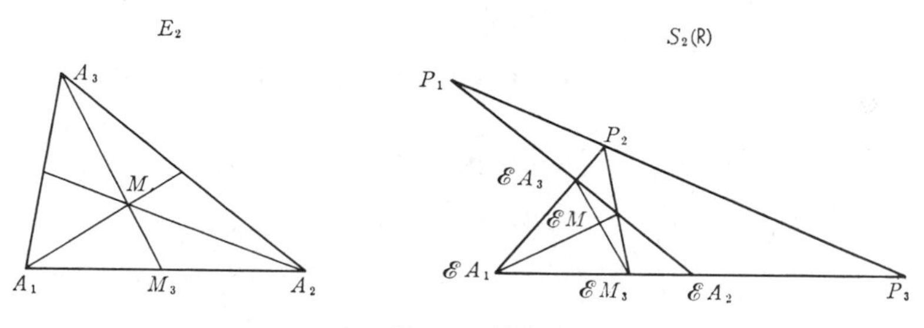

FIGURE 10.3

of $\mathscr{E}M_3$ with respect to $\mathscr{E}A_1$ and $\mathscr{E}A_2$, is the absolute point on $\mathscr{E}A_1 \oplus \mathscr{E}A_2$. P_1 and P_2 are constructed similarly. Thus the three harmonic conjugates are collinear. But in S_2, the quadrangle $\mathscr{E}A_1\mathscr{E}A_2\mathscr{E}A_3\mathscr{E}M$ is projectively equivalent to any other quadrangle, and therefore we have proved the sufficiency conclusion of Theorem 8.5. To prove the rest of Theorem 8.5 we can proceed as follows: If $A_1' A_2' A_3'$ is a triangle in $S_2(\mathsf{R})$, and P_1, P_2, P_3 three collinear points one on each of the three sides of the triangle, we choose an embedding of E_2 in $S_2(\mathsf{R})$ whose absolute line is the line of the three P's. Under the inverse of the embedding, the harmonic conjugates of the P's map onto the midpoints. We leave the remaining details to the reader.

We turn next to a theorem in $S_2(\mathsf{F})$.

THEOREM 10.6. *Let $A_1 A_2 A_3$ be a triangle in $S_2(\mathsf{F})$, and let B_1, B_2, B_3 and C_1, C_2, C_3 be two triples of points, distinct from the vertices, with B_i and C_i $(i = 1, 2, 3)$ incident to the side opposite A_i; then any two of the following assertions imply the third*:

(1) *The points B_i are collinear.*
(2) *The points C_i are collinear.*
(3) $(A_1 A_2, B_3 C_3)(A_2 A_3, B_1 C_1)(A_3 A_1, B_2 C_2) = 1.$

Proof. We show first that (3) is a consequence of (1) and (2). We let β and γ be the joins of the B's and C's respectively. If $\beta = \gamma$, $B_i = C_i$, and each of the cross ratios in (3) is 1 so the product is 1. If $\beta \neq \gamma$, the three cross ratios are equal to $(A_1 A_2, \beta\gamma)$, $(A_2 A_3, \beta\gamma)$, $(A_3 A_1, \beta\gamma)$ respectively; by the dual of Theorem 4.4 their product is 1.

To finish the proof, it suffices (because of symmetry) to show that (1) and (3) imply (2). We let $C_3' = (C_1 \oplus C_2) \cap (A_1 \oplus A_2)$. Then (3) holds by hypothesis, and (3), with C_3' replacing C_3, holds by the first part of our proof. Comparing the two products of cross ratios, we obtain that $(A_1 A_2, B_3 C_3) = (A_1 A_2, B_3 C_3')$, and therefore $C_3 = C_3'$. Hence the three C's are collinear, as required.

We obtain a theorem in E_2 from Theorem 10.6 by choosing the line γ to be the absolute line of an embedding. Then, by a slightly modified form of (II, Theorem 4.2), each of the cross ratios in (3) is equal to the negative of the ratio of directed distances; the resulting theorem is due to Ceva.

THEOREM OF CEVA. *In E_2, let points B_1, B_2, B_3 on the sides of the triangle $A_1 A_2 A_3$ divide the sides in the ratios k_1, k_2, k_3, respectively,*

$$A_2 B_1/B_1 A_3 = k_1, \qquad A_3 B_2/B_2 A_1 = k_2, \qquad A_1 B_3/B_3 A_2 = k_3$$

(where $A_2 B_1$, etc., represents the directed distance). Then the three points B_i are collinear if and only if $k_1 k_2 k_3 = -1$.

Although perpendicularity of lines is not a projective concept, we are able to generalize to the projective plane Euclidean properties that involve perpendicularity. We recall (see II, Corollary 6.3) that an embedding in $S_1(\mathsf{R})$ of a Euclidean pencil maps perpendicular lines onto pairs in an elliptic involution. Conversely, if an elliptic involution in $S_1(\mathsf{R})$ is given, we can find an embedding of a given Euclidean pencil of lines which maps perpendicular lines onto pairs in $S_1(\mathsf{R})$ that are conjugate in the given involution because we can choose coordinates in $S_1(\mathsf{R})$ in terms of which the involution is given by $x_1 x_1' + x_2 x_2' = 0$ (see II, Theorem 6.5). Theorem 10.1 enables us to extend these ideas to two dimensions; we leave the details of the proof of the following theorem to the reader.

THEOREM 10.7. *An embedding $\mathscr{E}$ given by* (10.1) *maps perpendicular lines of E_2 into lines of $S_2(\mathsf{R})$ which intersect the absolute line in points that are pairs in an elliptic involution. Conversely, if l is a line in $S_2(\mathsf{R})$ and σ is a given elliptic involution on l, there exists an embedding of E_2 in $S_2(\mathsf{R})$ which maps perpendicular lines of E_2 into lines of S_2 which intersect l in points that are pairs in σ.*

If $\mathscr{E}$ is the embedding (10.1), we call the involution, on $l(\mathscr{E})$, represented by $x_1 x_1' + x_2 x_2' = 0$ the *absolute involution*, and we denote it by $\sigma(\mathscr{E})$. If τ is any other involution on $l(\mathscr{E})$, there exist exactly two points on $l(\mathscr{E})$ which are conjugate in both τ and $\sigma(\mathscr{E})$ (II, 6, Exercise 10). The next corollary is a consequence of these remarks, of (II, Corollary 4.2), and of (II, Theorem 6.5).

COROLLARY 10.1. *If $\mathscr{E}$ is an embedding of E_2 in $S_2(\mathsf{R})$, the bisectors of the angles between two intersecting lines of E_2 are mapped by $\mathscr{E}$ into lines of $S_2(\mathsf{R})$ which intersect the absolute line of the embedding in points that are conjugate in the two involutions: the absolute involution $\sigma(\mathscr{E})$, and the involution τ on $l(\mathscr{E})$ whose fixed points are the absolute points on the maps of the two given lines.*

The two involutions of this corollary may equally well be regarded as involutions in the pencil of lines. From (II, (6.6)), the involution whose fixed elements have nonhomogeneous projective coordinates x satisfying

$$Ax^2 + 2Bx + C = 0 \tag{10.10}$$

is given by

$$Axx' + B(x + x') + C = 0. \tag{10.11}$$

In these coordinates, $\sigma(\mathscr{E})$ is given by

$$xx' + 1 = 0. \tag{10.12}$$

But if m is the slope of a variable line in a Euclidean pencil W, m is a projective coordinate in the pencil $\mathscr{E}W$. The involution whose fixed elements are given by

$$x^2 - (m_1 + m_2)x + m_1 m_2 = 0,$$

is represented by

$$xx' - \tfrac{1}{2}(m_1 + m_2)(x + x') + m_1 m_2 = 0. \tag{10.13}$$

Thus, in E_2, the bisectors of the angles formed by lines of slope m_1, m_2 have slope given by the solutions of (10.12) and (10.13).

Illustration 3. Prove the theorem in E_2 that the bisectors of the exterior angles of a nonisosceles triangle intersect the opposite sides in collinear points.

Proof. The two bisectors of an angle separate the sides harmonically (see II, Corollary 4.2), and therefore they intersect the opposite side in points which separate the vertices harmonically. Since the interior bisectors are concurrent, the conclusion of the theorem is a consequence of Theorem 8.5 and of embedding relations.

EXERCISES

1. Find a theorem in $S_2(\mathsf{R})$ which generalizes the theorem in E_2 that the altitudes of a triangle are concurrent. ANS. (see III, 8, Exercise 15).

2. Generalize to $S_2(\mathsf{R})$ the theorem that in E_2 the perpendicular bisectors of the sides of a triangle are concurrent.

3. Prove the following theorem in $S_2(\mathsf{F})$, where the notation is that used in Theorem 10.6. Any two of the following conditions imply the third:

(1) The lines $A_i \oplus B_i$ are concurrent.

(2) The points C_i are collinear.

(3) $(A_1 A_2, B_3 C_3)(A_2 A_3, B_1 C_1)(A_3 A_1, B_2 C_2) = -1$.

4. In E_2, the Theorem of Menelaus asserts that with the notation used in the statement of the Theorem of Ceva, the lines $A_i \oplus B_i$ are concurrent if and only if $k_1 k_2 k_3 = 1$. Prove this using Exercise 3.

5. Prove the theorem of Exercise 3 by proving the Theorem of Menelaus for a special triangle and generalizing the conclusion in the pattern of Illustrations 1 and 2.

6. Prove the Euclidean theorem of Illustration 3 by generalizing in E_2 the relevant properties of the exterior bisectors of an equilateral triangle.

7. Two triples of points, ABC and $A'B'C'$, on distinct lines satisfy $A \oplus A' \parallel B \oplus B'$, $A \oplus C' \parallel B' \oplus C$. Prove that $B \oplus C' \parallel A' \oplus C$.

8. The feet of the altitudes of a given oblique triangle are the vertices of its *pedal* triangle. Show that the altitudes and sides of the given triangle are the bisectors of the angles of its pedal triangle (see page 149).

9. What Euclidean theorem results from (III, 9, Exercise 11) if the points A, B are taken on the line at infinity of an embedding?

10. Adapt the solutions of Construction Problems 5.1 and 5.2 to E_2, by using lines parallel to a given line in addition to joins and intersections.

11. Give an interpretation, for a rectangle in E_2, of the paragraph following the statement of Corollary 8.2b.

12. Prove Theorem 10.5.

\#**13.** Let ABC be a triangle in E_2. Choose P on $A \oplus B$, and construct Q, R, P' so that $Q \in B \oplus C$, $R \in C \oplus A$, $P' \in A \oplus B$, and so that $P \oplus Q$, $Q \oplus R$, $R \oplus P'$ are respectively parallel to $C \oplus A$, $A \oplus B$, $B \oplus C$. Prove that the map $P \to P'$ is an involution, find its fixed points, and generalize this construction to $S_2(\mathsf{F})$.

\#**14.** A given line in E_2 intersects one pair of parallel sides of an unknown square in points A, A', the second pair in B, B', and one diagonal in C. Construct (in terms of joins, parallels, and intersections) the intersection of the given line and the second diagonal (see III, 8, Exercises 13, 14 and Corollary 8.1).

\#**15.** Prove the following theorem: Let $\mathscr{E}$ be a given embedding of E_2 in $S_2(\mathsf{R})$, and let (x, y) denote a given Cartesian coordinatization of E_2; then there exists a unique coordinatization of $S_2(\mathsf{R})$ in terms of which $\mathscr{E}$ is given by (10.1).

\#**16.** State and prove a converse of the theorem of Exercise 15.

11 Types of Collineations

We return to $S_2(\mathsf{F})$ to illustrate different types of collineations.

DEFINITION 11.1. A *harmonic homology* in $S_2(\mathsf{F})$ is the following point transformation: Let O be a given point, and let L be a given line, not incident to O; the transformation leaves O and the points of L fixed; any other point X is mapped onto X', the harmonic conjugate of X with respect to O and $X_1 = L \cap (O \oplus X)$ (Figure 11.1). The point O is called the *center*, and the line L the *axis*.

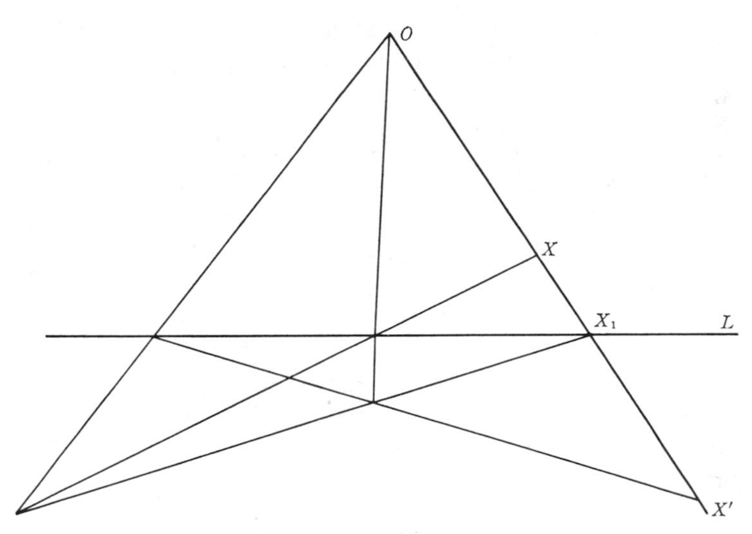

FIGURE 11.1

If we establish projective coordinates so that a representative of O is $(0, 0, 1)^T$, and the equation of L is $x_3 = 0$, the harmonic homology is given by the equations

$$(11.1) \qquad x_1' = x_1, \qquad x_2' = x_2, \qquad x_3' = -x_3.$$

Thus a harmonic homology is an involutory collineation.

LEMMA 11.1. *A collineation that interchanges two pairs of points (no three collinear) is involutory.*

Proof. Let $g \in G_8$ be defined by

$$gA = A', \qquad gA' = A, \qquad gB = B', \qquad gB' = B,$$

where A, B, A', B' are four points, no three collinear. Let $O = (A \oplus A') \cap (B \oplus B')$, and let L be the join of the remaining two diagonal points of the quadrangle $ABA'B'$. There exists a unique harmonic homology h with center O and axis L; furthermore (see Theorem 8.3a)

$$hA = A', \qquad hA' = A, \qquad hB = B', \qquad hB' = B.$$

Hence gh leaves the four vertices fixed, so that $gh = I$. Since h is involutory, $h = h^{-1}$, so that $gh = I$ implies $g = h$.

We have proved more.

THEOREM 11.1. *Harmonic homologies are the only involutory collineations in $S_2(\mathsf{F})$.*

From (11.1) we note that an embedding $\mathscr{E}$ of E_2 in $S_2(\mathsf{R})$ maps a point reflection in E_2 into a harmonic homology whose axis is the absolute line of the embedding; similarly $\mathscr{E}$ maps a line reflection into a harmonic homology with center on the absolute line.

In a harmonic homology we have (Figure 11.1)

$$(O\,X_1, X\,X') = -1,$$

where $X_1 = L \cap (O \oplus X)$. If $k \in \mathsf{F}$, $k \neq 0, 1$, we define a map g by the relations

$$\begin{gathered} gO = O; \qquad gX = X \quad \text{if} \quad X \in L; \\ gX \in O \oplus X_1, \quad (O\,X_1, X\,gX) = k \quad \text{if} \quad X \notin L. \end{gathered} \tag{11.2}$$

DEFINITION 11.2a. We call the map (11.2) a *homology* with characteristic k.

If coordinates are established as for (11.1), the homology (11.2) is given by

$$x_1' = x_1, \qquad x_2' = x_2, \qquad x_3' = kx_3. \tag{11.3}$$

Thus a homology is a collineation, and a homology with characteristic -1 is a harmonic homology. In any homology, every point on the axis and every line through the center are fixed.

A closely related class of collineations are the *elations*.

DEFINITION 11.2b. An *elation* in $S_2(\mathsf{F})$ is a collineation g with which are associated a line L and a point $O \in L$ such that

$$\begin{aligned} gX &= X \quad \text{for all } X \in L, \\ gl &= l \quad\ \ \text{for all lines incident to } O. \end{aligned}$$

The point and line are called the *center* and the *axis* of the elation.

Thus the center and axis of an elation are incident, whereas those of a homology are not.

Let us find a canonical representation of the elations with centers $A_1:(1,0,0)^T$ and axes $x_3 = 0$. We first note that $\mathbf{X}' = \mathbf{AX}$ leaves $(x_1, x_2, 0)^T$ fixed for all x_1, x_2 if and only if the elements a_{ij} of $\mathbf{A}$ satisfy

$$a_{12} = a_{21} = a_{31} = a_{32} = 0, \qquad a_{11} = a_{22}. \tag{11.4}$$

Requiring X, gX, and A_1 to be collinear imposes the further conditions

$$a_{11} = a_{33}, \qquad a_{23} = 0. \tag{11.5}$$

Hence the elations with centers $(1,0,0)^T$ and axes $x_3 = 0$ are given by

$$x_1' = x_1 + a_{13}x_3, \qquad x_2' = x_2, \qquad x_3' = x_3, \qquad a_{13} \neq 0. \tag{11.6}$$

It follows that under an embedding, a translation in E_2 corresponds to an elation with axis the absolute line of the embedding.

Homologies and elations constitute a class of collineations often called perspective collineations because they, unlike other collineations, can be expressed in three-space as the product of two planar perspectivities.†

Since $g \in G_8(\mathsf{F})$ is determined by the fate of four points (no three collinear), we can expect to find collineations that possess three independent fixed points. By taking these as the vertices of the reference triangle, we find that the matrix of the collineation is a diagonal matrix, and we obtain the canonical representation

$$x_1' = a_{11}x_1, \qquad x_2' = a_{22}x_2, \qquad x_3' = a_{33}x_3. \tag{11.7}$$

If each two of the coefficients are unequal, the number of fixed points is exactly three; otherwise (11.7) represents a homology or the identity.

Other types of collineations will occur to us if we attack directly the problem of finding the fixed points of a given collineation. If Y is a fixed point of a collineation g, with representation $\mathbf{X}' = \mathbf{AX}$, there exists $\lambda \in \mathsf{F}$ such that $\lambda\mathbf{Y} = \mathbf{AY}$, or

$$(\mathbf{A} - \lambda\mathbf{I})\mathbf{Y} = \mathbf{0}, \tag{11.8}$$

where $\mathbf{I}$ is the 3×3 unit matrix. The existence of fixed points implies that λ is a solution of

$$\det(\mathbf{A} - \lambda\mathbf{I}) = 0, \tag{11.9}$$

and conversely, when λ is a solution of (11.9), solutions of (11.8) exist.

The solutions of (11.9) are called the *characteristic* values (or eigenvalues) of $\mathbf{A}$. They are replaced by a proportional set when $\mathbf{A}$ is replaced by $\rho\mathbf{A}$, and they are unchanged when $\mathbf{A}$ is replaced by $\mathbf{B}^{-1}\mathbf{AB}$ (see III, 1, Exercise 11).

When λ_0 is a solution of (11.9), the rank of $\mathbf{A} - \lambda_0\mathbf{I}$ might be 2, 1, or 0; the set of fixed points would accordingly consist of just one point, a line

† See Veblen and Young, *op. cit.*, p. 72.

of points, or all the points of the plane. Thus the general collineation (11.7) with the a's all different yields three distinct characteristic values for each of which the rank of the characteristic matrix $\mathbf{A} - \lambda\mathbf{I}$ is 2. The homologies have one simple root for which the rank is 2 and one double root for which the rank is 1. The elation (11.6) and the identity both have one characteristic value of multiplicity three; the ranks of $\mathbf{A} - \lambda\mathbf{I}$ are 1 and 0 respectively. The reader should verify these assertions.

If the *characteristic polynomial*, det $(\mathbf{A} - \lambda\mathbf{I})$, is the product of three linear factors in F, two other possibilities occur. For example, the reader can verify that, if $a\lambda_1 \lambda_2(\lambda_1 - \lambda_2) \neq 0$, the matrix of the collineation

$$(11.10) \qquad x_1' = \lambda_1 x_1 + a x_2, \qquad x_2' = \lambda_1 x_2, \qquad x_3' = \lambda_2 x_3$$

has two characteristic values, one simple and one double, with characteristic rank equal to 2 for either value. Thus (11.10) has only two fixed points. Again, if $a_{12} a_{23} \neq 0$, the matrix of

$$(11.11) \quad x_1' = x_1 + a_{12} x_2 + a_{13} x_{13}, \quad x_2' = x_2 + a_{23} x_3, \quad x_3' = x_3$$

has one (triple) characteristic value, and the corresponding rank is 2. Thus (11.11) possesses exactly one fixed point when $a_{12} a_{23} \neq 0$.

If F is algebraically closed (for example, the complex field), it can be shown† that the six types of collineations already specified exhaust all possibilities. Otherwise, further types occur when the characteristic polynomial is not reducible. Thus, in $S_2(\mathsf{R})$, the collineation

$$(11.12) \qquad x_1' = a x_1 - b x_2, \qquad x_2' = b x_1 + a x_2, \qquad x_3' = x_3$$

has only one fixed point, whereas these equations represent, in $S_2(\mathsf{C})$, a collineation with three independent fixed points. Again, in $S_2(\mathsf{F}_7)$ (where coordinates are the residues mod 7), the equations

$$x_1' = x_2, \qquad x_2' = 2x_3, \qquad x_3' = x_1$$

represent a collineation with no fixed points.

The collineation $\mathbf{X}' = \mathbf{AX}$ has the representation (see (3.2)) $\mathbf{U}' = \mathbf{UA}^{-1}$ in terms of the associated line coordinates. If V is a fixed line, there exists $\mu \in \mathsf{F}$ so that $\mu\mathbf{V} = \mathbf{V}\mathbf{A}^{-1}$, or

$$(11.13) \qquad \mathbf{V}(\mathbf{A} - (1/\mu)\mathbf{I}) = \mathbf{0}.$$

Thus $\mu = 1/\lambda$, and each characteristic value determines a set of fixed points and a set of fixed lines, and these are dual sets.

A collineation, restricted to a fixed line, is a projectivity on the line. For example, an elation is the identity projectivity on the axis, and a parabolic

† See Veblen and Young, *op. cit.*, pp. 268–276; Hodge and Pedoe, *Methods of Algebraic Geometry*, Cambridge (England), 1947, pp. 322–357 treat the n-dimensional problem.

projectivity on any other fixed line; a similar result holds for pencils of lines with vertices fixed points. A homology restricted to a pencil with vertex on the axis is a projectivity with two fixed lines. We leave to the reader to examine the behavior of the different types of collineations on the fixed points and lines.

Although, as noted, there exist projective planes possessing collineations with no fixed points, $S_2(\mathsf{R})$ is not such a plane.

THEOREM 11.2. *A collineation in $S_2(\mathsf{R})$ leaves fixed at least one point, and at least one line.*

Proof. Since $\mathbf{A}$ is a 3×3 matrix, $\det(\mathbf{A} - \lambda\mathbf{I})$ is a cubic polynomial, with coefficients in R. Every such cubic has a zero, and hence (11.8) and (11.13) possess at least one solution $[\mathbf{Y}]$ and at least one solution $[\mathbf{V}]$ in Ω_3.

EXERCISES

1. Show that $x_1' = x_1, x_2' = x_2, x_3' = -2x_2 - x_3$ is a harmonic homology, and find its center and axis.

2. Show that $x_1' = x_1, x_2' = x_2, x_3' = x_1 - x_2 + x_3$ is an elation, and find its center and axis.

3. Find the fixed points and fixed lines of $x_1' = x_1$, $x_2' = 2x_1 - x_2, x_3' = -x_1 + 2x_2 + x_3$.

4. Find the fixed lines of (11.10) and (11.11).

5. Determine the type of projectivity induced by a collineation of type (11.10) on each of its fixed lines and at each of its fixed points.

6. Show that in $S_2(\mathsf{R})$, the collineations (11.12) possess one fixed line (not incident to the fixed point) and that the collineation, restricted to this line, is an elliptic projectivity.

7. Find all elations with given center and axis.

8. Prove that the set consisting of all elations having a given axis and the identity collineation is an Abelian group. Derive the dual result.

9. Prove that the product of two harmonic homologies with the same axis is an elation. Find its center and axis.

10. The map $x' = x + ky, y' = y$ of E_2 onto itself is a *shear*. What is its image under an embedding?

11. Prove that the set of all homologies with given center and axis (together with the identity) is an Abelian group.

#**12.** Show that in a finite projective plane with $p + 1$ points on a line there are $p - 2$ homologies with given axis and center.

#**13.** Prove that if $\mathbf{A}$ has three distinct characteristic values, the characteristic values of $\mathbf{A}^2$ are the squares of those of $\mathbf{A}$.

CHAPTER IV

Conics and Quadratic Forms

1 Curves in $S_2(\mathsf{R})$

In this chapter we shall be concerned with conics and quadratic forms; we begin this section with some general remarks about curves in $S_2(\mathsf{R})$, and we develop the idea that a curve is both a set of points and a set of lines. As in E_2, a curve (as a set of points) can be represented analytically in terms of a given coordinatization of $S_2(\mathsf{R})$ in two ways. We can regard it as the set of points whose coordinates annul a given function of the coordinates,

$$H(x_1, x_2, x_3) = 0. \tag{1.1}$$

For such a definition to be meaningful in $S_2(\mathsf{R})$, we must require that, for all $\rho \neq 0$, $H(x_1, x_2, x_3)$ and $H(\rho x_1, \rho x_2, \rho x_3)$ vanish simultaneously. When H is a polynomial, it will need to be a homogeneous polynomial.

Alternatively, we can define a (point) curve parametrically, that is, as the set of points whose coordinates are functions of a parameter t,

$$x_1 = f_1(t), \qquad x_2 = f_2(t), \qquad x_3 = f_3(t). \tag{1.2a}$$

We can write (1.2a) in matrix notation,

$$\mathbf{X} = \mathbf{F}(t), \qquad \text{where } \mathbf{F}(t) = (f_1(t), f_2(t), f_3(t))^T. \tag{1.2b}$$

But the function concept is too general to be useful here without some restrictions, and in $S_2(\mathsf{R})$ we shall require that the functions f_i of (1.2a, b) satisfy the following conditions:

(1.2c) They are real-valued functions defined over a common interval on the real axis; this interval may be finite or infinite, open or closed.

(1.2d) In this interval, they possess continuous derivatives of all orders.†

† For many purposes it would be sufficient to require the continuity of only a specific number of derivatives.

(1.2e) In this interval, the rank of the matrix $(\mathbf{F} \quad \mathbf{F}')$, where $\mathbf{F}' = d\mathbf{F}/dt = (df_1/dt, df_2/dt, df_3/dt)^T$, is 2.

Dually, if $\mathbf{\Phi}(t) = (\phi_1(t), \phi_2(t), \phi_3(t))$, and the functions ϕ_i satisfy conditions (1.2c, d, e), we say that the equations

$$\mathbf{U} = \mathbf{\Phi}(t) \tag{1.3}$$

represent a line curve.

We note that if $\rho(t)$ is a real-valued function of t with the same domain of definition as the functions f_i, possessing continuous derivatives of all orders, and not vanishing, then the curve (1.2) can be represented by the equations

$$x_i = \rho(t) f_i(t), \quad i = 1, 2, 3, \quad \text{or} \quad \mathbf{X} = \rho(t)\mathbf{F}(t). \tag{1.4}$$

If (1.2) represents a point rather than a curve, the functions $f_i(t)$ are proportional to constants,

$$f_i = \rho(t) c_i, \quad \text{that is,} \quad \mathbf{F} = \rho(t)\mathbf{C}, \tag{1.5}$$

where $\mathbf{C} \neq \mathbf{0}$; it follows by differentiation that the rank of $(\mathbf{F} \quad \mathbf{F}')$ is 1. Conversely, if the rank of $(\mathbf{F} \quad \mathbf{F}')$ is 1 throughout the domain of definition, there exists a function $\sigma(t)$ such that $df_i/dt = \sigma f_i$; by integration, we find that (1.5) holds. Thus condition (1.2e) guarantees that the locus of (1.2) does not consist of just one point.

We now define the *tangent line* at a point Y of a curve (1.2) to be the limit (if it exists) of the join of Y and Z, as Z approaches Y along the curve. If Y:$\mathbf{Y}$ and Z:$\mathbf{Z}$ correspond to parameter values t_0 and t respectively,

$$\mathbf{Y} = \mathbf{F}(t_0), \qquad \mathbf{Z} = \mathbf{F}(t),$$

$\mathbf{Z} - \mathbf{Y}$ and therefore also $(\mathbf{Z} - \mathbf{Y})/(t - t_0)$ represent a point of $Y \oplus Z$. From the differentiability of the functions $f_i(t)$, it follows that

$$\lim_{t \to t_0} \frac{\mathbf{Z} - \mathbf{Y}}{t - t_0} = \mathbf{F}'(t_0).$$

Let Y' denote the point with representative $\mathbf{F}'(t_0)$. Our earlier results on limits (see III, 7, Exercise 6) extended to continuous variables yield the conclusion that $\lim_{t \to t_0} (Y \oplus Z) = Y \oplus Y'$.

Thus we have proved that a (point) curve (1.2) in $S_2(R)$ possesses a tangent line at each of its points, and that the tangent line at a point Y is the join of Y and Y'. A representative $\mathbf{V} = (v_1, v_2, v_3)$ of the tangent line at Y is given by

$$v_1 = \begin{vmatrix} y_2 & y_2' \\ y_3 & y_3' \end{vmatrix}, \qquad v_2 = \begin{vmatrix} y_3 & y_3' \\ y_1 & y_1' \end{vmatrix}, \qquad v_3 = \begin{vmatrix} y_1 & y_1' \\ y_2 & y_2' \end{vmatrix}. \tag{1.6}$$

As t varies, Y varies over the curve, and V varies over the set of lines given by

$$(1.7)\quad u_1 = x_2 x_3' - x_3 x_2', \qquad u_2 = x_3 x_1' - x_1 x_3', \qquad u_3 = x_1 x_2' - x_2 x_1'.$$

Generally (1.7) represents a line curve; an exception occurs if (1.2) is a line, in which case the u's of (1.7) turn out to be proportional to constants. We leave to the reader the verification of this statement and also of the converse that if (1.7) fails to satisfy the three conditions (1.2c, d, e), the curve (1.2) is a line. Thus with a point curve (1.2), which is not a line, there is associated a line curve (1.7), the set of tangent lines.

Dually, we define *point of contact* on a line V of a line curve as the limit of the point of intersection of V and a line W as W approaches V through lines of the curve. Then with every line curve that is not a pencil, there is associated a point curve, the set of points of contact of the line curve.

If we start with a point curve and obtain its associated line curve, and then obtain the point curve associated with this line curve, what is the relation between this last point curve and the original point curve? We have the answer to this question in the following theorem.

THEOREM 1.1. *The points of contact of the line curve consisting of the tangent lines of a point curve $\mathscr{C}$ are the points of $\mathscr{C}$.*

Proof. Let the point curve $\mathscr{C}$ be given by equations (1.2). Then the tangent line U at a point X of this curve, the line joining X to the point $X'\colon(x_1', x_2', x_3')^T$, is given by (1.7). Since the point of contact of a line curve was defined as the dual of the tangent line of a point curve, it follows that the point of contact of the line curve (1.7) on a line U of this curve is the point of intersection of the line U and the line $U'\colon(u_1', u_2', u_3')$. We obtain the coordinates of the line U' by differentiating the determinants of (1.7):

$$(1.8)\qquad u_1' = \begin{vmatrix} x_2 & x_2'' \\ x_3 & x_3'' \end{vmatrix}, \qquad u_2' = \begin{vmatrix} x_3 & x_3'' \\ x_1 & x_1'' \end{vmatrix}, \qquad u_3' = \begin{vmatrix} x_1 & x_1'' \\ x_2 & x_2'' \end{vmatrix}.$$

Thus the line U' is the line joining X and X'', and since the lines U and U' are distinct, the intersection of U and U' is the point X. Since X was any point of the original curve $\mathscr{C}$, our theorem is proved.

Theorem 1.1 and its dual say that point curves and line curves are associated in pairs. We can think of a curve as consisting of both a set of points and a set of lines. Either set determines the other, so that it is immaterial whether we start with the point equations or the line equations of a curve.† It follows that the set of all curves (not lines, or pencils) is self-dual.

† One frequently speaks of a curve as the *envelope* of its tangent lines.

We can often obtain a single equation in the x's, such as (1.1), from (1.4). To do so, we first eliminate the factor of proportionality $\rho(t)$ to obtain $x_1/x_3 = f_1/f_3$, $x_2/x_3 = f_2/f_3$ (provided $f_3 \neq 0$); if the first of these determines t as a function of x_1/x_3, we can substitute this value of t in the second and obtain a homogeneous relation between the three x's. Conversely, if $H(x_1, x_2, x_3)$ is a homogeneous function, the conditions $H(x_1, x_2, x_3) = 0$, $x_3 \neq 0$ are equivalent to $H(x_1/x_3, x_2/x_3, 1) = 0$; if this equation determines x_2/x_3 as a function of x_1/x_3,

$$x_2/x_3 = \phi(x_1/x_3),$$

then $x_1 = t\rho(t)$, $x_2 = \rho(t)\phi(t)$, $x_3 = \rho(t)$, where ρ is a nonvanishing function of t, is a candidate for the representation (1.2). Whether conditions (1.2c, d, e) are satisfied will depend on the properties of $H(x_1, x_2, x_3)$.

We shall not seek conditions under which (1.1) and (1.2a) are equivalent. This question involves the implicit function theorem of analysis and a great deal more.† For example, in $S_2(R)$, the equation $x_1^2 + x_2^2 + x_3^2 = 0$ has no solution. Again, the equations $x_1 = \sin^2 t$, $x_2 = \cos^2 t$, $x_3 = 1$ represent points on one of the two segments determined by the points $(1, 0, 1)^T$ and $(0, 1, 1)^T$, that is, points on the line $x_1 + x_2 = x_3$; but this parametric representation does not cover the entire line.

Let us find the equation of the tangent line at a point Y of the curve (1.1) when we suppose that $H(x_1, x_2, x_3)$ is a homogeneous function possessing partial derivatives, and that the locus possesses a parametrization (1.2) so that $H(x_1(t), x_2(t), x_3(t)) = 0$. Then by differentiation with respect to t, we obtain

$$\frac{\partial H}{\partial x_1}\frac{dx_1}{dt} + \frac{\partial H}{\partial x_2}\frac{dx_2}{dt} + \frac{\partial H}{\partial x_3}\frac{dx_3}{dt} = 0.$$

This equation is valid for the point Y of the curve. It we write $\partial H/\partial y_i$ to denote $\partial H/\partial x_i$ evaluated at the point Y, and similarly for dy_i/dt, we have

$$\sum_{i=1}^{3} \frac{\partial H}{\partial y_i}\frac{dy_i}{dt} = 0. \tag{1.9}$$

By Euler's theorem on homogeneous functions,‡ we have

$$\frac{\partial H}{\partial x_1} x_1 + \frac{\partial H}{\partial x_2} x_2 + \frac{\partial H}{\partial x_3} x_3 = nH(x_1, x_2, x_3).$$

This equation is valid for all points X, and for a point Y of the curve, it becomes

$$\sum_{i=1}^{3} \frac{\partial H}{\partial y_i} y_i = 0. \tag{1.10}$$

† See John M. H. Olmsted, *Real Variables*, New York, Appleton-Century-Crofts, 1959, p. 419.

‡ See John M. H. Olmsted, *op. cit.*, p. 378.

Equation (1.9) says that the point Y' is incident to the line with coordinates $\partial H/\partial y_i$ $(i = 1, 2, 3)$; equation (1.10) says that the point Y is incident to this line. Therefore if Y and Y' are distinct, the line with representative

$$\left(\frac{\partial H}{\partial y_1}, \frac{\partial H}{\partial y_2}, \frac{\partial H}{\partial y_3}\right)$$

is the join of Y and Y'. By equations (1.6), this line is the tangent line at Y. We state this result in the following theorem and its dual:

THEOREM 1.2a. *If the curve* (1.2) *has the point equation* $H(x_1, x_2, x_3) = 0$, *then the coordinates of the tangent line at the point* Y *are* $\partial H/\partial y_i$ $(i = 1, 2, 3)$, *and the equation of this tangent line is*

$$\frac{\partial H}{\partial y_1} x_1 + \frac{\partial H}{\partial y_2} x_2 + \frac{\partial H}{\partial y_3} x_3 = 0. \tag{1.11}$$

THEOREM 1.2b. *Let the curve* (1.2) *have the line equation* $\Psi(u_1, u_2, u_3) = 0$. *Then the coordinates of the point of contact on the line* V *are* $\partial \Psi/\partial v_i$ $(i = 1, 2, 3)$, *and the equation of this point of contact is*

$$\sum_{i=1}^{3} \frac{\partial \Psi}{\partial v_i} u_i = 0. \tag{1.12}$$

Illustration 1. Let a curve $\mathscr{C}$ be given by the parametric line equations

$$u_1 = t, \qquad u_2 = t^3, \qquad u_3 = 1.$$

Then $\mathbf{U}' = (1, 3t^2, 0)$. The point of contact X, on U, is $U \cap U'$, so that

$$\mathbf{X} = (-3t^2, 1, 2t^3)^T.$$

These are parametric point equations of $\mathscr{C}$. The tangent line U of this curve at X is $U = X \oplus X'$. Since $\mathbf{X}' = (-6t, 0, 6t^2)^T$, $\mathbf{U} = (t, t^3, 1)$, as expected from the dual of Theorem 1.1.

We obtain a single line equation of $\mathscr{C}$ from the parametric representation given, by writing $u_1/u_3 = t$, $u_2/u_3 = t^3$, whence

$$\left(\frac{u_1}{u_3}\right)^3 = \frac{u_2}{u_3}, \quad \text{or} \quad u_1^3 - u_2 u_3^2 = 0.$$

We obtain a single equation of $\mathscr{C}$ from the parametric point equations by writing $x_1/x_2 = -3t^2$, $x_3/x_2 = 2t^3$, whence $4x_1^3 + 27x_3^2 x_2 = 0$.

We note that the line $(0, 1, 0)$ is not a line given by the parametric line equations, but is a line of the locus defined by the single line equation. If we introduce the factor of proportionality $1/t^3$ in the parametric line equation, then as $t \to \infty$, $U \to (0, 1, 0)$. A similar comment for the point $(0, 0, 1)$ applies to the point equations.

Illustration 2. Let the curve $\mathscr{C}$ be given by the equation

$$H = x_1^3 + x_2^3 + x_3^3 = 0.$$

Then

$$\frac{\partial H}{\partial x_1} = 3x_1^2, \qquad \frac{\partial H}{\partial x_2} = 3x_2^2, \qquad \frac{\partial H}{\partial x_3} = 3x_3^2,$$

and a representative of the tangent line U at a point X of the curve is

$$\mathbf{U} = (x_1^2, x_2^2, x_3^2).$$

Since X lies on the curve, the x's satisfy $H = 0$. Hence the line equation of $\mathscr{C}$ is

$$\pm u_1^{3/2} \pm u_2^{3/2} \pm u_3^{3/2} = 0,$$

or, after rationalizing,

$$u_1^6 + u_2^6 + u_3^6 - 2u_1^3 u_2^3 - 2u_1^3 u_3^3 - 2u_2^3 u_3^3 = 0.$$

From Illustration 2 we observe that the degrees of the point and line equations of an algebraic curve are not necessarily equal. We call the degree of the point equation of an irreducible algebraic curve the *order* of the curve, and the degree of the line equation the *class* of the curve. Thus the curve of Illustration 2 has order three and class six, that of Illustration 1 has order three and class three. We shall see later that an irreducible algebraic curve of order two has class two.

If the point equation of a curve has the form $y = f(x)$ in nonhomogenous coordinates (see III, (4.17)), we can find the equation of the tangent line at the point (x_0, y_0) by choosing a neighboring point $(x_0 + \Delta x, y_0 + \Delta y)$ and taking the limit of the line joining it to (x_0, y_0) as Δx approaches zero. We find that the equation of the tangent line at the point (x_0, y_0) has the familiar form

$$y - y_0 = \left.\frac{dy}{dx}\right|_{(x_0, y_0)} (x - x_0).$$

Dually, the equation of the point of contact on the line (u_0, v_0) of the curve with nonhomogeneous equation $v = \varphi(u)$ is

$$v - v_0 = \left.\frac{dv}{du}\right|_{(u_0, v_0)} (u - u_0).$$

EXERCISES

1. Find the line equation of the curve $x_1^4 - x_2 x_3^3 = 0$; from this line equation, find the point equation of the curve, and verify that it is the given equation.

2. Find the point equation of the curve $u_2 u_3^2 - u_1^3 - u_1 u_3^2 = 0$.

3. Find parametric line equations of the curve $\mathbf{X} = (\sin t, \cos t, e^t)^T$.

4. Show that the class and order of an algebraic curve are invariant under the group of collineations.

#**5.** Show directly that the line given by equation (1.11) is invariantly related to the curve (1.1) under the group of collineations.

#**6.** Prove: The curve $x_i = x_i(t)\ (i = 1, 2, 3)$ is a line (or a segment of a line) if and only if X, X', X'' are linearly dependent and X, X' are linearly independent.

7. Prove: If the coordinates u_i of the tangent line at a variable point X of a curve are proportional to constants, then the curve is a line.

8. Show that the curves $y = x^3$ and $y^2 = x^3$ are projectively equivalent, and find the cusp of the first.

2 Singular and Nonsingular Conics

In the last section, we defined point and line curves in $S_2(\mathsf{R})$; in this section we shall begin a more detailed study of curves of order two.

DEFINITION 2.1a. In $S_2(\mathsf{F})$ a point curve of order two, that is, a nonempty set of points whose coordinates satisfy a homogeneous quadratic equation

$$(2.1)\quad Q(x_1, x_2, x_3) = b_{11}x_1^2 + 2b_{12}x_1x_2 + b_{22}x_2^2 + 2b_{13}x_1x_3 + 2b_{23}x_2x_3 + b_{33}x_3^2 = 0,$$

is called a *point conic*.

In the complex field any homogeneous quadratic equation in three variables necessarily possesses solutions other than the trivial solution $(0, 0, 0)$. This is not the case for all fields; for example, the equation $x_1^2 + x_2^2 + x_3^2 = 0$ possesses no *real* solution other than $(0, 0, 0)$. Later (in Section 6) we shall consider such equations, but only those quadratic equations that possess nontrivial solutions in the given field represent a point conic in the sense of Definition 2.1a.

For the present, we shall consider conics in $S_2(\mathsf{R})$, and we shall understand that the b's in equation (2.1) are real numbers. Later in this section, we shall extend our results to $S_2(\mathsf{F})$.

The left side of equation (2.1), $Q = Q(x_1, x_2, x_3)$, is a *ternary quadratic form*, that is, a homogeneous polynomial of degree two in three variables. We can write the form Q more compactly if we introduce the symbols $b_{21} = b_{12}, b_{31} = b_{13}, b_{32} = b_{23}$. Then

$$(2.2)\qquad Q = \sum_{i,j=1}^{3} b_{ij}x_ix_j, \qquad b_{ij} = b_{ji}.$$

For many purposes, it is convenient to write the form Q in matrix notation†

$$Q = \mathbf{X}^T\mathbf{B}\mathbf{X}, \qquad \mathbf{B} = (b_{ij}), \quad \mathbf{X} = (x_1, x_2, x_3)^T. \tag{2.3}$$

In the expression (2.3), the matrix $\mathbf{B}$ is symmetric, that is, $b_{ij} = b_{ji}$, or $\mathbf{B} = \mathbf{B}^T$. Clearly the expression $\mathbf{X}^T\mathbf{C}\mathbf{X}$ is a ternary quadratic form, even if $\mathbf{C}$ is not symmetric. We can however replace $\mathbf{C}$ by the symmetric matrix $\frac{1}{2}(\mathbf{C} + \mathbf{C}^T)$ without changing the quadratic form.

DEFINITION 2.2. The symmetric matrix $\mathbf{B}$ is called the *matrix* of the quadratic form $Q = \mathbf{X}^T\mathbf{B}\mathbf{X}$, the determinant of this matrix, det $\mathbf{B}$, is called the *discriminant* or the *determinant* of the form Q, and the rank of the matrix $\mathbf{B}$, the *rank* of the form Q.

The equations $Q = 0$ and $\rho Q = 0$ $(\rho \neq 0)$ clearly represent the same point conic. If the matrix of Q is $\mathbf{B}$, the matrix of ρQ is $\rho\mathbf{B}$; since $\det \rho\mathbf{B} = \rho^3 \det \mathbf{B}$, in $S_2(\mathsf{R})$ a nonvanishing discriminant can, by a suitable choice of ρ, be made to take on any nonzero value. As with binary quadratic forms (see II, 5), the forms proportional to a given form constitute a geometric entity; for if $g \in G_8$ and $\mathbf{A}$ is a representative matrix of g, we can choose representatives of $X' = gX$ to satisfy $\mathbf{X}' = \mathbf{A}\mathbf{X}$. Then we have

$$\mathbf{X} = \mathbf{A}^{-1}\mathbf{X}', \qquad \mathbf{X}^T = \mathbf{X}'^T\mathbf{A}^{-T},$$

so that $\mathbf{X}^T\mathbf{B}\mathbf{X}$ remains a quadratic form,

$$\mathbf{X}^T\mathbf{B}\mathbf{X} = \mathbf{X}'^T\mathbf{B}'\mathbf{X}',$$

with matrix $\mathbf{B}'$ given by

$$\mathbf{B}' = \mathbf{A}^{-T}\mathbf{B}\mathbf{A}^{-1}. \tag{2.4}$$

If we now replace the representatives $\mathbf{X}, \mathbf{X}', \mathbf{A}$ by other representatives of their respective classes $[\mathbf{X}]$, $[\mathbf{X}']$, $[\mathbf{A}]$, and if we denote by $[\mathbf{X}^T\mathbf{B}\mathbf{X}]$ the class of forms proportional to $\mathbf{X}^T\mathbf{B}\mathbf{X}$,

$$[\mathbf{X}^T\mathbf{B}\mathbf{X}] = \{\rho\mathbf{X}^T\mathbf{B}\mathbf{X} \mid \rho \in \mathsf{F}, \rho \neq 0\},$$

it follows that we can extend the domain of definition of g to include classes $[\mathbf{X}^T\mathbf{B}\mathbf{X}]$, and that

$$g[\mathbf{X}^T\mathbf{B}\mathbf{X}] = [\mathbf{X}^T\mathbf{B}'\mathbf{X}], \tag{2.5a}$$

where

$$[\mathbf{B}'] = [\mathbf{A}^{-T}\mathbf{B}\mathbf{A}^{-1}]. \tag{2.5b}$$

THEOREM 2.1. *The rank of a quadratic form $Q = \mathbf{X}^T\mathbf{B}\mathbf{X}$ is a projective invariant of the conic $Q = 0$, or of the class $[Q]$.*

† We are identifying square matrices of order 1 with their elements, as we did earlier (see footnote, page 104).

Proof. Clearly the rank is independent of the choice of representatives; representatives **B**, **B′** satisfying (2.5b) have equal rank by (I, 5, Exercise 22).

When $Q = 0$ is the equation of a conic, we shall frequently denote the conic by $\mathscr{C}(Q)$, or if no ambiguity arises, simply by $\mathscr{C}$.

DEFINITION 2.3. A form Q, or the point conic $\mathscr{C}(Q)$ is *singular* if the discriminant of Q is zero, that is, if the rank of the matrix of Q is less than 3. If the discriminant of Q is not zero, the form and the point conic are *nonsingular*.

We can dualize Definition (2.1a) to obtain the definition of a line conic.

DEFINITION 2.1b. A line curve of class two, that is, the (nonempty) set of lines whose coordinates satisfy a homogeneous quadratic equation

$$\begin{aligned}(2.6)\quad Q(u_1, u_2, u_3) = c_{11}u_1^2 + 2c_{12}u_1u_2 + c_{22}u_2^2 \\ + 2c_{13}u_1u_3 + 2c_{23}u_2u_3 + c_{33}u_3^2 = 0,\end{aligned}$$

is called a *line conic*.

The quadratic form Q of equation (2.6) can be written

$$Q = \sum_{i,j=1}^{3} c_{ij}u_iu_j, \qquad c_{ij} = c_{ji},$$

or in matrix notation, $Q = \mathbf{UCU}^T$, where $\mathbf{C} = (c_{ij})$. By the dual of Definition 2.3, the line conic (2.6) is singular or nonsingular according as det $\mathbf{C}$ is or is not equal to zero.

THEOREM 2.2. *A nonsingular point conic* $\mathbf{X}^T\mathbf{BX} = 0$ *has a tangent at every point. The equation of the tangent at a point* Y *of the conic is*

$$(2.7)\qquad \mathbf{Y}^T\mathbf{BX} = 0.$$

Proof. By Theorem 1.2a, coordinates of the tangent line U at Y are $\partial Q/\partial y_i$, $i = 1, 2, 3$. From (2.1) we can choose the representative given by

$$(2.8)\qquad u_i = \sum_{j=1}^{3} b_{ij}y_j, \quad i = 1, 2, 3, \qquad \text{or} \qquad \mathbf{U} = \mathbf{Y}^T\mathbf{B},$$

so that the equation of the tangent line at Y is

$$(2.9)\qquad \sum_{i,j=1}^{3} b_{ij}y_ix_j = 0, \quad \text{or} \quad \mathbf{Y}^T\mathbf{BX} = 0.$$

The coordinates u_i, given by (2.8) cannot all be zero, since the conic is nonsingular.

THEOREM 2.3. *The line equation of the nonsingular point conic* $\mathbf{X}^T\mathbf{BX} = 0$ *is*

$$(2.10)\qquad \mathbf{UB}^{-1}\mathbf{U}^T = 0.$$

Proof. The tangent line U at a point X of the conic is, from (2.8),

$$\mathbf{U} = \mathbf{X}^T\mathbf{B}, \tag{2.11}$$

whence

$$\mathbf{X}^T = \mathbf{U}\mathbf{B}^{-1} \quad \text{and} \quad \mathbf{X} = \mathbf{B}^{-1}\mathbf{U}^T. \tag{2.12}$$

Eliminating $\mathbf{X}$ from the equation of the point conic, we obtain equation (2.10). Thus every tangent line to the point conic has representatives satisfying this equation. Conversely, if a line U is given with representatives satisfying (2.10), we can determine a point X by (2.12); then $\mathbf{X}$ satisfies $\mathbf{X}^T\mathbf{B}\mathbf{X} = 0$, so that X is a point of the point conic, and from Theorem 2.2 the given line is the tangent line at X.

Thus equation (2.10) represents the set of tangents to the nonsingular point conic $\mathbf{X}^T\mathbf{B}\mathbf{X} = 0$. By Definition 2.1b, it represents a line conic, so that the set of tangents to every nonsingular point conic is a line conic. Moreover, since (2.10) represents all nonsingular line conics (as $\mathbf{B}$ varies), every nonsingular line conic is the set of tangents to a nonsingular point conic. We shall henceforth use the term *nonsingular conic* to mean both the set of points of the point conic and the set of lines of the corresponding line conic. We can summarize the results of the preceding discussion in the following theorem.

THEOREM 2.4. *The set of nonsingular conics is self-dual.*

Let us now turn our attention to singular conics. Let

$$\mathbf{X}^T\mathbf{B}\mathbf{X} = 0, \qquad \det \mathbf{B} = 0, \tag{2.13}$$

be a singular point conic. Then (see I, 5, Exercise 12) the matrix equation

$$\mathbf{B}\mathbf{X} = \mathbf{0} \qquad (\mathbf{0} \text{ is the } 3 \times 1 \text{ zero matrix}) \tag{2.14}$$

has a solution $\mathbf{Y} \neq \mathbf{0}$. Under a collineation the conic (2.13) is transformed into the conic

$$\mathbf{X}^T\mathbf{B}'\mathbf{X} = 0,$$

where, by (2.5),

$$\mathbf{B}' = \mathbf{A}^{-T}\mathbf{B}\mathbf{A}^{-1}. \tag{2.15}$$

Then the equation

$$\mathbf{B}'\mathbf{X} = \mathbf{0} \tag{2.16}$$

also has a solution. If $\mathbf{Y}$ is a solution of (2.14), $\mathbf{AY}$ is a solution of (2.16), so that the solutions of (2.14) are invariantly related to the conic (2.13). This argument justifies the following definition.

DEFINITION 2.4. A point Y is called a *vertex* (or singular point) of the point conic $\mathbf{X}^T\mathbf{B}\mathbf{X} = 0$ if $\mathbf{B}\mathbf{Y} = 0$.

Clearly a vertex of a conic is a point of the conic.

THEOREM 2.5. *A point conic that has a vertex is singular, and a singular conic always has at least one vertex.*

We leave the proof to the reader.

It can be seen that if Y is a point of (2.13), but not a vertex, the tangent line at Y exists and is given by (2.7) If Y is a vertex, (2.7) is satisfied by every point X in the plane.

Let us now consider the intersections of a line with a point conic, singular or nonsingular. Let the conic be given by $\mathbf{X}^T\mathbf{B}\mathbf{X} = 0$, and let Y and Z be two points of the given line. Then any point of the line can be represented by $\lambda\mathbf{Y} + \mu\mathbf{Z}$. This point lies on the conic if and only if

$$(\lambda\mathbf{Y} + \mu\mathbf{Z})^T\mathbf{B}(\lambda\mathbf{Y} + \mu\mathbf{Z}) = 0. \tag{2.17}$$

Since a square matrix of order one is equal to its transpose, $\mathbf{Z}^T\mathbf{B}\mathbf{Y} = \mathbf{Y}^T\mathbf{B}\mathbf{Z}$, and equation (2.17) can be written in the form

$$\lambda^2\mathbf{Y}^T\mathbf{B}\mathbf{Y} + 2\lambda\mu\mathbf{Y}^T\mathbf{B}\mathbf{Z} + \mu^2\mathbf{Z}^T\mathbf{B}\mathbf{Z} = 0. \tag{2.18}$$

If the coefficients are not all zero, (2.18) is a homogeneous quadratic equation in λ, μ; it determines at most two points of intersection of the line and the conic. If the coefficients of (2.18) are all zero, then every pair of values (λ, μ) satisfies the equation and every point of the line lies on the conic. Then we say that the conic *contains* the line.

THEOREM 2.6. *A point conic that contains a line is singular.*

In order to illustrate different methods of proof, we shall give two independent proofs of this theorem.

First Proof. Let the point conic be given by $\mathbf{X}^T\mathbf{B}\mathbf{X} = 0$, and let V be the line contained in it. Let Y be a given point of V, and let X be a variable point of V. Then $\lambda\mathbf{Y} + \mu\mathbf{X}$ is a point of V, and since it lies on the conic, we have

$$\lambda^2\mathbf{Y}^T\mathbf{B}\mathbf{Y} + 2\lambda\mu\mathbf{Y}^T\mathbf{B}\mathbf{X} + \mu^2\mathbf{X}^T\mathbf{B}\mathbf{X} = 0.$$

Since this equation is satisfied for all values of λ, μ, each of its coefficients must be zero; in particular,

$$\mathbf{Y}^T\mathbf{B}\mathbf{X} = 0. \tag{2.19}$$

If $\mathbf{B}\mathbf{Y} = \mathbf{0}$, then Y is a vertex, and by Theorem 2.5 the conic is singular. If $\mathbf{B}\mathbf{Y} \neq \mathbf{0}$, then (2.19) is the equation of V, and

$$\mathbf{V}^T = \rho\mathbf{B}\mathbf{Y}, \qquad \rho \neq 0. \tag{2.20}$$

Now let Z be a second point of V distinct from Y, and by a precisely similar argument, either Z is a vertex or

$$\mathbf{V}^T = \sigma \mathbf{B} \mathbf{Z}, \qquad \sigma \neq 0. \tag{2.21}$$

Subtracting (2.21) from (2.20), we obtain

$$\mathbf{B}(\rho \mathbf{Y} - \sigma \mathbf{Z}) = 0.$$

We can conclude that at least one of $\mathbf{Y}$, $\mathbf{Z}$, $\rho \mathbf{Y} - \sigma \mathbf{Z}$ represents a vertex of the conic, and the conic is singular.

Second Proof. Let us choose a coordinate system so that the equation of the given line is $x_3 = 0$, and let the equation of the conic be given by (2.1). Since every point of $x_3 = 0$ is a point of the conic, the equation

$$b_{11} x_1^2 + 2b_{12} x_1 x_2 + b_{22} x_2^2 = 0$$

holds for all x_1, x_2. Then

$$b_{11} = b_{12} = b_{22} = 0.$$

The discriminant of Q is

$$\begin{vmatrix} 0 & 0 & b_{13} \\ 0 & 0 & b_{23} \\ b_{13} & b_{23} & b_{33} \end{vmatrix}.$$

Since this determinant equals zero, the conic is singular.

THEOREM 2.7. *A tangent line of a nonsingular conic intersects the conic in just one point, the point of contact. Conversely, if a line intersects a nonsingular conic in just one point, it is the tangent line to the conic at that point.*

Proof. Let the conic be given by $\mathbf{X}^T \mathbf{B} \mathbf{X} = 0$, and let Y be a point of the conic. By Theorem 2.2 the tangent line at Y has the equation $\mathbf{Y}^T \mathbf{B} \mathbf{X} = 0$. Let Z be a point, not Y, of the tangent line at Y. Then $\lambda \mathbf{Y} + \mu \mathbf{Z}$, a point of the tangent, lies on the conic if and only if (2.18) is satisfied. Since Y is a point of the conic, $\mathbf{Y}^T \mathbf{B} \mathbf{Y} = 0$, and since Z is a point of the tangent line, $\mathbf{Y}^T \mathbf{B} \mathbf{Z} = 0$, so that the first two coefficients of (2.18) both vanish. If the third coefficient also vanished, then the tangent line would be contained in the conic, and by Theorem 2.6 the conic would be singular, contrary to hypothesis. Therefore $\mathbf{Z}^T \mathbf{B} \mathbf{Z} \neq 0$, and the tangent line at Y intersects the conic only in the point Y. Conversely, let us suppose that a line intersects a nonsingular conic in just one point; let Y be that point, and let Z be any other point on the line. Then equation (2.18) can have only the solution $\mu = 0$, and this requires that $\mathbf{Y}^T \mathbf{B} \mathbf{Z} = 0$. But this says that Z lies on the tangent line at Y, and therefore the given line is the tangent line of the conic at Y.

THEOREM 2.8. *A line joining any point of a point conic to a vertex is contained in the conic, and conversely, a point of the conic is a vertex if the line joining it to any other point of the conic is contained in the conic.*

Proof. Let the point conic be given by $\mathbf{X}^T\mathbf{B}\mathbf{X} = 0$, let Y be a vertex, and let Z be any other point of the conic. Then $Y \oplus Z$ is contained in the conic if all the coefficients of (2.18) vanish. This is easily seen to be the case, since Y and Z are both points of the conic and $\mathbf{BY} = 0$. Conversely, let us suppose that a point Y of the conic has the property that every line joining it to a point of the conic is contained in the conic. Let Z be any point of the plane. Then the line joining Y and Z either is contained in the conic, or it intersects the conic only in the point Y. In the first case all the coefficients of (2.18) vanish; in the second case the first two coefficients vanish. In either case, $\mathbf{Z}^T\mathbf{B}\mathbf{Y} = 0$. Since this equation is valid for every point Z in the plane, $\mathbf{BY} = \mathbf{0}$, and Y is a vertex.

We close this section with a discussion of conics in a projective plane over an arbitrary field. In $S_2(\mathsf{F})$ a definition of tangent lines that depends on the concept of limit is not possible. Theorem 2.7, however, establishes a characterizing property of tangent lines to a nonsingular conic in $S_2(\mathsf{R})$, and this property has meaning in $S_2(\mathsf{F})$. The proof of Theorem 2.7 shows that with each point Y of a nonsingular conic $\mathbf{X}^T\mathbf{B}\mathbf{X} = 0$, there is associated a unique line whose only intersection with the conic is the point Y, and that the equation of this line is $\mathbf{Y}^T\mathbf{B}\mathbf{X} = 0$. We can then make the following definition which is consistent in $S_2(\mathsf{R})$ with the definition we have been using.

DEFINITION 2.5. In $S_2(\mathsf{F})$ a *tangent line* to a nonsingular conic is a line that intersects the conic in just one point; the tangent line to a singular conic $\mathbf{X}^T\mathbf{B}\mathbf{X} = 0$, $\det \mathbf{B} = 0$, at a point Y that is not a vertex, is the locus of the equation $\mathbf{Y}^T\mathbf{B}\mathbf{X} = 0$.

We do not define the tangent line at a vertex. We can dualize Definition 2.5 to obtain the definition of the point of contact of a line conic. With these definitions the reader can verify (making such modifications in the proofs as are necessary) that all of the theorems stated in this section are valid in $S_2(\mathsf{F})$.

EXERCISES

Unless otherwise specified, the following exercises refer to $S_2(\mathsf{R})$.

1. Show that the point conics

(a) $x_1^2 - 2x_1x_2 + 4x_1x_3 - 8x_2^2 + 2x_2x_3 + 3x_3^2 = 0$,

(b) $x_1^2 + x_2^2 + x_3^2 - 2x_1x_2 - 2x_1x_3 + 2x_2x_3 = 0$,

are singular, and find their vertices. ANS. (a) $(-5, 1, 3)$.

2. By means of Theorem 2.8, factor the quadratic forms of Exercise 1.

3. Show that each of the following line conics is singular, and determine their singular lines:

(a) $u_1^2 - u_1 u_2 = 0$, ANS. $(0, 0, 1)$.

(b) $(u_1 + u_2)^2 + (u_1 - 3u_3)^2 = 0$, ANS. $(3, -3, 1)$.

4. Show that the conic $x_1^2 - 2x_1 x_2 + x_2^2 - 2x_1 x_3 = 0$ is nonsingular, and find its line equation.

ANS. $u_2^2 - 2u_1 u_3 - 2u_2 u_3 = 0$.

5. Show that the conic $u_1^2 - 2u_1 u_2 - 4u_1 u_3 + u_2^2 + 2u_2 u_3 - 5u_3^2 = 0$ is nonsingular, and find its point equation.

ANS. $6x_1^2 + 14x_1 x_2 - 2x_1 x_3 + 9x_2^2 - 2x_2 x_3 = 0$.

6. Is the line $x_1 - x_2 + x_3 = 0$ tangent to the conic

$$2u_1^2 + 4u_1 u_3 - 5u_2^2 + u_2 u_3 = 0?$$

7. Find the envelope of the family of lines $tx_1 + t^2 x_2 + (3t^2 - 1)x_3 = 0$.

ANS. $x_1^2 + 4x_2 x_3 + 12x_3^2 = 0$.

8. Find the equations of the tangents to the conic of Exercise 4 from the point $(1, 1, -2)^T$.

ANS. $2x_2 + x_3 = 0$, $4x_1 - 2x_2 + x_3 = 0$.

9. Find the equation of the lines from the point $(2, 0, 1)^T$ tangent to the conic $u_1^2 + u_2^2 - u_3^2 = 0$.

ANS. $x_1 \pm \sqrt{3}\, x_2 - 2x_3 = 0$.

10. Find a necessary and sufficient condition on the elements of **B** that A_i (the ith vertex of the coordinate triangle) lie on the conic $\mathbf{X}^T\mathbf{B}\mathbf{X} = 0$.

11. Find a necessary and sufficient condition on the elements of **B** that $x_i = 0$ be tangent to the conic $\mathbf{X}^T\mathbf{B}\mathbf{X} = 0$.

#**12.** Let Y be a fixed point, and $\mathbf{X}^T\mathbf{B}\mathbf{X} = 0$ a given conic. Prove that the locus of the equation

$$(\mathbf{X}^T\mathbf{B}\mathbf{X})(\mathbf{Y}^T\mathbf{B}\mathbf{Y}) - (\mathbf{Y}^T\mathbf{B}\mathbf{X})^2 = 0$$

is invariantly related to the given conic under the group $G_8(\mathsf{F})$.

#**13.** Prove that in $S_2(\mathsf{C})$ the locus of Exercise 12 represents, when $\mathbf{X}^T\mathbf{B}\mathbf{X} = 0$ is nonsingular, the tangent lines from Y.

#**14.** State the dual of the result of Exercise 13.

15. State the duals of Theorems 2.6, 2.7, and 2.8, and of Definition 2.5.

#**16.** Find all points, in $S_2(\mathsf{F}_3)$, of the conics:

(a) $x_1^2 + x_2^2 + x_3^2 = 0$, (b) $x_1^2 + x_1 x_2 + x_2^2 + x_3^2 = 0$,
(c) $x_1^2 + x_1 x_2 + x_2^2 + 2x_3^2 = 0$.

Which of these conics is singular? (Recall that in F_3 coordinates are the residues modulo 3.)

3 Canonical Equations of Conics

In this section, we shall derive equations of nonsingular and singular conics in special coordinate systems and thereby classify them. Unless otherwise specified, we understand that we are considering conics in $S_2(\mathsf{F})$.

THEOREM 3.1. *The points of a nonsingular conic can be put in one-to-one correspondence with the points of a line.*

Proof. Let Y be a point of the conic, and let L be any line not incident to Y. We consider the pencil of lines with vertex Y. Let a line of this pencil, not tangent to the conic at Y, intersect the conic in a point Z and the line L in a point Z'. If we make Z' correspond to Z, and if to Y we make correspond the point in which the tangent at Y intersects L, we have established a correspondence which is one-to-one without exception.

If F is a finite field, a nonsingular conic in $S_2(\mathsf{F})$ contains exactly as many points as does a line in $S_2(\mathsf{F})$.

THEOREM 3.2. *A given nonsingular conic has the equation*

$$x_1 x_3 - x_2^2 = 0 \tag{3.1}$$

in a suitably chosen projective coordinate system.

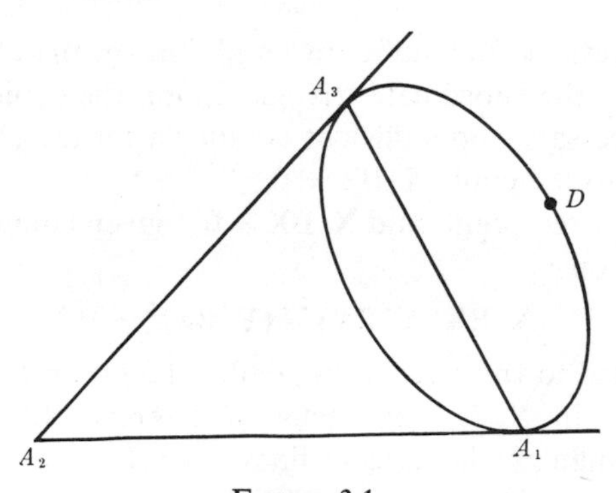

FIGURE 3.1

Proof. From the preceding theorem, every nonsingular conic contains at least three points. Let us introduce coordinates so that one of these points is the unit point D, and two others are the vertices A_1, A_3 of the reference triangle. We choose as the vertex A_2 of this triangle the point of intersection of the tangents at A_1 and A_3. We now show that we have enough data to determine the ratios of the coefficients b_{ij}. Since the tangents at the points $(1, 0, 0)^T$ and $(0, 0, 1)^T$ are the lines $(0, 0, 1)$ (that is, $x_3 = 0$) and $(1, 0, 0)$ $(x_1 = 0)$, respectively, we have from (2.8) that

$$(0, 0, 1) = (1, 0, 0)\mathbf{B}, \qquad (1, 0, 0) = (0, 0, 1)\mathbf{B}.$$

Expanding the matrix products on the right side of each of these equations, we find that $b_{11} = b_{12} = b_{23} = b_{33} = 0$. Since the unit point lies on the conic, $2b_{13} + b_{22} = 0$. Since the conic is nonsingular, $b_{22} \neq 0$, and the equation of the conic is given by (3.1).

THEOREM 3.3. *Two nonsingular conics are projectively equivalent.*

Proof. If we reinterpret Theorem 3.2 in terms of point transformations, we have the result that there exists a collineation that maps a given nonsingular conic onto the conic $x_1 x_3 - x_2^2 = 0$. If $\mathbf{X}^T\mathbf{B}\mathbf{X} = 0$, $\mathbf{X}^T\mathbf{C}\mathbf{X} = 0$ are two given conics, and if g_1, g_2 are collineations that map $\mathbf{X}^T\mathbf{B}\mathbf{X} = 0$, $\mathbf{X}^T\mathbf{C}\mathbf{X} = 0$, respectively, onto the conic $x_1 x_3 - x_2^2 = 0$, the map $g_2^{-1} g_1$ is clearly a collineation that maps $\mathbf{X}^T\mathbf{B}\mathbf{X} = 0$ onto $\mathbf{X}^T\mathbf{C}\mathbf{X} = 0$.

Theorems 3.1 and 3.2 suggest a coordinatization of the points of a nonsingular conic.

THEOREM 3.4. *The equations*

$$[x_1, x_2, x_3] = [t_1^2, t_1 t_2, t_2^2] \tag{3.2}$$

define a one-to-one map from Ω_2 *onto the conic* (3.1).

We leave the proof to the reader. We note that (3.2) can be interpreted as a one-to-one map from a line with projective coordinates $[t_1, t_2]^T$ onto the conic.

THEOREM 3.5. *In each projective coordinate system a nonsingular conic possesses a parametric representation*

$$[\mathbf{X}] = [\mathbf{A}\mathbf{T}], \qquad \textit{where } \mathbf{T} = (t_1^2, t_1 t_2, t_2^2)^T, \quad \det \mathbf{A} \neq 0; \tag{3.3}$$

conversely, conditions (3.3) *represent a nonsingular conic.*

Proof. The coordinate transformation $\mathbf{X}' = \mathbf{A}\mathbf{X}$ applied to the conic (3.1) with parametric representation (3.2) yields $\mathbf{X}' = \mathbf{A}\mathbf{T}$. Conversely, the coordinate transformation

$$\mathbf{X}' = \mathbf{A}^{-1}\mathbf{X}, \qquad \det \mathbf{A}^{-1} \neq 0, \tag{3.4}$$

reduces (3.3) to

$$x_1' = t_1^2, \qquad x_2' = t_1 t_2, \qquad x_3' = t_2^2, \tag{3.5}$$

and therefore (3.3) represents a nonsingular conic.

Thus we have in (3.3) a one-to-one map from Ω_2 onto the point conic. We call this map a *projective coordinatization* of the conic, and we call the elements t_1, t_2 of a representative element (t_1, t_2) of $[t_1, t_2]$ *projective coordinates* or *parameters*. The reason for this terminology will become apparent in Section 9 when we show that a conic in $S_2(\mathsf{F})$ possesses the inner structure of an $S_1(\mathsf{F})$. Here we merely note that, just as with projective coordinates in $S_1(\mathsf{F})$, we may replace $[t_1, t_2]$ by a nonhomogeneous coordinate $t = t_1/t_2$ and regard $t = \infty$ as the point $t_2 = 0$ of the conic.

THEOREM 3.6. *The tangent line to the conic* (3.2) *at the point with parametric values* (t_1, t_2) *is*

$$u_1 = t_2^2, \qquad u_2 = -2t_1 t_2, \qquad u_3 = t_1^2. \tag{3.6}$$

We leave the proof to the reader.

Equations (3.6) are parametric line equations of the conic (3.2) or (3.1).

We now turn our attention to singular conics.

THEOREM 3.7. *A singular point conic belongs to one of the following two types:*

(a) *those that have just one vertex* (*conics of rank* 2);

(b) *those that contain a line every point of which is a vertex* (*conics of rank* 1).

The theorem follows immediately from Definition 2.4 and from (I, Theorem 5.3) for $n = 3$.

THEOREM 3.8. *A given singular point conic of rank* 1 *has the equation*

$$x_1^2 = 0 \tag{3.7}$$

in a suitably chosen projective coordinate system.

Proof. From the preceding theorem, a singular conic of rank 1 contains a line every point of which is a vertex. We choose a coordinate system so that this line is the side $x_1 = 0$ of the coordinate triangle. In particular, the points $(0, 0, 1)^T$ and $(0, 1, 0)^T$ are vertices, and from

$$\mathbf{B}\begin{pmatrix}0\\0\\1\end{pmatrix} = \mathbf{0}, \qquad \mathbf{B}\begin{pmatrix}0\\1\\0\end{pmatrix} = \mathbf{0},$$

we find that $b_{13} = b_{23} = b_{33} = b_{12} = b_{22} = 0$. All the elements of $\mathbf{B}$, except b_{11}, vanish, and the equation of the conic is given by (3.7).

Thus a singular point conic of rank 1 always consists of one line every point of which is a vertex.

THEOREM 3.9. *A given singular point conic of rank* 2 *has an equation of the form*

$$(3.8) \qquad x_1^2 + dx_2^2 = 0, \qquad d \in \mathsf{F}, \quad d \neq 0,$$

in a suitably chosen projective coordinate system.

Proof. We first choose any coordinate system in which $A_3{:}(0, 0, 1)^T$ is the vertex of the conic. Since $\mathbf{B}(0, 0, 1)^T = \mathbf{0}$, we find that $b_{13} = b_{23} = b_{33} = 0$. Hence the matrix $\mathbf{B}$ has the form

$$\mathbf{B} = \begin{pmatrix} b_{11} & b_{12} & 0 \\ b_{12} & b_{22} & 0 \\ 0 & 0 & 0 \end{pmatrix}.$$

Since the rank of $\mathbf{B}$ is 2, $b_{11} b_{22} - b_{12}^2 \neq 0$, and the conic has the equation

$$(3.9) \qquad b_{11} x_1^2 + 2b_{12} x_1 x_2 + b_{22} x_2^2 = 0, \qquad \begin{vmatrix} b_{11} & b_{12} \\ b_{12} & b_{22} \end{vmatrix} \neq 0.$$

The coordinate transformation employed in the reduction of binary quadratic forms (page 87) becomes, when $x_3' = x_3$ is adjoined, a coordinate transformation in $S_2(\mathsf{F})$. If we apply this transformation (which leaves A_3 unchanged) to the conic (3.9), we obtain (3.8).

The canonical equation (3.8) for a point conic of rank 2 contains the element d of the ground field F. If $-d$ is a square, that is, if there exists an element α in F such that $\alpha^2 = -d$, the further transformation $x_1' = x_1$, $x_2' = \alpha x_2$, $x_3' = x_3$ reduces (3.8) to

$$(3.10) \qquad x_1^2 - x_2^2 = 0,$$

and the conic consists of two distinct lines that intersect in the vertex. In some fields, for example, the complex field, every element is a square; in such fields, every singular point conic of rank 2 consists of two distinct lines. If $-d$ is not a square, equation (3.8) is not satisfied for any values of x_1, x_2 except $x_1 = x_2 = 0$, and the only point on the conic is the vertex.

We summarize these results in the following theorems.

THEOREM 3.10. *In $S_2(\mathsf{F})$ a point conic of rank* 2 *either consists of two distinct lines (a_1, a_2, a_3), (b_1, b_2, b_3), and its equation is*

$$(a_1 x_1 + a_2 x_2 + a_3 x_3)(b_1 x_1 + b_2 x_2 + b_3 x_3) = 0;$$

or its locus contains only one point, the vertex, and the equation is of the form

$$(a_1 x_1 + a_2 x_2 + a_3 x_3)^2 + d(b_1 x_1 + b_2 x_2 + b_3 x_3)^2 = 0,$$

where the triples (a_1, a_2, a_3), (b_1, b_2, b_3) are linearly independent and $-d$ is an element of F that has no square root. A point conic of rank 1 *consists of a* *line* (a_1, a_2, a_3), *every point of which is a vertex, and its equation is*

$$(a_1 x_1 + a_2 x_2 + a_3 x_3)^2 = 0.$$

THEOREM 3.11. *In a projective plane over a field in which every element is a square, two point conics of the same rank are projectively equivalent.*

We leave the details of the proofs of Theorems 3.10 and 3.11 to the reader.

All of the preceding results for singular point conics can be dualized. Thus a singular line conic of rank 1 consists of the lines of one pencil, and its equation is reducible to $u_1^2 = 0$; every line of the pencil is a singular line. When the rank of a line conic is 2, its equation is reducible to $u_1^2 + du_2^2 = 0$. According as $-d$ is, or is not, a square, the line conic consists of two distinct pencils, with their common line as the singular line, or it consists only of the singular line.

We observe that the *self-dual* character of nonsingular conics does not extend to singular conics. A singular point conic is not a line curve, and a singular line conic is not a point curve.

EXERCISES

1. Find the line equation of the conic (3.1).

2. Find a coordinate transformation that reduces the equation of the conic $3x_1^2 - 2x_1 x_2 - x_3^2 = 0$ to (3.1).

3. Prove that a nonsingular conic has the line equation $u_1 u_3 - u_2^2 = 0$ in a suitably chosen coordinate system, and find a coordinate transformation that effects this reduction for the conic $u_1^2 + u_2^2 - u_3^2 = 0$.

4. Reduce the singular conics of (IV, 2, Exercises 1, 3) to the canonical forms (3.7), (3.8), (3.10), or their duals when the ground field of S_2 is (a) the real field, and (b) the complex field.

5. Find a parametric representation (3.3), in the field of rationals, for the conic $x_1^2 - 2x_1 x_2 - x_1 x_3 + x_2^2 - 4x_3^2 = 0$.

6. By means of the results of Exercise 5, show that the rational solutions of the equation $x^2 - 2xy + y^2 - x - 4 = 0$ can be expressed in the form $x = f_1(t)$, $y = f_2(t)$, where f_1, f_2 are rational functions and t takes on arbitrary rational values, and find functions f_1, f_2.

7. A given line and conic have one and just one point of intersection. What conclusions can you draw?

8. Prove Theorems 3.10 and 3.11.

9. Prove the following theorem: In $S_2(C)$ every point conic is projectively equivalent to one of the following nonequivalent conics:

$$\text{(a) } x_1^2 = 0, \qquad \text{(b) } x_1^2 + x_2^2 = 0, \qquad \text{(c) } x_1^2 + x_2^2 + x_3^2 = 0.$$

10. Show that the equation of the conic (3.3) is

$$(\alpha_{11} x_1 + \alpha_{12} x_2 + \alpha_{13} x_3)(\alpha_{31} x_1 + \alpha_{32} x_2 + \alpha_{33} x_3) - (\alpha_{21} x_1 + \alpha_{22} x_2 + \alpha_{23} x_2)^2 = 0,$$

where $(\alpha_{ij}) = \mathbf{A}^{-1}$.

11. Find the point equation of the conic

$$u_1 = t_1^2 + 2t_1 t_2, \qquad u_2 = (t_1 + t_2)^2, \qquad u_3 = t_1^2 - t_1 t_2.$$

ANS. $4x_2(x_1 + x_2 + x_3) = (2x_1 + 2x_2 - x_3)^2$.

12. Prove the following: The parametric point equations of the conic $\mathbf{U} = (t_1^2, t_1 t_2, t_2^2)\mathbf{A}$ are $\mathbf{X} = \mathbf{A}^{-1}(t_2^2, -2t_1 t_2, t_1^2)^T$.

13. State the dual of Theorem 3.5.

#**14.** Prove that every conic tangent to the lines $A:(a_1, a_2, a_3)$, $B:(b_1, b_2, b_3)$ at their intersections with the line $C:(c_1, c_2, c_3)$ (where A, B, C are three linearly independent lines) has an equation of the form $(\mathbf{AX})(\mathbf{BX}) + k(\mathbf{CX})^2 = 0$; find the equation of the conic tangent to the lines $x_1 + x_2 = 0$, $x_1 - x_3 = 0$ at their intersections with $x_1 + x_2 + x_3 = 0$, and through the point $(1, 1, 2)^T$.

#**15.** Dualize the theorem of Exercise 14.

#**16.** Prove that the locus of $\mathbf{U}\mathbf{B}^a\mathbf{U}^T = 0$ is invariantly related to the conic $\mathbf{X}^T\mathbf{B}\mathbf{X} = 0$ under the group of collineations (see I, (5.16)).

#**17.** What does the equation $\mathbf{U}\mathbf{B}^a\mathbf{U}^T = 0$ (see Exercise 16) represent if the rank of $\mathbf{X}^T\mathbf{B}\mathbf{X}$ is r $(r = 1, 2, 3)$?

#**18.** Let F_7 be the modular field with modulus 7; show that in $S_2(F_7)$ every singular point conic of rank 2 is projectively equivalent to one of the following conics

$$x_1^2 - x_2^2 = 0, \qquad x_1^2 + x_2^2 = 0,$$

and prove that these two are not projectively equivalent.

#**19.** Are the classes $[x_1^2 - 2x_2^2]$, $[x_1^2 - 3x_2^2]$ projectively equivalent in the rational projective plane?

20. Prove that in $S_2(F)$ the forms $x_1^2 + dx_2^2$, $x_1^2 + ex_2^2$ $(de \neq 0)$ are projectively equivalent if de is a square in F.

***21.** What is the locus of (3.3) if $\mathbf{A}$ is singular?

4 Nonsingular Conics in $S_2(R)$

We saw earlier (III, 6) that in $S_2(R)$ a simple closed curve may or may not be a bounding curve. In this section we shall see that every nonsingular conic is a bounding curve.

DEFINITION 4.1. In $S_2(\mathsf{R})$ a point, not on a given nonsingular conic, which lies on a line tangent to the conic is called an *exterior point* of the conic. A point that lies on no tangent line is called an *interior point*. The set of all exterior (interior) points is called the *exterior* (*interior*) of the conic.

Clearly, the three sets, the exterior, the interior, and the conic itself, are three disjoint sets whose union is the entire plane.

It is not immediately apparent that the interior is nonempty; this is established in the course of the proof of the next theorem.

We shall find it useful to use the signum function, defined for real numbers by

$$\operatorname{sgn} x = -1, 0, 1 \quad \text{according as} \quad x < 0, x = 0, x > 0.$$

THEOREM 4.1. *Two points* $Y, Z \in S_2(\mathsf{R})$ *are both interior or both exterior points of the conic* $\mathbf{X}^T\mathbf{B}\mathbf{X} = 0$ *if and only if*

$$\operatorname{sgn}(\mathbf{Y}^T\mathbf{B}\mathbf{Y})(\mathbf{Z}^T\mathbf{B}\mathbf{Z}) = 1. \tag{4.1}$$

Proof. Since the square of a nonzero real number is necessarily positive, sgn $(\mathbf{Y}^T\mathbf{B}\mathbf{Y})$ does not depend on the choice of representative $\mathbf{Y} \in [\mathbf{Y}]$, and similarly, sgn $(\mathbf{Y}^T\mathbf{B}\mathbf{Y})(\mathbf{Z}^T\mathbf{B}\mathbf{Z})$ is determined by the points Y, Z and the conic $\mathbf{X}^T\mathbf{B}\mathbf{X} = 0$.

Under a collineation g, given by $\mathbf{X}' = \mathbf{A}\mathbf{X}$, we can choose representatives which satisfy (see (2.4) and (2.5))

$$\mathbf{Y}^T\mathbf{B}\mathbf{Y} = \mathbf{Y}'^T\mathbf{B}'\mathbf{Y}', \qquad \mathbf{Z}^T\mathbf{B}\mathbf{Z} = \mathbf{Z}'^T\mathbf{B}'\mathbf{Z}'.$$

Hence sgn $(\mathbf{Y}^T\mathbf{B}\mathbf{Y})(\mathbf{Z}^T\mathbf{B}\mathbf{Z})$ is a projective invariant of the points Y, Z and the conic.

To prove the theorem, it suffices to prove it in a special coordinate system. We choose one in which the conic has the equation

$$x_1 x_3 - x_2^2 = 0. \tag{4.2}$$

For the parametrization (3.2) the coordinates of the tangent line U at the point with parametric values (t_1, t_2) are (see Theorem 3.6)

$$u_1 = t_2^2, \qquad u_2 = -2t_1 t_2, \qquad u_3 = t_1^2. \tag{4.3}$$

An arbitrary point X lines on some tangent line if and only if the equation in t_1, t_2,

$$\mathbf{U}\mathbf{X} = x_1 t_2^2 - 2x_2 t_1 t_2 + x_3 t_1^2 = 0, \tag{4.4}$$

possesses a nontrivial real solution. For this, it is necessary and sufficient that the discriminant of (4.4), regarded as a quadratic equation in t_1, t_2, be negative or zero. Since the discriminant in question is $x_1 x_3 - x_2^2$, the point X is an exterior point, or an interior point, of (4.2) according as

$$\text{(a) } x_1 x_3 - x_2^2 < 0, \quad \text{or} \quad \text{(b) } x_1 x_3 - x_2^2 > 0. \tag{4.5}$$

Therefore two interior points Y, Z, or two exterior points, satisfy the condition

$$\operatorname{sgn}(y_1 y_3 - y_2^2)(z_1 z_3 - z_2^2) = 1, \tag{4.6}$$

and two points in different regions satisfy the condition

$$\operatorname{sgn}(y_1 y_3 - y_2^2)(z_1 z_3 - z_2^2) = -1. \tag{4.7}$$

COROLLARY 4.1. *Two points Y, Z belong to different regions of the conic (that is, one is interior, the other exterior) if and only if* $\operatorname{sgn}(\mathbf{Y}^T\mathbf{B}\mathbf{Y})(\mathbf{Z}^T\mathbf{B}\mathbf{Z}) = -1$.

THEOREM 4.2. *Every line segment in $S_2(R)$ whose end points belong to different regions of a nonsingular conic has one and just one point of intersection with the conic; two points in the same region are the end points of at least one segment that has no point of intersection with the conic.*

Proof. Let the equation of the conic be $\mathbf{X}^T\mathbf{B}\mathbf{X} = 0$, and let Y and Z be the two given points. Then the intersections of the conic with the line $Y \oplus Z$ are determined by the solutions of the equation

$$\lambda^2\mathbf{Y}^T\mathbf{B}\mathbf{Y} + 2\lambda\mu\mathbf{Y}^T\mathbf{B}\mathbf{Z} + \mu^2\mathbf{Z}^T\mathbf{B}\mathbf{Z} = 0. \tag{4.8}$$

If Y and Z belong to different regions, then by the preceding corollary, $\operatorname{sgn}(\mathbf{Y}^T\mathbf{B}\mathbf{Y})(\mathbf{Z}^T\mathbf{B}\mathbf{Z}) = -1$, and (4.8) possesses two real solutions. If we denote the two solutions by (λ_1, μ_1) and (λ_2, μ_2), then $\operatorname{sgn}(\lambda_1 \mu_1 \lambda_2 \mu_2) = -1$, and by (III, Theorem 5.2), the two points of intersection with the conic lie in different segments with Y and Z as end points. If Y and Z belong to the same region of the conic, then $\operatorname{sgn}(\mathbf{Y}^T\mathbf{B}\mathbf{Y})(\mathbf{Z}^T\mathbf{B}\mathbf{Z}) = 1$, and equation (4.8) may have no solution, one solution, or two solutions. If it has no solution or one solution, the second statement of the theorem is clearly true. If it has two solutions, say, (λ_1, μ_1), (λ_2, μ_2), then $\operatorname{sgn}(\lambda_1 \mu_1 \lambda_2 \mu_2) = 1$, and both points of intersection lie in one segment with Y and Z as end points, leaving the other segment with no point of intersection with the conic.

THEOREM 4.3. *Two distinct points of a nonsingular conic in $S_2(R)$ determine two line segments, one of which consists solely of interior points of the conic and the other of which consists solely of exterior points.*

Proof. Let A and B be the two given points of the conic. Then, by Theorem 4.2, two points of the line $A \oplus B$ belonging to different regions of the conic separate A and B, while two points belonging to the same region do not. The theorem follows from (III, Theorem 5.1 and Definition 5.2).

The preceding definition and theorems show that a nonsingular conic in $S_2(R)$ separates the remaining points of the plane into two mutually exclusive sets such that two points of different sets cannot be joined by a line segment that does not intersect the conic. Furthermore, these sets, unlike the regions of (III, Theorem 6.2 or Theorem 6.4) are distinguishable.

DEFINITION 4.2. A line in $S_2(\mathsf{R})$ that is not a line of a given nonsingular conic and that contains a point of the conic is called an *interior* line of the conic. A line that contains no point of the conic is called an *exterior* line.

The reader will note that by this definition the dual of interior points is exterior lines and of exterior points is interior lines.

THEOREM 4.4. *In $S_2(\mathsf{R})$, two lines, one of which is exterior and the other of which is interior, separate the tangents to the conic through their point of intersection; two lines both of which are exterior or both interior, are not separated by the tangents to the conic (if any) through their point of intersection.*

This theorem is essentially the dual of Theorem 4.2.

THEOREM 4.5a. *A point in $S_2(\mathsf{R})$ is an interior point of a nonsingular conic if and only if every line through it is an interior line.*

Proof. Let Y be an interior point, and let V be any line incident to Y. Then V is not tangent to the conic and intersects a chosen tangent in a point Z. If Z is not a point of the conic, it is an exterior point, and by Theorem 4.2, V, the join of Y and Z, intersects the conic. If Z is a point of the conic, then clearly V intersects the conic. In either case V is an interior line. Conversely, let Y be a point such that every line through it is an interior line; then Y cannot lie on any tangent line and is an interior point.

By duality we have the following theorem.

THEOREM 4.5b. *A line in $S_2(\mathsf{R})$ is an exterior line of a nonsingular conic if and only if all of its points are exterior points.*

EXERCISES

Prove the following theorems in $S_2(\mathsf{R})$.

1. Every interior line of a nonsingular conic contains exterior points.
2. Every exterior point of a nonsingular conic lies on exactly two distinct tangents to the conic.
3. Every line through an interior point of a nonsingular conic intersects the conic in two distinct points.
4. Through every point of the plane there passes an interior line of a given nonsingular conic.
5. If L_1, L_2 are two tangents to a conic, the conic lies entirely in one of the two (closed) sectors determined by L_1, L_2.
6. A conic and its interior are contained in one of the four (closed) regions determined by a triangle circumscribing the conic.

7. Let L be an interior line of a nonsingular conic. Then the points in which L intersects the tangents to the conic constitute a closed segment of L.

8. The locus of the equation

$$\operatorname{sgn}\{(\mathbf{WX})^2 - (\mathbf{V}_1\mathbf{X})(\mathbf{V}_2\mathbf{X})\} = 1,$$

where V_1, V_2, W are three linearly independent lines, is the exterior of the conic $(\mathbf{WX})^2 - (\mathbf{V}_1\mathbf{X})(\mathbf{V}_2\mathbf{X}) = 0$.

9. A collineation of the plane that maps the interior of a conic onto itself maps the conic onto itself.

5 Conics as Projective Loci

In this section we shall develop theorems in $S_2(\mathsf{F})$ which enable us to describe a conic in purely geometric terms and to construct a conic from given geometric data. We begin with a theorem first published by Steiner, who in 1832 gave the first systematic treatment of real projective geometry from a synthetic point of view.

THEOREM 5.1. STEINER'S THEOREM. *The cross ratio of the lines joining a variable point of a nonsingular conic to four given points of the conic is constant.*

Proof. We establish a projective coordinate system in which the reference elements are the four given points. In this coordinate system the equation of the conic is

$$a_1 x_2(x_1 - x_3) + a_2 x_1(x_2 - x_3) = 0, \qquad a_1 a_2 \neq 0. \tag{5.1}$$

Let us denote by $(AB, CD)_X$ the cross ratio of the four lines joining the point X to each of the points A, B, C, and D. By (III, 4, Exercise 9),

$$(AB, CD)_X = \frac{\det(\mathbf{X}\ \ \mathbf{A}\ \ \mathbf{C})\det(\mathbf{X}\ \ \mathbf{B}\ \ \mathbf{D})}{\det(\mathbf{X}\ \ \mathbf{A}\ \ \mathbf{D})\det(\mathbf{X}\ \ \mathbf{B}\ \ \mathbf{C})}; \tag{5.2}$$

when A, B, C, and D have representatives $(1,0,0)^T$, $(0,1,0)^T$, $(0,0,1)^T$, and $(1,1,1)^T$, respectively, (5.2) becomes

$$(AB, CD)_X = \frac{\begin{vmatrix} x_1 & 1 & 0 \\ x_2 & 0 & 0 \\ x_3 & 0 & 1 \end{vmatrix} \begin{vmatrix} x_1 & 0 & 1 \\ x_2 & 1 & 1 \\ x_3 & 0 & 1 \end{vmatrix}}{\begin{vmatrix} x_1 & 1 & 1 \\ x_2 & 0 & 1 \\ x_3 & 0 & 1 \end{vmatrix} \begin{vmatrix} x_1 & 0 & 0 \\ x_2 & 1 & 0 \\ x_3 & 0 & 1 \end{vmatrix}} = \frac{x_2(x_1 - x_3)}{x_1(x_2 - x_3)}. \tag{5.3}$$

If the point X lies on the conic (5.1), the right side of (5.3) (if defined) reduces to the constant $-a_2/a_1$.

COROLLARY 5.1. *The cross ratio of the tangent to a nonsingular conic at one point and the lines joining that point to three other points of the conic is equal to the cross ratio of the lines joining any fifth point of the conic to these four points in the same order.*

Proof. We can, without loss of generality, suppose that the conic is given by (5.1) and that the one point is $(1,0,0)^T$; then the tangent line at $(1,0,0)^T$ has the equation

$$(a_1 + a_2)x_2 - a_2 x_3 = 0;$$

the lines joining $(1,0,0)^T$ to $(0,1,0)^T$, $(0,0,1)^T$, and $(1,1,1)^T$ have the equations

$$x_3 = 0, \qquad x_2 = 0, \quad \text{and} \quad x_2 = x_3,$$

respectively. The cross ratio of these four lines is found to have the previously noted value, $-a_2/a_1$.

THEOREM 5.2a. *The set of points whose joins to four given points (no three collinear) have cross ratio equal to a given constant $c \in \mathsf{F}$ is a conic through the four points. The conic is singular if and only if $c = 0$ or 1.*

Proof. We again choose the four given points as the reference frame. Then, from (5.3), the equation of the locus is

$$\frac{x_2(x_1 - x_3)}{x_1(x_2 - x_3)} = c. \tag{5.4}$$

Clearing of fractions, we obtain

$$x_2(x_1 - x_3) - cx_1(x_2 - x_3) = 0. \tag{5.5}$$

This is the equation of a conic which is singular if and only if $c = 0$ or 1.

The cross ratio $(A\,B, C\,D)_X$ does not exist when X coincides with one of the four points A, B, C, D. It is often convenient, in a real or complex plane, to understand by a locus not only the points that actually satisfy a given condition, but also all limits of such points. In $S_2(\mathsf{F})$, for an arbitrary F, we cannot speak of limits; nevertheless we shall find it convenient to regard the given points as part of the locus in view of the corollary to Steiner's Theorem. With this understanding every point whose coordinates satisfy (5.5) belongs to the set.

By duality we have the following theorem.

THEOREM 5.2b. *The lines that intersect four given lines (no three concurrent) in four points of constant cross ratio envelop a conic tangent to the given lines.*

Given a nonsingular conic and two of its points A, A', we can establish a one-to-one map between the pencils of lines with vertices at A, A', as follows:

Two lines, neither of which is $A \oplus A'$, correspond if their intersection lies on the conic; the line $A \oplus A'$ regarded as a line of the pencil A maps onto the tangent to the conic at A'; similarly, the tangent at A maps onto the line $A \oplus A'$ regarded as a line of the pencil A' (Figure 5.1). We speak of this map, between the pencils of lines at two points of the conic, as the map *established* by the conic.

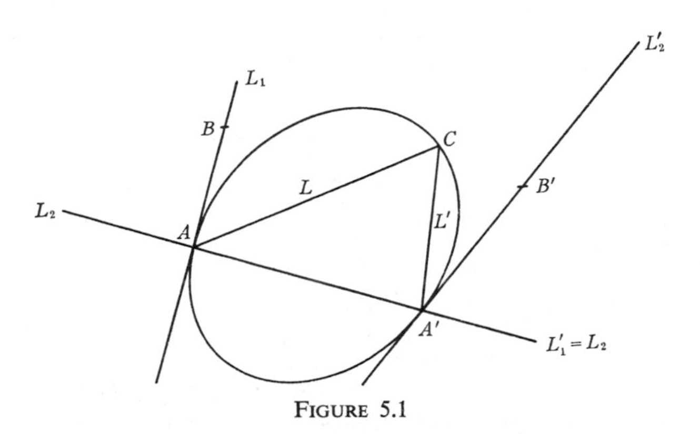

FIGURE 5.1

THEOREM 5.3. *The map established by the conic between the pencils of lines at any two of its points is a projectivity.*

Proof. Let L_i $(i = 1, 2, 3, 4)$ be any four lines of the pencil A, and let L_i' $(i = 1, 2, 3, 4)$ be the corresponding lines of the pencil A'; the points of intersection of L_i and L_i' are points of the conic, and by Steiner's Theorem (and Corollary 5.1) we have that

$$(L_1 L_2, L_3 L_4) = (L_1' L_2', L_3' L_4'). \tag{5.6}$$

Since equation (5.6) holds for every set of four distinct lines, the map is a projectivity.

THEOREM 5.4. *The set of intersections of corresponding lines of two distinct projective, nonperspective pencils of lines is a nonsingular conic through the vertices of the two pencils. The tangent to the conic at the vertex of either pencil is the line of the pencil that corresponds to the common line regarded as a line of the other pencil.*

Proof. Let the vertices of the pencils be A and A', let C be a point of intersection of one pair of corresponding lines, and let L_1, L_2', the lines that correspond to the common line, be specified by giving points $B \neq A$ and $B' \neq A'$ incident to L_1, L_2', respectively (Figure 5.1). Then a point X is a point of intersection of a pair of corresponding lines if and only if

$$(A' B, C X)_A = (B' A, C X)_{A'}. \tag{5.7}$$

If we expand both sides of this equation by means of (5.2), we obtain

(5.8) $h \det(\mathbf{A} \quad \mathbf{B} \quad \mathbf{X}) \det(\mathbf{A}' \quad \mathbf{B}' \quad \mathbf{X}) + k \det^2(\mathbf{A} \quad \mathbf{A}' \quad \mathbf{X}) = 0, \quad hk \neq 0,$

where

$$h:k = -\det^2(\mathbf{A} \quad \mathbf{A}' \quad \mathbf{C}) : \det(\mathbf{A} \quad \mathbf{B} \quad \mathbf{C}) \det(\mathbf{A}' \quad \mathbf{B}' \quad \mathbf{C}).$$

Noting that we can choose representatives so that

$$\det(\mathbf{A} \quad \mathbf{B} \quad \mathbf{X}) = \mathbf{L}_1 \mathbf{X}, \quad \det(\mathbf{A}' \quad \mathbf{B}' \quad \mathbf{X}) = \mathbf{L}_2' \mathbf{X}, \quad \det(\mathbf{A} \quad \mathbf{A}' \quad \mathbf{X}) = \mathbf{L}_2 \mathbf{X},$$

we can write (5.8) as

(5.9) $$h(\mathbf{L}_1 \mathbf{X})(\mathbf{L}_2' \mathbf{X}) + k(\mathbf{L}_2 \mathbf{X})^2 = 0.$$

Equation (5.9) is the equation of a nonsingular conic, since $hk \neq 0$. Clearly it is tangent to L_1 and L_2' at $A = L_1 \cap L_2$ and $A' = L_2' \cap L_2$ respectively.

The following theorem is the dual of Theorems 5.3 and 5.4. Its second statement was first published by Chasles in 1828.

THEOREM 5.5. *The intersections of a variable tangent to a nonsingular conic with two given tangents correspond in a projectivity; the points of contact of the given tangents correspond to their point of intersection. Conversely, the lines joining corresponding points of two projective, nonperspective lines envelop a nonsingular conic which is tangent to the two lines at the points that correspond to their point of intersection.*

THEOREM 5.6. *Let A, B, C, D, and E be five points, no three collinear. A conic is determined uniquely by any one of the following three conditions:*

(a) *it contains the points A, B, C, D, E;*

(b) *it contains the points A, B, C, D, and is tangent at A to $A \oplus E$;*

(c) *it contains the points A, B, C, and is tangent at A and B to $A \oplus E$ and $B \oplus D$, respectively.*

In each case the conic is nonsingular.

Proof. By Theorem 5.2a, the equation

(5.10) $$(AB, DE)_X = (AB, DE)_C$$

represents a conic satisfying condition (a), and by Theorem 5.4 the equation

(5.11) $$(BC, DX)_A = (BC, DX)_E$$

also represents such a conic. Similarly either of the equations

(5.12) $$(AB, CD)_X = (EB, CD)_A,$$

(5.13) $$(EB, CX)_A = (AB, CX)_D$$

represents a conic satisfying condition (b), and the equation

(5.14) $$(EB, CX)_A = (AD, CX)_B$$

represents a conic satisfying condition (c). Suppose there were two conics satisfying (a). Then by Steiner's Theorem every point X of either conic would satisfy equation (5.10), but by Theorem 5.2a the set of points that satisfy (5.10) is just one conic. Hence the two conics coincide. We can show the uniqueness of the conic satisfying (b) or (c) similarly. Since no three of the points A, B, C, D, E are collinear, each of the conics mentioned above is nonsingular.

Theorem 5.6 is concerned with a conic through five points, or with one through four points with a prescribed tangent at one of the points, or with one through three points with prescribed tangents at two of the points. We have specified the given points and lines in all cases by a set of five points; by Theorem 5.6 it is sufficient that no three of these five points be linearly dependent in order that there exist a unique nonsingular conic through the given points tangent to the given lines. Dually, there exists a unique nonsingular conic tangent to five given lines, or tangent to four lines with a prescribed point of contact on one of them, or tangent to three lines with prescribed points of contact on two of them if the five given lines in the first case, the four given lines and some line through the given point in the second case, the three given lines and some two lines, one through each given point, in the third case, have the property that no three lines are concurrent.

If three or more of the points of Theorem 5.5 are dependent, one can determine by inspection whether or not there exists a unique singular conic satisfying conditions (a), (b), (c) of the theorem. Thus five points, four of which are collinear, lie on every singular conic that consists of the line of the four points and any line through the fifth. On the other hand, the vertices of a quadrangle and one of the diagonal points lie on just one singular conic, the pair of sides through the diagonal point.

In dealing with singular point conics, it often makes for simplicity of expression if we admit as a tangent at a vertex of a conic, any line through the vertex. In this sense, the singular conic of rank one that consists of the line $A \oplus B$ with every point a vertex is one conic tangent at A and B to $A \oplus C$ and $B \oplus C$, respectively; the pair of lines $A \oplus C$ and $B \oplus C$ is another such conic. All other conics that satisfy these four conditions are nonsingular.

If we expand equations (5.10), (5.13), and (5.14), we obtain the respective equations

(5.15a)
$$h \det(\mathbf{X} \quad \mathbf{A} \quad \mathbf{D}) \det(\mathbf{X} \quad \mathbf{B} \quad \mathbf{E}) + k \det(\mathbf{X} \quad \mathbf{A} \quad \mathbf{E}) \det(\mathbf{X} \quad \mathbf{B} \quad \mathbf{D}) = 0,$$

(5.15b)
$$h \det(\mathbf{X} \quad \mathbf{A} \quad \mathbf{B}) \det(\mathbf{X} \quad \mathbf{A} \quad \mathbf{D}) + k \det(\mathbf{X} \quad \mathbf{A} \quad \mathbf{E}) \det(\mathbf{X} \quad \mathbf{B} \quad \mathbf{D}) = 0,$$

(5.15c) $$h \det^2(\mathbf{X} \quad \mathbf{A} \quad \mathbf{B}) + k \det(\mathbf{X} \quad \mathbf{A} \quad \mathbf{E}) \det(\mathbf{X} \quad \mathbf{B} \quad \mathbf{D}) = 0,$$

where h, k are constants that can be determined, for each equation, either in the course of the expansion of the original equation, or by requiring that the matrix **C** (which does not appear explicitly in (5.15)) satisfy the equation. However, it we allow h, k to vary independently, equations (5.15) represent *pencils* of conics satisfying conditions (a). (b), (c) of Theorem 5.5 except for the condition that C be a point of the conic. For $h = 0$, $k \neq 0$, or for $h \neq 0$, $k = 0$, equations (5.15) represent singular conics. Thus the equation of a conic through four points, or of a conic through three points with a given tangent at one of them, or of a conic through two points with given tangents at each of them (with suitable restrictions on dependency) is a linear combination of the equations of two singular conics that satisfy the same conditions.

The fact that there is a unique nonsingular conic through five points (no three collinear) leads us to seek conditions that characterize six points of a conic. For this purpose we define a *simple hexagon* as a set of six points in cyclic order, together with their sides, the lines joining consecutive vertices. We require further that the six sides be distinct. The following theorem was discovered by Pascal about 1640.

THEOREM 5.7. PASCAL'S THEOREM. *If six points lie on a nonsingular conic, the three points of intersection of pairs of opposite sides of any simple hexagon that they determine are collinear. Conversely, if the three points of intersection of pairs of opposite sides of a simple hexagon are collinear, and if no three of the vertices of the hexagon are dependent, the vertices lie on a nonsingular conic.*

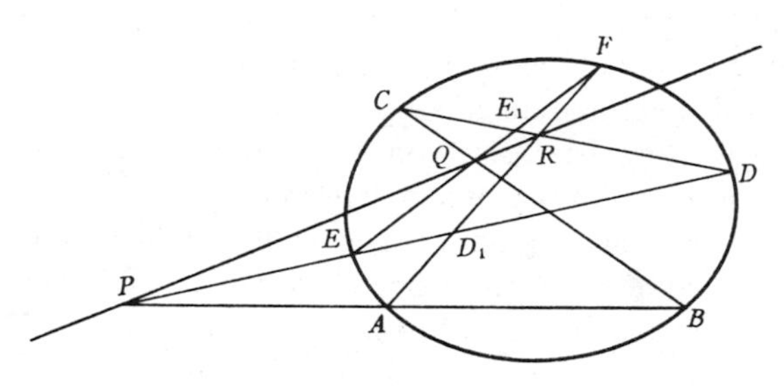

FIGURE 5.2

Proof. Let us denote the successive vertices of the hexagon by A, B, C, D, E, and F (Figure 5.2); let P, Q, R be the points of intersection of pairs of opposite sides:

$$P = (A \oplus B) \cap (D \oplus E), \quad Q = (B \oplus C) \cap (E \oplus F), \quad R = (C \oplus D) \cap (F \oplus A).$$

Let us first suppose that A, B, C, D, E, and F lie on a conic. Then

$$(5.16) \qquad (BD, EF)_A = (BD, EF)_C.$$

We intersect the first pencil by $D \oplus E$, and the second by $E \oplus F$; letting $D_1 = (A \oplus F) \cap (D \oplus E)$, and $E_1 = (C \oplus D) \cap (E \oplus F)$, we have

(5.17) $$(PD, ED_1) = (QE_1, EF).$$

There exists a projectivity between the points of $D \oplus E$ and $E \oplus F$ under which P, D, E, D_1 correspond to Q, E_1, E, F, respectively. Since the common point E of these lines is self-corresponding, the projectivity is a perspectivity (see III, Theorem 9.7), and $P \oplus Q$, $D \oplus E_1$, and $D_1 \oplus F$ are concurrent. Since $D \oplus E_1 = C \oplus D$, and $D_1 \oplus F = A \oplus F$, R lies on $P \oplus Q$, and the direct theorem has been proved.

Conversely, if the points P, Q, R are collinear, $R \in P \oplus Q$ so that, with the above notation, the lines $P \oplus Q$, $D \oplus E_1$, and $D_1 \oplus F$ are concurrent. Equation (5.17) holds, and therefore (5.16) holds. By Theorem 5.4, the points A, B, C, D, E, F lie on a conic.

A simple hexagon is called a *Pascal hexagon* if points of intersection of pairs of opposite sides are collinear.

The dual of Pascal's Theorem was discovered by Brianchon in 1806.

THEOREM 5.8. BRIANCHON'S THEOREM. *Six lines, no three dependent, are tangent to a nonsingular conic if and only if the three lines joining opposite vertices of any one of the simple hexagons they determine, are concurrent.*

If we are given five points of a conic and a tangent at one of them, and if we use the notation of equation (5.16) with $A = B$ and with $A \oplus B$ the tangent at A, equation (5.16) holds; we obtain in this way a theorem regarding pentagons. We leave it to the reader to obtain this theorem and similar theorems for quadrilaterals and triangles (see Exercises 7 to 10 below).

CONSTRUCTION PROBLEM 5.1. Given five points, no three collinear; construct additional points on the conic through the five points.

Procedure. Let the points be A, B, C, D, E, and let L be any line through A not incident to the remaining points (Figure 5.3). Let

$$P = (A \oplus B) \cap (D \oplus E), \qquad R = (C \oplus D) \cap L, \qquad Q = (P \oplus R) \cap (B \oplus C).$$

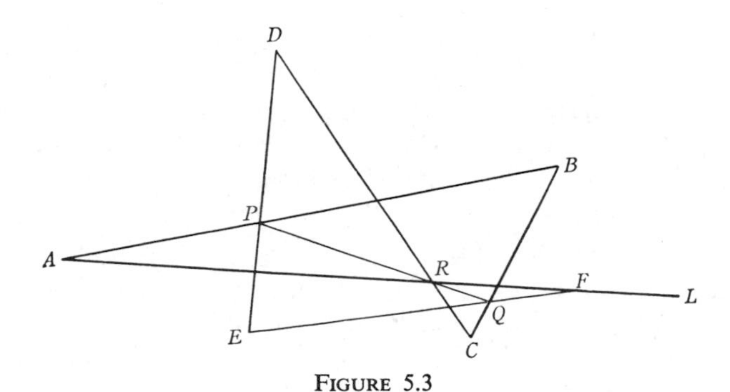

FIGURE 5.3

Then $F = L \cap (E \oplus Q)$ lies on the conic.

The proof follows from the second statement in Pascal's Theorem. We leave the details to the reader.

We leave to the reader to give the dual construction, and to extend this result to the construction of tangent lines and points of contact whenever a conic is given by conditions of the type appearing in Theorem 5.6 or its dual.

The fundamental theorems we have proved in this section provide a basis which enables us to develop a great variety of theorems on linear figures and conics and their relationships. We give two illustrations; further examples will be found in exercises at the end of this section.

THEOREM 5.9. *If the vertices of two triangles are distinct and lie on a conic, their sides are tangent to a conic.*

Proof. Let the triangles be ABC and DEF. Then $ADEFCB$ is a Pascal hexagon, so that P, Q, and R, the points of intersection of sides $A \oplus D$, $D \oplus E$, and $E \oplus F$ with their respective opposite sides, are collinear. If we now consider the hexagon $ACQDFR$, the lines joining opposite vertices are $A \oplus D$, $C \oplus F$, and $Q \oplus R$. These lines are concurrent in P, and by Brianchon's Theorem the sides of the hexagon $ACQDFR$ are tangent to a conic. But these are the sides of the given triangles.

PROBLEM 5.1. Two of the vertices of a triangle trace given lines, and each of the three sides is incident to one of three given points. What is the locus of the third vertex?

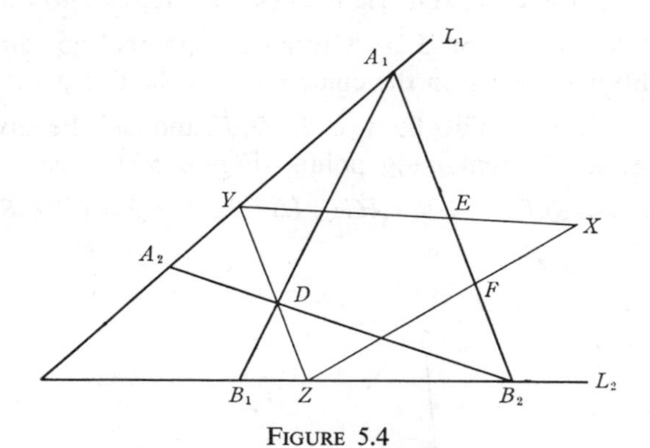

FIGURE 5.4

Solution. Let the given lines be L_1, L_2, and let Y, Z be the vertices that trace these respective lines. Let the third vertex be X, and let D, E, F be the given points on $Y \oplus Z$, $Y \oplus X$, and $Z \oplus X$, respectively (Figure 5.4). We consider first the case where D, E, F are independent, where none of these points is incident to L_1 or L_2, and where the lines $E \oplus F$, L_1, and L_2 are independent. Let $A_1 = (E \oplus F) \cap L_1$, $B_1 = (A_1 \oplus D) \cap L_2$, $B_2 = (E \oplus F) \cap L_2$, $A_2 = (B_2 \oplus D) \cap L_1$. We can establish a one-to-one map between the pencils E and F such that corresponding lines intersect in the point X. This map is projective since it is the product of a perspectivity between the pencils E and D from L_1 and a perspectivity between the pencils D and F from L_2. The common line of the pencils E and F is not self-corresponding (since the triples $E \oplus F$, L_1, L_2 and D, E, F are both independent); therefore the locus of X is a nonsingular conic. E, F, and $L_1 \cap L_2$ are points of the conic, and the lines $A_2 \oplus E$ and $B_1 \oplus F$ are the tangents at E and F, respectively. The points $(F \oplus D) \cap L_1$ and $(E \oplus D) \cap L_2$ are on the locus. Thus the locus of X is a nonsingular conic determined either by the five points mentioned above or by three of them including E, F, and the tangents at E and F.

If D, E, F are collinear, the variable triangles are all Desarguean, and the locus of X is a line concurrent with L_1 and L_2.

If $E \oplus F$, L_1, L_2 are concurrent, the projectivity between the pencils E and F is a perspectivity, and the locus of X is its central line.

If $E \in L_1$ and $F \in L_2$, the locus of X is the point $L_1 \cap L_2$. If only one of these incidence relations occurs, the locus of X is the line L_1 or the line L_2, according as $E \in L_1$ or $F \in L_2$. If $F \in L_1$ or $E \in L_2$, the general argument above is valid, and the locus is a nonsingular conic. If $D \in L_1$, the locus of X is the line $D \oplus E$, and if $D \in L_2$, the locus of X is $D \oplus F$.

EXERCISES

1. A projectivity between the pencils $\lambda x_1 + \mu(x_2 - x_3) = 0$ and $\lambda'(x_1 + x_2) + \mu'(x_2 - x_3) = 0$ is established by the condition $[\lambda', \mu'] = [\lambda + \mu, \mu]$. Find the locus of the points of intersection of corresponding lines.

ANS. $x_1^2 + x_1 x_2 - x_2^2 + x_2 x_3 = 0$.

2. The equations $\lambda' = 2\lambda - \mu$, $\mu' = \lambda + \mu$ establish a projectivity between the points $(\lambda, \mu, 0)^T$ and $(0, \lambda' \mu')^T$ of the lines $x_3 = 0$ and $x_1 = 0$. Find the equation of the envelope of the lines joining corresponding points.

ANS. $u_1(u_2 - u_3) + u_2(2u_2 + u_3) = 0$.

3. A projectivity between two pencils A, A' is given so that the lines L, L_1, L_2 of the pencil A correspond to the lines L', L_1', L_2', respectively, of the pencil A', and $L_2 = L_1'$ (see Figure 5.1). Show that, in a given coordinate system of $S_2(\mathsf{F})$, representatives of the five lines can be chosen so that the map of the line $\lambda \mathbf{L}_1 + \mu \mathbf{L}_2$ of the pencil A is the line $\lambda \mathbf{L}_1' + \mu \mathbf{L}_2'$ of the pencil A'.

4. Describe the set of conics through five given points when three or more of the points are collinear. Under what conditions is the set a pencil?

5. Find the equations of the following conics:

(a) Through the points $(1,1,1)^T$, $(3,-1,-1)^T$, $(1,1,0)^T$, $(4,-1,0)^T$, $(7,5,0)^T$. ANS. $x_1^2 + 3x_1x_2 - 4x_2^2 - x_1x_3 + 2x_2x_3 - x_3^2 = 0$.

(b) Through the points $(1,1,1)^T$, $(3,-1,-1)^T$, $(1,1,0)^T$, $(4,-1,0)^T$, tangent at $(1,1,1)^T$ to the line $x_1 + x_2 - 2x_3 = 0$.

ANS. $x_1^2 + 3x_1x_2 - 4x_2^2 - x_1x_3 + 9x_2x_3 - 8x_3^2 = 0$.

(c) Tangent to the lines $x_1^2 - x_2^2 = 0$ at the intersection of these lines with $x_3 = 0$, and through the point $(1,2,3)^T$.

ANS. $3x_1^2 - 3x_2^2 + x_3^2 = 0$.

(d) As in (c), with the last condition replaced by the condition that the conic be tangent to the line $x_1 + 2x_2 - x_3 = 0$.

ANS. $u_1^2 - u_2^2 + 3u_3^2 = 0$.

(e) Tangent to the lines $x_1 - x_3 = 0$, $x_1 + x_3 = 0$, $x_2 - x_3 = 0$, $x_2 + x_3 = 0$, and $3x_1 + 4x_2 - 5x_3 = 0$.

ANS. $u_1^2 + u_2^2 - u_3^2 = 0$.

(f) Tangent to the lines $x_1 - x_3 = 0$, $x_1 + x_3 = 0$, $x_2 - x_3 = 0$, and $3x_1 + 4x_2 - 5x_3 = 0$ with the point $(1,2,1)^T$ as a point of contact.

ANS. $-u_1^2 + 2u_1u_2 + 5u_2^2 + 6u_2u_3 + u_3^2 = 0$.

***6.** Show that the dual of (5.15a) represents, as h, k vary, the *pencil* of (line) conics tangent to the four sides of a quadrilateral, and that the singular conics in this pencil are the three pairs of opposite vertices of the quadrilateral. Describe geometrically the duals of (5.15b,c), and identify their singular conics.

7. Prove: If t_1, t_3, t_4, t_5, t_6 are the sides of a simple pentagon whose vertices lie on a given nonsingular conic, and if t_2 is the tangent at $t_1 \cap t_3$, the three points $t_1 \cap t_4$, $t_2 \cap t_5$, $t_3 \cap t_6$ are collinear. State and prove the converse.

8. Prove: If t_1, t_3, t_4, t_5 are the sides of a simple quadrilateral whose vertices lie on a given nonsingular conic, and if t_2 is the tangent at $t_1 \cap t_3$, and t_6 is the tangent at $t_5 \cap t_1$, the three points $t_1 \cap t_4$, $t_2 \cap t_5$, $t_3 \cap t_6$ are collinear. State and prove the converse.

9. Prove: If a quadrangle is inscribed in a nonsingular conic, the tangents at any two of its vertices intersect on the line joining the diagonal points not on the side joining these two vertices.

#**10.** Let $A_1A_2A_3$ and $B_1B_2B_3$ be two triangles with distinct vertices, and let the vertices B_1, B_2, and B_3 of the second triangle lie on the sides $A_2 \oplus A_3$, $A_3 \oplus A_1$, $A_1 \oplus A_2$, respectively, of the first. Prove that there exists a nonsingular conic circumscribing the second triangle and inscribed in the first if and only if the two triangles $A_1A_2A_3$ and $B_1B_2B_3$ are Desarguean.

11. State the duals of the theorems of Exercises 7, 8, 9, and 10.

12. Using the theorems of Exercises 7 to 9, construct the tangent line at a given point of a conic determined by conditions (a), (b), or (c) of Theorem 5.6.

13. Construct the point of contact, on a given tangent, of the conic tangent to five given lines, no three concurrent.

#**14.** If $A_1 A_2 A_3$ and $B_1 B_2 B_3$ are two Desarguean triangles, the six lines joining vertices of the first triangle to noncorresponding vertices of the second are six tangents to a conic. Prove this theorem and state the dual.

15. Prove: If two triangles are inscribed in a conic, the points in which two of the six sides intersect the remaining four sides have equal cross ratios.

16. Two vertices of a triangle move along two given tangents to a nonsingular conic so that their side always remains tangent to the conic. Each of the remaining two sides passes through a given point. Find the locus of the third vertex.

17. X and X'' are corresponding points in a given involution on a given line L, O is a given point and L' a given line, and $X' = (O \oplus X'') \cap L'$. Find the envelope of $X \oplus X'$ when L, L' are distinct and O is not incident to L or L'.

18. Let L_1, L_2, L_3 be concurrent lines, and let L_3 intersect a given nonsingular conic in two distinct points A, B. If X is an arbitrary point of the conic, and if $X_1 = (A \oplus X) \cap L_1$, $X_2 = (B \oplus X) \cap L_2$, find the envelope of $X_1 \oplus X_2$. Is the envelope ever a point?

#**19.** Reconcile the theorems of this section with the fact that a nonsingular conic in $S_2(\mathsf{F}_3)$ contains just four points.

20. Prove the converse of the Theorem of Pappus: If $ABCDEF$ is a Pascal hexagon and if A, C, and E are collinear, B, D, and F are collinear.

6 Polar Theory of Quadratic Forms

Let Q be a ternary quadratic form

$$Q = \mathbf{X}^T\mathbf{B}\mathbf{X}, \qquad \mathbf{B} = \mathbf{B}^T, \tag{6.1}$$

and let $[Q]$ be the class of forms ρQ ($\rho \neq 0$). In a projective plane over a field in which every element is a square (for example, the complex field), there is a one-to-one correspondence between the conics

$$Q = \mathbf{X}^T\mathbf{B}\mathbf{X} = 0 \tag{6.2}$$

and the classes $[Q]$, since every quadratic equation represents a conic, and every conic has an equation determined to within a factor of proportionality. However, if F is a field in which some elements are not squares (for example, the real field), there are in $S_2(\mathsf{F})$ forms (6.1) for which equation (6.2) has no locus. Thus the concept of classes of forms $[Q]$ is more general than that of conics. In this section we shall develop certain properties of the classes $[Q]$, but for simplicity of expression we shall generally speak of the form $[Q]$ or of the conic $\mathscr{C}(Q)$ rather than of the class of forms $[Q]$.

DEFINITION 6.1a. In $S_2(\mathsf{F})$, two points Y, Z whose representatives satisfy the equation

$$\mathbf{Y}^T\mathbf{B}\mathbf{Z} = 0 \tag{6.3}$$

are said to be *conjugate* with respect to the form $[Q] = [\mathbf{X}^T\mathbf{B}\mathbf{X}]$.

We leave to the reader to show that (6.3) represents a projective property of the points Y, Z and of the class $[Q]$. We note that equation (6.3) is symmetric in $\mathbf{Y}$ and $\mathbf{Z}$, since $\mathbf{Y}^T\mathbf{B}\mathbf{Z} = \mathbf{Z}^T\mathbf{B}\mathbf{Y}$; we say that either of the points Y or Z is conjugate to the other with respect to $[Q]$. A point Y is *self-conjugate* if and only if $\mathbf{X}^T\mathbf{B}\mathbf{X} = 0$ is a conic and Y is a point of the conic.

DEFINITION 6.2. The set of points in $S_2(\mathsf{F})$ conjugate to a given point, with respect to a given form, is called the *polar* of the point with respect to the form.

THEOREM 6.1. *If Y lies on the polar of Z, Z lies on the polar of Y.*

We leave the proof to the reader.

The equation of the polar of the point Y with respect to $[Q]$ is

$$\mathbf{Y}^T\mathbf{B}\mathbf{X} = 0, \tag{6.4}$$

so that the polar of a point not a vertex is a line. If Y lies on the conic $\mathscr{C}(Q)$ and is not a vertex, the polar of Y is the tangent at Y. If Y is a vertex, the polar of Y consists of all the points in the plane; hence if Q is singular, the polar of a given point contains all of the vertices of the conic $\mathscr{C}(Q)$. Thus if Q is singular of rank 1, the polar of a point of $\mathscr{C}(Q)$ consists of all the points of the plane, and the polar of a point not on $\mathscr{C}(Q)$ consists of the points of $\mathscr{C}(Q)$. If Q is singular of rank 2, the polar of a point (not the vertex) is a line through the vertex.

THEOREM 6.2. *The polars, with respect to a nonsingular form $[Q]$, of the points of a line are the lines of a pencil; the cross ratio of four collinear points is equal to the cross ratio of their polars.*

Proof. Let Z_1 and Z_2 be two distinct points of the given line V. Then from (6.4) their polars are the lines W_1 and W_2, where

$$\mathbf{W}_1 = \mathbf{Z}_1^T\mathbf{B}, \qquad \mathbf{W}_2 = \mathbf{Z}_2^T\mathbf{B},$$

and these lines are distinct. The polar of the point $\lambda\mathbf{Z}_1 + \mu\mathbf{Z}_2$ of V is, from (6.4), the line $\lambda\mathbf{W}_1 + \mu\mathbf{W}_2$, and hence the polars of the points of V are the lines of the pencil $W_1 \cap W_2$. Cross ratio is preserved since $[\lambda, \mu]^T$ is a projective coordinate both on the line and in the pencil.

DEFINITION 6.3. The vertex of the pencil of lines that consists of the polars of the points of a given line, with respect to a nonsingular form, is called the *pole* of the line.

Let us find the coordinates of the pole of V, that is, the vertex Y of the pencil of polars of points of V. If $X \in V$, we have

$$\mathbf{VX} = 0; \tag{6.5}$$

from equation (6.4), the polar U' of a point X is given by

$$\mathbf{U}' = \mathbf{X}^T\mathbf{B}, \qquad \text{or} \qquad \mathbf{X} = \mathbf{B}^{-1}\mathbf{U}'^T. \tag{6.6}$$

If we substitute this value of $\mathbf{X}$ in (6.5), we obtain

$$\mathbf{VB}^{-1}\mathbf{U}'^T = 0. \tag{6.7}$$

As X varies in (6.5), U' varies, and (6.7) is the line equation of a point Y, so that the pole of the line V is the point Y, where

$$\mathbf{Y}^T = \mathbf{VB}^{-1}, \qquad \text{or} \qquad \mathbf{Y} = \mathbf{B}^{-1}\mathbf{V}^T. \tag{6.8}$$

THEOREM 6.3. *If a given point is the pole of a given line, with respect to a nonsingular form, the line is the polar of the point.*

Proof. Equation (6.8) expresses the coordinates of Y, the pole of V. If we solve for $\mathbf{V}$, we obtain

$$\mathbf{V} = \mathbf{Y}^T\mathbf{B}. \tag{6.9}$$

By equation (6.4), V is the polar of Y.

We might expect to find two polar theories of nonsingular forms: the one we have been discussing, and the dual theory based on forms in line coordinates. Actually, there is but one polar theory of nonsingular forms, as the following discussion will show.

Let

$$Q^* = \mathbf{UB}^*\mathbf{U}^T, \qquad \mathbf{B}^* = \mathbf{B}^{*T}, \tag{6.10}$$

be an arbitrary quadratic form in line coordinates. If $Q^* = 0$ is a nonsingular conic, its point equation is $\mathbf{X}^T\mathbf{BX} = 0$, where

$$\mathbf{B}^* = \mathbf{B}^{-1}, \qquad \mathbf{B} = \mathbf{B}^{*-1}. \tag{6.11}$$

Whether or not $Q^* = 0$ has a locus, (6.11) enables us to associate with every nonsingular class $[Q^*]$, a unique class in point coordinates. We shall show that the polar theories of nonsingular forms $[Q]$ and $[Q^*]$ that satisfy (6.11) coincide. We begin with the dual of Definition 6.1a.

DEFINITION 6.1b. Two lines V, W are *conjugate* with respect to the form $[Q^*]$ if $\mathbf{VB^*W}^T = 0$.

We would naturally expect next to formulate the dual of Definition 6.2. This dual would give a name to the set of lines conjugate to a given line. The following theorem shows that, for nonsingular forms, we already have a name for this set.

THEOREM 6.4. *The set of lines conjugate to a given line with respect to a nonsingular form* $[\mathbf{UB}^{-1}\mathbf{U}^T]$ *is the pencil of lines with vertex at the pole, with respect to the form* $[\mathbf{X}^T\mathbf{BX}]$, *of the given line.*

Proof. The lines U conjugate to a given line V with respect to the form $[\mathbf{UB}^{-1}\mathbf{U}^T]$ satisfy the equation

$$\mathbf{UB}^{-1}\mathbf{V}^T = 0,$$

that is, they constitute a pencil of lines with vertex $Y{:}\mathbf{Y} = \mathbf{B}^{-1}\mathbf{V}^T$. But by equation (6.8) and Definition 6.3, Y is the pole of V with respect to $[\mathbf{X}^T\mathbf{BX}]$.

From Theorem 6.3, the pole-polar relationship between points and lines is reciprocal; from Theorem 6.4, this relationship is self-dual, that is, the dual theory with respect to the form $[\mathbf{UB}^{-1}\mathbf{U}^T]$ leads to exactly the same pole-polar relationship as did the original theory with respect to the form $[\mathbf{X}^T\mathbf{BX}]$. Henceforth, when we speak of poles and polars with respect to a nonsingular form, the form can be either of the pair of related forms $[\mathbf{X}^T\mathbf{BX}]$ or $[\mathbf{UB}^{-1}\mathbf{U}^T]$.

For the sake of completeness, we state the following theorem.

THEOREM 6.5. *Two lines are conjugate with respect to a given nonsingular form if and only if each contains the pole of the other.*

We leave the proof to the reader.

We have just seen that the pole-polar relationship, with respect to nonsingular forms, is one-to-one and self-dual. For singular forms, the situation is entirely different. As we have seen, the polar of a point with respect to a singular point conic may consist of all the points of the plane; again, even if distinct points have polar lines, these lines may coincide. The relationship between points and their polars, with respect to a singular form, is never one-to-one. We have, of course, defined conjugate lines, with respect to a singular form in line coordinates, by Definition 6.1b. The dual of Definition 6.2 would define the pole of a line with respect to a singular form in line coordinates. But this dual theory is different from the original theory, just as singular line conics are different from singular point conics.

In the next set of theorems and definitions, we develop further properties of the pole-polar relationship. Unless the contrary is stated, we understand that we are dealing with nonsingular forms.

THEOREM 6.6a. *Let L be a line not tangent to the conic $\mathscr{C}(Q)$ (if it exists). The map on L from a point X of L to the intersection of L with the polar of X is an involution.*

Proof. The map preserves cross ratio since the cross ratio of four points equals that of their polars, and the latter cross ratio is equal to the cross ratio of the points of intersection of the polars with L. Hence the map is a projectivity. By Theorem 6.1, the map is involutory.

DEFINITION 6.4. We say that $[Q]$ (or the conic $\mathscr{C}(Q)$) *induces* the involution of conjugate points on L.

If we use the convention suggested earlier, that any line through a vertex of a conic be regarded as a tangent to the conic at that vertex, Theorem 6.6a as stated can be seen to be valid for singular forms: for singular forms of

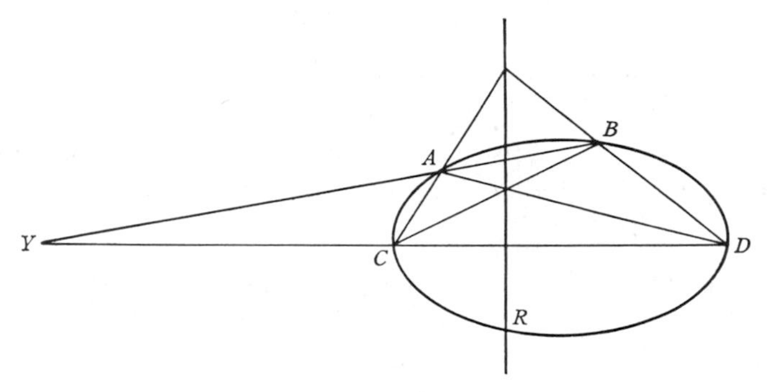

FIGURE 6.1

rank 1, the hypotheses of the theorem cannot be met; for singular forms of rank 2, the hypotheses must be interpreted as requiring that the line L does not contain the vertex. The proof as given is then valid. A similar situation exists for the next theorem and its first corollary: the hypotheses cannot be met by a singular conic of rank 1, and the theorems are valid for a singular conic of rank 2.

THEOREM 6.7. *Pairs of points on a line intersecting a conic in two distinct points are conjugate if and only if they separate harmonically the intersections of their line with the conic.*

Proof. The points of intersection of the line and the conic are self-conjugate, and therefore they are the fixed points of the induced involution.

COROLLARY 6.1. *If two lines through a point Y not on a conic intersect the conic in four distinct points A, B, C, D, then the polar of Y is the line joining the other two diagonal points of the quadrangle $ABCD$.*

We leave the proof to the reader (see Figure 6.1 and III, Theorem 8.3a).

The two preceding theorems and the corollary enable us to describe completely the polars of points with respect to a singular point conic of rank 2.

COROLLARY 6.2. *Pairs of lines through the vertex of a point conic of rank* 2 *that are conjugate with respect to the conic are pairs in an involution whose fixed lines* (*if any*) *are the lines of the conic. The polar of a point* (*not the vertex*) *is the line conjugate to the join of the point and the vertex.*

COROLLARY 6.3. *The polar of a point with respect to a nonsingular conic intersects the conic* (*if at all*) *in the points of contact of the tangents from the given point.*

Proof. Let Y be the given point, and let R be a point of intersection of the conic and the polar of Y (Figure 6.1). By Theorem 6.1, Y lies on the polar of R, that is, on the tangent to the conic at R.

For nonsingular forms, the following theorem is the dual of Theorem (6.6a).

THEOREM 6.6b. *Let* $[\mathbf{X}^T\mathbf{B}\mathbf{X}]$ *be a given nonsingular form, and let* Y *be any point for which* $\mathbf{Y}^T\mathbf{B}\mathbf{Y} \neq 0$; *the map in the pencil* Y *from a line* L *to the line joining* Y *to the pole of* L, *is an involution.*

We leave to the reader the statement of the duals of Theorem 6.6a for singular forms, and of Theorem 6.7 and Corollaries 6.1, 6.2, 6.3.

DEFINITION 6.5. If the polars, with respect to a given nonsingular form, of a set of points $\{X\}$ is a set of lines $\{U'\}$, the two sets $\{X\}$ and $\{U'\}$ are said to be *mutually polar* with respect to the given form. In particular, we speak of two mutually polar triangles, a quadrangle and quadrilateral that are mutually polar, etc.

DEFINITION 6.6. A triangle is *self-polar* (or *self-conjugate*), with respect to a given nonsingular form, if the polar of each vertex is the opposite side.

Clearly, if the polars of two of the vertices of a triangle are the opposite sides, the third side is the polar of the third vertex, and the triangle is self-polar.

That there exist triangles that are self-polar with respect to a given form can be seen as follows: Let Y be any point that is not self-conjugate, and let Z be a point (not self-conjugate) on the polar of Y; the polar of Z contains Y, and the pole of $Y \oplus Z$ is the point of intersection of the polars of Y and Z.

The equation of a conic can be simplified by choosing as the reference triangle of the coordinate system a triangle that is self-polar.

THEOREM 6.8. *The coordinate triangle is self-polar with respect to the nonsingular form* $[\mathbf{X}^T\mathbf{B}\mathbf{X}]$ *if and only if* $\mathbf{B}$ *is a nonsingular diagonal matrix* (*that is*, $\det \mathbf{B} \neq 0$; $b_{ij} = 0$, $i \neq j$).

Proof. From equation (6.4), the polar of the point $(1, 0, 0)^T$ is the line U where

$$\mathbf{U} = (1, 0, 0)\mathbf{B}, \quad \text{or} \quad \mathbf{U} = (b_{11}, b_{12}, b_{13}).$$

This is the line $(1, 0, 0)$ (that is, $x_1 = 0$) if and only if $b_{11} \neq 0$ and $b_{12} = b_{13} = 0$. Similarly, the point $(0, 1, 0)$ and the line $(0, 1, 0)$ are pole and polar if and only if $b_{22} \neq 0$ and $b_{21} = b_{23} = 0$, and the theorem is proved.

We have previously seen that in $S_2(\mathsf{C})$ all nonsingular conics, and consequently all nonsingular forms, are projectively equivalent. We could have proved this result by means of the polar theory of forms by reducing a given form first to the form

$$Q = b_1 x_1^2 + b_2 x_2^2 + b_3 x_3^2, \tag{6.12}$$

and then applying the transformation

$$x_i' = \sqrt{b_i}\, x_i. \tag{6.13}$$

In $S_2(\mathsf{C})$, $\sqrt{b_i}$ exists, and the coordinate transformation (6.13) preserves the triangle of reference while changing the unit point; it reduces the form (6.12) to the sum of squares

$$Q = x_1^2 + x_2^2 + x_3^2. \tag{6.14}$$

In $S_2(\mathsf{F})$, two nonsingular forms are not necessarily equivalent.

THEOREM 6.9. *In $S_2(\mathsf{R})$, the two classes of forms $[Q_1]$, $[Q_2]$, where*

$$Q_1 = x_1^2 + x_2^2 + x_3^2, \qquad Q_2 = x_1^2 + x_2^2 - x_3^2, \tag{6.15}$$

are not projectively equivalent; every nonsingular form Q belongs to a class $[Q]$ which is projectively equivalent to either $[Q_1]$ or $[Q_2]$.

Proof. The forms Q_1, Q_2 are clearly not projectively equivalent, since the equation $Q_2 = 0$ represents a conic, while $Q_1 = 0$ does not. By Theorem 6.8, any nonsingular form is reducible to (6.12); since we can, if necessary, renumber the x's and represent $[Q]$ by $-Q$ instead of Q, we can suppose that in (6.12) $b_1 > 0$, $b_2 > 0$. Then the transformation

$$x_1' = \sqrt{b_1}\, x_1, \qquad x_2' = \sqrt{b_2}\, x_2, \qquad x_3' = \sqrt{|b_3|}\, x_3$$

transforms (6.12) into one or the other of the two forms (6.15).

Clearly the reduction to the form (6.14) is possible in $S_2(\mathsf{F})$ whenever every element of F is a square, while Theorem 6.9 holds not only in the real field, but also in every field in which every element is either a square or the negative of a square.

The polar theory of quadratic forms plays a fundamental role in the development of relationships between projective geometry and either Euclidean geometry or the classical non-Euclidean geometries. This aspect of polar theory will be developed further in Sections 8, 9, 10 and in Chapter V. In the following two theorems, we illustrate the role this theory plays in the development of projective relations; further illustrations are to be found among the exercises.

THEOREM 6.10. *If two triangles with distinct vertices are mutually polar, they are Desarguean.*

Proof. Let the triangles be $A_1 A_2 A_3$ and $B_1 B_2 B_3$, where the polar of

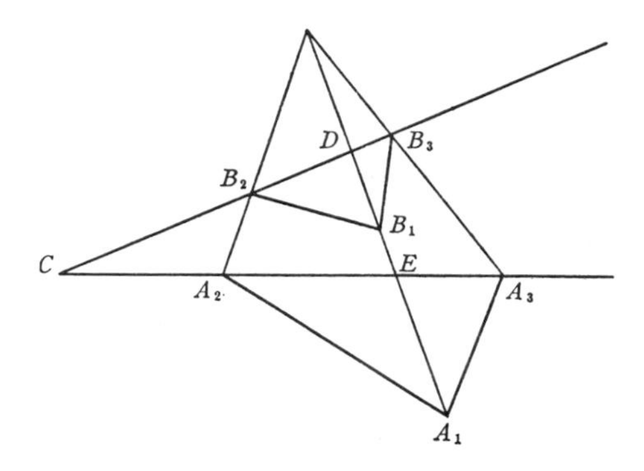

FIGURE 6.2

A_1 is the side opposite B_1. Let $C = (A_2 \oplus A_3) \cap (B_2 \oplus B_3)$, $D = (A_1 \oplus B_1) \cap (B_2 \oplus B_3)$, $E = (A_1 \oplus B_1) \cap (A_2 \oplus A_3)$ (Figure 6.2). Then the pole of $A_1 \oplus B_1$ is C, and we have

$$(A_2 E, A_3 C) = (A_2 B_1, A_3 C)_{A_1} = (B_3 C, B_2 D) = (B_2 D, B_3 C),$$

where the second equality is justified by Theorem 6.2. Comparing the first cross ratio with the last, we see that the projectivity that maps A_2, E, A_3 onto B_2, D, B_3 is a perspectivity. Since $E \oplus D = A_1 \oplus B_1$, the triangles are Desarguean. We note further that the point and line from which the triangles are perspective are pole and polar.

THEOREM 6.11. *If two pairs of opposite vertices of a quadrilateral are conjugate with respect to a form* $[Q] = [\mathbf{X}^T\mathbf{B}\mathbf{X}]$, *the third pair of opposite vertices is also conjugate with respect to the form.*

Proof. We can choose projective coordinates so that the reference lines of the coordinate system are the sides of the quadrilateral. Then the three pairs of opposite vertices are the three pairs of points:

$$(1,0,0)^T, (0,1,-1)^T; \qquad (0,1,0)^T, (1,0,-1)^T; \qquad (0,0,1)^T, (1,-1,0)^T.$$

A necessary condition that each of the first two pairs consist of mutually conjugate points is

$$(1,0,0)\mathbf{B}\begin{pmatrix}0\\1\\-1\end{pmatrix}=0, \qquad (0,1,0)\mathbf{B}\begin{pmatrix}1\\0\\-1\end{pmatrix}=0,$$

or

$$b_{12}-b_{13}=0, \qquad b_{21}-b_{23}=0.$$

Since $\mathbf{B}=\mathbf{B}^T$, we have that

$$b_{31}-b_{32}=0.$$

But this is a sufficient condition that the third pair be conjugate points.

We note that we did not require that the form Q be nonsingular.

EXERCISES

1. Determine which, if any, of the following pairs of points are conjugate with respect to $x_1^2+2x_1x_3-x_2^2+x_3^2$: $(1,2,3)^T$ and $(2,1,-1)^T$; $(2,1,1)^T$ and $(2,3,1)^T$; $(1,1,-1)^T$ and $(3,0,1)^T$.

2. Find the polar of the point $(1,2,3)^T$ and the pole of the line $(1,2,3)$ with respect to $x_1^2+2x_1x_2-x_3^2$.

ANS. $(3,1,-3)$; $(-2,1,3)^T$.

3. Find the polar of the point $(2,1,0)^T$ and the pole of the line $(1,-1,1)$ with respect to $u_1^2+2u_1u_2-2u_2u_3+u_3^2$.

ANS. $(3,1,1)$; $(0,0,1)^T$.

4. Find the matrix of a transformation in $G_8(\mathsf{R})$ that reduces the form $x_1^2+3x_1x_2+4x_2^2+2x_1x_3-4x_2x_3+x_3^2$ to one of the forms (6.15).

5. Find the matrix of a transformation that reduces the form $u_1^2+u_1u_2-2u_2^2+u_1u_3-u_3^2$ to the form (6.12) (take F as the field of rationals).

6. Prove that the points Y and Z are conjugate with respect to $[\mathbf{UBU}^T]$ ($\mathbf{B}=\mathbf{B}^T$, $\det \mathbf{B}\neq 0$) if and only if

$$\begin{vmatrix} b_{11} & b_{12} & b_{13} & y_1\\ b_{21} & b_{22} & b_{23} & y_2\\ b_{31} & b_{32} & b_{33} & y_3\\ z_1 & z_2 & z_3 & 0 \end{vmatrix}=0.$$

7. Let V, W be two nonconjugate lines (with respect to a given form). A point $X\in V$ determines a unique point $X'\in W$ conjugate to X. Prove: The map $X\to X'$ is a projectivity; it is a perspectivity if and only if $V\cap W$ is self-conjugate.

8. Show that if Z lies on the polar of Y with respect to a conic, the points of contact of the tangents to the conic from Z (when they exist) are collinear with Y.

9. Prove that if Y is an arbitrary point not on a given conic, if V is the polar of Y, and Z is any point on the conic, the points in which V is intersected by the line $Y \oplus Z$ and the tangent at Z are conjugate points.

10. Prove that if two lines are conjugate with respect to a nonsingular form, they intersect the polar of their intersection in conjugate points.

11. Let A, B be any two distinct points not incident to their polars, α, β. Prove that the points in which α is intersected by the lines $A \oplus B$ and β are conjugate points.

#***12.** Prove that if a quadrangle is inscribed in a nonsingular conic, its diagonal triangle is self-polar with respect to the conic, and conversely, every triangle self-polar with respect to a nonsingular conic is the diagonal triangle of an inscribed quadrangle one of whose vertices is any point of the conic, not on the sides of the given triangle (see Exercise 14).

13. Given six points A, B, C, D, E, Y, no three of which are collinear. Construct the polar of Y, with respect to the conic containing A, B, C, D, E, in terms of joins and intersections.

14. Let P and Q be conjugate points, and not self-conjugate, with respect to a nonsingular conic $\mathscr{C}$, and let $R \in \mathscr{C}$, $R \notin P \oplus Q$. If $P \oplus R$ and $Q \oplus R$ intersect $\mathscr{C}$ again in P' and Q', respectively, show that $(Q \oplus P') \cap (P \oplus Q') \in \mathscr{C}$ and that $P \oplus Q$ and $P' \oplus Q'$ are conjugate lines.

#**15.** Let A and B be given points not conjugate with respect to a given nonsingular form, and let α and β be their polars. A variable point Q of β determines a point R, on $A \oplus Q$, conjugate to Q. Find the locus of R.

16. Prove that if a line intersects two sides of a triangle inscribed in a nonsingular conic in conjugate points, it contains the pole of the third side.

***17.** Prove that in $S_2(\mathsf{R})$ the polar of an interior point is an exterior line and that of an exterior point is an interior line.

***18.** Prove that in $S_2(\mathsf{R})$, if α is a line not tangent to a nonsingular conic, the involution induced on α by the conic is elliptic or hyperbolic according as α is an exterior or interior line. State the dual.

19. Prove: If two nonsingular conics have four distinct points of intersection, there exists exactly one triangle which is self-conjugate with respect to both conics.

7 Conics in E_2

Let $\mathscr{E}$ be an embedding of E_2 in $S_2(\mathsf{R})$ (see III, 10). In the absence of a contrary statement, we shall suppose throughout this section that (x, y)

denotes Cartesian and [X] projective coordinates in terms of which $\mathscr{E}$ is given by

$$(7.1) \qquad x = x_1/x_3, \qquad y = x_2/x_3.$$

We shall let $\mathscr{C}_E$ denote a conic in E_2, the locus of a quadratic equation

$$(7.2) \qquad b_{11}x^2 + 2b_{12}xy + b_{22}y^2 + 2b_{13}x + 2b_{23}y + b_{33} = 0.$$

Then $\mathscr{E}\mathscr{C}_E$ is contained in the projective conic $\mathscr{C}_S$

$$(7.3) \qquad \mathbf{X}^T\mathbf{B}\mathbf{X} = 0, \qquad \mathbf{B} = (b_{ij}) = \mathbf{B}^T,$$

and since only points of $l(\mathscr{E})$, the absolute line of the embedding, are not in the range of $\mathscr{E}$, we have

$$\mathscr{E}\mathscr{C}_E = \mathscr{C}_S - (\mathscr{C}_S \cap l(\mathscr{E})).$$

We shall call $\mathscr{E}\mathscr{C}_E$ the *strict* image, $\mathscr{C}_S$ the *extended* image of $\mathscr{C}_E$ under $\mathscr{E}$, and $\mathscr{C}_E$ the *inverse* image of $\mathscr{C}_S$ under $\mathscr{E}$. For simplicity of expression, *image* will mean extended image.

Similar remarks apply to analogous situations. If L is a line in E_2, $\mathscr{E}L$ is the strict image, and the extended image is the unique line in S_2 that contains $\mathscr{E}L$. In a similar vein, we shall say that a point and a line are pole and polar with respect to a conic in E_2, if the extended images are in that relation in S_2.

For $\mathscr{C}_S$ nonsingular, the point set $\mathscr{C}_S \cap l(\mathscr{E})$ is empty, or consists of one or two points, according as $l(\mathscr{E})$ is an exterior line, or a tangent line, or an interior line of $\mathscr{C}_S$. If $l(\mathscr{E})$ is an exterior line, $\mathscr{C}_E$ is a closed curve; otherwise it is open, consisting of one or two branches. Taking for granted that these properties serve to distinguish Euclidean conics, we have proved the following theorem.

THEOREM 7.1. *An embedding $\mathscr{E}$ maps a Euclidean conic into a projective conic. Conversely, the inverse image under $\mathscr{E}$ of a nonsingular conic $\mathscr{C}_S$ in $S_2(\mathsf{R})$ is an ellipse, hyperbola, or parabola according as the absolute line of $\mathscr{E}$ is exterior, interior, or tangent to $\mathscr{C}_S$.*

THEOREM 7.2. *If $\mathscr{C}_E$ and $\mathscr{C}_S$ are given nonsingular conics in E_2 and $S_2(\mathsf{R})$ respectively, there exists an embedding $\mathscr{E}$ which maps $\mathscr{C}_E$ into $\mathscr{C}_S$.*

Proof. Let $\mathscr{C}_E$ be given by (7.2). In $S_2(\mathsf{R})$, two nonsingular conics are projectively equivalent, and therefore we can choose projective coordinates $\mathbf{X}$ in S_2 so that $\mathscr{C}_S$ is given by (7.3). Then (7.1) is the required embedding.

We can formulate a slightly stronger theorem than the preceding one.

THEOREM 7.3. *Let $\mathscr{C}_E$, $\mathscr{C}'_E$, $\mathscr{C}''_E$ be the circle $x^2 + y^2 = 1$, the hyperbola $xy = 1$, the parabola $y^2 = x$ respectively; let $\mathscr{C}_S$ be a given nonsingular conic in $S_2(\mathsf{R})$ and let l, l', l'' be an exterior line, an interior line, a tangent line of $\mathscr{C}_S$*

respectively. There exist embeddings $\mathscr{E}$, $\mathscr{E}'$, $\mathscr{E}''$ of E_2 in $S_2(\mathsf{R})$ whose absolute lines are l, l', l'' respectively, and whose inverse images of $\mathscr{C}_S$ are $\mathscr{C}_E$, $\mathscr{C}'_E$ $\mathscr{C}''_E$ respectively.

Proof. In the first case, we can choose in $S_2(\mathsf{R})$ a self-conjugate triangle $A_1 A_2 A_3$ where A_1 is the pole of l and A_2, A_3 are conjugate points on l. We then choose the unit point so that the equation of $\mathscr{C}_S$ is $x_1^2 + x_2^2 - x_3^2 = 0$, and that of l is $x_3 = 0$. The embedding (7.1) for this coordinatization is the required one. In the second and third cases we choose a coordinatization in which $\mathscr{C}_S$ has the equation $x_1 x_3 - x_2^2 = 0$ (see Theorem 4.2) with l':$x_2 = 0$, and l'':$x_3 = 0$, respectively. The embedding $x = x_1/x_2$, $y = x_3/x_2$ works in the second case, and (7.1) in the third.

These theorems enable us to interpret in E_2 projective properties of conics, and to generalize special Euclidean properties. We shall illustrate this procedure later in this section; first we need to formulate certain Euclidean relations and to reformulate others projectively.

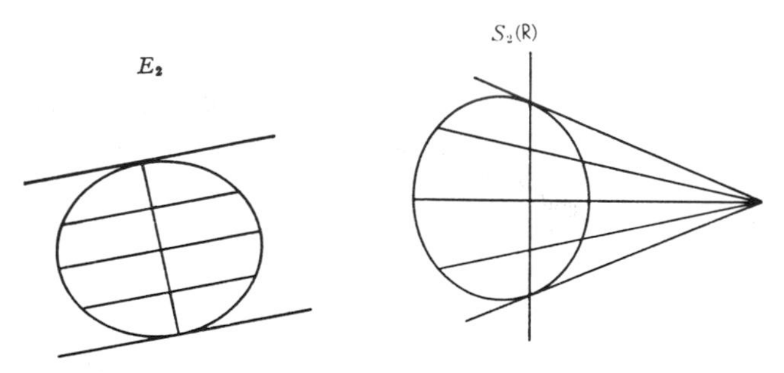

FIGURE 7.1

In E_2, a hyperbola and an asymptote have an empty intersection, and any other line parallel to the asymptote has one point of intersection; these intersection properties characterize an asymptote. Hence the image of an asymptote under an embedding must be the tangent line to the image conic at an absolute point. Similarly, the diameters of a parabola map into the pencil of lines through the point of contact of the image conic with the absolute line of the embedding.

The center of a central conic is the midpoint of all chords through it; hence an embedding $\mathscr{E}$ maps the center onto the pole of $l(\mathscr{E})$, and a diameter into a line incident to the pole of $l(\mathscr{E})$ (recall II, Corollary 4.1, and IV, Theorem 6.7). The locus of the midpoints of a family of parallel chords of a conic in E_2 is contained in a diameter, because the locus is the inverse image of the polar of the absolute point corresponding to the parallel pencil (Figure 7.1). Two diameters (of a central conic) each bisecting the chords parallel to the other are conjugate lines, in the projective sense, with respect to the conic. Therefore, two conjugate diameters in E_2 map into two lines which with the absolute line of the embedding form a self-conjugate triangle.

The conic (7.3) induces on $x_3 = 0$ the involution (see Theorem 6.6a) given by

$$b_{11}x_1x_1' + b_{12}(x_1x_2' + x_2x_1') + b_{22}x_2x_2' = 0. \tag{7.4}$$

This involution coincides with the absolute involution (see page 168) of $\mathscr{E}$

$$x_1x_1' + x_2x_2' = 0 \tag{7.5}$$

if and only if

$$b_{11} = b_{22}, \qquad b_{12} = 0. \tag{7.6}$$

But (7.6) characterizes nonsingular conics (7.2) that are circles. Hence $\mathscr{E}$ maps circles, and only circles, onto conics whose induced involution on $l(\mathscr{E})$ is the absolute involution. On the other hand, by Theorem 7.2, there exists an embedding which maps a given circle in E_2 onto a given nonsingular conic $\mathscr{C}_S$ in $S_2(\mathsf{R})$. To find such an embedding, we need only to characterize geometrically a reference frame in $S_2(\mathsf{R})$ in which (7.6) holds: We choose A_1, A_2 as conjugate points on an exterior line of $\mathscr{C}_S$, we choose D_3 as either point of the unique pair of points on $A_1 \oplus A_2$ which are conjugate with respect to $\mathscr{C}_S$ and which separate A_1, A_2 harmonically (see II, 6, Exercise 10). Then we choose A_3, D to satisfy $D_3 = (A_1 \oplus A_2) \cap (A_3 \oplus D)$. For this choice of reference frame, D_3 has coordinate $[1, 1, 0]^T$, and (7.6) can be verified.

The axes of a central conic, not a circle, are the only two conjugate diameters that are orthogonal; hence they map into lines whose absolute points are the unique common pair in the two involutions on $l(\mathscr{E})$: the absolute involution, and the involution induced by the conic.

Illustration 1. Identify the inverse image of the conic

$$x_1^2 + 4x_2^2 + 2x_3^2 - 4x_1x_2 - 6x_2x_3 = 0 \tag{7.7}$$

under the embedding (7.1).

Solution. We can replace x_1, x_2, x_3 by x, y, 1 respectively to obtain

$$x^2 - 4xy + 4y^2 - 6y + 2 = 0. \tag{7.8}$$

The matrix of (7.7) is nonsingular, and its locus is tangent to $x_3 = 0$ at $(2, 1, 0)^T$. Hence (7.8) is a parabola, and the lines $x - 2y + c = 0$ are diameters. Since $(2, 1, 0)^T$ and $(1, -2, 0)^T$ are conjugate points in the absolute involution, the axis of the parabola is the inverse image of the polar of $(1, -2, 0)^T$; since

$$\begin{pmatrix} 1 & -2 & 0 \\ -2 & 4 & -3 \\ 0 & -3 & 2 \end{pmatrix}\begin{pmatrix} 1 \\ -2 \\ 0 \end{pmatrix} = \begin{pmatrix} 5 \\ -10 \\ 6 \end{pmatrix},$$

it is the line $5x - 10y + 6 = 0$.

Illustration 2. Identify the inverse image of (7.7) under the embedding $x = x_2/x_1$, $y = x_3/x_1$.

Solution. Replacing x_1, x_2, x_3 in (7.7) by 1, x, y, respectively, we obtain

$$4x^2 - 6xy + 2y^2 - 4x + 1 = 0. \tag{7.9}$$

Since the line $x_1 = 0$ intersects the locus of (7.7) in $(0, 1, 2)^T$ and $(0, 1, 1)^T$, (7.9) is a hyperbola with the lines $x - y = 0$, $2x - y = 0$ parallel to the asymptotes. Since

$$\begin{pmatrix} 1 & -2 & 0 \\ -2 & 4 & -3 \\ 0 & -3 & 2 \end{pmatrix} \begin{pmatrix} 0 \\ 1 \\ 2 \end{pmatrix} = \begin{pmatrix} -2 \\ -2 \\ 1 \end{pmatrix},$$

the tangent to (7.7) at (0, 1, 2) is $2x_1 + 2x_2 - x_3 = 0$, and $2x - y + 2 = 0$ is one asymptote to (7.9).

Illustration 3. Find the center and axes of

$$x^2 + 2xy + 5y^2 + 6x - 4y = 0.$$

Solution. The center is the point (h, k) determined by

$$(0, 0, \rho)^T = \begin{pmatrix} 1 & 1 & 3 \\ 1 & 5 & -2 \\ 3 & -2 & 0 \end{pmatrix} \begin{pmatrix} h \\ k \\ 1 \end{pmatrix}.$$

The axes have slopes m, m' determined by the conditions that, in S_2, $(1, m, 0)^T$ and $(1, m', 0)^T$ satisfy (7.5) and (7.4) with $\mathbf{B}$ replaced by the above numerical matrix.

Illustration **4.** Find all parabolas tangent to the lines $x = 0$, $y = 0$, $x + y = 1$.

Solution. In S_2, we require the conics tangent to the lines (1, 0, 0), (0, 1, 0), (1, 1, −1), and (0, 0, 1). These conics constitute a pencil of line conics (see IV, 5, Exercise 6), and by the dual of (5.15a) their line equations are

$$h \begin{vmatrix} u_1 & u_2 & u_3 \\ 1 & 0 & 0 \\ 1 & 1 & -1 \end{vmatrix} \begin{vmatrix} u_1 & u_2 & u_3 \\ 0 & 1 & 0 \\ 0 & 0 & 1 \end{vmatrix} + k \begin{vmatrix} u_1 & u_2 & u_3 \\ 1 & 0 & 0 \\ 0 & 0 & 1 \end{vmatrix} \begin{vmatrix} u_1 & u_2 & u_3 \\ 0 & 1 & 0 \\ 1 & 1 & -1 \end{vmatrix} = 0.$$

Expanding these determinants, we obtain

$$(h + k)u_1 u_2 + h u_1 u_3 + k u_2 u_3 = 0.$$

Since

$$\begin{pmatrix} 0 & h + k & h \\ h + k & 0 & k \\ h & k & 0 \end{pmatrix}^{a} = \begin{pmatrix} -k^2 & hk & k(h + k) \\ hk & -h^2 & h(h + k) \\ k(h + k) & h(h + k) & -(h + k)^2 \end{pmatrix},$$

the required parabolas are

$$k^2x^2 - 2hkxy + h^2y^2 - 2k(h+k)x - 2h(h+k)y + (h+k)^2 = 0.$$

We note that a pencil of line conics need not be and generally is not a pencil of point conics.

Illustration 5. Find the equation of the hyperbolas with asymptotes the lines $x + y = 0$, $x - y - 2 = 0$.

Solution. In S_2 we would seek the conic tangent to two lines at their intersections with a third; the solution there is given by (5.15c). Hence the solution in E_2 is $(x+y)(x-y-2) + k = 0$, where k is arbitrary.

We commented earlier (page 80), that our definition of an embedding is incomplete. The incompleteness seems now to leave a hole in our logical structure; it would be reasonable to expect that there exist classes of embeddings of E_2 in $S_2(\mathsf{R})$, with the same absolute line, which possess the same absolute involutions. If that were not so, there would, for example, be no unique orthogonality in E_2. We shall find such related embeddings.

If m is a motion in E_2, and $\mathscr{E}$ an embedding of E_2 in S_2, $\mathscr{E}m$ is another embedding, and $\mathscr{E}m\mathscr{E}^{-1}$ is a map defined on $S_2 - l(\mathscr{E})$. By (III, Theorem 10.3) there exists a unique $g \in G_8$ which coincides with $\mathscr{E}m\mathscr{E}^{-1}$ on $S_2 - l(\mathscr{E})$; we shall refer to g as the *collineation corresponding to m*, under $\mathscr{E}$. We can show next that g leaves invariant a singular form $[\mathbf{UBU}^T]$ which, when $\mathscr{E}$ is given by (7.1), is the form $[u_1^2 + u_2^2]$. From our earlier equations of motions, we have that a representative matrix of g, when $\mathscr{E}$ is given by (7.1), is

$$\mathbf{A} = \begin{pmatrix} \cos\theta & \mp\sin\theta & e \\ \sin\theta & \pm\cos\theta & f \\ 0 & 0 & 1 \end{pmatrix}. \tag{7.10}$$

Since g acts on lines in accordance with $\mathbf{U} = \mathbf{U}'\mathbf{A}$ (see III, (3.2)), we have that $u_1 = u_1' \cos\theta + u_2' \sin\theta$, $u_2 = \mp(u_1' \sin\theta - u_2' \cos\theta)$, so that $u_1^2 + u_2^2 = u_1'^2 + u_2'^2$. Hence g leaves fixed the class of singular line forms $[Q]$, where $Q = u_1^2 + u_2^2$. The line conic $\mathscr{C}(Q)$ consists of just one line, $x_3 = 0$, which is the singular line of the conic. By the dual of Corollary 6.2, $\mathscr{C}(Q)$ establishes on $x_3 = 0$ the involution of conjugate points, and this involution is the absolute involution. Thus the two embeddings $\mathscr{E}$ and $\mathscr{E}m$ have the same absolute involution.

We are now able to give a projective interpretation of the foci of a conic $\mathscr{C}_E$. First let us consider the ellipse $x^2/a^2 + y^2/b^2 = 1$, where $0 < b \leqq a$. The embedding (7.1) maps the ellipse onto a conic whose equation, in line coordinates, is $a^2u_1^2 + b^2u_2^2 - u_3^2 = 0$. This conic and the singular line conic $u_1^2 + u_2^2 = 0$ determine the pencil of line conics

$$h(a^2u_1^2 + b^2u_2^2 - u_3^2) + k(u_1^2 + u_2^2) = 0. \tag{7.11}$$

The discriminant of (7.11) is $a(a^2h + k)(b^2h + k)h$, and hence the pencil (7.11) contains three singular line conics, with forms

$$(b^2 - a^2)u_2^2 - u_3^2, \qquad (a^2 - b^2)u_1^2 - u_3^2, \qquad u_1^2 + u_2^2$$

respectively. If $b < a$, the first of these forms does not possess real factors, so that only one of the singular line conics of the pencil (7.11) consists of two pencils of lines. This is the conic $(a^2 - b^2)u_1^2 - u_3^2 = 0$, which represents the points $(\pm\sqrt{a^2 - b^2}, 0, 1)^T$. Clearly $\mathscr{E}^{-1}$ maps these points onto the foci of the given ellipse. Because the conic $u_1^2 + u_2^2 = 0$ is invariant under the collineations in $S_2(\mathsf{R})$ that correspond to motions in E_2, it follows that the foci of any ellipse are the inverse images, under (7.1), of the unique two points that constitute a singular line conic in the pencil of line conics determined by $u_1^2 + u_2^2 = 0$ and the image under $\mathscr{E}$ of the given ellipse.

A similar conclusion holds for a hyperbola. The parabola $y^2 = 2px$ maps into the line conic $pu_2^2 = 2u_1 u_3$, and this conic, with $u_1^2 + u_2^2 = 0$, determines a pencil containing only two distinct singular line conics: $u_1^2 + u_2^2 = 0$ itself (counting doubly) and $pu_1^2 + 2u_1 u_3 = 0$. In $S_2(\mathsf{R})$, only the latter consists of pencils of lines: the pencils $u_1 = 0$ and $pu_1 + 2u_3 = 0$. $\mathscr{E}^{-1}$ maps the point $(p, 0, 2)^T$, the vertex of the second pencil, onto the focus of the given parabola.

These results might seem to take on a more simple form had we embedded E_2 in $S_2(\mathsf{C})$, the complex projective plane. In $S_2(\mathsf{C})$ the absolute involution (7.5) has two fixed points $(1, \pm i, 0)^T$ $(i^2 = -1)$, and the line conic $u_1^2 + u_2^2 = 0$ consists of two pencils of lines with $(1, \pm i, 0)^T$ as vertices. Many writers call these points *the circular points at infinity*, noting that they lie on every circle and that every conic through them is a circle. In this setting, the foci of a conic appear as the real intersections of tangents to the conic from the circular points. But such an approach would involve us in a detailed study of the structure of $S_2(\mathsf{C})$.†

We present two additional illustrations of the power of the methods that we have developed.

Illustration 6. Show that a variable tangent to a hyperbola determines with the asymptotes a triangle of constant area, and find a projective generalization.

Solution. We select two tangent lines to the hyperbola $xy = 1$, embed E_2 in $S_2(\mathsf{R})$, and label the various points as suggested by Figure 7.2. The reader can prove the theorem for this hyperbola by showing that

$$OP_1 \cdot OQ_1 = OP_2 \cdot OQ_2 \tag{7.12}$$

† From the point of view of real variables, $S_2(\mathsf{C})$ has real dimension four, and its lines have real dimension two. Moreover, any quadrangle in $S_2(\mathsf{C})$ determines a subspace with the properties of $S_2(\mathsf{R})$. For the analogous subspace in $S_1(\mathsf{C})$, see (V, Definition 10.1).

where OP_1, OQ_1, etc. denote directed lengths. Hence $OP_1/OP_2 = OQ_2/OQ_1$; letting the embedding be $\mathscr{E}$, we obtain (see II, (4.5) and (3.10)) the projective relation

$$(A_1\ \mathscr{E}O,\ \mathscr{E}P_2\ \mathscr{E}P_1) = (\mathscr{E}O\ A_2,\ \mathscr{E}Q_2\ \mathscr{E}Q_1). \tag{7.13}$$

By Theorem 7.3 the cross ratios are equal for any conic and $A_1 \oplus A_2$ any interior line; hence $A_1 \oplus \mathscr{E}O$, and $A_2 \oplus \mathscr{E}O$ are any two tangents, and we have proved the first part of Theorem 5.5. We can now choose an embedding whose inverse maps a given conic in $S_2(\mathsf{R})$ onto a given hyperbola; the equation corresponding to (7.12) will be a consequence of (7.13), and the Euclidean theorem is proved for any hyperbola.

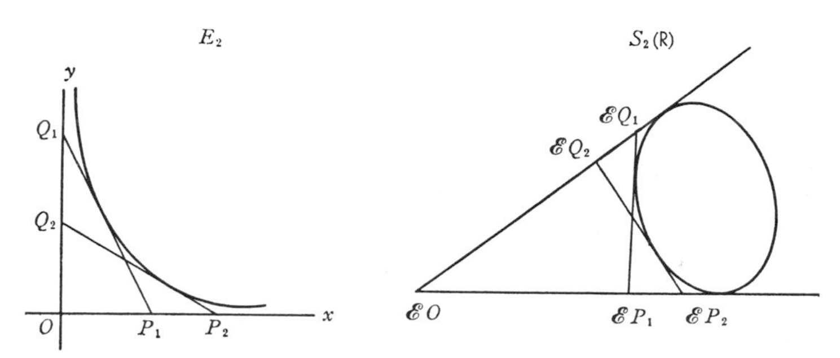

FIGURE 7.2

Let us digress briefly. We note that two conics in $S_2(\mathsf{R})$ induce the same involution on the join of any two of their points of intersection. On such a line, the involution is hyperbolic with fixed points the points of intersection. We have already seen (with the aid of circles) that there exist conics which induce the same elliptic involution on a given line. Can we characterize such pairs of conics without resorting to imaginary points of intersection? We proceed to do so. Without loss of generality, we suppose that in $S_2(\mathsf{F})$ the conics

$$\mathbf{X}^T\mathbf{B}\mathbf{X} = 0, \qquad \mathbf{X}^T\mathbf{B}'\mathbf{X} = 0$$

induce the same involution on the line $x_3 = 0$. Then by (7.4) there exists $\rho \neq 0$ such that

$$(b_{11}, b_{12}, b_{22}) = \rho(b'_{11}, b'_{12}, b'_{22});$$

this implies that $\mathbf{X}^T(\mathbf{B} - \rho\mathbf{B}')\mathbf{X}$ is the product of two linear forms, one of which is x_3 itself. The other will be proportional to x_3 if and only if the poles of the line $x_3 = 0$ with respect to the two conics coincide. Thus a line on which two conics induce the same involution of conjugate points is one component of a singular conic of their (point) pencil; the other component is another such line, and it is distinct from the first except as noted.

Some authors refer to these two lines in $S_2(\mathsf{R})$ as the (real) lines joining pairs of conjugate-imaginary points of intersection.

Illustration 7. Determine the projective content of the theorem that the radical axes of three circles not belonging to one pencil of circles are concurrent or parallel.

Solution. The radical axis of two nonconcentric circles,

$$x^2 + y^2 + 2b_{13}x + 2b_{23}y + b_{33} = 0,$$
$$x^2 + y^2 + 2b'_{13}x + 2b'_{23}y + b'_{33} = 0$$

is the line

$$2(b_{13} - b'_{13})x + 2(b_{23} - b'_{23})y + b_{33} - b'_{33} = 0.$$

An embedding $\mathscr{E}$ maps the circles onto two conics whose point pencil contains one real singular conic; this conic consists of $l(\mathscr{E})$ and the image of the radical axis. Our earlier results inform us that in E_2 the radical axis is the unique line on which the two circles induce the same involution. We might conjecture the following theorems.

(A) *If, in* $S_2(\mathsf{C})$, *three conics, not belonging to a point pencil, have in common two simple intersections, their opposite common chords are concurrent.*

In $S_2(\mathsf{R})$, our conjecture cannot take quite so simple a form:

(B) *If three conics in* $S_2(\mathsf{R})$, *not belonging to one point pencil, induce on a line L the same involution of conjugate points, each two conics determine a* (*point*) *pencil containing a singular* (*point*) *conic of which L is one component; the other three components are concurrent.*

We note that both of these conjectured theorems are stronger than what we obtain directly from the embedding relation: in (B) we have not retained the condition that the common involution be elliptic so that satisfaction of the hypothesis of (B) does not imply that an embedding exists which maps the three conics onto circles. Nevertheless we can prove both (A) and (B) directly, choosing coordinates in terms of which L (or the join of the two intersections) has the equation $x_3 = 0$. Then equations of three conics can be written as

$$(7.14)\qquad (x_1, x_2)\begin{pmatrix} b_{11} & b_{12} \\ b_{21} & b_{22} \end{pmatrix}\begin{pmatrix} x_1 \\ x_2 \end{pmatrix} + x_3(v^i_1 x_1 + v^i_2 x_2 + v^i_3 x_3) = 0, \qquad i = 1, 2, 3.$$

If we let $\mathbf{V}^i = (v^i_1, v^i_2, v^i_3)$, the three opposite common chords in $S_2(\mathsf{C})$ or the three other components in $S_2(\mathsf{R})$ have representatives $\mathbf{V}^1 - \mathbf{V}^2$, $\mathbf{V}^2 - \mathbf{V}^3$, and $\mathbf{V}^3 - \mathbf{V}^1$; clearly these lines are concurrent.

We obtain a new theorem in E_2 if we take the inverse map of the conics (7.14) under the embedding (7.1).

If three nonconcentric conics in E_2 are similar and have parallel axes, the three common chords are concurrent or parallel.

This theorem remains true if the conics do not intersect provided that we replace "the common chord" of each pair of conics by "the unique line on which the conics of the pair induce the same involution."

EXERCISES

1. Find the equation of the hyperbola through the point $(3, 1)$ with asymptotes $x - 2y = 0$, $x + y - 1 = 0$.

ANS. $(x - 2y)(x + y - 1) = 3$.

2. Find the diameter of the parabola $x^2 - 2xy + y^2 - 4x + 2y - 3 = 0$ that passes through the point $(1, 2)$.

ANS. $x - y + 1 = 0$.

3. Find the center and asymptotes (if any) of the conic

$$x^2 + 2xy + 3y^2 + 4x - 1 = 0.$$

ANS. $(-3, 1)$.

4. Find the equation of the conic, through the origin and unit point, for which the x-axis and the line $2x - y = 4$ are conjugate diameters.

ANS. $x^2 - xy + 2y^2 - 4x + 2y = 0$.

5. Prove that the center of the conic $f(x, y) = 0$ is given by solving $\dfrac{\partial f(x, y)}{\partial x} = 0$, $\dfrac{\partial f(x, y)}{\partial y} = 0$ simultaneously.

6. Prove: A necessary and sufficient condition that the center of a nonsingular conic be $(0, 0)$ is that the equation of the conic contain no linear terms.

7. Find the equations of all conics that have (x_0, y_0) as their center.

8. Prove: A necessary and sufficient condition that the lines $\lambda x + \mu y = 0$, $\lambda' x + \mu' y = 0$ be conjugate diameters of a nonsingular conic

$$Ax^2 + 2Bxy + Cy^2 + F = 0$$

is that

$$C\lambda\lambda' - B(\lambda\mu' + \lambda'\mu) + A\mu\mu' = 0.$$

9. Prove that the center of an ellipse is an interior point, and that of a hyperbola is an exterior point.

10. Find the foci of $x^2 + 2xy + 5y^2 = 10$.

11. Prove that the polar of a focus of a conic in E_2 is the directrix.

In Exercises 12, 13, 14 *it is assumed that one can draw a line through two points, a line through a given point parallel to a given line, and mark the point of intersection of nonparallel lines.*

#**12.** Construct the center of a conic through five given points (no three collinear), and thus derive a geometric condition that the conic through five given points be a parabola.

13. Construct additional points on the hyperbola through four given points with one asymptote parallel to a given line. What are the incidence relations that the line and the points must satisfy if the hyperbola is to exist?

14. Construct a diameter of a parabola, given four of its tangents.

15. A parallelogram is inscribed in an ellipse. Prove that the tangents at the four vertices are the sides of a circumscribed parallelogram and that its diagonals are conjugate diameters of the ellipse.

#**16.** Let t_i $(i = 1, 2, 3, 4, 5)$ be five given lines, no two of which are parallel and no three concurrent, and let P_j be the point of intersection of t_j and t_{j+1} $(j = 1, 2, 3, 4)$. Prove that a necessary and sufficient condition that there exist a parabola tangent to the five lines t_i is that the parallel to t_5 through P_2, the parallel to t_1 through P_3, and $P_1 \oplus P_4$ be concurrent.

17. Two opposite vertices of a parallelogram are points of a parabola, and two of the sides are the tangent lines to the parabola at these points. Prove that the diagonal determined by the other two vertices is a diameter of the parabola.

#**18.** Prove: If $\mathscr{E}$ and $\mathscr{E}'$, two embeddings of E_2 in $S_2(\mathsf{R})$, have the same absolute involution, $\mathscr{E}^{-1}\mathscr{E}'$ is a motion.

19. Prove: If Q_1, Q_2 are two nonsingular quadratic forms in $S_2(\mathsf{F})$, and if $\lambda, \mu \in \mathsf{F}$ exist for which $\lambda Q_1 + \mu Q_2$ is the product of linear forms $\mathbf{V}_1\mathbf{X}$ and $\mathbf{V}_2\mathbf{X}$, then the forms Q_1 and Q_2 induce the same involution of conjugate points on the lines V_1 and V_2.

#**20.** Let $ABCDEF$ be a simple hexagon with pairs of opposite sides parallel. Show that the three points of intersection of the diagonals of the simple quadrilaterals $ABCF$, $ABDE$, and $CFED$ are collinear.

#**21.** The vertices A, D and the parallel sides, $A \oplus B$ and $D \oplus C$, of a trapezoid $ABCD$ are given. Find the envelope of $B \oplus C$ if the product of the directed distances AB and DC is constant.

#**22.** The tangents at the vertices of an equilateral triangle inscribed in a circle are the sides of a second equilateral triangle, and the two triangles have the same medians and the same centroid. Verify this, and derive a projective generalization.

23. The tangent to a hyperbola at a point P intersects the asymptotes in A, B. Prove that the diameter through P and the lines through A and B respectively parallel to the other asymptote are concurrent.

8 Correlations

So far we have studied some of the properties of poles and polars and learned how to find the polar of a point or the pole of a line. We now wish to regard the pole-polar relationship dynamically, that is, as a map or transformation operating on all the points of the plane simultaneously. In order to make this concept clear and precise, we must reconsider our ideas of projective transformations.

We have previously defined a projective transformation of $S_2(\mathsf{F})$ onto itself. We now broaden this concept, to permit our speaking of projective transformations of one space $S_2(\mathsf{F})$ onto a second space $S_2'(\mathsf{F})$ over the same ground field. We let $(x_1, x_2, x_3)^T$ and $(x_1', x_2', x_3')^T$ be projective coordinates in S_2 and S_2', respectively. The equation

$$[\mathbf{X}'] = [\mathbf{AX}], \qquad \det \mathbf{A} \neq 0, \tag{8.1}$$

represents a map of the points of S_2 onto the points of S_2'; we can solve (8.1), since $\det \mathbf{A} \neq 0$, to obtain

$$[\mathbf{X}] = [\mathbf{A}^{-1}\mathbf{X}'], \tag{8.2}$$

so that either (8.1) or (8.2) determines a one-to-one map between the points of S_2 and S_2'.

DEFINITION 8.1. A one-to-one map between two projective spaces over the same ground field, which is linear and homogeneous in terms of projective coordinates in the two spaces, is called a *projective map*, or a *collineation* from either space onto the other.

Clearly this definition is consistent with our previous usage.

THEOREM 8.1. *A projective map from $S_2(\mathsf{F})$ onto $S_2'(\mathsf{F})$ maps the lines of S_2 onto the lines of S_2', pencils of lines of S_2 onto pencils of lines of S_2', conics of S_2 onto conics of S_2'. If A, B, C, D are any four elements of S_2 whose cross ratio is defined, their cross ratio is equal to the cross ratio of the transformed elements.*

Proof. If we transform coordinates in S_2' by the equations

$$\mathbf{X}'' = \mathbf{A}^{-1}\mathbf{X}',$$

the map (8.1) is given by

$$\mathbf{X}'' = \mathbf{X}.$$

Since collinear points, concurrent lines, points of a conic, and cross ratio are determined by conditions solely on the projective coordinates, the theorem is proved. More generally, any projective invariant (invariant property or relation) of S_2 is transformed into the same invariant in S_2'.

From (III, Theorem 8.6) we have the following theorem.

THEOREM 8.2. *A one-to-one map of* $S_2(\mathsf{R})$ *onto* $S_2'(\mathsf{R})$ *that maps collinear points onto collinear points is a collineation.*

DEFINITION 8.2. A transformation

$$\text{(8.3)} \qquad \text{(a)}\ [\mathbf{U}'] = [\mathbf{X}^T\mathbf{A}], \quad \text{or} \quad \text{(b)}\ [\mathbf{X}'] = [\mathbf{A}\mathbf{U}^T]$$

of the points (or lines) of a given $S_2(\mathsf{F})$ into its lines (or points) is called a *correlation.* The correlation is *singular* if its determinant vanishes.

THEOREM 8.3. *A nonsingular correlation transforms elements of* $S_2(\mathsf{F})$ *into their dual elements, and preserves cross ratio.*

Proof. A nonsingular correlation can be regarded as a projective correspondence between the given space S_2 and the space Σ_2, consisting of the lines of S_2 (see III, Theorem 3.1).

A nonsingular correlation (8.3a) maps the points of the line $\mathbf{UX} = 0$ onto the lines U' of the pencil $\mathbf{U}'\mathbf{A}^{-1}\mathbf{U}^T = 0$. Hence the map of the line U is the point X' where

$$\text{(8.4)} \qquad [\mathbf{X}'] = [\mathbf{A}^{-1}\mathbf{U}^T].$$

Thus (8.3a) and (8.4) represent the same correlation, and the class of nonsingular correlations (8.3b) coincides with the nonsingular correlations (8.3a).

The pole-polar relation determined by a nonsingular form $[\mathbf{X}^T\mathbf{B}\mathbf{X}]$ is given by

$$\text{(8.5)} \qquad [\mathbf{U}'] = [\mathbf{X}^T\mathbf{B}], \qquad \mathbf{X}' = [\mathbf{B}^{-1}\mathbf{U}^T], \qquad \mathbf{B} = \mathbf{B}^T.$$

Clearly, this is a correlation whose representative matrices are symmetric. Conversely, if one representative matrix of a correlation is symmetric, all are, independently of the reference frame (see Exercise 2 below), and the correlation is the pole-polar mapping of a quadratic form.

DEFINITION 8.3. A correlation $\mathbf{U}' = \mathbf{X}^T\mathbf{B}$ with symmetric matrix, $\mathbf{B} = \mathbf{B}^T$, is called the *polarity*† of the form $[Q] = [\mathbf{X}^T\mathbf{B}\mathbf{X}]$. The polarity is *singular* if Q is singular. A nonsingular polarity is *hyperbolic* or *elliptic* according as $\mathscr{C}(Q)$ does or does not exist.

From (8.5), the form $[\mathbf{X}^T\mathbf{B}\mathbf{X}]$ is transformed by its polarity into the form $[\mathbf{U}\mathbf{B}^{-1}\mathbf{U}^T]$; the polarity of the form $[\mathbf{U}\mathbf{B}^{-1}\mathbf{U}^T]$, regarded as a form in line coordinates, coincides with the polarity of the form $[\mathbf{X}^T\mathbf{B}\mathbf{X}]$. When

† The polarity of a conic is often called polar reciprocation with respect to the conic.

$\mathbf{X}^T\mathbf{B}\mathbf{X} = 0$ is a nonsingular conic, $\mathbf{U}\mathbf{B}^{-1}\mathbf{U}^T = 0$ is the line equation of the same conic; when the locus $\mathbf{X}^T\mathbf{B}\mathbf{X} = 0$ is empty, the form $\mathbf{U}\mathbf{B}^{-1}\mathbf{U}^T$ exists, and, from the point of view of polarities, the two forms are equivalent. We shall regard $\mathbf{X}^T\mathbf{B}\mathbf{X}$ and $\mathbf{U}\mathbf{B}^{-1}\mathbf{U}^T$ (det $\mathbf{B} \neq 0$) as the representation in point and line coordinates, respectively, of the same quadratic form.

In the rest of this section we consider only nonsingular correlations. We shall use the words pole and polar in the more general context.

DEFINITION 8.4. Let σ be a correlation, X a point, and U a line. The line σX is called the *polar* of X and the point σU the *pole* of U, under σ.

A point X lies on its polar U' under the correlation (8.3a) if and only if $\mathbf{U}'\mathbf{X} = 0$, or

$$\mathbf{X}^T\mathbf{A}\mathbf{X} = 0. \tag{8.6}$$

Note that a matrix of (8.6) is $\mathbf{A} + \mathbf{A}^T$, not $\mathbf{A}$. Similarly, a line U is incident to its pole X' if and only if

$$\mathbf{U}\mathbf{A}^{-1}\mathbf{U}^T = 0. \tag{8.7}$$

When F is algebraically closed, the correlation (8.3a) thus determines two conics, (8.6) and (8.7); one is the locus of points that lie on their polars, the other is the envelope of lines that contain their poles ($\mathbf{A}$ need not be symmetric, and (8.7) need not be the line equation of (8.6)). For any F, we call the forms that appear on the left sides of (8.6), (8.7) the *incidence forms* (conics) of the correlation (8.3a). If the correlation is a polarity, the incidence forms are equivalent. If $\mathbf{A} \neq \mathbf{A}^T$, the incidence forms are not equivalent, and the polar of a point of (8.6) under the correlation generally does not coincide with its polar under the polarity of (8.6).

THEOREM 8.4. *A nonsingular correlation in* $S_2(\mathsf{F})$ *is involutory if and only if it is a nonsingular polarity.*

Proof. A polarity is clearly involutory. Conversely, a given nonsingular correlation can be written as (8.3a) so that it induces the transformation (8.4) on the lines of $S_2(\mathsf{F})$. Hence its square is the collineation

$$\mathbf{X}' = \mathbf{A}^{-1}\mathbf{A}^T\mathbf{X}. \tag{8.8}$$

If the given correlation is involutory, the collineation (8.8) is the identity, that is,

$$\mathbf{A}^{-1}\mathbf{A}^T = \rho\mathbf{I}, \tag{8.9}$$

where $\mathbf{I}$ is the unit matrix; if we multiply on the left by $\mathbf{A}$, we obtain $\mathbf{A}^T = \rho\mathbf{A}$. Taking transposes, we have $\mathbf{A} = \rho\mathbf{A}^T$, and therefore $\mathbf{A} = \rho^2\mathbf{A}$. Since $\mathbf{A}$ is nonsingular, we can multiply by $\mathbf{A}^{-1}$ to obtain $\rho^2 = 1$. It follows that $\rho = 1$, or $\rho = -1$. In the latter case, $\mathbf{A}$ is skew-symmetric. But a skew-symmetric matrix of odd order is necessarily singular;† consequently $\rho = 1$, and $\mathbf{A}$ is symmetric.

THEOREM 8.5. *If a correlation maps each vertex of one triangle onto the opposite side, the correlation is a polarity, and the triangle is self-polar.*

The reader can give an analytic proof by choosing as the reference triangle the given triangle (see Theorem 6.8).

Let σ be a correlation, and let α be an arbitrary line not incident to its transform $\sigma\alpha$; let a transformation τ_α on the points of α be defined by $\tau_\alpha X = \alpha \cap \sigma X$. By Theorem 8.3 and (II, Theorem 3.4) τ_α is a projectivity on the line α. We call the projectivity τ_α the projectivity *induced* on α by the given correlation. We can now restate Theorem 6.6a as follows: *The projectivity induced by a polarity on any line not incident to its pole is an involution.*

LEMMA 8.1. *The projectivity induced by* (8.3a) *on the line* $x_3 = 0$ *is an involution if and only if* $a_{12} = a_{21}$, $a_{11}a_{22} - a_{12}^2 \neq 0$.

Proof. If X is the point $(x_1, x_2, 0)^T$, σX intersects $x_3 = 0$ in the point X':$(x_1', x_2', 0)^T$, where

$$(8.10) \qquad x_1' = a_{12}x_1 + a_{22}x_2, \qquad x_2' = -a_{11}x_1 - a_{21}x_2.$$

From (8.4) we see that $a_{11}a_{22} - a_{12}a_{21} = 0$ is equivalent to the condition that $x_3 = 0$ and its pole are incident, and then (8.10) maps all points into the pole. Otherwise $a_{12} = a_{21}$ is equivalent to the condition that (8.10) be an involution (see II, Theorem 6.3).

THEOREM 8.6. *A correlation which induces involutions on three independent lines is a polarity.*

An analytical proof based on the preceding lemma can be supplied by the reader.

We say that a correlation *interchanges* a point and a line if it maps each onto the other. Thus, if a correlation σ interchanges the point A and the line α,

$$(8.11) \qquad \sigma A = \alpha, \qquad \sigma\alpha = A, \qquad \sigma^2 A = A, \qquad \sigma^2\alpha = \alpha,$$

so that A and α are fixed under the collineation σ^2 given by (8.8). Conversely, if A is a fixed point of σ^2, $\sigma^2 A = A$, so that $\sigma(\sigma A) = A$ and $\sigma^2(\sigma A) = \sigma A$. Hence σA and A are interchanged by σ, and σA is a fixed

† A skew-symmetric matrix of even order need not vanish, and therefore involutory correlations that are not polarities exist in projective spaces of dimension three. These are called *null systems.*

line of σ^2. In $S_2(\mathsf{R})$, every collineation possesses at least one fixed point (see III, Theorem 11.2), and therefore every correlation interchanges at least one point-line pair.

THEOREM 8.7. *Let A_1, α and B_1, β be two point-line pairs with neither point incident to its line and with A_1, B_1, and $\alpha \cap \beta$ independent; a correlation which interchanges each of the two pairs is a polarity.*

Proof. Let σ be the correlation, and let $C = \alpha \cap \beta$, $\gamma = A \oplus B$. Then $\sigma C = \sigma\alpha \oplus \sigma\beta = \gamma$, and $\sigma\gamma = \sigma A \cap \sigma B = C$. It follows that the projectivity τ_α induced by σ on α interchanges C and $\alpha \cap \gamma$, so that this projectivity is an involution. A similar argument can be applied to τ_β and τ_γ, and the conclusion of the theorem is a consequence of Theorem 8.6.

We can classify correlations that are not polarities either by considering point-line pairs that are interchanged or by considering lines whose induced projectivities are involutions. For the latter, we let such a line be defined by points Y, Z. Introducing coordinates $(\lambda, \mu)^T$ on $Y \oplus Z$, we write

$$\mathbf{X} = \lambda\mathbf{Y} + \mu\mathbf{Z}, \qquad \mathbf{X}' = \lambda'\mathbf{Y} + \mu'\mathbf{Z}. \tag{8.12}$$

Then the induced projectivity maps X onto X' if X' and σX are incident. From (8.3a) the incidence condition is $\mathbf{X}^T\mathbf{A}\mathbf{X}' = 0$, which for (8.12) becomes

$$\mathbf{Y}^T\mathbf{A}\mathbf{Y}\,\lambda\lambda' + \mathbf{Y}^T\mathbf{A}\mathbf{Z}\,\lambda\mu' + \mathbf{Z}^T\mathbf{A}\mathbf{Y}\,\lambda'\mu + \mathbf{Z}^T\mathbf{A}\mathbf{Z}\,\mu\mu' = 0. \tag{8.13}$$

This bilinear form represents the projectivity (whenever the latter exists), and this projectivity is an involution if and only if (see II, (6.7a)),

$$\mathbf{Y}^T\mathbf{A}\mathbf{Z} = \mathbf{Z}^T\mathbf{A}\mathbf{Y}, \tag{8.14a}$$

$$(\mathbf{Y}^T\mathbf{A}\mathbf{Y})(\mathbf{Z}^T\mathbf{A}\mathbf{Z}) - (\mathbf{Y}^T\mathbf{A}\mathbf{Z})^2 \neq 0. \tag{8.14b}$$

Since a line is determined by any two of its points, (8.14) contains more variables than are needed. To simplify, we note that (8.14a) may be written

$$\mathbf{Y}^T(\mathbf{A} - \mathbf{A}^T)\mathbf{Z} = 0.$$

Since the rank of $\mathbf{A} - \mathbf{A}^T$ must be 2, the condition $(\mathbf{A} - \mathbf{A}^T)\mathbf{X} = 0$ determines a unique point K:$(a_{23} - a_{32}, a_{31} - a_{13}, a_{12} - a_{21})^T$. For $Z = K$, (8.14a) is satisfied for all Y; for $Z \neq K$, (8.14a) represents, as Y varies, a line incident to K. Hence the lines $Y \oplus Z$ for which (8.14a) holds belong to the pencil K. We can suppose $Z = K$; (8.14a) is satisfied identically, and (8.14b) becomes

$$(\mathbf{Y}^T\mathbf{A}\mathbf{Y})(\mathbf{k}\mathbf{K}) - (\mathbf{k}\mathbf{Y})^2 \neq 0, \tag{8.15}$$

where

$$\mathbf{k} = \mathbf{K}^T\mathbf{A}. \tag{8.16}$$

But (8.16) says that the line k is the polar of K, that is, $k = \sigma K$, and since

$$(8.17) \qquad \mathbf{AK} = \mathbf{A}^T\mathbf{K}, \quad \text{or equivalently,} \quad \mathbf{K} = \mathbf{A}^{-1}\mathbf{k}^T,$$

$K = \sigma k$. Thus the correlation interchanges K and k. We call K the *center*, and k the *axis* of σ.

Returning to the consideration of (8.15), we note that when K and k are incident, $\mathbf{kK} = 0$, so that (8.15) holds for any Y not on k. In this case, the correlation induces involutions on all lines through the center, except the axis.

When K and k are not incident, τ_k, the induced projectivity on k, may be the identity, or it may have 0, 1 or 2 fixed points. By taking Y on k the condition (8.15) for an involution becomes $\mathbf{Y}^T\mathbf{AY} \neq 0$, that is,

(i) Y is not incident to its polar, or equivalently,

(ii) Y is not a fixed point of τ_k.

Hence if τ_k is the identity, the correlation possesses no lines on which it induces involutions. More generally we can say that involutions are induced on and only on the lines through K that are not incident to fixed points of τ_k.

We have already seen that σ interchanges K and k. When K and k are incident, a geometric argument can show that σ interchanges no other pairs. When K and k are not incident, σ interchanges also the fixed points of τ_k and their polars, and again it can be shown that σ interchanges no other pairs.

Recalling that interchangeable pairs are the fixed points and fixed lines of the collineation σ^2, we have by referring to the six types of collineations (III, 11) that *the square of a correlation is never an elation.*

EXERCISES

1. Let σ be a given nonsingular correlation. Prove that the set σg as g runs through G_8 is the set of nonsingular correlations.

***2.** Find a representative matrix of the correlation $\mathbf{U}' = \mathbf{X}^T\mathbf{A}$ in terms of coordinates $\mathbf{Y}$, where $\mathbf{Y} = \mathbf{CX}$.

ANS. $\mathbf{C}^{-T}\mathbf{AC}^{-1}$.

3. Let a nonsingular polarity transform the quadratic form $\mathbf{X}^T\mathbf{CX}$ ($\mathbf{C} = \mathbf{C}^T$) into $\mathbf{UC}'\mathbf{U}^T$; show that the rank of $\mathbf{C}$ is equal to the rank of $\mathbf{C}'$.

4. A nonsingular conic $\mathbf{X}^T\mathbf{CX} = 0$ ($\mathbf{C} = \mathbf{C}^T$) is transformed by the correlation $\mathbf{U}' = \mathbf{X}^T\mathbf{A}$ into $\mathbf{X}^T\mathbf{C}'\mathbf{X} = 0$. Express $\mathbf{C}'$ in terms of $\mathbf{C}$ and $\mathbf{A}$.

5. Let $[\mathbf{UBU}^T]$ be a singular form of rank r ($r = 1, 2$). Describe the transformation $\mathbf{X}' = \mathbf{BU}^T$ (consider both values of r).

6. Prove that there exists one and just one correlation that transforms the (ordered) vertices of a given quadrangle into the (ordered) sides of a given quadrilateral.

7. Let ABC be a triangle, let P be a point not on any side, and let π be a line not through any vertex. Prove that there exists a unique polarity in which ABC is self-polar, and P and π are pole and polar.

8. Show that, in $S_2(\mathsf{R})$, a triangle self-polar with respect to a given conic has one interior vertex and two exterior vertices.

#**9.** Recalling that an involution in $S_1(\mathsf{R})$ is elliptic or hyperbolic according as pairs of corresponding points separate or fail to separate each other, prove that the polarity of Exercise 7 is the polarity of a conic if and only if there exists (at least one) point R of π that lies in the same region with respect to the given triangle as does P.

10. Prove: If each of two triangles is self-polar with respect to a form Q, there exists a conic in which the triangles are inscribed and another about which the triangles are circumscribed.

11. Prove: If two triangles with distinct vertices are Desarguean, there exists a polarity with respect to which they are mutually polar.

12. Prove that if X is a point interchanged with its polar under the correlation $\mathbf{U}' = \mathbf{X}^T\mathbf{A}$, $\mathbf{X}$ is a solution of $(\mathbf{A} - \rho\,\mathbf{A}^T)\mathbf{X} = 0$, where ρ satisfies $\det(\mathbf{A} - \rho\mathbf{A}^T) = 0$.

#**13.** Prove: If σ is a correlation which induces the identity transformation on its axis, coordinates can be chosen so that σ is represented by $u_1' = ax_1$, $u_2' = -x_3$, $u_3' = x_2$ $(a \neq 0)$.

14. Show that a coordinatization of $S_2(\mathsf{R})$ exists in terms of which a given polarity is expressed by $u_1' = x_1$, $u_2' = x_2$, $u_3' = \pm x_3$, where the upper or lower sign is to be taken according as the polarity is elliptic or hyperbolic.

#**15.** Find canonical representations for the three types of correlations in $S_2(\mathsf{C})$ not included in Exercises 13, 14.

#**16.** Prove geometrically that for each type of correlation there exist no point-line pairs that are interchanged other than those cited in the text.

#**17.** Let $\mathbf{A}$ be a given square matrix of order 3 with elements in R satisfying $\det \mathbf{A} = 1$. Discuss the problem of solving the matrix equation $\mathbf{M}^T = \mathbf{MA}$ geometrically.

18. Prove that a one-to-one map from the points of $S_2(\mathsf{F})$ onto its lines which maps collinear points onto concurrent lines need not be a correlation. Is the conclusion valid in $S_2(\mathsf{R})$?

9 Projectivities on a Nonsingular Conic

In this section we shall be dealing with an arbitrary but fixed nonsingular conic $\mathscr{C}$, and throughout this section when we speak of a conic, we shall mean a nonsingular conic. The ground field is F unless otherwise specified.

We saw (Theorem 3.5) that a conic can be represented by the equation

$$(9.1) \qquad \mathbf{X} = \mathbf{AT}, \qquad \text{where } \mathbf{T} = (t_1^2, t_1 t_2, t_2^2)^T, \quad \det \mathbf{A} \neq 0.$$

In these *parametric* equations of $\mathscr{C}$, the elements of a representative $\mathbf{X}$ are homogeneous quadratic forms in t_1, t_2, and this property is retained in all projective coordinatizations. Equation (9.1) establishes a one-to-one map from Ω_2 onto $\mathscr{C}$ (see II, Definition 1.2) and consequently the equations

$$(9.2) \qquad [t_1', t_2']^T = [\mathbf{B}(t_1, t_2)]^T, \qquad \text{where } \mathbf{B} = (b_{ij}), \quad \det \mathbf{B} \neq 0,$$

that is,

$$(9.2') \qquad [t_1', t_2'] = [b_{11}t_1 + b_{12}t_2, b_{21}t_1 + b_{22}t_2],$$

determine another map from Ω_2 onto $\mathscr{C}$. If we eliminate t_1, t_2 from (9.1) and (9.2), we see that the quadratic character of (9.1) is retained, and we have

$$(9.3) \qquad \mathbf{X} = \mathbf{A}'\mathbf{T}'$$

as another parametrization of $\mathscr{C}$. Moreover in (9.3), $\det \mathbf{A}' \neq 0$, as we can prove by noting that the contrary hypothesis would lead to the false conclusion that the locus (9.3) is contained in every line U satisfying the condition $\mathbf{UA}' = \mathbf{0}$.

Conversely, if we are given two parametrizations (9.1) of a conic $\mathscr{C}$, we naturally seek the relation between these parameters. Is it necessarily given by (9.2), for suitable $\mathbf{B}$? Let us first consider a special case. Suppose $\mathscr{C}$ is given by

$$(9.4) \qquad \mathbf{X} = (t_1^2, t_1t_2, t_2^2)^T, \qquad x_1x_3 - x_2^2 = 0,$$

and that (9.3) is a parametrization of $\mathscr{C}$ satisfying the further condition that the parametric values $[t_1', t_2']$ coincide with $[t_1, t_2]$ at the three points of $\mathscr{C}$ at which (t_1, t_2) has respective values $(1,0)$, $(0,1)$, and $(1,1)$. Then (9.3) and (9.4) imply that

$$\mathbf{A}'(1,0,0)^T = (\rho,0,0)^T, \quad \mathbf{A}'(0,0,1)^T = (0,0,\sigma)^T, \quad \mathbf{A}'(1,1,1)^T = (\tau,\tau,\tau)^T,$$
$$\rho, \sigma, \tau \in \mathsf{F}, \quad \rho\sigma\tau \neq 0.$$

It follows that

$$\mathbf{A}' = \begin{pmatrix} \rho & \tau-\rho & 0 \\ 0 & \tau & 0 \\ 0 & \tau-\sigma & \sigma \end{pmatrix}.$$

Imposing the further condition that $x_1x_3 - x_2^2 = 0$ for all (t_1', t_2'), we find that

$$\tau = \sigma = \rho, \quad \text{so that} \quad \mathbf{B} = \rho\mathbf{I} \quad \text{and} \quad [t_1', t_2'] = [t_1, t_2].$$

We thus can conclude that in the special case the two parametrizations coincide.

In the general case, we suppose that (9.1) and (9.3) are two parametrizations of $\mathscr{C}$. We can subject the second to a mapping (9.2) which assigns to three points of the conic chosen parametric values (see II, Theorem 2.3). In particular, we can choose (9.2) so that parametric values $(1,0)$, $(0,1)$, and $(1,1)$, in both (9.1) and the transform of (9.3) by (9.2), determine the same ordered triple of points of $\mathscr{C}$. If we now subject $S_2(\mathsf{F})$ to the coordinate transformation $\mathbf{X}^* = \mathbf{A}^{-1}\mathbf{X}$, we obtain the special situation considered above. From the coincidence of the final parametrizations, it follows that the original parameters are related by (9.2) for some choice of **B**. We have thus proved the following lemma.

LEMMA 9.1. *Two parametrizations* (9.1) *of a given conic are related by* (9.2), *for a suitable choice of* **B**.

This lemma will be used in proving the following theorem.

THEOREM 9.1. *The points of a nonsingular conic in* $S_2(\mathsf{F})$ *constitute a projective space of dimension one. If the conic is represented by* (9.1), *the parameters* $[t_1, t_2]^T$ *are projective coordinates.*

Proof. We need to show that collineations of S_2 which leave $\mathscr{C}$ fixed map the points of $\mathscr{C}$ in accordance with (9.2), and vice versa. The collineation $\mathbf{X}' = \mathbf{CX}$ maps $\mathbf{X} = \mathbf{AT}$ onto $\mathbf{X} = \mathbf{CAT}$. If these two conics coincide, there exists (see the preceding lemma) a parameter transformation (9.2) such that $\mathbf{CAT} = \mathbf{AT}'$ for all t_1, t_2. Now interpret the equation (9.2) thus found as representing a point transformation of the conic onto itself. It is the collineation restricted to the conic. Conversely, if we are given a point transformation (9.2) on $\mathscr{C}$, we write (9.2) as $\mathbf{T}' = \mathbf{CT}$, where $\mathbf{C}$ is a 3×3 nonsingular† matrix. Then $\mathbf{X}' = \mathbf{ACA}^{-1}\mathbf{X}$ is a collineation whose restriction to $\mathscr{C}$ coincides with (9.2).

Hence in dealing with the points of a conic we can apply the theory developed in Chapter II; we shall use the terminology introduced there. For clarity, however, we shall write $(A\,B, C\,D)_{\mathscr{C}}$ instead of $(A\,B, C\,D)$, the subscript being advisable since in most planes there is more than one conic containing four given points.

Whenever we are dealing with the properties of a subset of a given space, there is a natural division of those properties into two categories: the first consists of the properties that relate to and involve only the points of the subset; the second consists of properties of the subset in relationship to other sets in the space. We often use the term *inner structure* to describe the first, and *outer structure* to describe the second. Theorem 9.1 tells us that the inner structure of a conic, like that of a line, coincides with that of an $S_1(\mathsf{F})$. But from the properties of a conic already deduced, we know that there is a vast difference between the outer structures of lines and conics. This is the usual state of affairs; two subsets of a given space that have the same inner structure cannot be expected to be equivalent in the space.

As a further illustration of this point, the reader might consider in Euclidean three-space a parabolic cylinder. This surface can be flattened into a plane, and its two-dimensional geometry is identical with that of a Euclidean plane. But its relation to three-space is very different.

† The reader should prove that **C** is nonsingular by an argument that is partly geometric.

We naturally turn next to questions concerning the relationship of the inner structure of a conic to its outer structure. For example, four points of a conic $\mathscr{C}$ possess a cross ratio, as do points of any S_1; on the other hand, by Steiner's Theorem, $(A\,B,\,C\,D)_X$ is also determined uniquely by A, B, C, D, and $\mathscr{C}$, so that four points of $\mathscr{C}$ possess the *inner* cross ratio $(A\,B,\,C\,D)_{\mathscr{C}}$ and the *outer* cross ratio $(A\,B,\,C\,D)_X$, $X \in \mathscr{C}$. Are these two cross ratios related? Again, we have projectivities on a conic described analytically by equations (9.2); can we describe them in terms of outer relations? We shall devote the remainder of this section to answering these and similar questions.

THEOREM 9.2. *The inner and outer cross ratios of four points of a conic are equal, that is,*

$$(A\,B,\,C\,D)_{\mathscr{C}} = (A\,B,\,C\,D)_X \qquad \textit{for } X \in \mathscr{C}. \tag{9.5}$$

Proof. We can choose coordinates in S_2 and a parametrization on $\mathscr{C}$ so that $\mathscr{C}$ is given by (9.4) and A, B, C, and D are given by parametric values $(1,0)^T$, $(0,1)^T$, $(1,1)^T$, and $(t_1, t_2{}^T)$, respectively. Then $(A\,B,\,C\,D)_{\mathscr{C}} = t_1/t_2$.

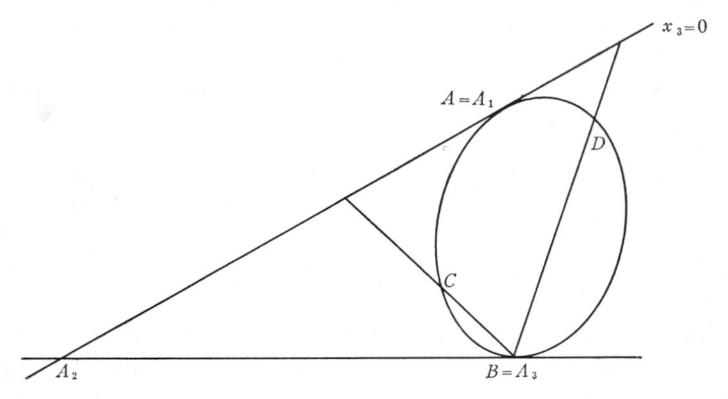

FIGURE 9.1

On the other hand, $(A\,B,\,C\,D)_X = (A\,B,\,C\,D)_B$, and this cross ratio is in turn equal to the cross ratio of the points in which the lines of the pencil at B intersect the line $x_3 = 0$. These points are $(1,0,0)^T$, $(0,1,0)^T$, $(1,1,0)^T$, and $(t_1^2, t_1\,t_2, 0)^T$. But $t_1^2/t_1\,t_2 = t_1/t_2$ is a projective coordinate on the line $x_3 = 0$, so that $(A\,B,\,C\,D)_X = t_1/t_2$, and our theorem is proved.

To dualize the preceding results, we establish a parametrization of the lines of the conic

$$\mathbf{U} = (s_1^2, s_1\,s_2, s_2^2)\mathbf{C}, \qquad \mathbf{C} = (c_{ij}), \quad \det \mathbf{C} \neq 0. \tag{9.6}$$

By the dual of Theorem 9.1, the lines of the conic constitute an S_1, and the parameters $[s_1, s_2]$ in (9.6) are projective coordinates. Let $\mathbf{U}' = \mathbf{X}^T\mathbf{B}$ be the polarity of (9.1); it maps the points of $\mathscr{C}$, $\mathbf{X} = \mathbf{AT}$, onto the tangent lines

$\mathbf{U} = (t_1^2, t_1 t_2, t_2^2)\mathbf{A}^T\mathbf{B}$. Since det $\mathbf{A}^T\mathbf{B} \neq 0$, the last is a representation (9.6) of the lines of the conic. Thus we can choose projective coordinates on the points and lines of a conic so that at each point the coordinates of the point and of the tangent line at the point are equal. As an immediate consequence of this fact, we have the following theorem.

THEOREM 9.3. *Four points of a conic and the four tangents at these points, in the same order, have equal cross ratios.*

With every projectivity σ on the points of $\mathscr{C}$, we associate the projectivity on its tangents determined by transforming the tangent U at X into the tangent U' at $X' = \sigma X$, and vice versa. Just as we use the term *nonsingular conic* to mean both the point conic and the line conic, we shall use the term *projectivity on a conic* to mean both the projectivity on the points of the conic and the associated projectivity on its lines.

THEOREM 9.4. *There exists a unique collineation whose restriction to a given conic is a given projectivity on the conic.*

Proof. We exhibited one collineation with the required property in the course of the proof of Theorem 9.1. To prove that the collineation is unique, we suppose there were two collineations g_1, g_2 coinciding on $\mathscr{C}$. Then $g_1 g_2^{-1}$ would leave every point of $\mathscr{C}$ fixed; by (III, Theorem 1.1) the identity is the only collineation that leaves fixed four points, no three collinear. Hence $g_1 g_2^{-1} = I$, and $g_1 = g_2$.

It is useful to give a geometric analysis. Let σ be the given projectivity on $\mathscr{C}$, let A, B, C, D be four points of $\mathscr{C}$, and let primes denote their maps under σ, $A' = \sigma A$, etc. By (III, Theorem 1.2) there exists a collineation g such that $gA = A'$, $gB = B'$, $gC = C'$, $gD = D'$. Let X be an arbitrary point of $\mathscr{C}$, and let $X' = \sigma X$, $X'' = gX$. To show that σ is the restriction of g to the conic, we need to show that X' and X'' coincide for all X on $\mathscr{C}$. We have

$$\begin{aligned} (A'B', C'D')_{X'} &= (A'B', C'D')_{\mathscr{C}} && \text{(by Theorem 9.2)} \\ &= (AB, CD)_{\mathscr{C}} && \text{(under the projectivity } \sigma) \\ &= (AB, CD)_X && \text{(by Theorem 9.2)} \\ &= (A'B', C'D')_{X''} && \text{(under the collineation } g). \end{aligned}$$

From Theorem 5.2a, X'' lies on $\mathscr{C}$. Furthermore

$$(A'B', C'X')_{\mathscr{C}} = (AB, CX)_{\mathscr{C}} = (A'B', C'X'')_{\mathscr{C}},$$

where the first equality expresses invariance of cross ratio under σ, and the second under g. Therefore $X' = X''$.

We can establish a projectivity on a conic $\mathscr{C}$ by a simple geometric construction. Let L be an arbitrary line, and let A and A' be two distinct points of $\mathscr{C}$ not incident to L (Figure 9.2). Consider the transformation τ that maps an arbitrary point X of $\mathscr{C}$ onto the point X' of $\mathscr{C}$ by projecting X from A' onto X'' on L, and then projecting X'' from A onto the conic. (We understand by the projection on L, from A', of A' itself, the point of intersection

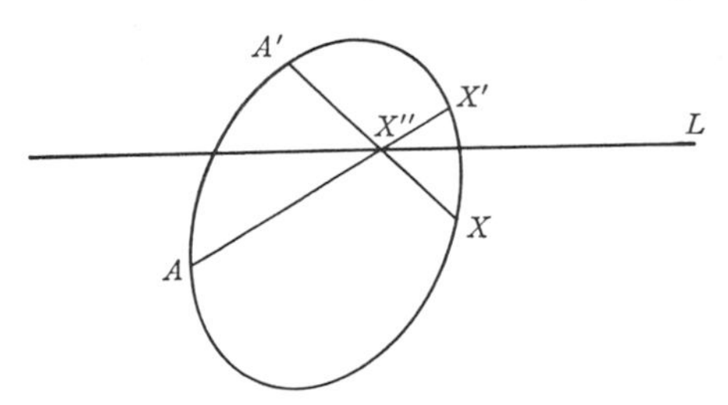

FIGURE 9.2

with L of the tangent at A', and similarly, a point X'' of L projects from A onto A itself if $A \oplus X''$ is tangent to $\mathscr{C}$ at A.) If we denote by X_i $(i = 1, 2, 3, 4)$ any four points of $\mathscr{C}$, by X_i'' the projection of X_i from A' on L, and by X_i' the projection of X_i'' from A, we have

$$\begin{aligned}(X_1\, X_2\,,\, X_3\, X_4)_{\mathscr{C}} &= (X_1\, X_2\,,\, X_3\, X_4)_{A'} = (X_1''\, X_2''\,,\, X_3''\, X_4'') \\ &= (X_1'\, X_2'\,,\, X_3'\, X_4')_A = (X_1'\, X_2'\,,\, X_3'\, X_4')_{\mathscr{C}}\,.\end{aligned}$$

Thus the transformation τ preserves cross ratio and is a projectivity. In the following theorem we prove that every projectivity on $\mathscr{C}$ can be described by the above construction for a suitable choice of A, A', and L.

THEOREM 9.5. *Let $\sigma \neq I$ be a given projectivity on a conic $\mathscr{C}$; there exists a line L with the following property: If Y, Z are any two distinct points of $\mathscr{C}$, $(Y \oplus \sigma Z) \cap (Z \oplus \sigma Y) \in L$.*

Proof. Let σ be given by the relations

$$\sigma A = A', \qquad \sigma B = B', \qquad \sigma C = C', \qquad A' \neq A, \tag{9.7}$$

and Let $L = B'' \oplus C''$, where $B'' = (A \oplus B') \cap (A' \oplus B)$, $C'' = (A \oplus C') \cap (A' \oplus C)$ (Figure 9.3(a)). If we project the points of $\mathscr{C}$ from A' onto L, and then project from A onto $\mathscr{C}$, we obtain a projectivity which by (II, Theorem 2.2) must be σ. Hence $(A \oplus \sigma Y) \cap (A' \oplus Y) \in L$, $(A \oplus \sigma Z) \cap (A' \oplus Z) \in L$. We now consider the hexagon with vertices A, σY, Z, A', Y, σZ; by Pascal's Theorem, $(\sigma Y \oplus Z) \cap \sigma Z) \in L$.

DEFINITION 9.1. The line L of Theorem 9.5 is called the *axis* of the projectivity; the point determined by the dual of Theorem 9.5 is called the *center*.

THEOREM 9.6. *The axis and the center of a projectivity on a conic are pole and polar. They are fixed under the collineation that induces the projectivity.*

We leave the proof to the reader.

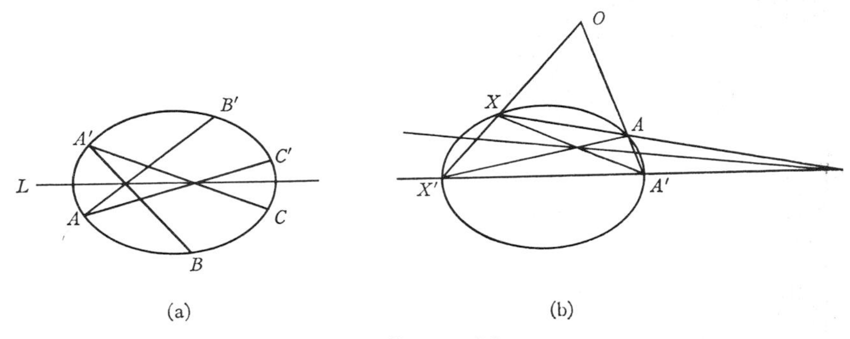

FIGURE 9.3

THEOREM 9.7. *The fixed points, if any, of a projectivity (not the identity) on a conic are the intersections of the conic and the axis. The fixed lines, if any, are the tangents to the conic from the center.*

We leave the proof to the reader.

In $S_2(\mathsf{R})$, the three types of projectivities on a conic are characterized by the relationship of the axis to the conic. A projectivity is hyperbolic, parabolic, or elliptic according as its axis intersects the conic in distinct points, is tangent to it, or fails to intersect it.

We see from the next theorem that involutions on a conic in $S_2(\mathsf{F})$ have a particularly simple structure.

THEOREM 9.8. *The lines of a pencil with vertex not on the conic intersect the conic in points that are pairs in an involution whose center is the given vertex; conversely, in every involution on a conic, the lines joining pairs of corresponding points are concurrent in the center.*

Proof. Let O be the vertex of the pencil, and let L be the polar of O (Figure 9.3(b)). Let a chosen line of the pencil intersect the conic in A and A', and let a variable line of the pencil intersect it in X and X'. Then by Corollary 6.1, $(A \oplus X') \cap (A' \oplus X) \in L$. Hence the map $X \to X'$ is that described in the discussion preceding Theorem 9.5 and is a projectivity with L as axis. Since $X' \to X$, the projectivity is an involution. Conversely, if σ is an involution, and if $\sigma Y = Y'$, $\sigma Z = Z'$, then $\sigma Z' = Z$, and by Theorem 9.5, the axis is the join of $(Y \oplus Z') \cap (Y' \oplus Z)$ and $(Y \oplus Z) \cap (Y' \oplus Z')$. Then the pole of the axis must be $(Y \oplus Y') \cap (Z \oplus Z')$.

Many properties of involutions in $S_1(\mathsf{F})$ take on particularly elegant forms when they are expressed in terms of the geometry of a conic. To illustrate, we shall describe geometrically pairs of involutions which commute; these are called harmonic involutions by some writers. We begin with a triangle $D_1 D_2 D_3$ which is self-conjugate with respect to a conic $\mathscr{C}$, and we let σ_i $(i = 1, 2, 3)$ be the involution on $\mathscr{C}$ with center D_i (Figure 9.4(a)). If P is

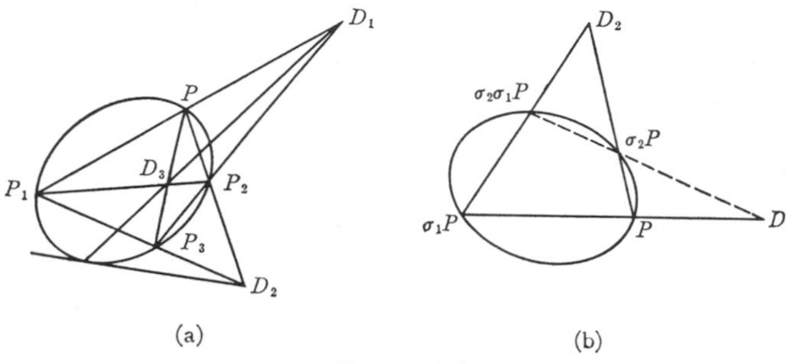

FIGURE 9.4

any point of $\mathscr{C}$ not on the sides of the triangle, and if $P_i = \sigma_i P$, $D_1 D_2 D_3$ is the diagonal triangle (Corollary 6.1) of the quadrangle $P\,P_1 P_2 P_3$, so that $D_i = (P \oplus P_i) \cap (P_j \oplus P_k)$ for i, j, k any permutation of 1, 2, 3. Thus σ_1 interchanges P_2 and P_3 as well as P and P_1. More generally, σ_i interchanges P_j and P_k as well as P and P_i, and this conclusion is valid also if P is a point of intersection of a side of the triangle and the conic. It follows readily that $\sigma_1 = \sigma_2 \sigma_3 = \sigma_3 \sigma_2$, and similarly,

$$\sigma_i = \sigma_j \sigma_k = \sigma_k \sigma_j . \tag{9.8}$$

Thus we have three involutions each two of which commute, and the product of any two is the third.

This situation is less special than we might suppose, for we can show that two commutative involutions on a conic have conjugate centers, that their product is a third involution, and that the three centers are the vertices of a self-conjugate triangle. Letting σ_1, σ_2 be two involutions (Figure 9.4(b)) with centers D_1, D_2, we recognize that $\sigma_1 \sigma_2 = \sigma_2 \sigma_1$ if and only if the three points D_1, $\sigma_2 P$, and $\sigma_2 \sigma_1 P$ are collinear for all P, or equivalently, if and only if D_1 and D_2 are conjugate with respect to $\mathscr{C}$.

We can summarize these and earlier results (see II, especially Theorem 6.7 and the remarks following it, Exercise 19, equation (6.7b)) as follows.

THEOREM 9.9. *The involutions which commute with a given involution (other than the given involution itself) constitute a pencil of involutions. If the involutions are represented on a conic, their centers describe the axis of the given involution, and their axes are the lines through its center. Their quadratic forms constitute the pencil apolar to the form of the given involution, and their matrix representations constitute a pencil of matrices.*

In $S_2(\mathsf{C})$ this pencil of involutions contains two distinct singular involutions; their centers lie on the conic, their axes are tangent to the conic, their quadratic forms and their representative matrices are singular. These singular involutions map all points onto the center; yet they satisfy, trivially, the commutativity condition. In $S_2(\mathsf{R})$, this situation will not occur if the center of the given involution is an interior point of the conic (that is, if the given involution is elliptic).

We note further that if either of two commutative involutions in $S_2(\mathsf{F})$ possesses fixed points, these points are pairs in the other; if both possess fixed points, one pair separates the other harmonically.

We suggested earlier (II, 6, Exercise 11) that any projectivity in $S_1(\mathsf{F})$ is expressible as the product of two involutions. The factorization will be seen not to be unique, and we shall show that one factor can be selected arbitrarily in a certain pencil of involutions. Let the projectivity π be represented on a conic $\mathscr{C}$, and let L be its axis. Choose a point D on $L - (\mathscr{C} \cap L)$ and A on $\mathscr{C} - (\mathscr{C} \cap L)$ (Figure 9.5(a)). The projectivity is determined by specifying the

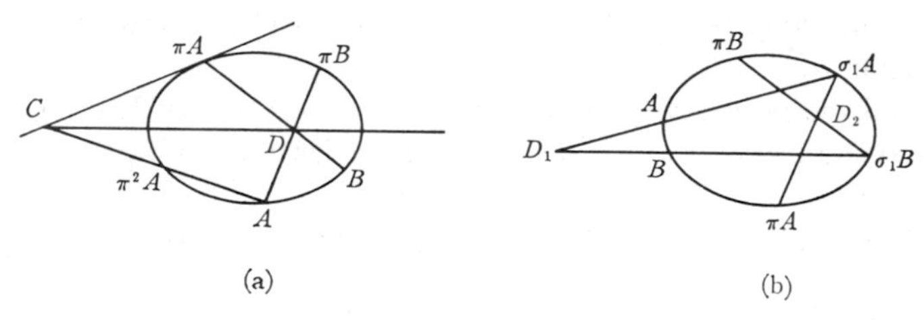

FIGURE 9.5

point πA on $\mathscr{C} - (\mathscr{C} \cap L)$. Let the second intersection of $\mathscr{C}$ and $D \oplus \pi A$ be B. Then $A \oplus D$ intersects $\mathscr{C}$ again in πB. Let σ be the involution with center D, and let $\sigma' = \pi\sigma$. Clearly σ' interchanges πB and πA, so that σ' is an involution and $\pi = \sigma'\sigma$. We could show similarly that $\sigma\pi$ is an involution, say σ'', so that $\pi = \sigma\sigma''$.

Thus the center of σ can be any point of $L - (L \cap \mathscr{C})$. That the center of the other factor also lies on L is seen as follows. Let σ_1, σ_2 be any two involutions, D_1 and D_2 their centers, and $\pi = \sigma_2\sigma_1$ (Figure 9.5(b)). If A, B are two points of $\mathscr{C}$, the points $\sigma_1 A, A, \pi B, \sigma_1 B, B$, and πA lie on $\mathscr{C}$; by Pascal's Theorem the three points of intersection of pairs of opposite sides are collinear. Since

$$(\sigma_1 A \oplus A) \cap (\sigma_1 B \oplus B) = D_1, \qquad (\pi B \oplus \sigma_1 B) \cap (\pi A \oplus \sigma_1 A) = D_2,$$

we have that $(A \oplus \pi B) \cap (B \oplus \pi A) \in D_1 \oplus D_2$. Thus every point of the axis of $\pi = \sigma_2\sigma_1$ lies on the join of the centers D_1, D_2.

We can summarize these results in the following theorem.

THEOREM 9.10. *The product of two involutions on a conic is a projectivity whose axis is the join of the centers of the involutions. Conversely, a projectivity can be factored into the product of two involutions. When the projectivity is represented on a conic, the center of one involution can be chosen to be any point on the axis of the projectivity not on the conic; the other is determined uniquely by the choice of the first.*

EXERCISES

1. Verify that the collineation $x_1' = x_3$, $x_2' = x_2$, $x_3' = x_1$ is a harmonic homology leaving the conic $x_1 x_3 - x_2^2 = 0$ fixed. Describe the projectivity established on the conic, and find a matrix representation (9.2) for the parametrization (9.4).

2. The tangents to a conic are given by $u_1 = s_1^2$, $u_2 = 2s_1 s_2 + s_2^2$, $u_3 = s_1^2 - s_2^2$. Verify that the lines $x_1 + x_3 = 0$, $x_2 - x_3 = 0$, $x_1 + 3x_2 = 0$, $4x_1 - 3x_2 + 3x_3 = 0$ are tangent lines. Their points of contact are joined to that of the tangent for which $[s_1, s_2]^T = [1, -1]^T$. Find the cross ratio of the four lines.

3. Find the projectivity induced by the collineation of Exercise 1 on the tangents to the conic in terms of the parametrization for which the conic is given by (3.6).

4. Show that the collineations leaving the conic (9.4) fixed are given by

$$x_1' = \alpha^2 x_1 + 2\alpha\beta x_2 + \beta^2 x_3, \qquad x_2' = \alpha\gamma x_1 + (\alpha\delta + \beta\gamma)x_2 + \beta\delta x_3,$$

$$x_3' = \gamma^2 x_1 + 2\gamma\delta x_2 + \delta^2 x_3,$$

where $\alpha, \beta, \gamma, \delta$ are any four elements of F for which $\alpha\delta - \beta\gamma \neq 0$.

5. Define the duals of inner and outer cross ratio, and give independent proofs of the duals of Theorems 9.2 and 9.4.

6. A projectivity π on a conic $\mathscr{C}$ maps a given tangent p onto p', and has as its center a given point O. Describe πU, where U is an arbitrary tangent, in terms of incidence relations involving $\mathscr{C}$, p, p', O, and U.

7. Let the projectivity π on $\mathscr{C}$ be defined by $\pi a = a'$, $\pi b = b'$, $\pi c = c'$, where a, a', etc. are given tangents to $\mathscr{C}$. Describe πU, for any tangent U, in terms of incidence relations.

8. Prove Theorem 9.6.

9. Prove Theorem 9.7.

#**10.** Prove that an elation leaves no conic fixed.

11. Let $g \in G_8$ map a conic $\mathscr{C}$ onto $\mathscr{C}' \neq \mathscr{C}$. Prove that g restricted to $\mathscr{C}$ is given by a map (9.2) where $[t_1, t_2]^T$, $[t_1', t_2']^T$ are projective coordinates on $\mathscr{C}$, $\mathscr{C}'$, respectively. Show, conversely, that a given projectivity (9.2) from a conic $\mathscr{C}$ to a conic $\mathscr{C}'$ is the restriction to $\mathscr{C}$ of a unique collineation.

12. Let $g \in G_8$, and let π be a projectivity on $\mathscr{C}$. Prove that the map $gX \to g\pi X$ is a projectivity on $g\mathscr{C}$.

13. Prove that the set of three involutions whose centers are vertices of a self-polar triangle, together with the identity, is a group.

14. Prove that if $\mathbf{A}$, $\mathbf{A}'$ are matrices of two involutions in $S_1(\mathsf{R})$ which commute with a given elliptic involution, the equation $\det(\mathbf{A} - \lambda\mathbf{A}') = 0$ has no (real) solution in λ.

***15.** Prove that the pencil of involutions which commute with an elliptic involution in $S_1(\mathsf{R})$ consists of hyperbolic involutions exclusively.

***16.** Prove: Every projectivity in $S_1(\mathsf{R})$ is the product of three or fewer hyperbolic involutions.

10 The Group of a Quadratic Form

In this section we shall consider projectivities associated with *binary* quadratic forms in $S_1(\mathsf{F})$, and collineations associated with *ternary* quadratic forms in $S_2(\mathsf{F})$. When we write $\mathbf{X}' = \mathbf{AX}$ and $Q = \mathbf{X}^T\mathbf{BX}$ $(\mathbf{B} = \mathbf{B}^T)$, the matrices $\mathbf{X}$, $\mathbf{A}$, $\mathbf{B}$, etc. have two rows or three rows according as the dimension of the space is one or two. As already remarked, the class $[Q]$ consisting of all forms ρQ $(\rho \in \mathsf{F}, \rho \neq 0)$ is mapped by $[\mathbf{X}'] = [\mathbf{AX}]$ onto a class $[Q']$, and a matrix $\mathbf{B}'$ of Q' satisfies

$$(10.1) \qquad \mathbf{B}' \in [\mathbf{A}^{-T}\mathbf{B}\mathbf{A}^{-1}], \quad \text{that is,} \quad \mathbf{B}' = \rho\mathbf{A}^{-T}\mathbf{B}\mathbf{A}^{-1}, \quad \rho \neq 0.$$

Of great significance are the collineations which (using historical language) preserve a given quadratic form. By this one means that the transformed *class* $[Q']$ coincides with $[Q]$. Since $[Q'] = [Q]$ is equivalent to $\mathbf{B}' \in [\mathbf{B}]$, the following theorem is a consequence of (10.1).

THEOREM 10.1 *A projective transformation with representative matrix* $\mathbf{A}$ *leaves fixed the form* $[Q]$ *with representative matrix* $\mathbf{B}$ $(= \mathbf{B}^T)$ *if and only if there exists* ρ *in* F, $\rho \neq 0$, such *that*

$$(10.2) \qquad \mathbf{B}\mathbf{A}^{-1} = \rho\mathbf{A}^T\mathbf{B}.$$

It is clear that in $S_1(\mathsf{F})$ as well as in $S_2(\mathsf{F})$, condition (10.2) defines a subgroup of the projective group. The quadratic form itself defines an involutory transformation: an involution in S_1, a polarity in S_2. We shall denote this transformation by $\sigma = \sigma(Q)$; vice versa, if σ is an involution or a polarity, it belongs to a class of quadratic forms $[Q]$, and we shall let $Q(\sigma)$ denote a member of the class.

DEFINITION 10.1. The group of projective transformations satisfying (10.2) is called the *group of* (*the quadratic form*) $[Q]$ or *of* (*the involution* or *polarity*) σ. We shall denote this group by $G(Q)$ or by $G(\sigma)$.

The same analytical machinery can be used in S_1 as in S_2 if we introduce in S_1 the analogue of line coordinates. In S_1, a linear equation, $u_1 x_1 + u_2 x_2 = 0$, has as its locus a single point; we might call the row matrix (u_1, u_2) the dual or associated coordinates of the point $(u_2, -u_1)^T$. In terms of the dual coordinates, the involution determined by the binary form $\mathbf{X}^T\mathbf{B}\mathbf{X}$ has the representation (see II, (6.7a)) $\mathbf{U}' = \mathbf{X}^T\mathbf{B}$, so that the involution bears the same matrix relation to the binary form as does the polarity to the ternary form.

THEOREM 10.2. *The three following conditions are equivalent:*

(a) $g \in G(\sigma)$;

(b) $g\sigma = \sigma g$;

(c) *g maps pairs of points conjugate in* σ *onto pairs that are conjugate in* σ.

Proof. If a projective transformation g has the representation $\mathbf{X}' = \mathbf{A}\mathbf{X}$ in point coordinates, it has the representation $\mathbf{U}' = \mathbf{U}\mathbf{A}^{-1}$ in the dual (line) coordinates. Then $g\sigma$ is the correlation† $\mathbf{U}' = \mathbf{X}^T\mathbf{B}\mathbf{A}^{-1}$, and σg is the correlation $\mathbf{U}' = \mathbf{X}^T\mathbf{A}^T\mathbf{B}$. If $g \in G(\sigma)$, (10.2) holds, so that the correlations coincide, and thus (a) implies (b). Next, $g\sigma = \sigma g$ implies that the maps of X and σX by g are gX and $g(\sigma X) = (g\sigma)X = \sigma(gX)$, and thus (b) implies (c). Finally, if g preserves conjugacy in σ, it maps the conjugate pair X and σX onto gX and σgX; the correlations σg and $g\sigma$ must coincide, and (10.2) holds. Hence (c) implies (a). The chain is completed, and each one of the three conditions implies any other one.

COROLLARY 10.1. *The set of self-conjugate points in* σ *is mapped onto itself by every* $g \in G(\sigma)$.

Thus in, $S_1(\mathsf{F})$, g in $G(\sigma)$ either leaves fixed or interchanges the fixed points of σ; in $S_2(\mathsf{F})$, the locus of self-conjugate points is either a conic or empty, and g in $G(\sigma)$ leaves the conic fixed.

When σ is an involution in $S_1(\mathsf{F})$, we can find $G(\sigma)$ by representing σ on a conic in $S_2(\mathsf{F})$. If F is algebraically closed (so that every involution possesses fixed points), it follows from Corollary 10.1 that g in $G(\sigma)$ either interchanges the fixed points of σ or leaves both fixed. In the first case g is an involution that commutes with σ; by Theorem 9.9, it belongs to a pencil of involutions whose centers lie on the axis of σ. In the second case the axis of g coincides with the axis of σ; by Theorem 9.10, g is expressible as the product of two involutions belonging to the first pencil. From our earlier results (see II, (5.10))

† In S_1, a correlation $\mathbf{U}' = \mathbf{X}^T\mathbf{A}$ is a projectivity, and vice versa.

the projectivities that possess a given pair of fixed elements constitute a pencil of projectivities† containing the identity and the one involution.

We might suspect, as is the case, that these conclusions are valid even if F is not algebraically closed.

THEOREM 10.3. *Let $\Sigma(\sigma)$ be the pencil of involutions in $S_1(\mathsf{F})$ which commute with a given involution σ. Then every finite product of elements of $\Sigma(\sigma)$ is an element of $G(\sigma)$. Conversely, every element of $G(\sigma)$ is either in $\Sigma(\sigma)$ or it is the product of two elements of $\Sigma(\sigma)$.*

Proof. The first conclusion is obvious. If $g \in G(\sigma)$, by Theorem 10.2, $g\sigma = \sigma g$. We represent σ on a conic $\mathscr{C}$ in $S_2(\mathsf{F})$. Letting O be the center (Figure 10.1), we recall that for $X \in \mathscr{C}$ the point $Y = (X \oplus \sigma g X) \cap (\sigma X \oplus g X)$

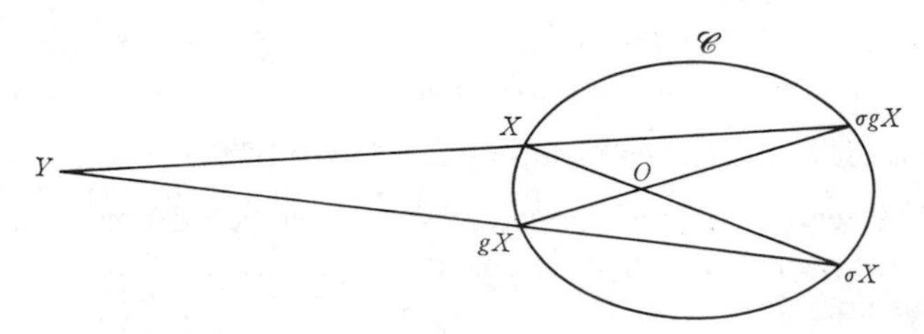

FIGURE 10.1

lies on the axis of σ, and that $Y' = (X \oplus g\sigma X) \cap (\sigma X \oplus g X)$ lies on the axis of g. Hence $g\sigma = \sigma g$ implies $Y' = Y$. If $g\sigma$ is an involution, Y is its center. Then $g\sigma$ commutes with σ, and the product, $g = g\sigma\sigma$, is an involution (see (9.8)). By Theorem 9.9, $g \in \Sigma(\sigma)$. If $g\sigma$ is not an involution, the map from $X \in \mathscr{C}$ to Y is *onto* the axis of σ, and $g\sigma = \sigma g$, $g^2 \neq I$ implies that g and σ have the same axis. By Theorem 9.10, g is the product of two involutions in $\Sigma(\sigma)$.

It is instructive to outline an algebraic proof of the preceding theorem. If we coordinatize $S_1(\mathsf{F})$ so that σ is given by $[x_1', x_2'] = [\gamma x_2, x_1]$ $(\gamma \in \mathsf{F}, \gamma \neq 0)$, a projectivity g given by $[x_1', x_2'] = [ax_1 + bx_2, cx_1 + dx_2]$ satisfies $g\sigma = \sigma g$ if and only if there exists λ in F, $\lambda \neq 0$, such that

$$\begin{pmatrix} 0 & \gamma \\ 1 & 0 \end{pmatrix}\begin{pmatrix} a & b \\ c & d \end{pmatrix} = \lambda \begin{pmatrix} a & b \\ c & d \end{pmatrix}\begin{pmatrix} 0 & \gamma \\ 1 & 0 \end{pmatrix}.$$

† The representative matrix

$$\begin{pmatrix} a & b \\ b & a \end{pmatrix}$$

can be written as a pencil of matrices,

$$a\begin{pmatrix} 1 & 0 \\ 0 & 1 \end{pmatrix} + b\begin{pmatrix} 0 & 1 \\ 1 & 0 \end{pmatrix}.$$

A straightforward calculation shows that $\lambda = \pm 1$, and we verify that the solutions consist of the pencil of projectivities determined by I and σ, with representative matrix

$$a\begin{pmatrix}1 & 0\\0 & 1\end{pmatrix} + c\begin{pmatrix}0 & \gamma\\1 & 0\end{pmatrix}, \tag{10.3}$$

and the pencil of involutions with representative matrix

$$a\begin{pmatrix}1 & 0\\0 & -1\end{pmatrix} + c\begin{pmatrix}0 & -\gamma\\1 & 0\end{pmatrix}. \tag{10.4}$$

We shall leave it to the reader to show that if a pencil of lines in E_2 is embedded in $S_1(\mathsf{R})$ so that orthogonal lines map onto pairs in a given elliptic involution, the pencil of projectivities is the image of the rotations in the pencil, and the pencil of involutions the image of the reflections.

COROLLARY 10.2. *If Y and Z are not self-conjugate points of an involution σ in $S_1(\mathsf{F})$, there exists two transformations g in $G(\sigma)$ which map Y onto Z.*

We leave it to the reader to supply the details of the proof.

We shall see in Chapter V, Section 4, that we can define *sense* in $S_1(\mathsf{R})$ and that the pencil of projectivities preserves sense while the pencil of involutions does not.

In $S_2(\mathsf{F})$ harmonic homologies play the role played by involutions in $S_1(\mathsf{F})$.

LEMMA 10.1. *A harmonic homology leaves fixed a polarity σ in $S_2(\mathsf{F})$ if and only if the center and axis of the homology are pole and polar in σ.*

Proof. The theorem is obvious if σ is the polarity of a conic, but an analytic proof covers all cases. Choose coordinates so that the center O and axis L of the homology are $(0, 0, 1)^T$ and $x_3 = 0$. Then the homology is given by $x_1' = x_1, x_2' = x_2, x_3' = -x_3$ (see III, (11.1)). Since $O = \sigma L$ implies $b_{12} = b_{13} = 0$, the homology leaves $[\mathbf{X}^T\mathbf{B}\mathbf{X}]$ fixed. Conversely, if the homology leaves $[\mathbf{X}^T\mathbf{B}\mathbf{X}]$ fixed, either $\det \mathbf{B} = 0$ or $b_{12} = b_{13} = 0$. The first is excluded from our considerations, and the second implies that $O = \sigma L$.

LEMMA 10.2. *An involution on a conic is the restriction to the conic of a harmonic homology whose center and axis are the center and axis of the involution. Conversely, a harmonic homology restricted to a conic with respect to which the center and axis are pole and polar is an involution.*

For the proof, use the preceding lemma and (III, Lemma 11.1 and Theorem 11.1).

When F is algebraically closed or, more generally, when σ is the polarity of a conic $\mathscr{C}$, the determination of $G(\sigma)$ follows from our previous conclusions. If $g \in G(\sigma)$, g maps $\mathscr{C}$ onto itself. Thus the restriction of g to $\mathscr{C}$ is a projectivity which can be factored into the product of two involutions. By Lemma 10.2, the involutions are the restrictions to $\mathscr{C}$ of harmonic homologies whose product coincides with g on $\mathscr{C}$, and therefore throughout $S_2(\mathsf{F})$. We have proved the following theorem.

THEOREM 10.4. *Let $\Sigma(\sigma)$ be the set of harmonic homologies in $S_2(\mathsf{F})$ with centers and axes that correspond in σ, a given hyperbolic polarity. The product of any finite number of elements of $\Sigma(\sigma)$ is in $G(\sigma)$; every element of $G(\sigma)$ either is in $\Sigma(\sigma)$ or is the product of two elements of $\Sigma(\sigma)$.*

We can extend this result to elliptic polarities σ in $S_2(\mathsf{R})$ by analytic methods. Let $g \in G(\sigma)$, so that $g\sigma = \sigma g$, and let O be a fixed point of g (see III, Theorem 11.2). Since $g\sigma O = \sigma g O = \sigma O$, the line $L = \sigma O$ is a fixed line, and since σ is elliptic, O and L are not incident. Let us choose a reference frame so that $A_3 : (0, 0, 1)^T$ is O and so that (see (6.15)),

$$\mathbf{B} = \mathbf{I}, \qquad Q(\sigma) = x_1^2 + x_2^2 + x_3^2. \tag{10.5}$$

Then L is the line $x_3 = 0$. If g is given by $[\mathbf{X}'] = [\mathbf{AX}]$, we must have that

$$a_{13} = a_{23} = a_{31} = a_{32} = 0,$$

and we can choose $\mathbf{A} \in [\mathbf{A}]$ so that

$$a_{33} = 1.$$

Denoting by $\tilde{\mathbf{A}}$ the 2×2 matrix whose elements are the elements of the first two rows and columns of $\mathbf{A}$,

$$\tilde{\mathbf{A}} = \begin{pmatrix} a_{11} & a_{12} \\ a_{21} & a_{22} \end{pmatrix},$$

we find that the condition (10.2) on $\mathbf{A}$ implies that $\rho = 1$ and that

$$\tilde{\mathbf{A}}^{-1} = \tilde{\mathbf{A}}^T. \tag{10.6}$$

We note that $\tilde{\mathbf{A}}$ is the matrix of g_L, the restriction of g to L, and that $g_L \in G(\sigma_L)$, where σ_L is the involution induced on L by σ. Moreover (10.6) implies the normalizing condition $\det^2 \tilde{\mathbf{A}} = 1$. We can now use our earlier conclusions; $\tilde{\mathbf{A}}$ is contained in the set of matrices (10.3) and (10.4), with $\gamma = -1$ and $a^2 + c^2 = 1$. If g_L is an involution, $\tilde{\mathbf{A}}$ belongs to the pencil (10.4), and we have

$$\mathbf{A} = \begin{pmatrix} a & c & 0 \\ c & -a & 0 \\ 0 & 0 & 1 \end{pmatrix}, \qquad a^2 + c^2 = 1. \tag{10.7}$$

To show that in this case g is a harmonic homology, we can simplify the numerical work by letting $a = \cos 2\alpha$, $c = \sin 2\alpha$, $0 \leqq \alpha < \pi$; we find that the center is $(-\sin\alpha, \cos\alpha, 0)^T$ and the axis is $x_1 \sin\alpha - x_2 \cos\alpha = 0$. On the other hand, if g_L is not an involution, $\tilde{\mathbf{A}}$ is included in (10.3). Since

$$\tilde{\mathbf{A}} = \begin{pmatrix} a & -c \\ c & a \end{pmatrix} = \begin{pmatrix} a & c \\ c & -a \end{pmatrix}\begin{pmatrix} 1 & 0 \\ 0 & -1 \end{pmatrix},$$

we can factor $\mathbf{A}$,

$$\mathbf{A} = \begin{pmatrix} a & -c & 0 \\ c & a & 0 \\ 0 & 0 & 1 \end{pmatrix} = \begin{pmatrix} a & c & 0 \\ c & -a & 0 \\ 0 & 0 & 1 \end{pmatrix}\begin{pmatrix} 1 & 0 & 0 \\ 0 & -1 & 0 \\ 0 & 0 & 1 \end{pmatrix}, \tag{10.8}$$

and g is the product of two harmonic homologies. Thus we have proved the following theorem.

THEOREM 10.5. *The group of a polarity in $S_2(\mathsf{R})$ is generated by the harmonic homologies whose center and axis are pole and polar in the polarity. Every member of the group is expressible as the product of at most two such harmonic homologies.*

We need to introduce the concept of isomorphic groups.

DEFINITION 10.2. Two groups G and G' are *isomorphic* if there exists a one-to-one mapping from one onto the other which maps the product of every two elements in the one group onto the product of their maps in the second group. If G and G' are isomorphic, we write $G \cong G'$. The mapping is called an *isomorphism.*

Thus if f is an isomorphism from a group G onto a group G', it follows that $f(g) \in G'$ for all $g \in G$, and that

$$f(g_1 g_2) = f(g_1) f(g_2), \qquad g_1, g_2 \in G.$$

Isomorphic groups are abstractly equivalent, that is, they have the same inner structure. They may however appear in a concrete setting in terms of which they are distinguishable. As an example of isomorphic groups, we have the following theorem.

THEOREM 10.6. *The set of collineations in $S_2(\mathsf{F})$ that leave a given non-singular conic invariant is a group isomorphic to the group of projectivities of $S_1(\mathsf{F})$.*

Proof. We establish a mapping between the two groups by associating with a given element in the group of the conic the projectivity induced on the conic by the collineation. By Theorem 9.4, this map is one-to-one. We leave to the reader to prove that this map preserves multiplication.

We give further examples of isomorphic groups in the exercises below. The following theorem yields a single criterion for the requirement that a given set be a group and that the group be isomorphic to a given group.

THEOREM 10.7. *Let H be a set in which a multiplication is defined, and let f be a one-to-one map with domain H and range a group G; if f maps the product of elements in H onto the product, in G, of their maps under f,*

$$f(h_1 h_2) = f(h_1)f(h_2), \qquad h_1, h_2 \in H,$$

then H is a group isomorphic to G, and f is an isomorphism.

Proof. Since f is one-to-one, $f(a) = f(b)$ implies $a = b$, so that f^{-1} exists. Let e_G be the unit in G, and let $e_H = f^{-1}(e_G)$. Since $f(e_H h) = f(e_H)f(h) = e_G f(h) = f(h)$, and since $f(e_H h) = f(h)$ implies $e_H h = h$, it follows that e_H is a left unit in H. We can show in a similar manner that $he_H = h$, and that every element in H possesses an inverse. We leave the rest of the proof to the reader.

EXERCISES

1. In $S_1(\mathsf{F})$ let π be a projectivity (not an involution) in the group of an involution σ. Prove that for all points $X \neq \pi X$

$$(\pi^{-1}X\ \pi X,\ X\ \sigma X) = -1.$$

2. Prove that in $S_2(\mathsf{F}_7)$ (where coordinates are residues mod 7) the collineation $x_1' = x_2, x_2' = 2x_3, x_3' = x_1$ leaves no conic fixed.

3. Prove the assertion in the text (following the proof of Theorem 10.3) regarding rotations and reflections in a Euclidean pencil of lines.

4. Prove Corollary 10.2.

5. Relate the theorem that every rotation in a Euclidean pencil of lines is the product of two line reflections to the work of this section.

6. Prove that the group of an elliptic involution in $S_1(\mathsf{R})$ is isomorphic to the group of rotations and line reflections in a Euclidean pencil of lines.

#***7.** Let σ be a polarity in $S_2(\mathsf{R})$, and σ_L the involution of conjugate points on a line L. If π is a projectivity on L and $\pi\sigma_L = \sigma_L\pi$, there exists $g \in G(\sigma)$ such that the restriction of g to L is π. (*Hint*: factor π into the product of three (or fewer) hyperbolic involutions.)

8. Complete the proofs of Theorems 10.6 and 10.7.

9. Prove that the set of elations in $S_2(\mathsf{R})$ with a given axis is a group isomorphic to the group of translations in E_2.

11 Pencils of Quadratic Forms

In $S_2(\mathsf{F})$, we let

$$Q = \mathbf{X}^T\mathbf{B}\mathbf{X}, \qquad \mathbf{B} = \mathbf{B}^T = (b_{ij}). \tag{11.1}$$

If we seek all conics in $S_2(\mathsf{F})$ which are incident to a given point Y, or equivalently all forms Q which vanish at Y, we must have

$$\mathbf{Y}^T\mathbf{B}\mathbf{Y} = 0. \tag{11.2}$$

Because $\mathbf{B} = \mathbf{B}^T$, we can regard (11.2) as a homogeneous linear equation in six unknowns. Our earlier results (see I, Theorem 5.4) permit us to conclude that there exist quintuples of solutions of (11.2) such that every solution is a linear combination of these five solutions. Denoting one such quintuple by $b_{ij}^{(h)}$ $(h = 1, 2, 3, 4, 5)$, we have

$$b_{ij} = \lambda_1 b_{ij}^{(1)} + \lambda_2 b_{ij}^{(2)} + \lambda_3 b_{ij}^{(3)} + \lambda_4 b_{ij}^{(4)} + \lambda_5 b_{ij}^{(5)}. \tag{11.3}$$

Each solution $b_{ij}^{(h)}$ determines the symmetric matrix $\mathbf{B}_h = (b_{ij}^{(h)})$ and the form $Q_h = \mathbf{X}^T\mathbf{B}_h\mathbf{X}$; the matrix $\mathbf{B}$ and the form Q of the solution (11.3) are given by

$$\mathbf{B} = \lambda_1 \mathbf{B}_1 + \lambda_2 \mathbf{B}_2 + \lambda_3 \mathbf{B}_3 + \lambda_4 \mathbf{B}_4 + \lambda_5 \mathbf{B}_5, \tag{11.4}$$

$$Q = \lambda_1 Q_1 + \lambda_2 Q_2 + \lambda_3 Q_3 + \lambda_4 Q_4 + \lambda_5 Q_5. \tag{11.5}$$

Thus the linear relation (11.3) on the coefficients b_{ij}, $b_{ij}^{(h)}$ implies the linear relations (11.4) and (11.5) on the corresponding matrices $\mathbf{B}$, $\mathbf{B}_h$, and on the forms Q, Q_h. Conversely, either of the linear relations (11.4) or (11.5) implies the other and (11.3).

More generally, we can replace (11.2) by a system, say of n independent homogeneous linear equations; if $n \leqq 5$, there exist $6 - n$ independent solutions which generate (or span) the set of all solutions. As in the case discussed, the coefficients b_{ij}, the matrix $\mathbf{B} = (b_{ij}) = (b_{ji})$, and the form $Q = \mathbf{X}^T\mathbf{B}\mathbf{X}$ of an arbitrary solution are linear combinations of the independent solutions (coefficients, matrices, or forms respectively), with the same coefficients of dependence.

Definition 11.1. We call $[Q]$, that is, the set of forms ρQ for $\rho \in \mathsf{F}$, $\rho \neq 0$, and Q given by (11.1), a *linear system of dimension zero*. We define a *linear system of dimension*† k inductively: If $Q_1, Q_2, \ldots, Q_{k+1}$ are $k + 1$ forms which do not belong to a linear system of dimension $k - 1$, the set of forms

$$Q = \lambda_1 Q_1 + \lambda_2 Q_2 + \ldots + \lambda_{k+1} Q_{k+1}, \qquad \lambda_i \in \mathsf{F}, \quad (\lambda_1, \lambda_2, \ldots, \lambda_{k+1}) \neq (0, 0, \ldots, 0), \tag{11.6}$$

(and the set of conics $Q = 0$) is called a linear system of dimension k. A linear system of dimension one (two) is called a *pencil* (*bundle*). The forms $Q_1, Q_2, \ldots, Q_{k+1}$ constitute a *basis* of the linear system.

Although Definition 11.1 is in terms of a particular coordinatization, it is readily verified that the concept of a linear system is geometric, that is, it is

† This dimension is relative to F.

independent of the chosen projective point-coordinate system. Equivalently, a collineation maps a linear system onto a linear system, and the basis of the first system onto a basis of the second.

Belonging to a linear system is algebraically equivalent to linear dependence; thus two forms (conics) are dependent if and only if they belong to a linear system of dimension zero, and three if and only if they belong to a pencil, etc.

THEOREM 11.1. *The set of forms Q (or conics $\mathscr{C}(Q)$) whose coefficients satisfy a system of homogeneous linear conditions of rank r $(r \leqq 5)$ constitute a linear system of dimension $5 - r$. Conversely, every linear system of forms (conics) of dimension k is the solution set of a system of homogeneous linear conditions of rank $5 - k$.*

Since any set consisting of the appropriate number of independent solutions generates all the solutions of a system of linear equations, we have the following theorem.

THEOREM 11.2. *Any $k + 1$ forms (conics) which belong to a given linear system of dimension k and which do not belong to a linear system of smaller dimension constitute a basis for the system.*

Thus any two distinct conics of a pencil generate the pencil; any three conics in a bundle and not belonging to a pencil generate the bundle.

THEOREM 11.3. *The set of all forms Q is a linear system of dimension 5.*

Proof. Q is in the linear system spanned by the six forms $x_1^2, x_2^2, x_3^2, x_1x_2, x_1x_3, x_2x_3$. The 6×6 matrix of coefficients of these forms has rank 6, whereas the rank of the coefficients of six forms belonging to a linear system of dimension $k < 5$ cannot exceed 5 (see I, Theorem 5.5).

The set of all forms Q can be regarded as a vector space of dimension 6, and what we have called linear systems of dimension k would be vector spaces of dimension $k + 1$. Our dimensions are one less because we regard Q and ρQ as equivalent forms, in the same way that $\mathbf{X}$ and $\rho\mathbf{X}$ are equivalent representations of one point. Moreover the zero form, important in the algebraic theory of vector spaces, has somewhat less geometric significance.

The algebraic theory of linear systems of quadratic forms provides us with two geometric theories, one relating to conics as sets of points, and the other as sets of lines. Although the set of all nonsingular conics is self-dual, a linear system is not self-dual: the set of tangent lines to the conics $Q = 0$, where Q is given by (11.6), is a quadratic system because the elements of $\mathbf{B}^{-1}$ are proportional to quadratic functions of the λ's. Thus, the set of all conics through a given point is not a linear system of line conics; the dual set, the set of all conics tangent to a given line, is a linear system of line conics and not a linear system of point conics.

In the early part of this section we shall use linear systems, pencils, etc., in the sense of Definition 11.1; later we apply the algebraic theory to quadratic forms in line coordinates $\mathbf{U}$, and we shall then distinguish between the two kinds of pencils by means of the terms *point-pencils* and *line-pencils*.

Let us turn to the consideration of pencils, writing

$$Q = \lambda Q_1 + \mu Q_2, \qquad [Q_1] \neq [Q_2]. \tag{11.7}$$

Then

$$\mathbf{B} = \lambda \mathbf{B}_1 + \mu \mathbf{B}_2, \tag{11.8}$$

where $\mathbf{B}$, $\mathbf{B}_1$, $\mathbf{B}_2$ are the respective matrices of Q, Q_1, Q_2.

THEOREM 11.4. *A pencil of forms in $S_2(\mathsf{F})$ contains at most three singular forms, unless it consists exclusively of singular forms.*

Proof. Q is singular if and only if λ, μ satisfy

$$\det(\lambda \mathbf{B}_1 + \mu \mathbf{B}_2) = 0. \tag{11.9}$$

This is a homogeneous cubic equation in λ, μ unless all coefficients vanish.

The two pencils $\lambda x_1^2 + \mu x_2^2$ and $\lambda x_1 x_2 + \mu x_1 x_3$ illustrate that a pencil may consist exclusively of singular forms. We shall leave consideration of such pencils to the reader (see Exercises 4, 5, 6 below); in the rest of this section pencils of forms (conics) shall mean pencils that do not consist exclusively of singular forms (conics).

Notation. We shall denote a pencil of forms (11.7) not all of which are singular by $\mathscr{L}$. The *conics and the polarities in* $\mathscr{L}$ are the conics and polarities determined by the forms in $\mathscr{L}$.

THEOREM 11.5. *A point of intersection of two conics is incident to all conics of their pencil; two points conjugate with respect to two conics are conjugate with respect to all conics of their pencil.*

Proof. We can choose the two conics as a basis for the pencil. If Y is a point of intersection, Q_1 and Q_2 vanish at Y; from (11.7), Q vanishes at Y for all λ, μ. We leave the rest of the proof to the reader.

DEFINITION 11.2. The set of intersections of the conics of a pencil is called the set of *base points* of the pencil.

THEOREM 11.6. *A point not a base point of a pencil is incident to exactly one conic of the pencil.*

We leave the proof to the reader.

We shall see that the set of base points together with a set of integers called their multiplicities, characterize pencils in many projective planes (for example, in $S_2(\mathsf{C})$). To this end, we select in $S_2(\mathsf{F})$ two conics $\mathscr{C}_1$ and $\mathscr{C}_2$ in a given pencil $\mathscr{L}$. We suppose $\mathscr{C}_1$ is nonsingular. We choose a coordinate system in which $A_3:(0,0,1)^T$ is a point of $\mathscr{C}_1$ and not of $\mathscr{C}_2$, and in which the forms Q_1, Q_2 of $\mathscr{C}_1, \mathscr{C}_2$ are respectively

$$Q_1 = x_1 x_3 - x_2^2, \qquad Q_2 = \mathbf{X}^T\mathbf{B}\mathbf{X}, \qquad b_{33} \neq 0. \tag{11.10}$$

Since no base point lies on the line $x_1 = 0$, we can introduce nonhomogeneous coordinates

$$x = x_2/x_1, \qquad y = x_3/x_1,$$

and represent base points by $(1, x, y)^T$ where x, y, satisfy $y = x^2$ and the nonhomogeneous equation corresponding to $Q_2 = 0$. Eliminating y, we obtain the quartic equation

$$b_{33}x^4 + 2b_{23}x^3 + (2b_{13} + b_{22})x^2 + 2b_{12}x + b_{11} = 0. \tag{11.11}$$

Each solution of this equation determines one base point, and the base points corresponding to distinct solutions are distinct. Thus the number of base points is four or less.

The reader can verify that the multiplicities of the solutions of (11.11) are associated with the pencil $\mathscr{L}$ rather than with the basis Q_1, Q_2 by showing that each two forms in the pencil determine the same equation (11.11).

If the left side of (11.11) is the product of four linear factors, as is the case when F is the complex field C (or any other algebraically closed field), there are exactly five possibilities as regards multiplicities of the roots of (11.11):

I four simple roots;
II one double root and two simple roots;
III two double roots;
IV one triple and one simple root;
V one quadruple root.

We shall denote these five cases as follows:

$$\text{I: } (1,1,1,1); \quad \text{II: } (2,1,1); \quad \text{III: } (2,2); \quad \text{IV: } (3,1); \quad \text{V: } (4). \tag{11.12}$$

These cases exist in $S_2(\mathsf{F})$ for every F, but in some planes (for example, in $S_2(\mathsf{R})$) additional possibilities may occur.

Let us first examine the consequences in $S_2(\mathsf{F})$ of the existence of a base point. We specialize the coordinate system of (11.10) further by requiring that $A_1:(1,0,0)^T$ be the base point. Then $x = 0$ is a solution of (11.11), $b_{11} = 0$, and basis forms Q_1, Q_2 are given by

$$Q_1 = x_1 x_3 - x_2^2, \qquad Q_2 = 2b_{12}x_1x_2 + b_{22}x_2^2 + 2b_{13}x_1x_3 + 2b_{23}x_2x_3 + b_{33}x_3^2. \tag{11.13}$$

Letting m be the multiplicity of $x = 0$ as a root of (11.11), we note the following double implications:

$$\begin{aligned} m = 1 &\quad \Leftrightarrow \quad b_{12} \neq 0; \\ m = 2 &\quad \Leftrightarrow \quad b_{12} = 0, \quad 2b_{13} + b_{22} \neq 0; \\ m = 3 &\quad \Leftrightarrow \quad b_{12} = 2b_{13} + b_{22} = 0, \quad b_{23} \neq 0; \\ m = 4 &\quad \Leftrightarrow \quad b_{12} = 2b_{13} + b_{22} = b_{23} = 0. \end{aligned}$$

Since the tangent line at A_1 to $\mathscr{C}_2$ is the line $b_{12}x_2 + b_{13}x_3 = 0$, and the tangent line at A_1 to the conic $\lambda Q_1 + \mu Q_2 = 0$ is the line $\lambda x_3 + \mu(b_{12}x_2 + b_{13}x_3) = 0$, we can conclude that

$$\begin{aligned} m = 1 &\quad \Leftrightarrow \quad \text{two conics of the pencil are not tangent† at } A_1; \\ m > 1 &\quad \Leftrightarrow \quad \text{each two conics of the pencil are tangent at } A_1. \end{aligned}$$

If $m \geqq 2$, we find that

$$\det(2\lambda Q_1 + Q_2) = (\lambda + b_{13})^2(2\lambda - b_{22}).$$

Thus the existence of a base point of multiplicity 2 or more implies that, in $S_2(\mathsf{F})$, the left side of (11.9) is the product of three linear factors, at least one of which is repeated. If $m = 2$, the pencil contains two singular conics; one, corresponding to the double root of (11.9), is given by

$$(2b_{13} + b_{22})x_2^2 + 2b_{23}x_2x_3 + b_{33}x_3^2 = 0, \tag{11.14}$$

and the second, corresponding to the simple root of (11.9), is given by

$$x_3\{(2b_{13} + b_{22})x_1 + 2b_{23}x_2 + b_{33}x_3\} = 0. \tag{11.15}$$

If $m = 3$, the pencil contains just one singular conic,

$$x_3(2b_{23}x_2 + b_{33}x_3) = 0, \tag{11.16}$$

and this conic has rank 2. Finally, if $m = 4$, the pencil contains just one singular conic,

$$x_3^2 = 0. \tag{11.17}$$

We can describe the singular conic (or conics) geometrically. If $m = 4$, it consists of the tangent line at the base point regarded as a conic of rank 1. If $m = 3$, we see from (11.16) that it consists of two distinct lines incident to the base point and one of which is the tangent line. In this case there must exist a second base point which is simple (that is, of multiplicity 1). If $m = 2$, there may or may not exist further base points; (11.15) represents two distinct lines, of which one is the tangent line at the base point and the other can be any other line not incident to the first base point. If this line is a tangent line, (11.14) has rank 1, we have two base points, each of multiplicity 2, and

† A singular conic with vertex at A_1 is to be regarded as tangent to any conic incident to A_1.

(11.14) is the chord of contact counted doubly. Otherwise, (11.14) has rank 2; it is a pair of lines if and only if the second line of (11.15) intersects $\mathscr{C}_1$. Conversely, a pencil containing two singular conics of the kinds just described possesses a base point of multiplicity 2.

In $S_2(\mathsf{C})$ (or in $S_2(\mathsf{F})$, where F is algebraically closed), the sum of the multiplicities of the base points is 4, and the preceding characterization of pencils is categorical. We can summarize the foregoing results for $S_2(\mathsf{C})$ in the following table.

TYPES OF PENCILS IN $S_2(\mathsf{C})$

Type	*Number and Multiplicity of Base Points*		*Multiplicity and Rank of Singular Conics*		*Vertices of Singular Conics*
I	4	1,1,1,1	1,1,1	2,2,2	three independent points
II	3	2,1,1	1,2	2,2	two points
III	2	2,2	1,2	2,1	the points of one line and one other point
IV	2	3,1	3	2	one point
V	1	4	3	1	the points of one line

In Figure 11.1, we show two nonsingular conics in each of the five types of pencils in $S_2(\mathsf{C})$.

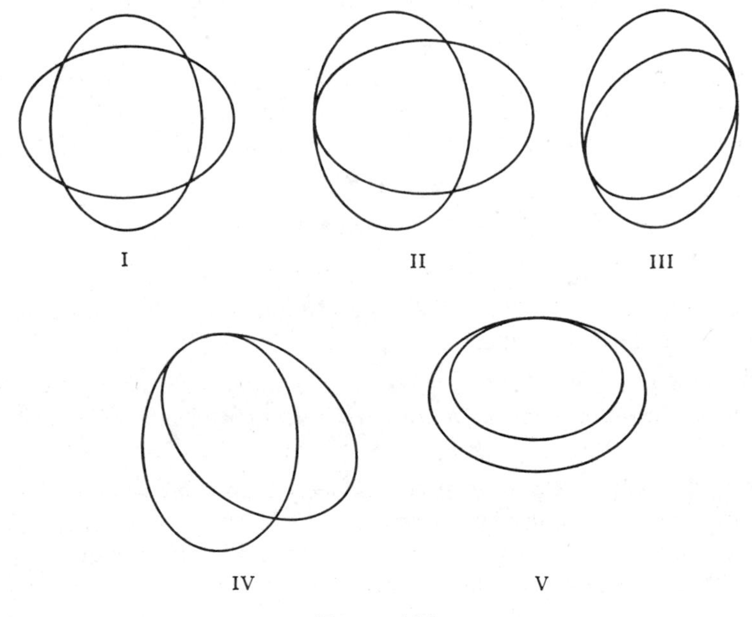

FIGURE 11.1

The preceding analysis shows that in $S_2(\mathsf{F})$ different values for the multiplicities of the roots of (11.11) give rise to different types of pencils, and we can conclude that the multiplicities of the base points are indeed projective invariants of the pencil.

We say that two conics have *k-point* contact at a point if the point is a base point of multiplicity k of their pencil. Frequently, k-point contact is called contact of *order* $k - 1$. A base point of multiplicity 1 is called a *simple* base point. Two conics have *double contact* at two points if they have 2-point contact at each of them; their pencil is of type III.

A pencil $\mathscr{L}$ in $S_2(\mathsf{F})$ which possesses base points the sum of whose multiplicities is 4 is necessarily one of the five types pictured in Figure 11.1 and listed in the preceding table. We can derive canonical equations for these pencils.

For a pencil of type I, the diagonal triangle of the quadrangle whose vertices are the four points of intersection is self-conjugate with respect to all the conics of the pencil. If we choose this triangle as the reference triangle, and choose the unit point as one of the intersections, the four intersections will be $(\pm 1, \pm 1, 1)^T$, and the pencil of forms becomes

$$Q = \lambda(x_1^2 - x_2^2) + \mu(x_1^2 - x_3^2). \tag{11.18}$$

For a pencil of type II, we choose the vertices of the coordinate triangle to be the base points, with A_1 the base point of multiplicity 2, and we choose the unit point on the tangent at A_1. Then the two singular forms are $x_2 x_3$ and $x_1(x_2 - x_3)$, so that the pencil of forms is given by

$$Q = \lambda x_2 x_3 + \mu x_1(x_2 - x_3). \tag{11.19}$$

Since two tangents to a nonsingular conic and the chord of contact can always be taken as the lines $x_1 = 0$, $x_3 = 0$, $x_2 = 0$ respectively, pencils of types III, IV, or V possess the respective canonical forms

$$Q = \lambda x_1 x_3 + \mu x_2^2, \tag{11.20}$$

$$Q = \lambda(x_1 x_3 - x_2^2) + \mu x_1 x_2, \tag{11.21}$$

$$Q = \lambda(x_1 x_3 - x_2^2) + \mu x_1^2. \tag{11.22}$$

Since equations (11.18)–(11.22) contain no arbitrary constants, we have proved the following theorem.

THEOREM 11.7. *In $S_2(\mathsf{F})$, two pencils possessing base points the sum of whose multiplicities is 4 are projectively equivalent if and only if they are of the same type.*

In $S_2(\mathsf{R})$ there exist pencils of conics other than those already described since the sum of the multiplicities of the (real) solutions of (11.11) could be 0 or 2, as well as 4. We list below these new possibilities, using the notation of (11.12) and letting 0 denote the absence of any base point. For each type in $S_2(\mathsf{R})$, we include the type symbol when the pencil is regarded as one in $S_2(\mathsf{C})$.

(11.23)

$S_2(\mathsf{R})$		$S_2(\mathsf{C})$	
Ia:	(0)	I:	(1, 1, 1, 1)
Ib:	(1, 1)	I:	(1, 1, 1, 1)
IIa:	(2)	II:	(2, 1, 1)
IIIa:	(0)	III:	(2, 2)

We can show by examples that these four types exist in $S_2(\mathsf{R})$ (or in $S_2(\mathsf{F})$ whenever there exist quadratic equations that have no solution in F). Consider a pencil with basis a nonsingular conic and a singular conic consisting of two lines. The four types (11.23) arise in the following situations:

(11.24)

Ia: The two lines are distinct exterior lines of the conic.
Ib: One line is exterior, the other interior.
IIa: One line is a tangent line, the other exterior.
IIIa: The two lines coincide, and are exterior.

Although (11.23) exhausts all possibilities in $S_2(\mathsf{R})$, it is not apparent that (11.24) does so since we have not yet proved that every pencil in $S_2(\mathsf{R})$ contains a singular conic consisting of two (distinct or coincident) lines. However, pencils of types Ib and IIa do possess such a singular conic: We let P be a point (not a base point) on the join of the two base points if the pencil is of type Ib, or on the common tangent if the pencil is of type IIa; the (unique) conic of the pencil incident to P must consist of two lines. Following Theorem 11.8, we shall prove that every pencil of forms in $S_2(\mathsf{R})$ contains at least one which is the product of linear factors, so that (11.24) is equivalent to (11.23).

There exist fields F such that $S_2(\mathsf{F})$ possesses more types of pencils than exist in $S_2(\mathsf{R})$. For example, a pencil may contain no singular conics, and it may possess only one simple base point (see Exercises 9, 10, 11 below).

DEFINITION 11.3. The vertices of the singular forms in a pencil $\mathscr{L}$ are called the *singular points* of $\mathscr{L}$.

The following theorem in $S_2(\mathsf{F})$ plays a particularly important role in the further development of the theory.

THEOREM 11.8. *A point in $S_2(\mathsf{F})$, not a singular point of a pencil $\mathscr{L}$, determines uniquely a point to which it is conjugate with respect to all the forms in $\mathscr{L}$. A singular point is conjugate to the points of a line, the polar of the singular point with respect to all except one of the forms in $\mathscr{L}$.*

Proof. In general, the polars of Y with respect to the forms (11.7) in $\mathscr{L}$ is a pencil of lines, given by

(11.25) $$\lambda \mathbf{Y}^T\mathbf{B}_1\mathbf{X} + \mu\mathbf{Y}^T\mathbf{B}_2\mathbf{X} = 0.$$

The vertex of this pencil is the only point conjugate to Y with respect to all the forms (11.7). (11.25) fails to represent a pencil of lines if and only if there exist $\rho_1, \rho_2 \in \mathsf{F}$, $(\rho_1, \rho_2) \neq (0, 0)$, such that

$$\rho_1 \mathbf{Y}^T\mathbf{B}_1 + \rho_2 \mathbf{Y}^T\mathbf{B}_2 = 0. \tag{11.26}$$

Then $(\rho_1\mathbf{B}_1 + \rho_2\mathbf{B}_2)\mathbf{Y} = 0$, and Y is a vertex of $\rho_1 Q_1 + \rho_2 Q_2$; in this contingency, (11.25) represents the common polar of Y with respect to all forms (11.7) of which Y is not a vertex.

We can now show that a pencil $\mathscr{L}$ in $S_2(\mathsf{R})$ necessarily contains at least one form which is the product of two linear factors. First we note that since (11.9) is of degree three, every pencil contains at least one singular form. Denote such a form by Q_2, let $\mathscr{C}_2$ be the conic $Q_2 = 0$, and let Y be a vertex of $\mathscr{C}_2$. The polars of Y with respect to the forms in the pencil (except Q_2) coincide (see Theorem 11.8); let W be this polar. If Y is a base point, W is tangent at Y to all the conics in the pencil, and the multiplicity of Y is at least 2. Then the pencil is necessarily of type II, III, IV, V, or IIa, and it contains a singular form of which $\mathbf{WX}$ is one factor. If Y is not a base point, and Q_2 is not reducible (that is, $\mathscr{C}_2$ consists solely of Y), we let Q_1 be an arbitrary form in the pencil, not Q_2, and we let σ_1 and σ_2 be the involutions of conjugate points on W, with respect to Q_1 and Q_2 respectively. Then σ_2 is elliptic, so that there exist points Z, Z' which are pairs in both σ_1 and σ_2. Thus Z, Z' are conjugate with respect to two forms, and therefore they are conjugate with respect to every form belonging to the pencil. Hence YZZ' is a self-conjugate triangle. By choosing coordinates with this triangle as the reference triangle, the matrices of Q_1 and Q_2 become diagonal matrices; for a suitable choice of the unit point, $[Q_1]$ and $[Q_2]$ can be represented by

$$Q_1 = \pm x_1^2 + x_2^2 + cx_3^2, \qquad Q_2 = x_2^2 + x_3^2. \tag{11.27}$$

Then one of the forms $Q_1 - Q_2$ or $Q_1 - cQ_2$ is reducible. Hence every pencil in $S_2(\mathsf{R})$ contains at least one reducible form, and the four types (11.24) represent all possibilities not included in the earlier table.

We can derive canonical forms corresponding to these four types. For a pencil of type Ia, we choose the sides $x_1 = 0$, $x_3 = 0$ of the coordinate triangle as the given exterior lines, and the side $x_2 = 0$ as the polar of their intersection. If $Q_1 = \mathbf{X}^T\mathbf{B}\mathbf{X}$ is a form in the pencil, $b_{12} = b_{23} = 0$. Since the lines $x_1 = 0, x_3 = 0$ have no intersection with $Q_1 = 0$, we must have $\operatorname{sgn} b_{11} = \operatorname{sgn} b_{22} = \operatorname{sgn} b_{33}$. Hence we can choose the unit point so that $b_{ii} = 1$. Every pencil of type Ia can therefore be reduced to

$$Q = \lambda(x_1^2 + x_2^2 + x_3^2) + \mu x_1 x_3. \tag{11.28}$$

If the pencil is of type Ib, a similar choice of coordinates leads to the canonical form

$$Q = \lambda(x_1^2 + x_2^2 - x_3^2) + \mu x_1 x_3. \tag{11.29}$$

Our choice of coordinates for a pencil of type IIa resembles that made for one of type II. We let the lines $x_3 = 0$, $x_1 = 0$ be the tangent line and the exterior line which constitute the reducible conic in the pencil, and $x_2 = 0$ the polar of their intersection. If we choose the unit point on one of the nonsingular conics of the pencil and conjugate to A_3 (Figure 11.2), the equation of that conic becomes $x_2^2 + x_3^2 - 2x_1 x_3 = 0$, and the pencil is given by

$$Q = \lambda(x_2^2 + x_3^2) + \mu x_1 x_3 . \tag{11.30}$$

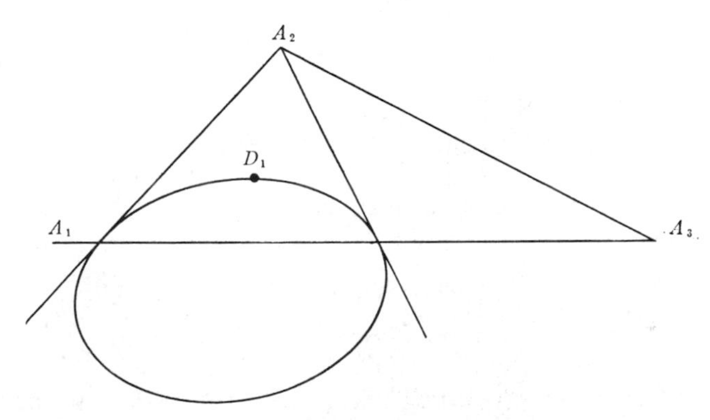

FIGURE 11.2

We shall leave it to the reader to verify that a pencil of type IIIa possesses the canonical form

$$Q = \lambda(x_1^2 + x_2^2) + \mu x_3^2 . \tag{11.31}$$

The canonical forms are devoid of arbitrary constants, and they yield the following theorem.

THEOREM 11.9. *In $S_2(\mathsf{R})$ two pencils of quadratic forms are projectively equivalent if and only if they are of the same type.*

We note that in mapping one pencil projectively onto a second (of the same type) we cannot necessarily preassign in the second pencil the map of a given conic of the first pencil.

THEOREM 11.10. *The matrix of a pencil of quadratic forms in $S_2(\mathsf{C})$ is equivalent to a diagonal matrix if and only if the pencil is of type* I *or* III.

Proof. If the matrix is diagonal, the reference triangle is self-conjugate with respect to all the forms; by Theorem 11.8, its vertices must be vertices of singular forms in the pencil. From the table (page 257) the pencil cannot be of type II, IV, or V. A pencil of type I possesses a unique self-conjugate triangle, the diagonal triangle of the base quadrangle. A pencil of type III possesses infinitely many self-conjugate triangles, since one vertex can be taken arbitrarily as a point, not a base point, on the line of contact.

COROLLARY 11.1. *In* $S_2(\mathsf{R})$, *the matrix of a pencil is equivalent to a diagonal matrix if and only if the pencil is of type* I, Ia, III, *or* IIIa.

In our earlier work we have emphasized the point of view that a nonsingular conic is a self-dual structure, determined either by its constituent points, as a locus $\mathbf{X}^T\mathbf{B}\mathbf{X} = 0$, or by its constituent lines, as the locus $\mathbf{U}\mathbf{B}^{-1}\mathbf{U}^T = 0$. Two nonsingular forms

$$Q_1 = \mathbf{X}^T\mathbf{B}_1\mathbf{X}, \qquad Q_2 = \mathbf{X}^T\mathbf{B}_2\mathbf{X}$$

determine the dual forms

$$Q_1^* = \mathbf{U}\mathbf{B}_1^{-1}\mathbf{U}^T, \qquad Q_2^* = \mathbf{U}\mathbf{B}_2^{-1}\mathbf{U}^T,$$

and vice versa. Either pair of forms (conics, polarities) determines the two pencils

$$Q = \lambda Q_1 + \mu Q_2, \tag{11.32}$$

$$Q^* = \lambda Q_1^* + \mu Q_2^*. \tag{11.33}$$

Although the algebraic properties of a pencil of quadratic forms are independent of the particular interpretation of the variables of the form, and although the conics $Q_i = 0$ and $Q_i^* = 0$ $(i = 1 \text{ or } 2)$ (and their polarities) coincide, the two pencils may be, and generally are, distinct. Thus the conics of the pencil (11.32) are incident to the points of intersection of the two basis conics, whereas the conics belonging to (11.33) are tangent to those lines which are tangent to both basis conics.

By applying the algebraic conclusions implicit in our earlier analysis, we can conclude that in $S_2(\mathsf{C})$ a pencil of line conics not consisting exclusively of singular line conics is of one of five types. We portray these five types in Figure 11.3, where we have drawn two nonsingular conics in the line-pencil and the base lines, that is, the lines tangent to all the conics of the pencil.

The preceding analysis yields the following dual conclusions. The points of contact of two conics of a line-pencil with a base line are distinct if and only if the base line is a line of multiplicity 1. The table (page 257) permits us to describe the five types of line-pencils in $S_2(\mathsf{C})$ in terms of the singular conics of the line-pencil. A pencil of type I is the set of conics tangent to the four sides of a quadrilateral, and the three pairs of opposite vertices, regarded as three pairs of pencils of lines, are the three singular line conics of the pencil. A pencil of type II consists of the conics inscribed in a given triangle, with prescribed point of contact on a given one of the three sides. The two vertices on that side constitute one singular line conic (of multiplicity 2); the given point of contact and the point of intersecion of the other two tangents is the other singular line conic. In a pencil of type III, the point of intersection of the given tangents is one singular conic (of rank 1, and multiplicity 2) and the pair of points of contact is the other. Pencils of types IV and V possess only one singular line conic (of rank 2 and 1, respectively); the reader should identify these.

THEOREM 11.11. *Two nonsingular conics in $S_2(\mathsf{C})$ generate a point-pencil and a line-pencil which are of the same type.*

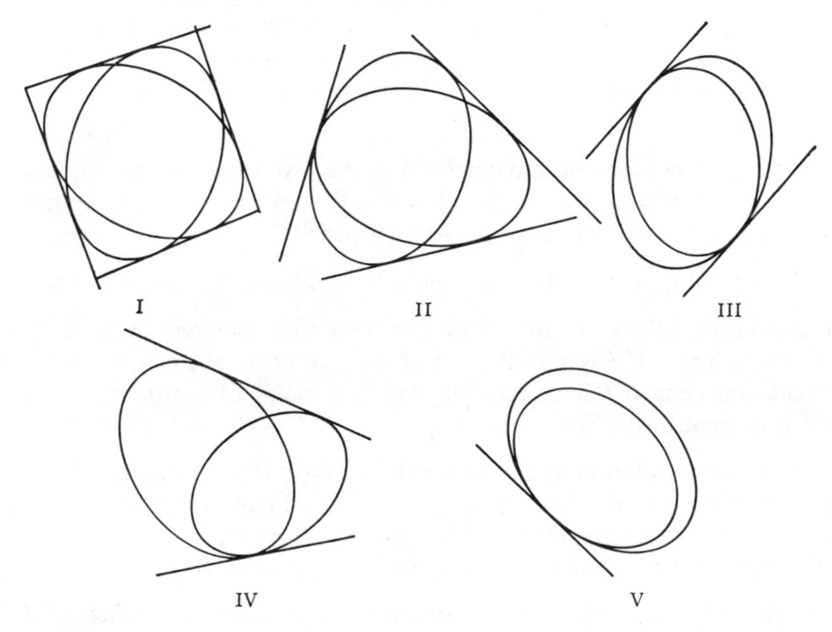

FIGURE 11.3

Proof. Although we could verify the assertion by means of the canonical representations given in (11.18) to (11.22), we prefer the following argument: The singular forms in the line-pencil (11.33) are given by the values of λ, μ which satisfy

$$\det(\lambda \mathbf{B}_1^{-1} + \mu \mathbf{B}_2^{-1}) = 0. \tag{11.34}$$

Since $\lambda \mathbf{B}_1^{-1} + \mu \mathbf{B}_2^{-1} = \mathbf{B}_1^{-1}(\lambda \mathbf{B}_2 + \mu \mathbf{B}_1)\mathbf{B}_2^{-1}$, the set of multiplicities of the solutions of (11.34) is the set of multiplicities of the solutions of (11.9), and the set of ranks of the singular conics of one pencil is the set of ranks of the singular conics of the other pencil. From our earlier table these arithmetic invariants characterize the pencil.

We cannot conclude that Theorem 11.11 is valid in $S_2(\mathsf{R})$ because in the real field a quadratic form of rank 2 may or may not be reducible. It can be shown that in $S_2(\mathsf{R})$ the two pencils are of the same type except if one is of type I or Ia. Then the other is either of type I or Ia, independently.

In the development of the geometry of conics, the theorems of Steiner, Pascal, Desargues, and their duals, due to Chasles, Brianchon, and Sturm, are outstanding. The first two of these together with their duals were discussed earlier in this chapter.

THEOREM 11.12a. DESARGUES' INVOLUTION THEOREM. *The pairs of points in which the conics of a pencil of point conics in $S_2(\mathsf{C})$ intersect a given line not incident to a base point of the pencil are pairs in an involution whose fixed points are the points of contact of the conics of the pencil which are tangent to the given line.*†

Proof. We choose coordinates so that the given line has the equation $x_3 = 0$. If the pencil is given by $Q = \mathbf{X}^T(\lambda\mathbf{B} + \mu\mathbf{B}')\mathbf{X}$, the pairs of intersections are cut out by the one-dimensional pencil

$$\lambda(b_{11}x_1^2 + 2b_{12}x_1x_2 + b_{22}x_2^2) + \mu(b'_{11}x_1^2 + 2b'_{12}x_1x_2 + b'_{22}x_2^2) = 0.$$

The conclusion follows in part from the involution theorem in $S_1(\mathsf{C})$ (see II, Theorem 6.6). If F is a fixed point of the involution, the unique conic of the pencil incident to F intersects the line in a point of multiplicity 2 and hence is tangent to the line.†

Desargues' Involution Theorem is valid in $S_2(\mathsf{F})$ if we restrict the line by requiring that on it the involutions (or singular involutions) of conjugate points with respect to the forms of the pencil be distinct.

We state next the dual of Theorem 11.12a, due to Sturm.

THEOREM 11.12b. *The pairs of tangents to the conics of a pencil of line conics in $S_2(\mathsf{C})$ from a point not incident to a base line of the pencil are pairs in an involution whose fixed lines are the tangent lines to the two conics of the pencil which are incident to the given point.*

COROLLARY 11.2. *In $S_2(\mathsf{C})$ a given point-pencil contains two conics tangent to a given line not incident to a base point of the pencil.*

The familiar property of quadrangles stated earlier (III, 8, Exercise 13) is a special case of Desargues' Involution Theorem. When the pencil is of type I, the following geometric proof of Theorem 11.12a is of interest. In the notation suggested by Figure 11.4, where $\mathscr{C}$ is a nonsingular conic through K, L, M, and N, we have

$$\begin{aligned}(AB, CC') &= (AB, CC')_K = (LN, CC')_{\mathscr{C}} \\ &= (LN, CC')_M = (B'A', CC') = (A'B', C'C).\end{aligned}$$

† Tangency is here used in the algebraic sense; a singular conic is tangent to any line through its vertex.

Hence the projectivity mapping A, B, C onto A', B', C' is an involution, and therefore C and C' are a pair in the involution mapping A, B onto A', B'.

We return to Theorem 11.8 to consider some consequences thereof. Let $\mathscr{L}$ be a given point-pencil in $S_2(\mathsf{F})$, and for $X \in S_2(\mathsf{F})$ let fX be the point (or points) conjugate to X with respect to all forms Q in $\mathscr{L}$. We can regard f as mapping the points of $S_2(\mathsf{F})$ into themselves with the singular points of $\mathscr{L}$ as singular points of the map; f maps each such point onto a line. Moreover $fX = fY$ does not imply $X = Y$, as we can verify, for example, by letting X and Y be incident to the join of two vertices in a pencil of type I. Despite these disadvantages, f is typical of a class of transformations which play an important role in geometry and algebra, the class of birational transformations.

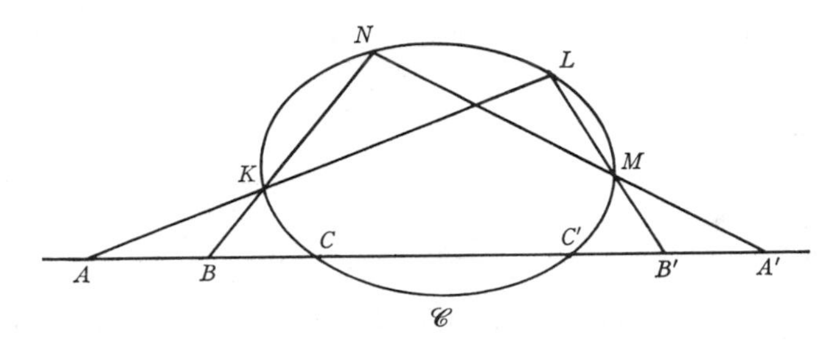

FIGURE 11.4

We let L be an arbitrary line, and we seek to identify fL, that is, the set of points fX for $X \in L$. Let σ_1, σ_2 be two nonsingular polarities in $\mathscr{L}$, and let Z_1, Z_2 be the respective poles of L: $Z_1 = \sigma_1 L$, $Z_2 = \sigma_2 L$. For any $X \in L$, $\sigma_i X$ is a line of the pencil Z_i $(i = 1, 2)$, and $fX = \sigma_1 X \cap \sigma_2 X$. Since the map $\sigma_1 X \to \sigma_2 X$ is a projectivity, fX is the intersection of corresponding lines of two projective pencils. Complications arise when these pencils of lines possess the same vertex $(Z_1 = Z_2)$, or when the common line of the two pencils, $Z_1 \oplus Z_2$, is self-corresponding.

In the latter event, there exists $Z \in L$ such that $\sigma_1 Z = \sigma_2 Z = Z_1 \oplus Z_2$. Hence Z is a singular point of the pencil, and fL consists of the polar of the singular point incident to L, and another line.

If $Z_1 = Z_2$, L is the polar of a singular point; the map $\sigma_1 X \to \sigma_2 X\,(X \in L)$ is a projectivity of a pencil of lines onto itself, and fL is the set of fixed lines of the projectivity. If the projectivity is the identity, every point of L is a vertex and fL is the entire plane. If the projectivity is not the identity, it possesses at most two fixed lines; fL is a singular conic, with vertex the pole of L, incident to those singular points of $\mathscr{L}$ which lie on L.

We summarize our conclusions when the locus is not a singular conic in the following theorem.

THEOREM 11.13. *The set of points fX conjugate to the points X of a line L, with respect to all the forms of a point-pencil is a nonsingular conic unless L contains a singular point of the pencil or is the polar of a singular point.*

We note that in $S_2(\mathrm{C})$ the second restriction on L is redundant.

The conic fL is of particular interest when the pencil is of type I. We denote the base points of $\mathscr{L}$ by P_i $(i = 1, 2, 3, 4)$, and we let $P_{ij} = L \cap (P_i \oplus P_j)$ (Figure 11.5); then the point $P'_{ij} = fP_{ij}$ is the harmonic conjugate of P_{ij} with

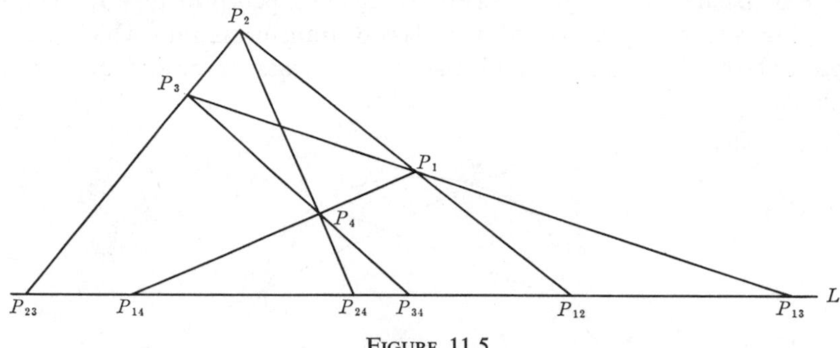

FIGURE 11.5

respect to P_i and P_j. Thus we have six points on the conic fL. The three vertices of the diagonal triangle are the maps by f of the intersections of L and the respective sides of the diagonal triangle. Lastly, the fixed points (if any exist) of the involution cut out on L by the pencil $\mathscr{L}$ (see Theorem 11.12a) separate pairs in the involution harmonically and therefore are paired in f. We have therefore the following conclusion.

COROLLARY 11.3. *Let a line L intersect the sides of a quadrangle $P_1 P_2 P_3 P_4$ in six distinct points. Then the following points lie on a nonsingular conic:*

(i) *the six points, one on each side, which are the harmonic conjugates, with respect to the vertices on that side, of the intersection of that side and L;*
(ii) *the three diagonal points of the quadrangle;*
(iii) *the points of contact with L of the conics* (*two, or possibly none*) *circumscribing the quadrangle and tangent to L.*

This conic is called the *eleven-point conic*.

We close this section with a presentation of two problems which can be solved by means of the ideas we have been discussing. Many more such problems will be found in the exercises at the end of the section.

Problem 1. Discuss a system of confocal ellipses and hyperbolas in E_2 from the projective point of view.

Solution. In E_2, the equations

$$x^2/(a^2+\lambda)+y^2/(b^2+\lambda)=1, \qquad b^2<a^2,$$

represent for $\lambda > -a^2$, the set of all central conics with foci at $(\pm\sqrt{(a^2-b^2)}, 0)$. An embedding of E_2 in $S_2(\mathsf{R})$ maps these conics into the pencil of line conics

$$(a^2+\lambda)u_1^2+(b^2+\lambda)u_2^2-u_3^2=0.$$

This pencil possesses one real singular line conic which consists of the two foci (see (7.11)). Can we discover any property of the pencil by using Sturm's Theorem? Since $u_1^2+u_2^2=0$ is a singular conic of the pencil, we can say (using the language of the complex plane) that the two tangents to the two conics of the pencil through a given point separate harmonically the joins of that point and the circular points., Thus in E_2 the two tangents are orthogonal, and confocal ellipses and hyperbolas intersect orthogonally.

Problem 2. Prove that if each of two conics in $S_2(\mathsf{C})$ has double contact with a third, a pair of opposite common chords of the two conics and the two chords of contact are four concurrent lines.

Proof. We can write the equations of the two conics as $Q+L_1^2=0$, $Q+L_2^2=0$, where $Q=0$ is the equation of the third conic, and $L_1=0$, $L_2=0$ are equations of the chords of contact. The conic $L_1^2-L_2^2=0$ belongs to the pencil of the first two, and it decomposes into the two lines $L_1 \pm L_2=0$, which clearly are lines incident to the intersection of $L_1=0$ and $L_2=0$.

EXERCISES

1. Which, if any, of the following sets of conics are (or are contained in) linear systems of point conics, which are linear systems of line conics, and which are neither? Determine the dimension of each linear system:

(a) the conics in $S_2(\mathsf{R})$ with respect to which a given point and a given line are pole and polar;

(b) the conics in $S_2(\mathsf{F})$ in which a given triangle is self-conjugate;

(c) the conics in $S_2(\mathsf{F})$ whose involutions of conjugate points on a given line coincide with a given involution on the line.

2. An embedding maps the following sets of curves in E_2 into conics in $S_2(\mathsf{R})$. Answer the question of Exercise 1 for them.

(a) circles through a given point;

(b) circles tangent to a given line;

(c) circles with a given center;

(d) parabolas tangent to two lines;

(e) hyperbolas with one given asymptote.

3. What can one say about the conics which belong to each of two given linear systems?

4. Prove that a point which is a vertex of two independent forms of a point-pencil is a vertex of all the forms of the pencil.

5. Determine necessary and sufficient conditions that a pencil contain more than two independent singular forms of rank 1.

6. Characterize pencils which consist exclusively of singular forms, using the results of Exercises 4, 5.

7. Two conics have double contact. What are the singular conics (a) in their point-pencil, and (b) in their line-pencil?

8. Two nonsingular conics determine a point-pencil and a line-pencil with the property that the nonsingular conics of either pencil belong to the other. Characterize such pencils.

#**9.** Show that in $S_2(\mathsf{F}_3)$ (where the coordinates are the residues mod 3) the two conics

$$x_1 x_3 - x_2^2 = 0, \qquad x_1 x_2 + x_3^2 = 0$$

have a triple intersection and a simple one.

#**10.** Show that in $S_2(\mathsf{F}_7)$ (where coordinates are residues mod 7) the conics

$$x_1x_3 - x_2^2 = 0, \qquad 2x_1^2 + x_3^2 - 2x_1x_2 - x_2x_3 = 0$$

have just one intersection (which is simple), and that their pencil contains only one singular conic.

#**11.** Show that in $S_2(\mathsf{F}_7)$ the pencil

$$\lambda(x_1^2 + 4x_2 x_3) + \mu(x_3^2 + x_1 x_2)$$

possesses just one base point (which is simple) and no singular forms.

12. Find an equation of the parabola in E_2 which has double contact with the circle $x^2 + y^2 = 25$ at the points $(\pm 3, 4)$. Is your result consistent with the corollary to Theorem 11.12b and the dual of Theorem 11.6?

13. Find the circle in E_2 which has at least three-point contact with the parabola $y^2 = 2x$ at the point $(8, 4)$.

14. Is the set of all osculating circles to a given conic a linear system?

15. Let A, P, Q, R be four points, no three collinear. Prove that the set of conics incident to A and in which PQR is a self-conjugate triangle is a pencil of point conics of type I, and determine the base points of the pencil.

16. How are your conclusions modified if in Exercise 15 A is a point on a side of the triangle PQR?

17. State the dual of the conclusions of Exercises 15, 16.

18. Let the conics of a point-pencil of type II be mutually tangent at a point A, and let P, not A, be a point on the tangent at A. Let Q be the point of contact of the second tangent from P to an arbitrary conic of the pencil. Find the locus of Q.

19. Let Y be a point of the nonsingular conic $\mathbf{X}^T\mathbf{B}\mathbf{X} = 0$, and let V be a line incident to Y. If $U(\lambda, \mu)$ is the tangent line to $\lambda\mathbf{X}^T\mathbf{B}\mathbf{X} + \mu(\mathbf{Y}^T\mathbf{B}\mathbf{X})^2 = 0$ at its intersection with V, find the envelope of $U(\lambda, \mu)$.

#**20.** Prove that the set of all conics tangent to a given conic at a given point is a linear system, whereas the set of all conics tangent to a given conic is not.

#**21.** Let σ_1 and σ_2 be distinct polarities. Prove that the fixed points and lines of the collineation $\sigma_2 \sigma_1$ are the vertices and singular lines of the point and line pencils determined by the quadratic forms of σ_1 and σ_2.

22. Prove that the Euclidean theorem that the altitudes of a triangle are concurrent can be regarded as a consequence of Desargues' Involution Theorem.†

23. In E_2, let a variable circle in a given pencil of circles intersect a given line L in points X, X', and let L intersect the radical axis of the pencil in the point A. Prove that the product of directed distances AX, AX' is constant, provided that L contains no base point of the pencil.

24. Let ABC be a triangle in E_2. Prove that the hyperbolas with asymptotes $A \oplus B$ and $A \oplus C$ intersect $B \oplus C$ in points having the same midpoint.

#**25.** Find the locus of the centers of the rectangular hyperbolas circumscribing a given triangle.

ANS. The nine-point circle.

26. State the dual of the theorem of Problem 2 of the text.

#**27.** Use the method employed in Problem 2 to discover a theorem about conics each of which have four-point (or line) contact with a third.

28. Let $Q(x, y) = 0$ be a parabola in E_2. Describe the system of curves $Q(x, y) = c$, where c is a parameter.

29. An ellipse in E_2 is tangent to the asymptotes of a hyperbola and intersects the hyperbola in four points. Prove that two common chords are parallel to the chord of contact, and that the latter lies midway between the two common chords.

30. Prove that in general a pencil of point conics in E_2 contains two parabolas, and a pencil of line conics contains one parabola. A point-pencil of type III is also a line-pencil of type III. How many parabolas does such a pencil contain, and how do you resolve the seeming paradox (see Exercise 7)?

31. Prove that the locus of the poles of a given line with respect to a pencil of line conics is a line except if the given line is a singular line of the pencil.

32. Prove that the set of all hyperbolas and ellipses tangent to the four sides of a parallelogram are concentric.

#**33.** Prove that the foci of the parabolas in E_2 tangent to the sides of a triangle describe the circle circumscribing the triangle.

† See Coxeter, *The Real Projective Plane*, Cambridge, England, Cambridge University Press, 1954, p. 139.

CHAPTER V

Subgeometries of Real Projective Geometry

1 Isomorphic Geometries, Subgeometries, and Embeddings

So far we have been primarily concerned with the development of plane projective geometry. This development is logically complete since it rests on our definitions of projective spaces (see II, Definition 2.2 and III, Definition 1.1) and is therefore independent of any intuitive or subjective geometrical notions. A secondary feature of our development has been the study of interrelations between the real projective plane and the Euclidean plane. This portion of our treatment may seem to the reader to be on somewhat shaky grounds since, at this stage in his mathematical studies, he is probably unfamiliar with a logically complete development of Euclidean geometry. Later in this chapter (Section 8) we shall remedy this logical defect by defining a Euclidean plane in purely projective terms. In the meantime we shall continue to use the term in our earlier sense (see I, Definition 6.2).

The relationship between Euclidean geometry and projective geometry embodies two essential ingredients. Originally we were concerned with one of these ingredients, namely a map from the points of the one onto a subset of the other. Later we discovered (IV, (7.10)) the existence of collineations corresponding to Euclidean motions. The reader can verify that this set of collineations is a group isomorphic to the group of motions. In this section we shall discuss these ideas in a more general form, and in the following sections we shall apply them to several different geometries. We begin by formulating the concept of a geometry suggested by our earlier definitions.

Definition 1.1. Let S be a set of objects, which we call points, and let G be a group of transformations whose elements map the points of S one-to-one onto S. The set of invariants, invariant relations, and invariant properties of S (and of subsets of S) is called *the geometry of S under G*. We shall denote the geometry defined by the point set S and the group G by $\Gamma(S, G)$.

Notation. In this section we shall frequently suppress the arguments, and Γ, Γ', Γ'' will denote the geometries whose respective point sets and groups are S, S', S'' and G, G', G''.

DEFINITION 1.2. Two geometries $\Gamma(S, G)$, $\Gamma'(S', G')$ are *isomorphic*, provided that

(a) there exists a one-to-one map from S onto S';
(b) there exists an isomorphism between the groups G and G';
(c) the isomorphism preserves the map, that is, gX and $g'X'$ correspond under (a) whenever X and X' are corresponding points and g and g' are corresponding transformations.

If f denotes the map from S onto S' and h the isomorphism from G to G', condition (c) asserts that

$$f(gX) = (hg)(fX), \qquad \text{for all } X \in S,\ g \in G.$$

This relation can be clarified by means of the following diagram.

$$\begin{array}{ccc} X & \xrightarrow{\quad f \quad} & X' = fX \\ g \Big\downarrow & & \Big\downarrow g' = hg \\ gX & & X'' = hgX' \end{array}$$

Condition (c) asserts that f maps gX onto X''.

LEMMA 1.1. *If a geometry Γ is isomorphic to Γ', and if Γ' is isomorphic to Γ'', then Γ is isomorphic to Γ''. In other words, isomorphism of geometries is transitive.*†

We leave the proof to the reader.

Two geometries that are isomorphic are abstractly equivalent; if we introduce a vocabulary in one geometry, we can, by using the same vocabulary in the second geometry, have precisely the same theorems in both geometries. The two geometries would thus be intrinsically indistinguishable.

If a geometry $\Gamma(S, G)$ is given, a new geometry can be constructed by considering the action of a subgroup of G on a subset of S that is invariant under the subgroup.

DEFINITION 1.3. Let Γ and Γ' be two given geometries with the following properties:

(a) the group G' of Γ' is a subgroup of the group G of Γ;

† Isomorphism of geometries is indeed an equivalence relation since it obviously is reflexive and symmetric.

(b) the point set S' of Γ' is a subset of the point set S of Γ.
The geometry Γ' is said to be a *subgeometry* of Γ.

It is not necessary in the above definition that G' be a proper subgroup of G, nor that S' be a proper subset of S. In our applications, however, we shall usually be interested in subgeometries whose group is a proper subgroup of the original group.

Since invariants under a group are invariants under a subgroup, a subgeometry possesses the structural relations of the parent geometry, in addition to the specialized relations that arise from those invariants of the subgroup that are not invariants of the full group. We shall find that certain geometries, of major importance in mathematics and the applications of mathematics, are subgeometries of projective geometry, and thus they will have in common properties which, one might say, are due to their common parentage.

Previously we have used the symbol $S_2(\mathsf{R})$ primarily as a symbol for the point set of the real projective plane. It will cause no confusion if we use the same symbol to denote real projective geometry, that is the geometry of the point set under $G_8(\mathsf{R})$, the group of real collineations.

THEOREM 1.1. *Euclidean geometry is isomorphic to a subgeometry of* $S_2(\mathsf{R})$.

Proof. We have already remarked that we are using the term Euclidean geometry in the sense of (I, Definition 6.2). We let (x, y) be rectangular Cartesian coordinates in E_2, and $\mathbf{X} = (x_1, x_2, x_3)^T$ projective coordinates in $S_2(\mathsf{R})$. The equations

$$x = x_1/x_3, \qquad y = x_2/x_3 \tag{1.1}$$

establish a one-to-one map from E_2 onto $S_2(\mathsf{R}) - l$, where l is the line $x_3 = 0$. The group of motions M^* in E_2 is given by

$$M^*: \begin{array}{l} x' = x \cos\theta \mp y \sin\theta + e, \\ y' = x \sin\theta \pm y \cos\theta + f, \end{array} \qquad e, f, \theta \in \mathsf{R},\ 0 \leqq \theta < 2\pi, \tag{1.2}$$

and the set of corresponding collineations (see IV, (7.10)) is given by

$$\mathbf{X}' = \mathbf{A}\mathbf{X}, \qquad \text{where } \mathbf{A} = \begin{pmatrix} \cos\theta & \mp\sin\theta & e \\ \sin\theta & \pm\cos\theta & f \\ 0 & 0 & 1 \end{pmatrix}. \tag{1.3}$$

This set is clearly a group, isomorphic to M^*, and condition (c) of Definition 1.2 is trivially satisfied. Thus Euclidean geometry is isomorphic to the subgeometry of $S_2(\mathsf{R})$ whose point set is $S_2(\mathsf{R}) - l$, and whose group is given by (1.3) where e, f take on all real values and θ real values in the interval $[0, 2\pi)$.

From this proof we note that two isomorphic geometries may be isomorphic in more than one way (see also Exercise 6 below).

We leave the proofs of the next two theorems to the reader.

THEOREM 1.2. *Projective geometry of dimension one over a field* F *is isomorphic to a subgeometry of projective geometry of dimension two over the same field.*

THEOREM 1.3. *If* F_1 *is a subfield of* F_2, *the geometry of the projective space* $S_2(F_1)$ *is isomorphic to a subgeometry of the geometry of* $S_2(F_2)$.

In particular, real projective geometry is isomorphic to a subgeometry of complex projective geometry.

Saccheri, Bolyai, Lobachevski, and Gauss are a few of the many geometers who made significant contributions to the study of the role played by Euclid's parallel postulate; their investigations culminated in the creation of the two classical non-Euclidean geometries. We shall define these geometries as geometries isomorphic to subgeometries of projective geometry. We shall return to a more detailed study of these geometries later.

DEFINITION 1.4. Let σ be a hyperbolic polarity in $S_2(R)$, $\mathscr{C}$ its conic of self-conjugate points, S the interior of $\mathscr{C}$, and G the group of σ (the subgroup of $G_8(R)$ leaving S invariant; see IV, 10). Any geometry $\Gamma'(S', G')$ that is isomorphic to the geometry $\Gamma(S, G)$ is called (real) *hyperbolic geometry* (of dimension two); the point set S', with the structure determined by the group G', is called a (real) *hyperbolic plane.*

DEFINITION 1.5. Let σ be an elliptic polarity in $S_2(R)$, let S be the point set of $S_2(R)$, and let G be the group of σ (the group of collineations that leaves σ invariant). Any geometry $\Gamma'(S', G')$ that is isomorphic to $\Gamma(S, G)$ is called (real) *elliptic geometry* (of two dimensions). The point set S' with the structure determined by the group G' is called a (real) *elliptic plane.*

Another geometry even more closely related to Euclidean geometry than are the two non-Euclidean geometries just defined is *affine* geometry.

DEFINITION 1.6. Let l be an arbitrary line in $S_2(R)$, and let S be the set of points $S_2(R) - l$. We denote by G the subgroup of the real projective group that has l (and therefore S) as an invariant subspace. The geometry $\Gamma(S, G)$, or any geometry isomorphic to it, is called (real) *affine geometry* (of dimension two). If $\Gamma'(S', G')$ is an affine geometry, S' is called an *affine plane*, and G' is called an *affine group.*

For the sake of completeness, we state the following theorem which is an obvious consequence of the preceding definitions.

THEOREM 1.4. *Real hyperbolic geometry, real elliptic geometry, and real affine geometry are each isomorphic to a subgeometry of real projective geometry.*

THEOREM 1.5. *Any two affine geometries are isomorphic.*

Proof. Let l and l' be two lines of $S_2(\mathsf{R})$, and let

$$S = S_2(\mathsf{R}) - l, \qquad S' = S_2(\mathsf{R}) - l'.$$

Denote by G and G' the subgroups of G_8 leaving S and S' respectively invariant. By our lemma it suffices to prove that $\Gamma(S, G)$ is isomorphic to $\Gamma'(S', G')$. Let π be any collineation that maps l onto l'. Then if $g \in G$, the collineation $\pi g \pi^{-1}$ leaves l' fixed and therefore belongs to G'. Conversely, if $g' \in G'$, $\pi^{-1} g' \pi$ is a transformation of G, say g. From the equation

$$g = \pi^{-1} g' \pi, \tag{1.4}$$

we obtain

$$g' = \pi g \pi^{-1}. \tag{1.5}$$

Equation (1.4) (or its equivalent (1.5)) establishes a one-to-one correspondence between the groups G and G'. We can see as follows that this correspondence is an isomorphism: let $g, \bar{g}$ be in G, and let $g', \bar{g}'$ be the corresponding transformations of G'. Then besides (1.5) we have that $\bar{g}' = \pi \bar{g} \pi^{-1}$. Consequently,

$$g'\bar{g}' = (\pi g \pi^{-1})(\pi \bar{g} \pi^{-1}) = \pi g(\pi^{-1}\pi)\bar{g}\pi^{-1} = \pi g \bar{g} \pi^{-1}.$$

That is, to the product $g\bar{g}$ corresponds the product $g'\bar{g}'$, and hence G and G' are isomorphic. Furthermore, π itself establishes a one-to-one map from S onto S'. If $X' = \pi X$,

$$g'X' = \pi g \pi^{-1} \pi X = \pi g X,$$

and the isomorphism preserves this correspondence. By Definition (1.2), $\Gamma(S, G)$ and $\Gamma'(S', G')$ are isomorphic geometries.

THEOREM 1.6. *Any two hyperbolic geometries are isomorphic, and any two elliptic geometries are isomorphic.*

This theorem can be proved by an argument essentially the same as that used in the proof of Theorem 1.5. We leave the proof to the reader.

We can obtain analytical machinery for the study of affine geometry as follows. In $S_2(\mathsf{R})$ we choose projective coordinates so that l is the line $x_3 = 0$. The collineations that leave l fixed are found to be

$$\mathbf{X}' = \mathbf{A}\mathbf{X}, \tag{1.6a}$$

where

$$\mathbf{A} = \begin{pmatrix} a_{11} & a_{12} & a_{13} \\ a_{21} & a_{22} & a_{23} \\ 0 & 0 & a_{33} \end{pmatrix}, \qquad \det \mathbf{A} \neq 0. \tag{1.6b}$$

We introduce nonhomogeneous coordinates (x, y) given by

$$x = x_1/x_3, \qquad y = x_2/x_3\,; \tag{1.7}$$

in terms of these coordinates, the group (1.6) has the representation

$$\begin{aligned} x' &= \alpha_{11}x + \alpha_{12}y + \alpha_{13}, \\ y' &= \alpha_{21}x + \alpha_{22}y + \alpha_{23}, \end{aligned} \qquad \begin{vmatrix} \alpha_{11} & \alpha_{12} \\ \alpha_{21} & \alpha_{22} \end{vmatrix} \neq 0, \tag{1.8}$$

where

$$\alpha_{ij} = a_{ij}/a_{33}, \qquad i = 1, 2;\, j = 1, 2, 3. \tag{1.9}$$

Hence we can represent the points of a real affine plane by ordered pairs of real numbers (x, y), and the affine group by the transformations (1.8).

THEOREM 1.7. *Euclidean geometry is isomorphic to a subgeometry of affine geometry.*

Proof. We can establish, in the affine plane, a coordinate system (x, y) in terms of which the affine group is given by equations (1.8). If we let the point (x, y) of the affine plane correspond to the point of the Euclidean plane with rectangular Cartesian coordinates (x, y), we have a one-to-one correspondence between the two point sets. If we let a motion (1.2) of the Euclidean plane correspond to the affine transformation (1.8) for which

$$\begin{aligned} \alpha_{11} &= \cos\theta, & \alpha_{12} &= \mp\sin\theta, & \alpha_{13} &= e, \\ \alpha_{21} &= \sin\theta, & \alpha_{22} &= \pm\cos\theta, & \alpha_{23} &= f, \end{aligned}$$

we have an isomorphism between the group of motions and a subgroup of the affine group. Finally, it is obvious that this isomorphism preserves the correspondence between the point sets.

We need to elaborate one further idea. In our first applications of projective geometry to Euclidean (and vice versa) we mapped the Euclidean plane onto a subset of the projective plane. Later (IV, (7.10)) we discovered that this map determined a subgroup of G_8 that corresponds to Euclidean motions, and we noted a projective property of the group. For our present purposes we need to define an embedding abstractly,† and the following definition is consistent with our previous usage.

DEFINITION 1.7. We say that a geometry $\Gamma(S, G)$ can be *embedded* in a geometry $\Gamma'(S', G')$ whenever Γ is isomorphic to a subgeometry of Γ'. We *embed* Γ in Γ' by giving

(a) a one-to-one correspondence between S and a subset of S';
(b) an isomorphism between G and a subgroup of G' that preserves this correspondence.

† The reader will find in his later mathematical studies a more general class of maps that are called embeddings. From this broader point of view, the maps with which we shall be concerned could be called *isomorphic* embeddings.

We can regard an embedding as an operation carried out simultaneously on the points and the transformations of a given geometry. For a given embedding of $\Gamma(S, G)$ in $\Gamma'(S', G')$, we shall denote by $\mathscr{E}$ the operator on the points and transformations of Γ. Thus, if $g \in G$ and $X \in S$, $\mathscr{E}g$ is the transformation of G' that corresponds to g under the isomorphism given by the embedding, $\mathscr{E}G$ is the subgroup of G' isomorphic to G; $\mathscr{E}X$ is the point of S' which corresponds to X and $\mathscr{E}S$ is the subset of S' which corresponds to S under the point correspondence given by the embedding. With this notation, we can express the fact that the isomorphism preserves the correspondence by the equation

$$\mathscr{E}(gX) = (\mathscr{E}g)(\mathscr{E}X). \tag{1.10}$$

It is natural to denote by $\mathscr{E}^{-1}$ the inverse operator on the points of the subset $\mathscr{E}S$ of S' and on the transformations of the subgroup $\mathscr{E}G$ of G'.

Equations (1.6) to (1.9) are the equations of an embedding of the affine plane in the projective plane, and equations (1.1), (1.2), and (1.3) are those of an embedding of the Euclidean plane in the projective plane.

When an affine plane is embedded in $S_2(\mathsf{R})$, the line of Definition 1.6 is called the *absolute line* of the embedding. Similarly the polarities and the conic of Definitions 1.4 and 1.5 are called the *absolute polarities* and the *absolute conic*.

Since we can embed E_2 in $S_2(\mathsf{R})$ in many ways, we would not expect in the general case that an embedding, when it exists, is unique. The following diagram suggests a way of combining a given embedding of Γ in Γ' and an arbitrary transformation $h \in G'$. Our next theorem asserts that the composite map $X \to h\mathscr{E}X$, $g \to h(\mathscr{E}g)h^{-1}$ is an embedding.

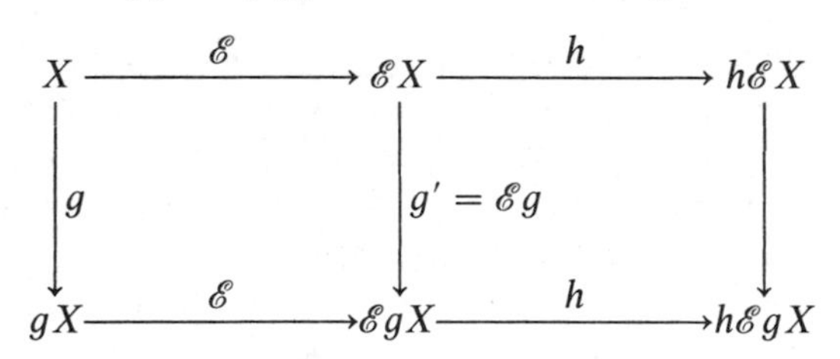

THEOREM 1.8. *If $\mathscr{E}$ in an embedding of $\Gamma(S, G)$ in $\Gamma'(S' G')$, and if h is an arbitrary, but fixed, transformation of G', the operator $\mathscr{E}'$ (on elements X of S and g of G) defined by*

$$\mathscr{E}'X = h(\mathscr{E}X), \qquad \mathscr{E}'g = h(\mathscr{E}g)h^{-1}, \qquad X \in S, g \in G, \tag{1.11}$$

is an embedding of Γ in Γ'.

Proof. Since $\mathscr{E}$ is an embedding, $\mathscr{E}g$ is an element of G', and $\mathscr{E}X$ is a point of S'. Hence $\mathscr{E}'$ maps the points (and transformations) of $\Gamma(S, G)$ into the set of points (and transformations) of $\Gamma'(S', G')$. The map between S and

$\mathscr{E}'S$ is one-to-one, since $\mathscr{E}'X$ determines $\mathscr{E}X = h^{-1}(\mathscr{E}'X)$ uniquely, and $\mathscr{E}X$ determines X uniquely. The map between G and $\mathscr{E}'G$ is one-to-one, since $\mathscr{E}g = h^{-1}(\mathscr{E}'g)h'$, and $\mathscr{E}g$ determines g uniquely. This map can be seen to be an isomorphism as follows: if $g, \bar{g}$ are any two transformations of G,

$$(\mathscr{E}'g)(\mathscr{E}'\bar{g}) = h(\mathscr{E}g)h^{-1}h(\mathscr{E}\bar{g})h^{-1} = h(\mathscr{E}g)(\mathscr{E}\bar{g})h^{-1}.$$

Since $\mathscr{E}$ establishes an isomorphism between G and $\mathscr{E}G$,

$$(\mathscr{E}g)(\mathscr{E}\bar{g}) = \mathscr{E}(g\bar{g}),$$

and therefore

$$(\mathscr{E}'g)(\mathscr{E}'\bar{g}) = h\mathscr{E}(g\bar{g})h^{-1} = \mathscr{E}'(g\bar{g}).$$

Hence to the product $g\bar{g}$ corresponds the product of their maps $(\mathscr{E}'g)(\mathscr{E}'\bar{g})$, and $\mathscr{E}'$ establishes an isomorphism between G and $\mathscr{E}'G$. It remains to show that equation (1.10) is valid for $\mathscr{E}'$.

$$\begin{aligned}(\mathscr{E}'g)(\mathscr{E}'X) &= \big(h(\mathscr{E}g)h^{-1}\big)\big(h(\mathscr{E}X)\big)\\ &= h(\mathscr{E}g)(\mathscr{E}X)\\ &= h\mathscr{E}(gX)\\ &= \mathscr{E}'(gX).\end{aligned}$$

Therefore $\mathscr{E}'$ is an embedding of Γ in Γ'.

The reader should note that $\mathscr{E}S$ and $\mathscr{E}'S$ are distinct unless h is sufficiently restricted.

Let $\Gamma(S, G)$ be isomorphic to a subgeometry of $\Gamma'(S', G')$, and let $\mathscr{E}$ be an embedding of Γ in Γ'. When $\mathscr{E}G$ is a proper subgroup of G', we can expect to find invariants under G that are not invariants under G', and from such invariants we obtain geometric properties of Γ that have no counterpart in the geometry Γ'. For example, theorems in the Euclidean plane involving lengths, circles, foci of a conic, etc., have no projective counterparts. Yet in the development of such geometric properties, we shall see that the embedding relationship often suggests the construction of invariants in the subgeometry, as was indeed the case earlier when we characterized the foci of a conic in E_2.

On the other hand, invariants under G' are also invariants under its subgroup $\mathscr{E}G$. In discussing these invariants, two types of situations arise, depending on whether the point set $\mathscr{E}S$ does, or does not, coincide with the point set S'. When we embed elliptic geometry in projective geometry, we establish a one-to-one correspondence between the point set of the elliptic plane and that of the projective plane, so that $\mathscr{E}S = S'$. Similarly, the relation $\mathscr{E}S = S'$ holds when we embed Euclidean geometry in affine geometry. On the other hand, $\mathscr{E}S$ is a proper subset of S' when we embed Euclidean (or affine, or hyperbolic) geometry in projective geometry.

Whenever we have a geometry $\Gamma(S, G)$ embedded in a geometry $\Gamma'(S', G')$ so that the relation $\mathscr{E}S = S'$ holds for the given embedding $\mathscr{E}$, we can introduce in Γ the vocabulary of Γ' (naturally, we shall need additional vocabulary—to reflect invariants under G that are not invariants under G'). Thus a conic in the elliptic plane is a curve $\mathscr{C}$ whose image $\mathscr{E}\mathscr{C}$ is a conic in the projective plane, and the cross ratio (AB, CD) of four points in the elliptic plane is the cross ratio $(\mathscr{E}A\,\mathscr{E}B, \mathscr{E}C\,\mathscr{E}D)$ of their images in the projective plane. In this situation, many theorems of Γ' hold, without exception, in Γ. For example, Desargues' triangle theorem is necessarily valid in the elliptic plane, and a projective classification of pairs of conics in terms of the nature of their intersections would furnish an elliptic classification of pairs of conics in the same terms.

When $\mathscr{E}S$ is a proper subset of S', the relationship between theorems of Γ and those of Γ' is more complex. Let us consider, first, how to define *line* in hyperbolic geometry. It would be useless to say that a line in the hyperbolic plane is a point set whose image in the projective plane is a line, because no point set of the hyperbolic plane can have such an image—every line in the projective plane contains exterior points of a given conic. Instead, we shall understand by a line in the hyperbolic plane a point set whose image is that segment of a projective line that is interior to the absolute conic (that is, the conic of Definition 1.4). Similarly, a curve $\mathscr{C}$ in the affine plane (or in the hyperbolic plane) is a conic (with respect to an embedding $\mathscr{E}$) if $\mathscr{E}\mathscr{C}$ in the projective plane is the intersection of a projective conic and the point set $\mathscr{E}S$. More generally, let $\Gamma(S, G)$ be isomorphic to a subgeometry of $S_2(\mathsf{R})$; a curve $\mathscr{D}$ in Γ is an irreducible algebraic curve (under an embedding $\mathscr{E}$) if there exists an irreducible algebraic curve $\mathscr{D}'$ in $S_2(\mathsf{R})$ such that $\mathscr{E}\mathscr{D} = \mathscr{D}' \cap \mathscr{E}S$. In the kind of situations with which we shall be concerned, the existence of $\mathscr{D}'$ will imply its uniqueness. Usually we shall assign to $\mathscr{D}$ the same name that we have given to $\mathscr{D}'$, and we shall speak of $\mathscr{E}\mathscr{D}$ as the *strict image* of $\mathscr{D}$, and of $\mathscr{D}'$ as its *extended image*. As earlier (page 219), it will be convenient to let *image* mean extended image.

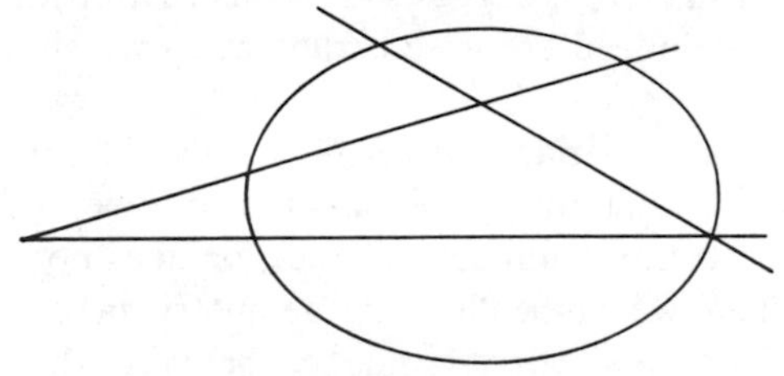

FIGURE 1.1

A theorem of Γ' will frequently need further examination before it can be applied in the geometry Γ. For example, let us consider the theorem of the projective plane: any two distinct lines intersect in one and just one point. Referring to Figure 1.1, we see that in the hyperbolic plane, there are three types of pairs of lines according as the intersection of the image lines in the projective plane lies inside, on, or outside the absolute conic. In the hyperbolic plane, pairs of lines of the first type intersect, those of the other two types do not intersect. If we define two lines in the hyperbolic plane to be *parallel* if their image lines intersect on the absolute conic, and two lines to be *ultraparallel* if their image lines intersect in an exterior point of the absolute conic, we obtain, in place of the simple projective theorem, the theorem that *two lines of the hyperbolic plane are either intersecting, parallel, or ultraparallel.* Another obvious theorem of hyperbolic geometry is that *through a given point not on a given line there are exactly two lines parallel to the given line.*

When we look at the geometry of $\Gamma(S, G)$ from the point of view of a geometry $\Gamma'(S', G')$ in which the first is embedded, we will find very frequently that diverse theorems of Γ are brought together as special cases of one theorem in Γ'. By embedding one geometry in another, we may find in the first geometry a unity that otherwise could not have been anticipated.

EXERCISES

1. Verify directly that the embedding of E_2 in $S_2(\mathsf{R})$, given by equations (1.1) to (1.3), possesses the property expressed by equation (1.10).

2. Verify directly that the embedding given by equations (1.6) to (1.9) possesses the property expressed by (1.10).

3. By means of Theorem 1.8 give the equations of an embedding of the affine plane in $S_2(\mathsf{R})$ which maps the points of the affine plane onto $S_2(\mathsf{R}) - V$, where V is the line (v_1, v_2, v_3).

4. Prove Theorem 1.6 for hyperbolic (or elliptic) geometry by modifying suitably the proof of Theorem 1.5.

5. Prove Theorem 1.6 for elliptic (or hyperbolic) geometry by applying Theorem 1.8.

6. Let $\mathscr{E}$ be an embedding of $\Gamma(S, G)$ in $\Gamma'(S', G')$, and let $g_1 \in G$. Prove that $\mathscr{E}''$ defined by

$$\mathscr{E}''X = \mathscr{E}g_1 X, \qquad \mathscr{E}''g = \mathscr{E}(g_1 g g_1^{-1}), \qquad X \in S, g \in G,$$

is an embedding of Γ in Γ'.

7. Prove that if $S \subset S'$, $G \subset G'$, the embeddings $\mathscr{E}''$ of Exercise 6 obtained by varying g_1 constitute a proper subset of the embeddings $\mathscr{E}'$ of Theorem 1.8 with variable h.

8. How could one define a pencil of lines in the hyperbolic plane? How many types of pencils exist?

#**9.** Classify nonsingular conics in the hyperbolic plane in terms of their intersections with the absolute (see IV, (11.12) and (11.23)), and show that there are eleven types if one takes into account the number of branches and the connectedness of the interior.†

† See Felix Klein, *Vorlesungen über Nicht-Euclidsche Geometrie*, Berlin, Julius Springer, 1928, p. 229.

#**10.** A line in the hyperbolic plane is an *asymptote* to a conic if the image line under an embedding in $S_2(\mathsf{R})$ is tangent to the image conic at an intersection of the latter with the absolute conic. Find the number of asymptotes possessed by each of the eleven types of conics of Exercise 9.

#**11.** Two lines in the elliptic (or hyperbolic) plane are said to be *orthogonal* if their image lines under an embedding in $S_2(\mathsf{R})$ are conjugate with respect to the absolute polarity. Formulate and prove some elementary properties of orthogonality. In E_2 a pencil of parallel lines determines a new pencil each of whose lines is orthogonal to every line of the first pencil. Do the elliptic or hyperbolic planes possess any such pencils?

2 The Affine Plane

Throughout this section we shall be considering affine geometry. We shall denote both the point set of the affine plane and its geometry by A_2, and its group by G_6. We shall denote a given embedding of A_2 in $S_2(\mathsf{R})$ by $\mathscr{E}$ and the absolute line of $\mathscr{E}$ by l or $l(\mathscr{E})$. Images under $\mathscr{E}$ will refer to extended images, and the inverse image of a point set $\mathscr{D}$ in $S_2(\mathsf{R})$ will be the set $\mathscr{E}^{-1}(\mathscr{D} - \mathscr{D} \cap l(\mathscr{E}))$.

In accordance with the discussion at the end of the preceding section, we define an affine line to be a (nonempty) point set whose strict image in $S_2(\mathsf{R})$ is the intersection of a projective line and $S_2(\mathsf{R}) - l$. If L is an affine line, $\mathscr{E}L$ is contained in a unique projective line L'. We call the point $L' \cap l(\mathscr{E})$ the *absolute point* on the (extended) image of L, or, for brevity, on $\mathscr{E}L$.

The images of two lines in the affine plane necessarily intersect in a point of $S_2(\mathsf{R})$. But two cases arise, according as this point does, or does not, lie on $l(\mathscr{E})$. Since the group $\mathscr{E}G_6$ leaves l invariant, the affine group G_6 preserves the two kinds of intersection.

Definition 2.1. Two lines of the affine plane are *parallel* if their images and the absolute line are dependent.

If lines L and L' are parallel, we write $L \parallel L'$.

Thus a line of the affine plane is parallel to itself, and two distinct lines are parallel if and only if they do not intersect. Through a given point, there is one and just one line parallel to a given line.

A projective line is a closed curve; hence an affine line is not a closed curve. Two points on a projective line separate the remaining points of the line into two mutually exclusive segments (see III, Theorem 5.1). If we choose a point A on an affine line L, and apply this theorem to the two points $\mathscr{E}A$ and the absolute point on $\mathscr{E}L$, we see that one point on an affine line separates the remaining points of the line into two mutually exclusive sets. We call each of these sets a *ray* (with A as end point). If we choose two points A, B on an affine line and apply the cited theorem to the two points $\mathscr{E}A$ and $\mathscr{E}B$, we find that two points on an affine line are end points of a unique *segment*, seg AB, the set whose image does not contain the absolute point. If $X \in$ seg AB, we say that X is *between* A and B. We can combine these properties in the first sentence of the following theorem. The proof of the remainder of the theorem uses projective properties of segments (see III, 5, Exercise 6).

THEOREM 2.1. *Two points A, B of an affine line separate the remaining points of the line into three mutually exclusive subsets: the segment AB, the ray with end point A not containing B, and the ray with end point B not containing A. A closed segment with end points C, D is contained in one of the three subsets if and only if C and D are contained in that subset.*

We denote the ray with end point A containing B by $r(A, B)$, and that not containing B by $r(A/B)$.

The next theorem is the analogue of (III, Theorem 6.2); the two lines in $S_2(\mathsf{R})$ are the image of the given affine line and the absolute line.

THEOREM 2.2. *Every line in the affine plane separates the remaining points of the plane into two mutually exclusive subsets. The segment joining a point of one subset to a point of the other subset intersects the line.*

The two sets are called the *sides* of the line, or *half-planes*.

In the projective plane three distinct collinear points possess no (non-trivial) invariant since they are projectively equivalent to any such triple. Four collinear points possess an invariant cross ratio. With every three collinear points of the affine plane, we can associate four points in $S_2(\mathsf{R})$, namely, the images of the three points under $\mathscr{E}$ and the absolute point of their line; the cross ratio of these four points is an invariant of three collinear points in A_2.

DEFINITION 2.2. Let A, B, C be three collinear points in A_2 where $A \neq B$. Let Q be the absolute point of $\mathscr{E}A \oplus \mathscr{E}B$. The cross ratio $(Q\ \mathscr{E}A,\ \mathscr{E}B\ \mathscr{E}C)$ is called the *affine ratio in which C divides the points A, B*, and is written AC/AB.

The reader should note that the affine ratio is not a quotient, and that we have not given any meaning to the symbols AC and AB.

If $\mathscr{E}C$ is the harmonic conjugate of Q with respect to $\mathscr{E}A$ and $\mathscr{E}B$, $(\mathscr{E}A\ \mathscr{E}B,\ \mathscr{E}C\ Q) = -1$, or $(Q\ \mathscr{E}A,\ \mathscr{E}B\ \mathscr{E}C) = 1/2$. In this case, C divides the points A, B in the ratio $1/2$, and we call C the *midpoint* of seg AB, and we say that C *bisects* seg AB.

Clearly A divides the points A, B in the ratio $0, B$ divides them in the ratio 1; each of the points of the segment divides them in a ratio t, where $0 < t < 1$. A point of the ray $r(B/A)$ divides the points A, B in a ratio $t > 1$, while a point of the ray $r(A/B)$ divides them in a negative ratio. If the ratio in which C divides A, B is t $(AC/AB = t)$, the ratio in which C divides B, A is $1 - t$ since

$$(Q\ \mathscr{E}A,\ \mathscr{E}B\ \mathscr{E}C) + (Q\ \mathscr{E}B,\ \mathscr{E}A\ \mathscr{E}C) = 1.$$

If A, B, C, D are four collinear points in A_2, we define

$$(A\,B,\ C\,D) = (\mathscr{E}A\ \mathscr{E}B,\ \mathscr{E}C\ \mathscr{E}D).$$

In $S_2(\mathsf{R})$, the four image points and Q, the absolute point of their line satisfy the relation

$$(\mathscr{E}C\ \mathscr{E}D,\ \mathscr{E}A\ \mathscr{E}B)(\mathscr{E}C\ \mathscr{E}D,\ \mathscr{E}B\ Q)(\mathscr{E}C\ \mathscr{E}D,\ Q\ \mathscr{E}A) = 1.$$

This relation can be rewritten

$$(\mathscr{E}A\ \mathscr{E}B,\ \mathscr{E}C\ \mathscr{E}D) = \frac{(Q\ \mathscr{E}A,\ \mathscr{E}D\ \mathscr{E}C)}{(Q\ \mathscr{E}B,\ \mathscr{E}D\ \mathscr{E}C)} = AC/AD \div BC/BD.$$

Thus $(A\,B,\ C\,D)$ is the quotient of the ratio in which C divides the points A, D by the ratio in which C divides the points B, D.

Parallelograms, trapezoids, medians of a triangle are some of the concepts of Euclidean geometry that are strictly affine, and some of our previous results belong to both geometries. However the following theorem has no Euclidean counterpart.

THEOREM 2.3. *Any two triangles are affinely equivalent.*

Proof. In $S_2(\mathsf{R})$ two quadrilaterals are projectively equivalent, so that there exists $g \in G_8$ that maps the image (under an embedding $\mathscr{E}$) of one triangle onto the image of the other and leaves $l(\mathscr{E})$ fixed. Hence $g \in \mathscr{E}G_6$, and $\mathscr{E}^{-1}g \in G_6$.

We note further that the map is unique if we preassign pairs of corresponding vertices.

The next theorem, like the preceding, is not valid in Euclidean geometry. It is the affine form of a projective theorem (III, Theorem 8.6), and in its proof the reader can use (III, Theorem 10.3).

THEOREM 2.4. *A one-to-one map of the affine plane onto itself which preserves collinearity is an affine transformation.*

Although many Euclidean properties of conics are likewise affine, and some such properties were discussed earlier, our present point of view requires affine definitions. The reader will note that although the definitions which follow are expressed in terms of a particular embedding, the relationships in the affine plane are independent of the choice of the embedding since different embeddings lead to isomorphic geometries (Theorem 1.5). We could state and prove a theorem for A_2 which is the counterpart of (III, Theorem 10.5), but this is unnecessary in view of Theorem 1.5. As suggested in the preceding section, we define an affine conic to be the inverse image of a projective conic that does not contain the absolute line. A nonsingular affine conic is called an *ellipse*, *hyperbola*, or *parabola* according as the absolute line is an exterior line, an interior line, or a tangent line of the projective image.

An ellipse is a closed curve, since it is in one-to-one continuous correspondence with a nonsingular projective conic which is a closed curve. In the affine plane, an exterior line of a hyperbola divides the plane into two regions each of which contains points of the hyperbola. The points in one region constitute a *branch* of the hyperbola. Thus every hyperbola consists of two branches. A parabola consists of just one branch, but is not a closed curve.

The polar theory of quadratic forms in the projective plane leads to further special properties of affine conics.

We define the *center* of a conic to be the inverse image, if it exists, of the pole of the absolute line with respect to the image conic in the projective plane.

Clearly a parabola has no center, whereas the center of an ellipse or of a hyperbola is the unique point which bisects every chord incident to it. Ellipses and hyperbolas are called *central* conics.

A line is called a *diameter* of a conic if its image in the projective plane is conjugate, with respect to the image conic, to the absolute line. Two diameters are said to be *conjugate* if their images are conjugate.

Hence diameters of a central conic pass through the center, while those of a parabola form a pencil of parallel lines. Two diameters of a parabola are never conjugate, while every diameter of a central conic determines one and just one diameter conjugate to it. The absolute line and the images of two conjugate diameters are the sides of a self-polar triangle (with respect to the image conic).

A self-conjugate diameter is called an *asymptote*. A hyperbola possesses two asymptotes; their images under an embedding $\mathscr{E}$ are the tangent lines to the image conic at its intersections with the absolute line.

THEOREM 2.5. *Any two ellipses, any two hyperbolas, and any two parabolas are affinely equivalent.*

This theorem is the affine form of the following projective theorem.

THEOREM 2.6. *In $S_2(\mathsf{R})$ a nonsingular conic and an exterior line is projectively equivalent to another nonsingular conic and a line exterior to it. A similar result is valid when both lines are interior lines, and again when both are tangents.*

Proof. Let L be an exterior line of the conic $\mathscr{C}$, let A_2, A_3 be conjugate points on L, and let their polars intersect $\mathscr{C}$ in P_2, Q_2, P_3, Q_3 (Figure 2.1).

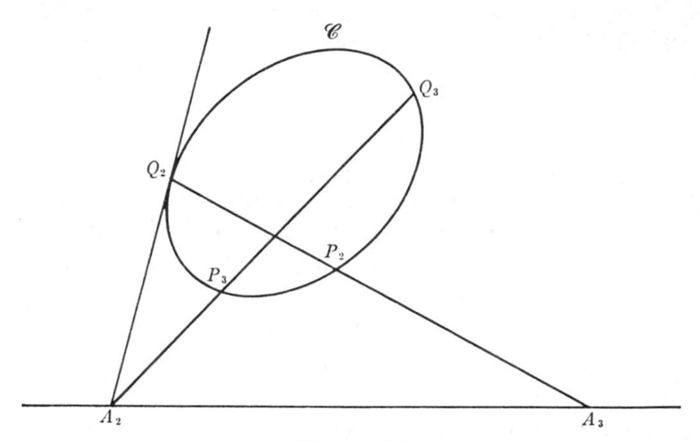

FIGURE 2.1

Then $A_2 \oplus P_2$ and $A_2 \oplus Q_2$ are tangents, so that $(P_2 Q_2, P_3 Q_3)_{\mathscr{C}} = -1$, and $\mathscr{C} = \{X \mid (P_2 Q_2, P_3 Q_3)_X = -1\}$. Hence the collineation that maps $P_2 P_3 Q_2 Q_3$ onto a quadrangle constructed similarly from the second conic and line maps the first conic and line onto the second.

We leave the proof for the other two cases to the reader.

We have already coordinatized A_2 by assigning to a point P the ordered pair of real numbers (x, y), where $(x, y, 1)^T$ is a projective representative of $\mathscr{E}P$ in a coordinate system in which $l(\mathscr{E})$ is the line $x_3 = 0$. The coordinates (x, y) are called *affine coordinates*. If (x', y') are affine coordinates related to an embedding $\mathscr{E}'$ with the same absolute line, it follows that the image coordinatizations in $S_2(\mathsf{R})$ can be related by

$$(2.1) \qquad \mathbf{X}' = \mathbf{A}\mathbf{X}, \qquad \text{where } \mathbf{A} = \begin{pmatrix} a_{11} & a_{12} & a_{13} \\ a_{21} & a_{22} & a_{23} \\ 0 & 0 & 1 \end{pmatrix}, \qquad \det \mathbf{A} \neq 0,$$

and therefore the two affine coordinate systems are related by

$$(2.2) \qquad \begin{aligned} x' &= a_{11}x + a_{12}y + a_{13}, \\ y' &= a_{21}x + a_{22}y + a_{23}, \end{aligned} \qquad a_{11}a_{22} \neq a_{21}a_{22}.$$

Conversely, any coordinatization (x', y') related to affine coordinates (x, y) by (2.2) is affine. Thus both the affine group G_6 and transformations of affine coordinates are represented by (2.2).

We can give a strictly affine interpretation of affine coordinates, in terms of affine ratios. Let A_3, D_2, D_1 be the points with affine coordinates $(0, 0)$, $(1, 0)$, $(0, 1)$ respectively; if P is an arbitrary point, let the parallel through P to $A_3 \oplus D_1$ intersect $A_3 \oplus D_2$ in P_2 (Figure 2.2), and let P_1 be

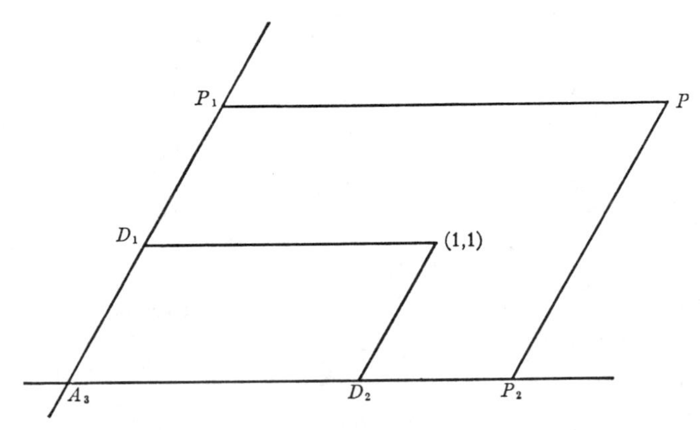

FIGURE 2.2

defined by interchanging D_1 and D_2. Then the coordinates (x, y) of P are the affine ratios $x = A_3P_2/A_3D_2$, $y = A_3P_1/A_3D_1$, as can be seen from (III, (4.11)) and Definition 2.2. Conversely, if A_3, D_1, D_2 are any three noncollinear points, the coordinates (x, y) defined by the above affine ratios are affine.

When we use analytical methods to study properties of A_2 that involve the embedding relation, it is frequently more convenient to denote affine coordinates by (x_1, x_2) rather than by (x, y). For then we can retain the matrix notation used in $S_2(\mathsf{F})$ by associating with an arbitrary point X with affine coordinates (x_1, x_2) the column matrix $\mathbf{X}$, where $\mathbf{X}^T = (x_1, x_2, 1)$; similarly we can associate with an arbitrary affine transformation (2.2), the matrix $\mathbf{A}$ given by (2.1). In terms of these representations,

$$\text{(2.3)} \qquad \text{(a) } \mathbf{X} = \begin{pmatrix} x_1 \\ x_2 \\ 1 \end{pmatrix}, \qquad \text{(b) } \mathbf{A} = \begin{pmatrix} a_{11} & a_{12} & a_{13} \\ a_{21} & a_{22} & a_{23} \\ 0 & 0 & 1 \end{pmatrix},$$

the affine group is given by

$$\text{(2.4)} \qquad \mathbf{X}' = \mathbf{A}\mathbf{X}, \qquad \det \mathbf{A} \neq 0.$$

Then the image, under the embedding $\mathscr{E}$ given by (1.6) to (1.9), of the affine point with representation **X** is the point in $S_2(\mathsf{R})$ with **X** as one of its representatives, and the image of the affine transformation with matrix **A** is the collineation with **A** as one of its representatives. Thus in terms of these matrix representations, we can represent the embedding $\mathscr{E}$ by the equations

$$\mathscr{E}\mathbf{X} = \mathbf{X}, \qquad \mathscr{E}\mathbf{A} = \mathbf{A}. \tag{2.5}$$

Can we adapt the representation

$$\mathbf{X} = \lambda\mathbf{Y} + \mu\mathbf{Z}, \tag{2.6}$$

which we use in $S_2(\mathsf{R})$ for the points X of the line $Y \oplus Z$, to A_2? In $S_2(\mathsf{R})$, the condition

$$\lambda + \mu = 1 \tag{2.7}$$

amounts to choosing a particular representative for the homogeneous class $[\lambda, \mu]$, and this is possible except if $\lambda + \mu = 0$. On the other hand, (2.7) guarantees that the matrix (2.6) be of the form (2.3a) whenever **Y** and **Z** are of this form. For such matrices, $\lambda + \mu = 0$ represents a point on the line $x_3 = 0$. Hence we can regard (2.6) and (2.7) as representing the affine line joining the affine points Y and Z; $\mathbf{Y} - \mathbf{Z}$ represents the absolute point on the image line in $S_2(\mathsf{R})$.

In A_2, we may eliminate λ from (2.6) by means of (2.7); then

$$\mathbf{X} = (1 - \mu)\mathbf{Y} + \mu\mathbf{Z}. \tag{2.8}$$

From Definition 2.2 we find that μ is the affine ratio YX/YZ, and hence (see Exercise 8 below) μ is an affine coordinate on the line. The ray from Y, the segment YZ, and the ray from Z are represented by (2.8) together with the respective inequality

$$\mu < 0, \qquad 0 < \mu < 1, \qquad 1 < \mu. \tag{2.9}$$

In $S_2(\mathsf{R})$, the point of intersection R of the line $Y \oplus Z$ and a line V is represented by $\mathbf{R} = (\mathbf{VZ})\mathbf{Y} - (\mathbf{VY})\mathbf{Z}$. Since the absolute point of $Y \oplus Z$ is $\mathbf{Y} - \mathbf{Z}$, we have (see III, Theorem 5.2) that R and the absolute point lie on different segments if and only if $(\mathbf{VY})(\mathbf{VZ}) < 0$. Then from Theorem 2.2 we have the following result.

THEOREM 2.7. *In A_2, the (open) half-planes of the line V are given by*

$$\operatorname{sgn}(\mathbf{VX}) = +1 \quad \textit{and} \quad \operatorname{sgn}(\mathbf{VX}) = -1. \tag{2.10}$$

COROLLARY 2.1. *The (open) half-planes of the line joining points Y, Z in A_2 are given by*

$$\operatorname{sgn}\det(\mathbf{X}\ \ \mathbf{Y}\ \ \mathbf{Z}) = +1 \quad \textit{and} \quad \operatorname{sgn}\det(\mathbf{X}\ \ \mathbf{Y}\ \ \mathbf{Z}) = -1. \tag{2.11}$$

We shall find frequent occasion to refer to the determinant appearing in (2.11). Under any linear transformation $\mathbf{X}' = \mathbf{A}\mathbf{X}$, the maps of $\mathbf{P}$, $\mathbf{Q}$, $\mathbf{R}$ given by $\mathbf{P}' = \mathbf{A}\mathbf{P}$, $\mathbf{Q}' = \mathbf{A}\mathbf{Q}$, $\mathbf{R}' = \mathbf{A}\mathbf{R}$ satisfy

$$\text{(2.12)} \qquad \det(\mathbf{P}' \quad \mathbf{Q}' \quad \mathbf{R}') = \det \mathbf{A} \det(\mathbf{P} \quad \mathbf{Q} \quad \mathbf{R}).$$

Because of the homogeneity of projective coordinates, the value of each of the determinants in (2.12) has no projective significance (except if they vanish). But in A_2, where matrix representations are of the form (2.3), equation (2.12) will be seen to play an important role. It could have been the point of departure for an algebraic formulation of the concept of "sides" of a line.

We close this section with several problems that illustrate how the embedding relation can be used to develop affine geometry.

Problem 1. Let P_0, P_0', P_4, P_4' be four points with

$$P_0 \oplus P_4 \nparallel P_0' \oplus P_4', \qquad P_0 \oplus P_0' \nparallel P_4 \oplus P_4'.$$

Let P_i divide the points P_0, P_4, and P_i' the points P_0', P_4', in the ratios $i/4$ $(i = 1, 2, 3)$. Prove that the conic tangent to the lines $P_j \oplus P_j'$ $(j = 0, 1, 2, 3, 4)$ is a parabola.

Solution. Under an embedding $\mathscr{E}$ in $S_2(\mathsf{R})$ we obtain on each of two lines, the five images and the absolute point. Clearly there exists a projectivity which maps the six points of one line onto the six of the other, respectively. This projectivity can not be a perspectivity since

$$P_0 \oplus P_0' \nparallel P_4 \oplus P_4'$$

implies that $\mathscr{E}P_0 \oplus \mathscr{E}P_0'$ and $\mathscr{E}P_4 \oplus \mathscr{E}P_4'$ are not concurrent with the absolute line. Hence the joins of points corresponding under the projectivity envelop a conic, and since the absolute line is one of the tangents, the inverse image in A_2 of the conic is a parabola.

Problem 2. Find affine coordinates (x', y') in terms of which the conic $x^2 - 4xy - 5y^2 - 4x - 6y + 4 = 0$ has the equation $x'^2 \pm y'^2 = 1$.

Solution. There are infinitely many such coordinate systems, and any pair of conjugate diameters can be chosen to be the coordinate axes. In $S_2(\mathsf{R})$ we recall that the matrix of a quadratic form is a diagonal matrix (see III, Theorem 6.8) in any coordinate system in which the triangle of reference is self-polar with respect to the form. Since the absolute line is not tangent to the conic, there exist self-polar triangles with the absolute line as one of the sides, and hence we can retain this line as one of the sides of the new triangle of reference. To find two other sides, we choose any point on the absolute line, say $(1, 0, 0)^T$, and find its polar, and then find the polar of its intersection with the absolute line. The polar of $(1, 0, 0)^T$ is the line

$$(1 \quad 0 \quad 0)\begin{pmatrix} 1 & -2 & -2 \\ -2 & -5 & -3 \\ -2 & -3 & 4 \end{pmatrix} = (1 \quad -2 \quad -2).$$

This line intersects the line $x_3 = 0$ in the point $(2, 1, 0)^T$, and the polar of this point is the line

$$(2 \quad 1 \quad 0)\begin{pmatrix} 1 & -2 & -2 \\ -2 & -5 & -3 \\ -2 & -3 & 4 \end{pmatrix} = (0 \quad -9 \quad -7).$$

The collineation

$$x_1' = x_1 - 2x_2 - 2x_3, \qquad x_2' = 9x_2 + 7x_3, \qquad x_3' = x_3$$

reduces the image form to the form (IV, (6.12)). In the affine plane, the two lines $x - 2y - 2 = 0$, $9y + 7 = 0$ are conjugate diameters, and the affine transformation

$$x' = x - 2y - 2, \qquad y' = 9y + 7$$

reduces the equation of the given conic to

$$-9x'^2 + y'^2 = 49.$$

The further transformation

$$x'' = \tfrac{1}{7}y', \qquad y'' = \tfrac{3}{7}x'$$

reduces the equation of the conic to $x''^2 - y''^2 = 1$. The product of the two transformations is

$$x'' = \tfrac{1}{7}(9y + 7), \qquad y'' = \tfrac{3}{7}(x - 2y - 2), \tag{2.13}$$

which is a coordinate transformation that effects the desired result.

Problem 3. Define "interior of a triangle" in A_2, and characterize it analytically.

Solution. In $S_2(\mathsf{R})$ any triangle determines four regions that are projectively equivalent. Can we discover an affine distinction between these regions? We leave to the reader to show that in $S_2(\mathsf{R})$ a given line, not incident to any vertex of the triangle, contains points of just three of the four regions. Hence a suitable definition of *interior of a triangle* in A_2 is the point set whose image, under $\mathscr{E}$, is that one of the four regions (determined in $S_2(\mathsf{R})$ by the image triangle) that contains no point of the absolute line. Such a point set is clearly affinely invariant.

In $S_2(\mathsf{R})$ the equations

$$\mathbf{X} = \lambda\mathbf{P} + \mu\mathbf{Q} + \nu\mathbf{R}, \qquad \det(\mathbf{P} \quad \mathbf{Q} \quad \mathbf{R}) \neq 0, \tag{2.14}$$

can be interpreted as a coordinate transformation with the triangle PQR as the reference triangle of the $(\lambda, \mu, \nu)^T$ coordinate system. To impose on $(\lambda, \mu, \nu)^T$ the condition

$$\lambda + \mu + \nu = 1 \tag{2.15}$$

amounts to choosing a particular representation for the homogeneous class $[\lambda, \mu, \nu]$, and this is possible except for the points of the line $\lambda + \mu + \nu = 0$. The regions determined by PQR are given by inequalities on λ, μ, ν of the form of (III, (6.5)), and the region that contains no point of the line $\lambda + \mu + \nu = 0$ is the region for which

$$\lambda > 0, \qquad \mu > 0, \qquad \nu > 0. \tag{2.16}$$

Equation (2.15) ensures that the matrix $\mathbf{X}$ of (2.14) be of the form (2.3a) whenever $\mathbf{P}$, $\mathbf{Q}$, $\mathbf{R}$ are of this form. For such matrices the line $\lambda + \mu + \nu = 0$ is the line $x_3 = 0$. Hence we can regard equations (2.14) and (2.15) as representing all the points X of A_2, and (2.16) characterizes the interior of the triangle PQR.

In A_2, the coordinates (λ, μ, ν) of a point X determined by (2.14) and (2.15) are called *areal coordinates*; homogeneous coordinates proportional to areal coordinates are called *barycentric coordinates*. The reader can verify that the unit point of barycentric coordinates is the point of intersection of the medians of the reference triangle.†

EXERCISES

1. Prove that the affine ratios AC/AB and AB/AC are reciprocals, and that $AC/AB \div AD/AB = AC/AD$.

2. Express CB/CA in terms of AC/AB.

3. Prove that if three parallel lines a, b, and c intersect a transversal in A, B, and C, respectively, the ratio AC/AB is independent of the transversal.

4. Prove Theorem 2.4.

5. Interpret (x, y) in (IV, 7, Exercises 1–8) as affine coordinates in A_2. Which, if any, of these exercises have meaning, and how does the solution differ from the solution in E_2?

6. Let A, B, A', B' be four points in A_2, no three collinear. Define points Y, Z by the conditions

$$A \oplus Y \parallel A' \oplus B' \parallel B \oplus Z, \qquad A' \oplus Y \parallel A \oplus B \parallel B' \oplus Z.$$

Prove that $Y \oplus Z$, $A \oplus B'$, and $A' \oplus B$ are concurrent.

#7. Define one-dimensional affine geometry in terms of $S_1(\mathsf{R})$, and prove that your definition is consistent with the structure of a line in the affine plane.

† See H. S. M. Coxeter, *Introduction to Geometry*, New York, John Wiley & Sons, 1961, pp. 216–221.

8. If A, B are distinct points of a line L in A_2, the equation $AX/AB = \mu$, $X \in L$, $\mu \in \mathsf{R}$ defines a one-to-one map with domain L and range R. Such a map is called an *affine* coordinatization of L. Characterize affine coordinates algebraically, and show that the coordinate x in A_2 is an affine coordinate on any line not parallel to the y axis.

#**9.** Let A_1 and A_1' be two one-dimensional affine spaces (see Exercise 7). Define an affine map from A_1 to A_1', and characterize such maps algebraically and geometrically.

10. Let L, L' be lines in A_2, and let π map L onto L' so that the lines $X \oplus \pi X$ are parallel for all $X \in L$ (except $L \cap L'$) and $\pi(L \cap L') = L \cap L'$. Prove that π is a one-dimensional affine transformation (see Exercise 9). This map is called a *parallel projection* from L onto L'. Does there exist $g \in G_6$ whose restriction to L coincides with π? Is g unique?

#**11.** Prove that every affine transformation from a line L in A_2 onto L' is the product of at most two parallel projections (see Exercise 10), and give an affine construction for the axis.

#**12.** Let $g \in G_6$ map a line L onto itself, and let A, B, gA, gB be two given points on L and their images. Give an affine construction for gX where $X \in L$.

#**13.** Prove that A_2 induces on a pencil of parallel lines the structure of a one-dimensional affine space (see Exercise 7). How would you interpret affine ratio in such a pencil?

#**14.** Prove that A_2 induces on a pencil of concurrent lines the structure of an $S_1(\mathsf{R})$.

15. Which of the relations set forth in (IV, 7, Exercises 8–16) are affine rather than Euclidean?

#**16.** Let (x, y) be a given affine coordinatization of A_2, and let a, b, c be real numbers with a, b not both zero. Denote the coordinates of $P \in A_2$ by $(x(P), y(P))$, and define the map τ by $\tau P = ax(P) + by(P) + c$, for $P \in A_2$. Show that the restriction of τ to a line L is an affine coordinatization of L unless L is parallel to the line $ax + by + c = 0$.

17. Prove that the locus of the midpoints of a family of parallel chords of a nonsingular conic is contained in a diameter, and that for central conics this diameter and the diameter of the family are conjugate.

18. A variable line intersects three given independent lines in three points of constant affine ratio. Find the envelope of the variable line.

19. If two tangents to a hyperbola intersect one asymptote in A, B, and the other in A', B', respectively, and if O is the center of the hyperbola, prove that the sum of the ratios AO/AB, $A'O/A'B'$ is 1.

20. Prove the projective theorem: Three points of a conic and the three tangents at these points are Desarguean triangles. Apply this theorem to a hyperbola, its asymptotes, and an arbitrary tangent.

21. Let ABC be a triangle circumscribing a given parabola, and let D be any point exterior to the parabola and not incident to the sides of the triangle. Prove that there exists a hyperbola through A, B, C, and D with asymptotes parallel to the tangents to the parabola from D.

22. Prove that the locus of the equation

$$a_{11}x^2 + 2a_{12}xy + a_{22}y^2 + 2a_{13}x + 2a_{23}y + a_{33} = 0$$

is an ellipse, hyperbola, or parabola according as

(i) $a_{11}a_{22} - a_{12}^2 > 0, \qquad a_{11}\det(a_{ij}) < 0;$
(ii) $a_{11}a_{22} - a_{12}^2 < 0, \qquad \det(a_{ij}) \neq 0;$
(iii) $a_{11}a_{22} - a_{12}^2 = 0, \qquad \det(a_{ij}) \neq 0.$

23. Give an affine construction for the points $(a + b, 0)$ and $(ab, 0)$ when $(a, 0)$ and $(b, 0)$ are two given points (see III, Construction Problems 5.1 and 5.2).

3 Affine Transformations

We turn our attention to the transformations g of the affine group G_6. Representations (2.4) of g in different affine coordinate systems have matrices $\mathbf{A}, \mathbf{A}'$ satisfying $\mathbf{A}' = \mathbf{BAB}^{-1}$, where the four matrices are each of the form (2.3b). Hence $\det \mathbf{A}' = \det \mathbf{A}$, and we can define the *determinant* of g as $\det \mathbf{A}$. We denote it by $\det g$. Clearly

$$\det(gg') = (\det g)(\det g'), \qquad \text{for all } g, g' \in G_6. \tag{3.1}$$

Under an embedding $\mathscr{E}$ of A_2 in $S_2(\mathsf{R})$, the image of g, $\mathscr{E}g$, is a collineation which maps $l(\mathscr{E})$ onto itself. We shall denote by g_l the restriction of $\mathscr{E}g$ to $l(\mathscr{E})$,

$$g_l X = (\mathscr{E}g)X, \qquad \text{for all } X \in l(\mathscr{E}), \tag{3.2}$$

so that g_l is a projectivity on $l(\mathscr{E})$. Let us recall (III, 11) that if g^* is a collineation in $S_2(\mathsf{R})$, the following three conditions are equivalent.

(i) g^* is either an elation or a homology.
(ii) g^* possesses an axis, that is, there exists a line L such that $g^*X = X$, for all $X \in L$.
(iii) g^* possesses a center, that is, there exists a point C such that $g^*L = L$ for all lines L incident to C.

The center and axis of an elation are incident, whereas those of a homology are not.

We define three classes of affine transformations g for each of which $\mathscr{E}g$ is either an elation or homology.

(1) g is a *dilation* whenever the axis of $\mathscr{E}g$ is $l(\mathscr{E})$, so that $g_l = I$.

(2) g is a *line reflection* whenever $\mathscr{E}g$ is a harmonic homology with center on $l(\mathscr{E})$.

(3) g is a *shear* whenever $\mathscr{E}g$ is an elation with center on $l(\mathscr{E})$ and axis not $l(\mathscr{E})$.

In (2), g_l is a hyperbolic involution, and in (3), g_l is a parabolic projectivity with fixed point the center of $\mathscr{E}g$, but it is not true that (2) or (3) can be characterized by properties of g_l. However the dilations are so characterized, and equivalently, they are the affine transformations g such that $gL \parallel L$ for every line L. They have the representation

$$x' = ax + e, \qquad y' = ay + f, \qquad a \neq 0, \tag{3.3}$$

in every affine coordinate system.

The set of all dilations is a group, the *dilation group*. In the rest of this section we shall use H to denote this group, and h, h', etc., its elements. We note that if h is given by (3.3), $\det h = a^2$, so that

$$\det h > 0, \qquad \text{for all } h \in H.$$

If $a^2 \neq 1$, h is said to be *proper*; its projective image is a nonharmonic homology with characteristic $1/a$ (III, (11.2)). If $a = -1$, $\mathscr{E}h$ is a harmonic homology, and h is called a *point reflection*. Dilations h with $a \neq 1$ possess a center C ($hC = C$), and for $X \in A_2$, $X \neq C$ the affine ratio $ChX/CX = a$. If coordinates are chosen with C as the origin, h is given by

$$x' = ax, \qquad y' = ay. \tag{3.4}$$

If in (3.3) $a = 1$, $\mathscr{E}h$ is an elation, and h has no fixed points (unless it is the identity). Such a dilation is called a *translation*. Its equations are

$$x' = x + e, \qquad y' = y + f. \tag{3.5}$$

The set of all translations is a group. If A, A' are given points in A_2, there exists a unique translation t such that $tA = A'$. We can construct tX by referring to the properties of the image elation $\mathscr{E}t$: If $X \notin A \oplus A'$, tX is the intersection of the parallel to $A \oplus A'$ through X and the parallel to $A \oplus X$ through A'; if $X \in A \oplus A'$, we select $Y \notin A \oplus A'$, we construct tY, and lastly we use Y, tY in place of $A, A' = tA$ to construct tX.

If $A \oplus B \parallel A' \oplus B'$, a dilation h is determined uniquely by the conditions $hA = A'$, $hB = B'$. If $ABB'A'$ is a proper trapezoid, the center is $C = (A \oplus A') \cap (B \oplus B')$.

The centered dilations ($a \neq 1$) possess a fixed pencil of concurrent lines, that is, $hL = L$ for every line L incident to the center. On the other hand, translations, line reflections, and shears possess a fixed pencil of parallel lines. The reader should state and prove an appropriate converse.

In E_2 the axis of a line reflection determines the reflection, whereas in A_2 there are infinitely many reflections in a given line for we can choose the fixed pencil as any pencil of parallels not containing the axis. If we choose affine coordinates so that the axis is the line $x = 0$, and the fixed pencil $y =$ const., the line reflection is given by (see III, (11.1))

$$x' = -x, \qquad y' = y. \tag{3.6}$$

Either from the definition, or from (3.6), it is clear that if X is not on the axis of a line reflection r, $X \oplus rX$ belongs to the fixed pencil, and that seg XrX is bisected by the axis. Accordingly, there exists a unique line reflection leaving fixed one vertex of a given triangle and interchanging the other two vertices.

If the axis of a shear is taken as the x axis, its equation becomes (see III, (11.6))

$$x' = x + ay, \qquad y' = y. \tag{3.7}$$

We note that if ABC is a triangle, there exists a unique shear leaving A fixed and mapping B on C, for the axis must be incident to A and parallel to $B \oplus C$ (Figure 3.1). The map X' of an arbitrary point X is obtained

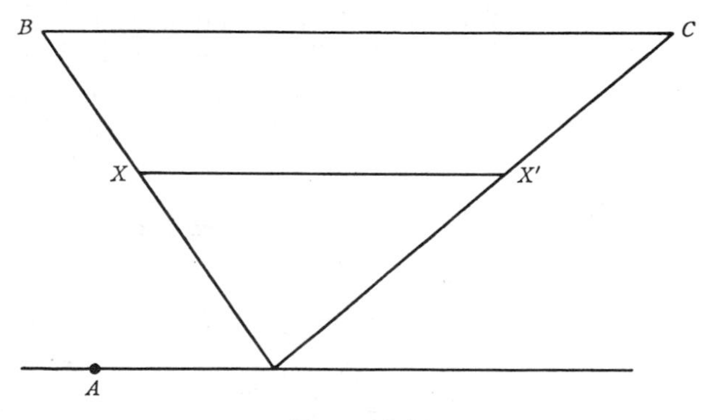

FIGURE 3.1

by an affine construction which is suggested by Figure 3.1.

THEOREM 3.1. *An involutory collineation in the affine plane is either a point reflection or a line reflection.*

The proof follows from earlier results (see (III, Theorem 11.1) and Theorem 2.4).

Point reflections, translations, and shears are examples of *equiaffine* transformations. These are defined by the condition det $g = 1$. From (3.1) it follows that they form a group, the *equiaffine group*. We note from (3.6) that if r is a line reflection, $\det r = -1$. From (3.1) we have the following theorem.

THEOREM 3.2. *The product of an even number of line reflections is equiaffine.*

The next theorem will be very useful.

THEOREM 3.3. *If $g, g' \in G_6$ have coincident restrictions on $l(\mathscr{E})$, there exist dilations $h, h' \in H$ such that*

$$g' = hg, \qquad g' = gh'.$$

Proof. $g_l = g_l'$ implies that $(g'g^{-1})_l$ and $(g^{-1}g')_l$ are the identity, and therefore $g'g^{-1}$ and $g^{-1}g'$ are dilations.

We propose to show that line reflections and dilations are the generating transformations of G_6, that is, that every $g \in G_6$ can be expressed as the product of a finite number of dilations and line reflections. We shall prove this by factoring g_l into the product of hyperbolic involutions. We need to recall that in $S_1(\mathsf{R})$ every projectivity π is the product $\sigma_1 \sigma_2$ of two involutions, of which σ_1 can be chosen to have one of its fixed points any point X not a fixed point of π (see II, 6, Exercise 11). Thus σ_1 can always be chosen hyperbolic. If π is a parabolic or an elliptic projectivity, both factors are necessarily hyperbolic (IV, Theorem 9.10). Since an elliptic involution is the product of two hyperbolic involutions, every hyperbolic projectivity is expressible as the product of either two or three hyperbolic involutions.†

THEOREM 3.4. *An affine transformation g whose determinant is neither 1 nor -1 is the product of a proper dilation and at most three line reflections.*

Proof. We express g_l as the product of three (or fewer) hyperbolic involutions. Suppose

$$g_l = \sigma_1 \sigma_2 \sigma_3. \tag{3.8}$$

Let r_1, r_2, r_3 be line reflections chosen so that $(r_i)_l = \sigma_i$, that is, the center of $\mathscr{E}r_i$ is one fixed point of σ_i and the axis is incident to the other. Then

$$g_l = (r_1 r_2 r_3)_l.$$

By Theorem 3.3., there exists $h \in H$ such that

$$g = hr_1 r_2 r_3, \tag{3.9}$$

† We shall see, in Section 4, that we can define sense in $S_1(\mathsf{R})$, and that hyperbolic involutions reverse sense, whereas a hyperbolic projectivity may either preserve or reverse sense.

and then

$$\det g = -\det h. \tag{3.10}$$

If g_l were the product of two involutions we would have

$$g = hr_1 r_2, \qquad \det g = \det h \tag{3.11}$$

in place of (3.9) and (3.10). In either case, h is a proper dilation.

If $\det g = \pm 1$, the preceding analysis shows that the factorization (3.9) or (3.11) is possible, with h either a point reflection or a translation. Actually we shall obtain the stronger conclusion that, for a suitable choice of the reflections, h is the identity.

We turn to the factorization of point reflections and translations. Let us choose, in $S_2(\mathsf{R})$, any two distinct points F, F' on $l(\mathscr{E})$, and let r, r' be distinct line reflections whose restrictions to $l(\mathscr{E})$ have F, F' as their fixed points (Figure 3.2). Then $r_l = r'_l$ and $(rr')_l = I$. Moreover $\det(rr') = 1$, and

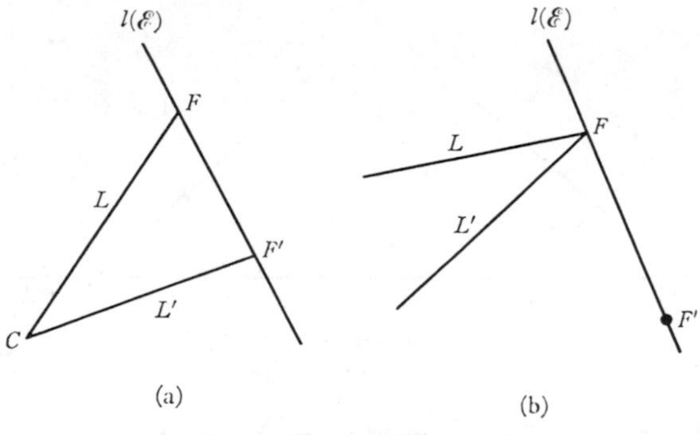

FIGURE 3.2

therefore rr' must be either a point reflection or a translation. If the axes L, L' of the homologies $\mathscr{E}r$, $\mathscr{E}r'$ are not concurrent on $l(\mathscr{E})$, their intersection C is fixed under $\mathscr{E}rr'$, and rr' is a point reflection. If the axes are concurrent on $l(\mathscr{E})$, rr' has no fixed points and is a translation. We leave to the reader the proof of the converse, that every point reflection and every translation can be factored in this manner. For convenience, we state the conclusion as follows.

THEOREM 3.5. *A point reflection is the product of two line reflections. The axes are any distinct lines through the center, and the fixed pencil of each reflection is the pencil of lines parallel to the axis of the other. A translation is the product of two reflections with axes which are parallel, and fixed pencils which coincide with the fixed pencil of the translation. Conversely, every product of the first kind is a point reflection, and every product of the second kind a translation.*

We next show that a shear can be factored.

THEOREM 3.6. *A shear is the product of two line reflections. The axis of one is any line that intersects the axis of the shear, and that of the second is a determined line concurrent with the two. The fixed pencils of both reflections coincide with that of the shear. Conversely, the product of two reflections in intersecting lines with a common fixed pencil is a shear whose axis is concurrent with the axes of the two reflections, and whose fixed pencil coincides with the common fixed pencil of the two reflections.*

Proof. Let g be the shear with axis L, let L' be any line not parallel to the axis, and let $A = L \cap L'$. In $S_2(\mathsf{R})$ (Figure 3.3) we let $F = \mathscr{E}L \cap l(\mathscr{E})$,

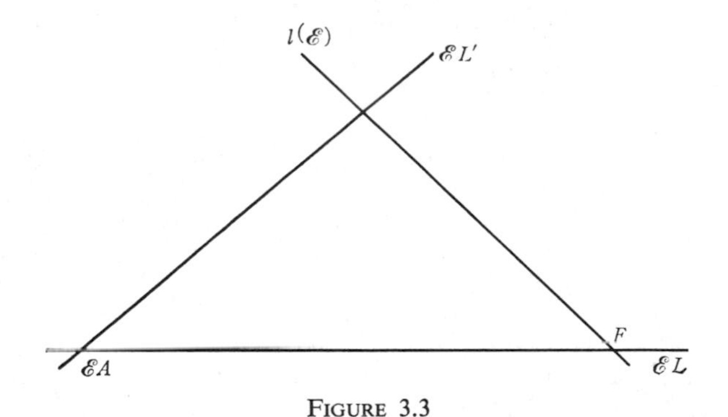

FIGURE 3.3

$P = \mathscr{E}L' \cap l(\mathscr{E})$. Then g_l is a parabolic projectivity with center F, and $P \neq F$. If σ is the involution on $l(\mathscr{E})$ defined by $\sigma P = P$, $\sigma g_l P = g_l^{-1}P$, the other fixed point of σ is F (see II, 5, Exercise 9) and $g_l = \sigma\sigma'$, where σ' is an involution with fixed points F and Q. (It can be shown that Q is defined by$(Q\ F,\ P\ g_l^{-1}P) = -1$.) Then in A_2 we choose reflections r, r' with axes L' and $L'' = \mathscr{E}^{-1}(\mathscr{E}A \oplus Q)$, and with fixed pencil that of g, so that $g_l = (rr')_l$. Moreover the restrictions of both g and rr' to L coincide with the identity, so that $g = rr'$.

We are now ready to prove the theorem suggested earlier.

THEOREM 3.7. *Every equiaffine map is the product of two line reflections.*

Proof. We let $g \in G_6$ be given, with $\det g = 1$. We can suppose that g is neither a translation, a point reflection, nor a shear. Then there exists a point $A \in A_2$ such that $A \oplus gA$ is not a fixed line.

In $S_2(\mathsf{R})$, we let F be the absolute point on $\mathscr{E}(A \oplus gA)$. Then we can write $g_\iota = \sigma\sigma'$,† where σ and σ' are hyperbolic involutions with fixed points F, F' and F'', F''' respectively, where we have chosen our notation so that $F''' \neq F'$ (Figure 3.4). We select the harmonic homology with axis $\mathscr{E}A \oplus F'''$

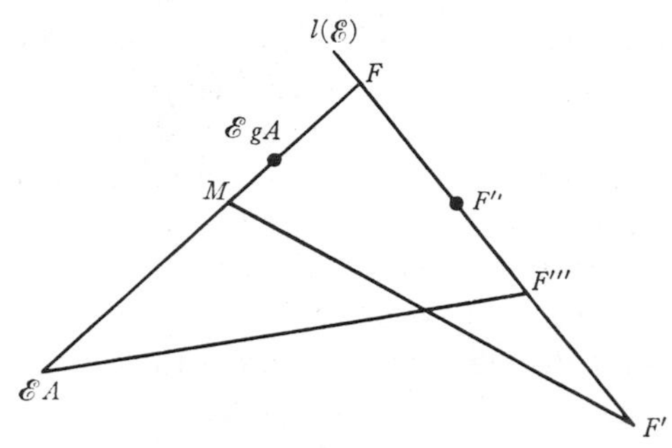

FIGURE 3.4

and center F'', and let r' be the corresponding line reflection in A_2. Similarly, let r be the line reflection with image harmonic homology having center F and axis $F' \oplus M$, where M is defined by $(F\ M,\ \mathscr{E}A\ \mathscr{E}gA) = -1$. Then, in A_2, $r'A = A$, $rA = gA$. Hence $g = rr'h$ where h is a dilation satisfying $\det h = 1$, $hA = A$. Consequently at worst h is a point reflection with center A, and a line reflection r'' exists such that $h = r'r''$. Then $g = rr'r'r'' = rr''$, as was to have been proved.

COROLLARY 3.1. *If* $\det g = -1$, *g is the product of three line reflections.*

Clearly, the product of three line reflections might reduce to a single reflection.

To summarize, we have shown that every affine transformation is the product of a dilation (which may be the identity) with either two or three line reflections.

The translation group, the dilation group, and the equiaffine group are examples of *invariant*, or *normal*, subgroups, and the next theorem is equivalent to this assertion (see Definition 4.3 below).

THEOREM 3.8. *If t is a translation, so is $g^{-1}tg$ for all $g \in G_6$. If h is a dilation, and k an equiaffine map, so are $g^{-1}hg$ and $g^{-1}kg$ respectively, for all $g \in G_6$.*

† The hypothesis that $\det g = 1$ guarantees that g_ι can be expressed as the product of two hyperbolic involutions. Although this conclusion will follow later when we consider sense (see footnote, page 294), we can prove it now by noting that $x' = kx$ is the product of $x' = 1/x$ and $x' = k/x$, and that $k > 0$ implies that both involutions are hyperbolic.

Proof. By (3.1), $\det(g^{-1}kg) = \det k$, and consequently k and $k' = g^{-1}kg$ are simultaneously equiaffine. If $h \in H$, $h_l = I$ and $(g^{-1}hg)_l = I$, so that $g^{-1}hg \in H$. If h possesses a center C, $hC = C$, and then $g^{-1}hg$ leaves $g^{-1}C$ fixed. Since the relation between h and $h' = g^{-1}hg$ is reciprocal ($h = gh'g^{-1}$), h' is a translation if and only if h is a translation.

Although affine geometry is not a metric geometry in that there is no intrinsic way of defining distance between points, or length of a segment (except trivially), the first statement in Theorem 3.8 leads to a definition of relative length of a segment with respect to a parallel segment.

We shall see that relative lengths can be negative as well as positive, and this is so because in reality relative length is a measure of directed line segments. However for convenience we shall postpone a definition of *directed* until Section 5, and for the present it will suffice to let seg $\overrightarrow{PQ}$ denote seg PQ together with the specification of P as the *initial* point and Q as the *terminal* point (that is, we have selected a particular ordering of the end points). Thus seg PQ = seg QP since the two segments are coincident point sets, but seg $\overrightarrow{PQ} \neq$ seg $\overrightarrow{QP}$.

DEFINITION 3.1. Two segments are *congruent* if there exists a translation which maps the end points of one segment onto the end points of the other.

If there existed translations t_1, t_2 such that

$$t_1 P = P', \qquad t_1 Q = Q', \qquad t_2 P = Q', \qquad t_2 Q = P',$$

the product $t_2^{-1}t_1$ would be a translation interchanging P and Q; this is impossible, and congruent segments are congruent in just one way. Thus congruent segments are congruent directed segments, and we shall write

$$\text{seg } \overrightarrow{PQ} \cong \text{seg } \overrightarrow{P'Q'}$$

to denote that there exists a translation mapping P on P' and Q on Q'.

It may be surprising that one can define congruent segments in the absence of a metric, and we need to show that congruence of segments is indeed an affine property. From our earlier observations (following (3.5)) we note that seg $\overrightarrow{PQ} \cong$ seg $\overrightarrow{P'Q'}$ implies that $P \oplus Q \parallel P' \oplus Q'$, and that $P \oplus P' \parallel Q \oplus Q'$. Conversely, whenever $PQQ'P'$ is a parallelogram,† seg $\overrightarrow{PQ} \cong$ seg $\overrightarrow{P'Q'}$, and seg $\overrightarrow{PP'} \cong$ seg $\overrightarrow{QQ'}$; if P, P', Q, Q' are collinear, and if there exist points Y, Z such that $PQYZ$ and $P'Q'YZ$ are parallelograms, then again seg $\overrightarrow{PQ} \cong$ seg $\overrightarrow{P'Q'}$ and seg $\overrightarrow{PP'} \cong$ seg $\overrightarrow{QQ'}$. Since all affine transformations map parallelograms onto parallelograms, congruence of segments is an affine invariant. However it is instructive to give another

† $PQQ'P'$ is a parallelogram means that $P \oplus Q \parallel P' \oplus Q'$, that $P \oplus P' \parallel Q \oplus Q'$, and that the four points are not collinear.

argument, based on Theorem 3.8, of the affine character of Definition 3.1. Let t be a translation and $g \in G_6$. Then g maps seg $\overrightarrow{PQ}$ and t(seg $\overrightarrow{PQ}$) onto g(seg $\overrightarrow{PQ}$) and gt(seg $\overrightarrow{PQ}$). The latter two segments are surely affinely equivalent, and indeed gtg^{-1} maps the first on the second. By Theorem (3.8), gtg^{-1} is a translation, and hence every $g \in G_6$ maps a pair of congruent segments onto another such pair.

We are now ready to define relative length.

DEFINITION 3.2. Let seg $\overrightarrow{PQ}$ and seg $\overrightarrow{AB}$ lie on parallel lines, let C be any point, and let Q' and B' be determined by the conditions (Figure 3.5)

$$\text{seg } \overrightarrow{CQ'} \cong \text{seg } \overrightarrow{PQ}, \qquad \text{seg } \overrightarrow{CB'} \cong \text{seg } \overrightarrow{AB}.$$

The *relative length* of seg $\overrightarrow{PQ}$ with respect to seg $\overrightarrow{AB}$ is the affine ratio CQ'/CB'.

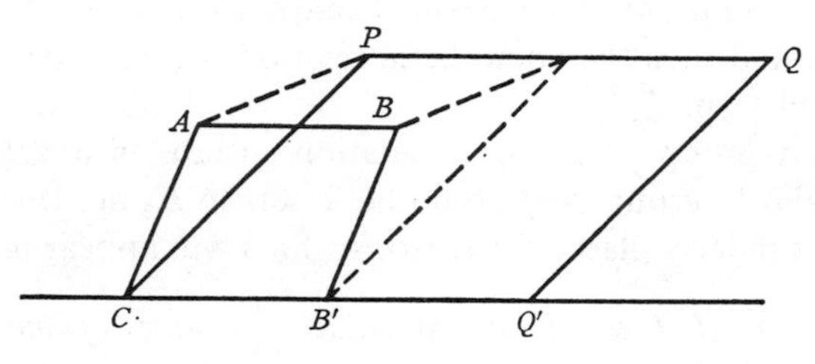

FIGURE 3.5

We can, without ambiguity, denote relative length by PQ/AB. The reader should verify that our definition of PQ/AB is independent of the choice of C, that $PQ/QP = -1$, and that $PQ/AB = -QP/AB$.

THEOREM 3.9. *If seg PQ and seg AB lie on parallel lines, the relative length of seg $\overrightarrow{PQ}$ with respect to seg $\overrightarrow{AB}$ is given by*

$$PQ/AB = (q_1 - p_1)/(b_1 - a_1), \qquad \textit{if } a_1 \neq b_1,$$

and

$$PQ/AB = (q_2 - p_2)/(b_2 - a_2), \qquad \textit{if } a_2 \neq b_2,$$

where $\mathbf{P} = (p_1, p_2, 1)^T$ *is the matrix representation* (2.3a) *of* P, *and similarly for* $\mathbf{A}$, $\mathbf{B}$, *and* $\mathbf{Q}$.

Proof. $P \oplus Q \parallel A \oplus B$ implies that there exists a real number μ such that $\mathbf{Q} - \mathbf{P} = \mu(\mathbf{B} - \mathbf{A})$. Then the translation $\mathbf{X}' = \mathbf{X} + \mathbf{A} - \mathbf{P}$ maps P onto A, and Q onto Q':$\mathbf{Q} + \mathbf{A} - \mathbf{P}$. Therefore $\mathbf{Q}' = \mathbf{A} + \mu(\mathbf{B} - \mathbf{A})$. Since $PQ/AB = AQ'/AB$, the relative length is μ, which in turn, expressed in terms of the elements of the matrices $\mathbf{A}, \mathbf{B}, \mathbf{P}, \mathbf{Q}$, gives the desired result.

Thus in A_2 we can assert that one of two parallel segments is, for example, twice as long as the other, but there does not exist in A_2 any intrinsic calibration of nonparallel segments. Nevertheless we can select arbitrarily a *unit* segment on each line of a concurrent pencil, and refer all relative lengths to the chosen unit segment on the parallel line. For example, we can select as our unit segments the radial segments from the center of a given ellipse. In this case the resulting geometry would be Euclidean. However other calibrations are possible, and they lead to other geometries.†

The property of the dilation group and of the equiaffine group expressed by Theorem 3.8 leads to further concepts which are strictly affine and have no projective counterpart. We shall give two examples of such concepts.

DEFINITION 3.3. Two point sets in A_2 are *homothetic* if there exists a dilation which maps one onto the other.

If $\mathscr{D}$ is a given point set and $h \in H$, $\mathscr{D}$ and $h\mathscr{D}$ are mapped by an arbitrary $g \in G_6$ onto $g\mathscr{D}$ and $gh\mathscr{D}$. Hence ghg^{-1} maps $g\mathscr{D}$ onto $gh\mathscr{D}$. By Theorem 3.8, $ghg^{-1} \in H$, and thus the homothetic relation is preserved by G_6, that is, it is an affine relation.

The dilation group, like the translation group, is a subgroup of the Euclidean similarity group, and homothetic sets in E_2 are frequently said to be similar and similarly placed for reasons which will appear more fully later.

THEOREM 3.10. *If L and L' are conjugate diameters of one conic, the two parallel diameters of a second conic homothetic to the first are conjugate with respect to the second.*

The proof follows from the observation that the images, under an embedding, of homothetic (central) conics induce the same involution (IV, Definition 6.4)) on the absolute line of the embedding.

Further homothetic properties appear in the exercises at the end of this section.

Area, like length, does not exist in A_2, but equality of area and relative area do have meaning. In the development of these ideas, the equiaffine group plays the leading role. In developing areal properties we shall consider only triangular regions, for the theory for more general classes of regions can be developed from the theory for triangular regions by standard processes.‡ Our "areas" will be signed, and the sign will depend on the order of enumeration of the vertices. We shall see in Section 5, where we discuss orientation, that the sign is determined by the orientation of the triangle in

† See H. Busemann and P. J. Kelly, *Projective Geometry and Projective Metrics*, New York, Academic Press Inc., 1953.

‡ For curvilinear regions, by the methods of the calculus. For polygonal regions see Exercises 25–26 below, and Veblen and Young, *op. cit.*, II, p. 104.

exactly the way we expect, but in our present treatment we shall not be concerned with questions of orientation.

DEFINITION 3.4. Two ordered triangles, PQR and $P'Q'R'$, are *equiareal* if there exists an equiaffine map g ($g \in G_6$, $\det g = 1$) such that $gP = P'$, $gQ = Q'$, $gR = R'$.

Theorem 3.8 guarantees that equiareal triangles are part of the structure of the affine plane.

Since $g \in G_6$ is determined uniquely by the conditions $gP = P$, $gQ = R$, $gR = Q$, and the solution is a line reflection, we see that PQR and PRQ are not equiareal. From Theorem 3.2 we see that each two of the three ordered triangles PQR, QRP, and RPQ are equiareal.

In E_2, the areas of triangles with congruent bases are in the ratio of their altitudes, or, when the bases are parallel, in the ratio of the lengths of parallel segments intercepted between the respective congruent bases and the opposite vertices. This suggests a way of defining relative area in A_2, but we shall need the following two lemmas.

LEMMA 3.1. *There exist infinitely many equiaffine maps of one of two given segments onto the other.*

Proof. Let seg PQ and seg $P'Q'$ be given; if g is equiaffine, and $g(\text{seg } PQ) = \text{seg } P'Q'$, then $g'g(\text{seg } PQ) = \text{seg } P'Q'$ when g' is a shear with axis $P' \oplus Q'$, or a point reflection with center the midpoint of seg $P'Q'$, or the product of any of these. Clearly $g'g$ is equiaffine, and thus if one g exists, there are infinitely many.

To show that one g exists, we can suppose $PP'QQ'$ is a quadrangle (if not, replace seg $P'Q'$ by $t(\text{seg } P'Q')$, where t is a suitably chosen translation). Then the line reflection in the median through P of the triangle PQQ' followed by the reflection in the median through Q' of triangle $PQ'P'$ satisfies our requirements.

LEMMA 3.2. *If triangles PQR and PQR' are equiareal, $R \oplus R' \parallel P \oplus Q$.*

Proof. $gP = P$, and $gQ = Q$ implies that $gX = X$ for all $X \in P \oplus Q$. The subgroup of G_6 leaving fixed all points of a line consists of the shears with the line as axis and the transformations whose projective images are the homologies with center on the absolute line (see Exercise 6 below). The intersection of this group and the equiaffine group consists of the shears, and therefore $R \oplus R'$ is parallel to the common axis.

Thus the locus of gR as g runs through all equiaffine maps satisfying $gP = P'$, $gQ = Q'$ is a line parallel to $P' \oplus Q'$.

DEFINITION 3.5. Let PQR and ABC be given ordered triangles. Select a segment KL and points R', C' so that PQR, KLR' are equiareal, and

ABC, KLC' are equiareal. Choose M, N on $K \oplus L$ so that $R' \oplus N \parallel C' \oplus M$. The *relative area* of PQR with respect to ABC is the relative length NR'/MC'.

If we introduce the parallels to $K \oplus L$ through C' and R', respectively, and use Exercise 3 above, we can see that Definition 3.5 is independent of the choice of M (or N), and of the shears entering through Lemmas 3.1 and 3.2.

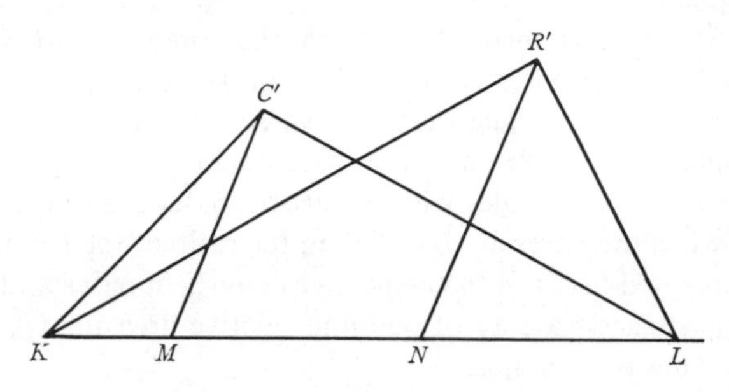

FIGURE 3.6

If we choose affine coordinates with K the origin, L the unit point on the line $x_2 = 0$, and the line $x_1 = 0$ parallel to $C' \oplus M$, we have that $NR'/MC' = x_2(R')/x_2(C')$. In this coordinate system

$$x_2(R') = \det(\mathbf{K} \quad \mathbf{L} \quad \mathbf{R}'), \quad \text{and} \quad x_2(C') = \det(\mathbf{K} \quad \mathbf{L} \quad \mathbf{C}').$$

From (2.12),

$$\det(\mathbf{A} \quad \mathbf{B} \quad \mathbf{C}) = \det(\mathbf{K} \quad \mathbf{L} \quad \mathbf{C}'), \quad \text{and} \quad \det(\mathbf{P} \quad \mathbf{Q} \quad \mathbf{R}) = \det(\mathbf{K} \quad \mathbf{L} \quad \mathbf{R}').$$

Hence we have proved the following theorem.

THEOREM 3.11. *The relative area of the ordered triangle PQR with respect to the ordered triangle ABC is, in terms of matrix notation* (2.3), *the ratio* $\det(\mathbf{P} \quad \mathbf{Q} \quad \mathbf{R})/\det(\mathbf{A} \quad \mathbf{B} \quad \mathbf{C})$.

We note that a formal analytical approach to this subject could have been based on (2.12).

EXERCISES

1. Find equations of the following transformations in A_2:
(a) The reflection in the point $(1, 2)$.
(b) The dilation with center $(2, 3)$ mapping $x + y = 0$ onto $x + y = 1$.
(c) The line reflection with axis $x - 2 = 0$ and fixed pencil the parallels to $x - y = 0$.
(d) The shear with axis $y - 2 = 0$ mapping $(0, 0)$ to $(0, 3)$.

2. Identify the following transformations in A_2:
(a) $x' = -x + 4, \quad y' = -y + 2.$
(b) $x' = x - 2y + 4, \quad y' = -y + 4.$
(c) $x' = y, \quad y' = x.$

3. Characterize g_l as hyperbolic, elliptic, involutory, etc., when $g \in G_6$ is given by
(a) $x' = x + 2y + 3, \quad y' = y + 1,$
(b) $x' = -x + 2y - 4, \quad y' = -y + 4,$
and find the fixed points and lines of g.

4. Factor g, given by 3(b), into the product of line reflections.

5. Find the equation of the line reflection with axis $v_1 x_1 + v_2 x_2 + v_3 = 0$, and with fixed pencil the lines parallel to $q_2 x_1 - q_1 x_2 = 0$.

ANS. $\mathbf{X}' = \mathbf{X} - 2\mathbf{Q}(\mathbf{VX})/(\mathbf{VQ})$, where $\mathbf{Q} = (q_1, q_2, 0)^T$.

6. Characterize the transformations $g \in G_6$ such that $\mathscr{E}g$ is a homology with center on $l(\mathscr{E})$. Show that in a suitably chosen coordinate system, they can be expressed by $x' = x, \quad y' = ay, \quad a \neq 0$.

7. Identify the affine transformations which leave fixed all points of one line (see Exercise 6).

8. Prove that in the factorization of Theorem 3.4, the center of the dilation may be preassigned.

9. Give an affine construction for hX if h is the dilation determined by
(a) $hC = C, \quad hA = A' \qquad (A' \in A \oplus C);$
(b) $hA = A', \quad hB = B' \qquad (A \oplus B \parallel A' \oplus B').$

10. Prove that the set of shears with a given axis is a group isomorphic to the additive group of the reals.

11. Prove that the set of dilations with a given center is a group isomorphic to the multiplicative group of the nonzero reals.

12. Identify the product of two point reflections.

13. Let g_1, g_2 be the shears determined by $g_1 A = A, g_1 B = B', g_2 B = B, g_2 A = A'$, where $ABB'A'$ is a parallelogram. Show that g_1 and g_2 commute, and that their product is a translation.

14. Let g be the shear $x' = x + ay, \ y' = y$, and r the line reflection $x' = -x, \ y' = y$. Verify that gr and rg are line reflections, and find their axes (see Theorem 3.6).

15. Let g_1, g_2 be harmonic homologies in $S_2(\mathsf{R})$ with distinct centers and with distinct axes which intersect on the join of the centers. Show that $g_1 g_2$ has only one fixed point and only one fixed line.

16. The parallels to every pair of conjugate diameters of one conic which are incident to the center of a second conic are conjugate with respect to the second conic. Are the conics homothetic (see Theorem 3.10)?

17. Prove that two homothetic conics have at most two (real) intersections.

18. Prove that there exists exactly one conic homothetic to a given conic and circumscribing a given triangle.

19. Find necessary and sufficient conditions that two parabolas be homothetic.

20. Prove that if each two of three mutually homothetic conics intersect, their common chords are dependent.

21. Prove that relative lengths of corresponding sides of two homothetic triangles is the same for all three pairs of sides.

22. Prove that if two hyperbolas are homothetic, they have parallel asymptotes.

23. Prove that the relative area of the triangle determined by two asymptotes of a hyperbola and a variable tangent is constant.

#**24.** Identify the triangles of maximum relative area inscribable in a given ellipse.

25. Let $m(PQR)$ denote the relative area of a variable triangle PQR with respect to a fixed triangle, and let $m(PQR) = 0$ if P, Q, R are collinear. Prove that for all points O

$$m(OPQ) + m(OQR) + m(ORP) = m(PQR).$$

#**26.** Prove that the sum (see Exercise 25)

$$m(OP_1 P_2) + m(OP_2 P_3) + \dots + m(OP_{n-1} P_n) + m(OP_n P_1)$$

is independent of the point O. This sum can be defined as the relative area of the polygon $P_1 P_2 \dots P_n$ and can be denoted by $m(P_1 P_2 \dots P_n)$.

#**27.** Prove that for any four points,

$$m(P_1 P_2 P_3 P_4) = m(P_1 P_2 P_3) + m(P_1 P_3 P_4)$$

(see Exercise 26).

#**28.** Define "distance" between two points $P, Q \in A_2$ as twice the relative length of seg PQ with respect to the parallel diameter of a given ellipse. Prove that if ABC is a triangle inscribed in the ellipse and if $B \oplus C$ is a diameter, the Pythagorean theorem holds for ABC, with seg BC as the hypotenuse.

4 Sense Classes in $S_1(\mathsf{R})$

We are all familiar with the fact that on the Euclidean line we have not merely length, but directed length based on a choice of a *positive direction* on the line. It is a fact that $S_2(\mathsf{R})$, unlike the Euclidean plane, cannot be oriented; it is also true that $S_1(\mathsf{R})$ can be oriented, and in this and the following section we define and study, first an oriented $S_1(\mathsf{R})$, and then an oriented affine plane.

We first describe a subdivision of the set of all projectivities in $S_1(\mathsf{R})$ into two mutually exclusive, nonempty classes. If a projectivity π has, in a particular coordinate system, the representation

$$\mathbf{X}' = \mathbf{AX}, \quad \text{where} \quad \mathbf{X} = \begin{pmatrix} x_1 \\ x_2 \end{pmatrix}, \quad \mathbf{A} = \begin{pmatrix} a_{11} & a_{12} \\ a_{21} & a_{22} \end{pmatrix}, \tag{4.1}$$

π can equally well be represented by the matrix $\rho\mathbf{A}$, where ρ is a nonzero scalar, or, in terms of coordinates $\mathbf{Y} = \mathbf{CX}$, by the matrix $\mathbf{CAC}^{-1}$. Since sgn det $(\rho\mathbf{A})$ = sgn det $\mathbf{A}$, and since sgn det $(\mathbf{CAC}^{-1})$ = sgn det $\mathbf{A}$, the following definition is meaningful.

DEFINITION 4.1. A projectivity in $S_1(\mathsf{R})$ is said to be *direct* or *opposite*, according as its determinant is positive or negative.

THEOREM 4.1. *The set of all direct projectivities is a group. If π_1 is a given opposite projectivity, every opposite projectivity is the product of π_1 and some direct projectivity. The product of two projectivities of the same kind is direct, of different kinds is opposite.*

We leave the proof to the reader.

In $S_1(\mathsf{R})$, any two ordered triples of distinct points are equivalent under the group of all projectivities, and there is just one transformation that maps the one triple onto the other. This transformation need not be direct, and two triples are not necessarily equivalent under the group of direct projectivities. We can show, for example, that the projectivity mapping points P, Q, R onto Q, P, R, respectively, is opposite by noting that this projectivity is a hyperbolic involution, and verifying that such an involution is necessarily opposite.

Let us denote by $(P\,Q\,R)$ the ordered triple consisting of the points P, Q, and R, and by $\{P\,Q\,R\}$ the class of all triples *directly* equivalent to $(P\,Q\,R)$. Let $(P'\,Q'\,R')$ be an arbitrary triple.

LEMMA 4.1. *If $(P'\,Q'\,R')$ is contained in $\{P\,Q\,R\}$, $\{P'\,Q'\,R'\} = \{P\,Q\,R\}$.*

Proof. Our hypothesis implies that there exists a direct projectivity, say π_1, that maps $(P\,Q\,R)$ onto $(P'\,Q'\,R')$:

$$\pi_1(P\,Q\,R) = (P'\,Q'\,R').$$

Let $(P^*\,Q^*\,R^*)$ belong to $\{P'\,Q'\,R'\}$. Then there exists a direct projectivity π_2 such that

$$(P^*\,Q^*\,R^*) = \pi_2(P'\,Q'\,R') = \pi_2\pi_1(P\,Q\,R).$$

By the first statement in Theorem 4.1., $\pi_2\pi_1$ is direct, and therefore $(P^*\,Q^*\,R^*)$ belongs to $\{P\,Q\,R\}$. By a similar argument, every triple contained in $\{P\,Q\,R\}$ belongs to $\{P'\,Q'\,R'\}$. Hence the two classes coincide.

LEMMA 4.2. *If $(P'\,Q'\,R')$ is not contained in $\{P\,Q\,R\}$,*

$$\{P'\,Q'\,R'\} = \{Q\,P\,R\}.$$

Proof. Let $(P'\,Q'\,R') = \pi_1(P\,Q\,R)$; by hypothesis, π_1 is opposite. But the projectivity that maps $(P\,Q\,R)$ onto $(Q\,P\,R)$ is also opposite; denote it by π_2 so that

$$(P\,Q\,R) = \pi_2^{-1}(Q\,P\,R),$$

and therefore

$$(P'\,Q'\,R') = \pi_1\,\pi_2^{-1}\,(Q\,P\,R).$$

The inverse of any projectivity is one of the same kind, and by the last part of Theorem 4.1, $\pi_1\,\pi_2^{-1}$ is direct. Hence $(P'\,Q'\,R')$ is contained in $\{Q\,P\,R,\}$ and by the preceding lemma, $\{P'\,Q'\,R'\} = \{Q\,P\,R\}$.

DEFINITION 4.2. In $S_1(\mathsf{R})$, a *sense class* $\mathscr{S}$ is the class of all ordered triples of points that are directly equivalent to a given triple.

There exist in $S_1(\mathsf{R})$ two sense classes $\mathscr{S}_1$ and $\mathscr{S}_2$, each determined by any one of its constituent triples; if $\mathscr{S}_1 = \{P\,Q\,R\}$, $\mathscr{S}_2 = \{Q\,P\,R\}$.

Our definition of a sense class as an infinite collection of triples of points may seem somewhat abstruse. But our experience with directing a Euclidean line leads us to observe that however we may there define *direction from A to B* we do want the concept to satisfy two requirements: first, that there are only two directions on the line; second, that for every pair of points P, Q, the direction from P to Q is either that from A to B, or that from B to A. The second requirement makes it clear that the concept of direction is in essence that of a class. That on $S_1(\mathsf{R})$ three points are needed for the specification of a sense class seems natural when we recall that the projective line is a topological image of a circle. For the purpose of visualizing sense classes, we should draw the projective line as a circle rather than as a line.

Just as the defining structure of $S_2(\mathsf{R})$ led to the existence of various types of sets of points (lines, conics), so in $S_1(\mathsf{R})$ there exist two objects which we call the two sense classes. That these are in reality part of the structure of $S_1(\mathsf{R})$ is seen in the next theorem.

THEOREM 4.2. *Every projectivity between two real S_1's maps sense classes onto sense classes.*

Proof. Denote the projectivity by A and represent it by $\mathbf{Y} = \mathbf{AX}$, where $[x_1, x_2]^T$ and $[y_1, y_2]^T$ are coordinates in S_1 and S_1', respectively. If $\mathbf{B}$ is the matrix of a projectivity B of S_1 onto itself, X and $X' = BX$ are mapped by A onto $Y = AX$ and $Y' = AX' = ABX$, or $Y' = ABA^{-1}Y$. Since $\det(\mathbf{A}\quad\mathbf{B}\quad\mathbf{A}^{-1}) = \det \mathbf{B}$, the projectivities in S_1 and S_1' with matrices $\mathbf{B}$ and $\mathbf{B}' = \mathbf{ABA}^{-1}$ respectively, are either both direct or both opposite. Now consider a sense class $\mathscr{S}_1$ of S_1; any two representative triples of $\mathscr{S}_1$ can be mapped, one onto the other, by some direct projectivity B. Hence their transforms, under **A**, can be mapped, one onto the other, by a direct projectivity, so that these two transformed triples belong to the same sense class, say $\mathscr{S}_1'$ of S_1'. Thus the maps of all triples of $\mathscr{S}_1$ belong to $\mathscr{S}_1'$. By reversing the argument, it follows that all triples in $\mathscr{S}_1'$ are the maps of triples of $\mathscr{S}_1$, and therefore the map of $\mathscr{S}_1$ is $\mathscr{S}_1'$.

The next theorem involves the concept of direct equivalence in a more general form than appears in the preceding theorem, but it does not involve the logical concept of equivalence of classes.

THEOREM 4.3. *Every projectivity maps directly equivalent point sets onto directly equivalent points sets.*

We leave the proof to the reader.

From Theorems 4.2 and 4.3 we see that the structure of an $S_1(\mathsf{R})$ is in part derived from the existence of the subgroup of direct projectivities, and we naturally seek a characterizing property of a subgroup that does contribute to the structure determined by the full group. Let H be a subgroup of a group G; if $\mathscr{C}$ and $\mathscr{C}'$ are any two point sets (or classes of point sets) that are equivalent under H, there exists an element h in H such that

$$\mathscr{C}' = h\mathscr{C}.$$

Then, for any g in G, we let

$$\mathscr{C}_1 = g\mathscr{C}, \qquad \mathscr{C}_1' = g\mathscr{C}',$$

and it follows that

$$\mathscr{C}_1' = gh\mathscr{C} = ghg^{-1}\mathscr{C}_1.$$

Thus $\mathscr{C}_1$ is transformed into $\mathscr{C}_1'$ by ghg^{-1}. In order that equivalence under H be an invariant relation under G, it is therefore necessary and sufficient that ghg^{-1} belong to H for all $h \in H$ and $g \in G$. We are thus led to the following definition.

DEFINITION 4.3. A subgroup H of a group G is said to be an *invariant*, or *normal, subgroup* if $ghg^{-1} \in H$ for all $h \in H$ and $g \in G$.

Thus we have the equivalent form of Theorem 4.3.

THEOREM 4.3′. *The group of direct projectivities of* $S_1(\mathsf{R})$ *is an invariant subgroup of the group of all projectivities.*

Since a collineation in $S_2(\mathsf{R})$ induces a projectivity from a given line to its transform, the following two theorems are immediate consequences of Theorems 4.2. and 4.3.

THEOREM 4.4. *Every collineation of* $S_2(\mathsf{R})$ *maps the sense classes of a line onto the sense classes of the transformed line.*

THEOREM 4.5. *Every collineation of* $S_2(\mathsf{R})$ *maps directly equivalent point sets on a line onto directly equivalent point sets on the transformed line.*

These last two theorems enable us to speak of the sense classes of a line in $S_2(\mathsf{R})$.

THEOREM 4.6. *Every direct projectivity of* $S_1(\mathsf{R})$ *onto itself leaves each sense class fixed; every opposite projectivity interchanges them.*

We leave the proof to the reader.

In the next two theorems we characterize sense classes, first geometrically, then analytically.

THEOREM 4.7. *Two points* C *and* D *lie on the same one of the two segments determined by* A *and* B *if and only if* $\{A\,B\,C\}$ *and* $\{A\,B\,D\}$ *coincide.*

Proof. We establish coordinates in $S_1(\mathsf{R})$ with A, B, C as reference frame. Let a representative of D in this system be $(d_1, d_2)^T$. Then the projectivity π that maps the triple $(A\,B\,C)$ onto $(A\,B\,D)$ is $x_1' = d_1 x_1$, $x_2' = d_2 x_2$. But by (III, Theorem 5.1 and Definition 5.2), C and D lie on the same one of the two segments determined by A and B if and only if $(A\,B, C\,D) = d_1/d_2 > 0$. This clearly is equivalent to the condition that π be direct.

THEOREM 4.8. $\{P\,Q\,R\} = \{P'\,Q'\,R'\}$ *if and only if*

$$\begin{aligned}\operatorname{sgn}(\det(\mathbf{P}'\quad\mathbf{Q}')\det(\mathbf{Q}'\quad\mathbf{R}')\det(\mathbf{R}'\quad\mathbf{P}'))\\ = \operatorname{sgn}(\det(\mathbf{P}'\quad\mathbf{Q}')\det(\mathbf{Q}'\quad\mathbf{R}')\det(\mathbf{R}'\quad\mathbf{P}')).\end{aligned}$$

Proof. Let a matrix of the projectivity mapping $(P\,Q\,R)$ onto $(P'\,Q'\,R')$ be $\mathbf{A}$. Then for suitably chosen representatives,

$$\mathbf{P}' = \mathbf{A}\mathbf{P}, \qquad \mathbf{Q}' = \mathbf{A}\mathbf{Q}, \qquad \mathbf{R}' = \mathbf{A}\mathbf{R},$$

so that the determinant of the chosen representatives of each two of the points multiplied by $\det \mathbf{A}$ is equal to the determinant of the transformed representatives. From this we can obtain the following equation, which is independent of the representatives chosen:

$$\begin{aligned}\operatorname{sgn}(\det(\mathbf{P}'\quad\mathbf{Q}')\det(\mathbf{Q}'\quad\mathbf{R}')\det(\mathbf{R}'\quad\mathbf{P}'))\\ = \operatorname{sgn}(\det(\mathbf{P}\quad\mathbf{Q})\det(\mathbf{Q}\quad\mathbf{R})\det(\mathbf{R}\quad\mathbf{P}))(\operatorname{sgn}\det\mathbf{A}).\end{aligned}$$

The theorem follows from this equation.

COROLLARY 4.1. *According as* $\{P\,Q\,R\}$ *is equal to* $\{A_1\,A_2\,D\}$ *or* $\{A_2\,A_1\,D\}$ *(where* A_1, A_2, D *are the reference elements of* $S_1(\mathsf{R})$*),* $\operatorname{sgn}(\det(\mathbf{P}\quad\mathbf{Q})\det(\mathbf{Q}\quad\mathbf{R})\det(\mathbf{R}\quad\mathbf{P}))$ *is equal to* $+1$ or -1.

DEFINITION 4.4. If S is the point set of $S_1(\mathsf{R})$, $\mathscr{S}_1$ a specified sense class, and G_3^+ the group of direct projectivities in $S_1(\mathsf{R})$, the geometry† $\Gamma(S, G_3^+)$,

† Strictly, we should write $\Gamma((S,\mathscr{S}_1), G_3^+)$.

or any isomorphic geometry, is called the *geometry of an oriented* $S_1(\mathsf{R})$; the point set S, together with the chosen sense class $\mathcal{S}_1$, with the structure imposed by G_3^+, constitute an *oriented* $S_1(\mathsf{R})$. We denote an oriented $S_1(\mathsf{R})$ by $\overrightarrow{S_1}$, and we call the chosen sense class the *positive* sense class of $\overrightarrow{S_1}$, and the other the *negative* sense class of $\overrightarrow{S_1}$.

Corresponding to the two sense classes $\mathcal{S}_1$ and $\mathcal{S}_2$, $S_1(\mathsf{R})$ *carries* two $\overrightarrow{S_1}$'s. Clearly in their inner structure these two $\overrightarrow{S_1}$'s are isomorphic. But in their relationship to each other, or to $S_1(\mathsf{R})$, or to a plane in which they may be embedded, they are different. Thus the positive sense class of one $\overrightarrow{S_1}$ is the negative sense class of the other; a direct projectivity in $S_1(\mathsf{R})$ leaves both $\overrightarrow{S_1}$'s fixed, while an opposite one interchanges them. In $S_2(\mathsf{R})$, the collineation $x_1' = x_1$, $x_2' = 2x_2$, $x_3' = -3x_3$ leaves fixed each of the sense classes of one of the three fixed lines ($x_3 = 0$) and interchanges those of each of the other two.

We have thus formalized the process, familiar in the case of a Euclidean line, of orienting the projective line by affixing an arrow.

On $\overrightarrow{S_1}$ we call a coordinate system *positively oriented* if the sense class $\{A_1 A_2 D\}$ of its reference frame is the positive sense class† of $\overrightarrow{S_1}$. One usually chooses in $\overrightarrow{S_1}$ positively oriented coordinates, and by the corollary to Theorem 4.8, the positive sense class has the same analytical description in all such coordinate systems. Clearly equation (4.1) interpreted as a coordinate transformation represents a transformation between positively oriented coordinates if and only if $\det \mathbf{A} > 0$. Thus the equations of the direct group admit the two usual interpretations.

The above procedure cannot be generalized to $S_2(\mathsf{R})$, since here multiplication of the elements of $\mathbf{A}$ by -1 changes the sign of $\det \mathbf{A}$. Does there exist some other method of orienting the projective plane? The answer is in the negative, but a proof of this statement is beyond the scope of this book. Closely related to this question is the following: Given two projective transformations (either in S_1 or in S_2) can we always find a family of projective transformations that vary continuously from the first to the second? The reader might try to prove that, in S_1, the answer to this question is negative; in S_2 it is more difficult to prove that the answer is in the affirmative.

Theorem 4.7 guarantees that $\{A\,X\,B\} = \{A\,C\,B\}$ for all $X \in \text{seg } ACB$, and we can define directed segments in conformity with our intuitive ideas.

DEFINITION 4.5. In $S_1(\mathsf{R})$, the *directed segment*, with initial point A and *terminal* point B is the pair: a specified sense class $\mathcal{S}$ and the set of points X such that $(A\,X\,B) \in \mathcal{S}$.

† This choice is quite arbitrary. What is essential is that the positive sense class have the same description in terms of the reference frames.

If C is a point of the directed segment, $\mathscr{S} = \{A\,C\,B\}$, and we denote the directed segment by seg $\overrightarrow{ACB}$. Thus seg $\overrightarrow{ACB}$ and seg $\overrightarrow{BCA}$ are distinct even though they carry the same point set. Two directed segments, seg $\overrightarrow{ACB}$ and seg $\overrightarrow{PQR}$ are *oppositely* directed if $\{A\,C\,B\} \neq \{P\,Q\,R\}$ and identically directed if $\{A\,C\,B\} = \{P\,Q\,R\}$.

On $\overrightarrow{S_1}$ a segment is positively directed if its sense class is the positive sense class of $\overrightarrow{S_1}$. There exists just one positively directed segment with preassigned initial and terminal points.

EXERCISES

1. Prove Theorem 4.1.

2. Prove that the sense class $\{P\,Q\,R\}$ is unaltered by even permutations of the three points P, Q, R, and is altered by odd permutations.

3. Prove: If P, Q, R are three distinct points of $S_1(\mathsf{R})$, the locus of points X for which $\{P\,X\,R\} = \{P\,Q\,R\}$ is seg PQR.

***4.** Prove that $\{A_1\,Y\,Z\} = \{A_1\,A_2\,D\}$ if and only if $z_1/z_2 > y_1/y_2$, and that $\{A_1\,Y\,Z\} = \{A_2\,A_1\,D\}$ if and only if $y_1/y_2 > z_1/z_2$.

***5.** Prove: If σ is an elliptic involution in $S_1(\mathsf{R})$, and if P, Q are distinct points not conjugate in σ, $\{P\,Q\,\sigma P\} = \{P\,Q\,\sigma Q\}$.

6. Prove: If π is a projectivity of S_1 onto S_1', and if $\mathscr{S}_i$ and $\mathscr{S}_i' = \pi\mathscr{S}_i$ $(i = 1, 2)$ are the sense classes of S_1 and S_1', respectively, a projectivity of S_1 onto S_1' that maps $\mathscr{S}_1$ onto $\mathscr{S}_1'$ is the product $g\pi$, where g is a suitably selected direct projectivity in S_1'. What can you say about the projectivities that map $\mathscr{S}_1$ onto $\mathscr{S}_2'$?

7. Prove Theorem 4.3.

8. Prove Theorem 4.6.

9. Show that coordinates can be chosen in a given $S_1(\mathsf{R})$ so that a given projectivity from S_1 to S_1' can be represented by $\mathbf{Y} = \mathbf{X}$. Now reproduce the proof of Theorem 4.2 taking into account the simplification brought about by the choice $\mathbf{A} = \mathbf{I}$.

10. If $\mathscr{B}$ is the set of all pairs of points of $S_1(\mathsf{R})$ directly equivalent to a given pair, and $\mathscr{D}$ is the set of all pairs of points of $S_1(\mathsf{R})$, what is the relationship of $\mathscr{B}$ and $\mathscr{D}$?

#**11.** Characterize the classes consisting of all ordered quadruples of distinct points of $S_1(\mathsf{R})$ any two of which are directly equivalent.

***12.** Apply the definition of sense classes of $S_1(\mathsf{R})$ to a pencil of lines in $S_2(\mathsf{R})$, and state for pencils the analogue of Exercise 3.

13. State the duals of Theorems 4.4 and 4.5.

14. If $\mathscr{C}$ is a point set of $S_1(\mathsf{R})$, and $\mathscr{D}$ is the class of point sets directly equivalent to $\mathscr{C}$, show that the transform of $\mathscr{D}$ under a projectivity is the class of point sets directly equivalent to the transform of $\mathscr{C}$.

***15.** Let τ be a harmonic homology in $S_2(\mathsf{R})$ that leaves fixed a conic $\mathscr{C}$. Prove that τ leaves fixed or interchanges the sense classes of $\mathscr{C}$ according as the center of τ is an interior or exterior point of $\mathscr{C}$.

#16. When a projectivity π is represented on a conic it is determined uniquely by its axis and two points A and πA. Characterize direct and opposite projectivities in terms of relations determined by the conic, the axis, and the two points.

17. Prove that parabolic and elliptic projectivities are direct, that every opposite projectivity is hyperbolic, and that direct hyperbolic projectivities exist.

18. Prove that every direct hyperbolic projectivity is the product of two hyperbolic involutions, and every opposite one is the product of three.

19. Find all projectivities that map a given directed segment onto itself.

20. Prove that if n points $A_1, A_2, \ldots, A_n$ are in the projective order $\langle A_1 A_2 \ldots A_n \rangle$ (see (III, Definition 5.3)), the sense classes $\{A_1 A_i A_n\}$, for $i = 2, 3, \ldots, n-1$, coincide.

21. Prove that for the points of Exercise 20, $\{A_i A_j A_k\} = \{A_1 A_2 A_n\}$ if $i < j < k$.

5 The Oriented Affine Plane

Although $S_2(\mathsf{R})$ cannot be oriented, the real affine plane can be. Intuitively we can regard $S_2(\mathsf{R})$ as having a twist (something like a Möbius band) which renders the plane nonorientable and which can be removed when the plane is cut along a line. The structure of the oriented affine plane is part of the structure of the affine plane—an affine plane *carries* two oriented planes just as $S_1(\mathsf{R})$ carries two $\overrightarrow{S_1}(\mathsf{R})$'s—and we could define and develop the orientation structure from a purely affine point of view. However it is preferable for us to do it from the projective point of view because such a development will be adapted to other geometries in later sections.

To define the oriented affine plane $\overrightarrow{A_2}$, we modify Definition 1.6 by adjoining to the absolute line l a chosen sense class, $\mathscr{S}_1$. That is, we replace l by $\vec{l}$. The point set of $\overrightarrow{A_2}$ is that of A_2, and its group is isomorphic to the subgroup of G_8 that leaves l and $\mathscr{S}_1$ fixed.

To coordinatize $\overrightarrow{A_2}$, we usually choose projective coordinates in $S_2(\mathsf{R})$ so that l is the line $x_3 = 0$ (Figure 5.1) and

$$(5.1) \qquad \mathscr{S}_1 = \{A_2 A_1 D_3\}, \qquad \text{where } \mathbf{D}_3 = (1, 1, 0)^T.$$

THEOREM 5.1. *The group of* $\overrightarrow{A_2}$ *is represented by equations* (2.1), *where*

$$\text{det } \mathbf{A} = \begin{vmatrix} a_{11} & a_{12} \\ a_{21} & a_{22} \end{vmatrix} > 0. \tag{5.2}$$

Proof. An affine transformation (2.4) induces on l, the absolute line, a projectivity whose determinant is the left side of (5.2.). Hence (5.2) is a necessary and sufficient condition that both sense classes of the absolute line be left invariant.

We call the group of $\overrightarrow{A_2}$ the *direct affine group* and denote it by G_6^+, and we note that equations (2.3) to (2.5) with the further restrictions (5.1) and (5.2), represent an embedding of $\overrightarrow{A_2}$ in $S_2(\mathsf{R})$. Transformations of G_6 that do not satisfy (5.2) are called *opposite*. Clearly, $g \in G_6^+$ implies that $g_l \in G_3^+$.

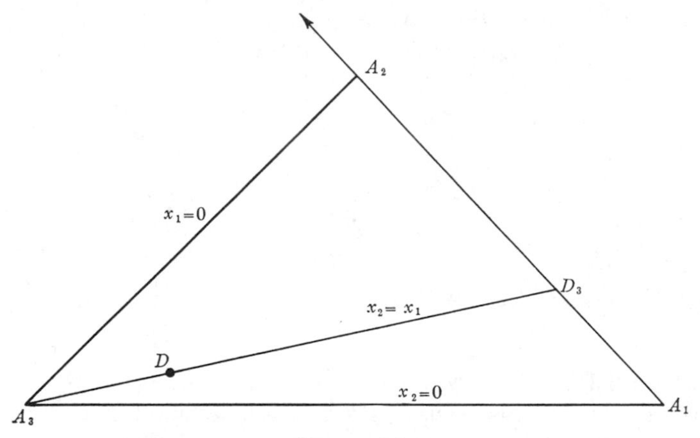

FIGURE 5.1

In our treatment of the affine plane in Section 2 we distinguished very sharply between the point set (and the transformation group) of A_2 and the images of these under an embedding in $S_2(\mathsf{R})$. But since any two oriented affine geometries are isomorphic, we can without loss of generality take the point set S of Definition (1.6) as representing the point set of the affine plane. We thus identify each point of the affine plane with its image in $S_2(\mathsf{R})$, under a particular embedding. It must be kept in mind, however, that a point of these identified point sets plays two roles simultaneously. In order to avoid the somewhat cumbersome notation that was used in Section 2, we shall generally denote by the same letter, a point in either of its roles, when the context makes it clear which one is meant. In the same way we can identify each affine transformation (whose domain of definition is the affine plane) with its image collineation under an embedding. Since the domain of definition of the image collineation is the entire projective plane, no confusion will arise if we speak of the image of an absolute point under an affine transformation.

In A_2, let (pqr) be any ordered triple of distinct concurrent lines, intersecting the absolute line in (PQR). Let $\{pqr\}$ denote the class of all triples of concurrent lines whose ordered triples of absolute points belong to the sense class $\{PQR\}$ of l. Clearly every ordered triple of distinct concurrent lines in A_2 belongs to one and just one of the two classes $\{pqr\}$ and $\{qpr\}$, and each of the two classes in turn is completely determined by any one of its constituent triples.

DEFINITION 5.1. In A_2, the classes $\{pqr\}$ and $\{qpr\}$ described above are called the *sense classes of pencils*.

THEOREM 5.2. *Every affine transformation maps sense classes of pencils onto sense classes of pencils.*

Proof. If two triples of lines belong to the same sense class of pencils in A_2, their ordered triples of absolute points belong to the same sense class of l, and by Theorem 4.4, the maps under $g \in G_6$, of the absolute triples also belong to the same sense class of l. But the maps under $g \in G_6$ of the absolute triples are the triples of absolute points on the maps of the original lines. Consequently the transformed triples of lines belong to the same sense class of pencils in A_2. A similar argument shows that if two triples of lines belong to different sense classes of pencils, so do their maps under $g \in G_6$.

Thus sense classes of pencils constitute part of the structure of A_2.

THEOREM 5.3. *The direct group of G_6^+ leaves invariant each of the two sense classes of pencils; opposite transformations of G_6 interchange them.*

We leave the proof to the reader.

DEFINITION 5.2. In $\overrightarrow{A_2}$, the *positive* sense class of pencils is the sense class determined by a triple (pqr) whose absolute points belong to $\mathscr{S}_1$, the positive sense class of l.

From (5.1) it follows that in any pencil the positive sense class is that determined by the lines of the pencil that are parallel to $x_2 = 0$ (the x-axis), $x_2 = x_1$ ($y = x$), and $x_1 = 0$ (the y-axis), respectively (see Figure 5.1).

THEOREM 5.4. *If (p_1, p_2), (q_1, q_2), (r_1, r_2) are projective coordinates of the lines p, q, r of a nonparallel pencil in $\overrightarrow{A_2}$, the sense class $\{pqr\}$ is the positive sense class if and only if* $\operatorname{sgn}(\det(\mathbf{p} \quad \mathbf{q}) \det(\mathbf{q} \quad \mathbf{r}) \det(\mathbf{r} \quad \mathbf{p})) = -1$.

We leave the proof to the reader (see Corollary 4.1).

Thus the orientation of l induces *simultaneously* an orientation in all nonparallel pencils. But this is not all. In A_2, an ordered triple of noncollinear points $(P\,Q\,R)$ determines the triple $(P^*\,Q^*\,R^*)$ of points P^*, Q^*, R^* in which the lines $Q \oplus R$, $R \oplus P$, and $P \oplus Q$, respectively, intersect the absolute line, and $(P^*\,Q^*\,R^*)$ in turn determines the sense class $\{P^*\,Q^*\,R^*\}$ on l. Let us for brevity refer to $(P^*\,Q^*\,R^*)$ as the triple *associated* with $(P\,Q\,R)$.

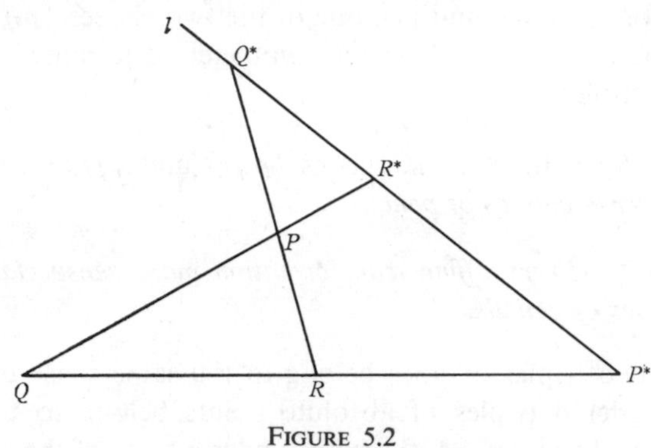

FIGURE 5.2

DEFINITION 5.3. *A sense class of A_2* is the class of all ordered triples of noncollinear points with associated triples that belong to the same sense class on l.

We see that there are just two sense classes of A_2; we shall denote them by $\mathscr{T}_1$ and $\mathscr{T}_2$. If $(P\,Q\,R)$ belongs to $\mathscr{T}_1$, we write $\mathscr{T}_1 = \{P\,Q\,R\}$, and it follows that $\mathscr{T}_2 = \{Q\,P\,R\}$.

THEOREM 5.5. *Every affine transformation maps the sense classes of A_2 onto themselves. The direct affine transformations leave each invariant, and the opposite transformations interchange them.*

Outline of Proof. Since the triple associated with a given triple transforms under G_6 into the triple associated with the transformed triple, the proof of the first statement is similar to the proof of Theorem 5.2. We leave the details to the reader.

From Theorem 5.1 it follows that for any transformations g, g^+ in G_6, G_6^+, respectively, the transformation gg^+g^{-1} belongs to G_6^+. Hence G_6^+ is an invariant subgroup of G_6. It can be seen that a sense class of A_2 consists of all triples of points equivalent under G_6^+ to a given triple, and the preservation of sense classes by G_6 itself is another illustration of the more general result that equivalence under an invariant subgroup is preserved by all transformations of the group.

DEFINITION 5.4. In $\overrightarrow{A_2}$ the ordered triple of noncollinear points P, Q, R shall be said to be *positively oriented*, or to have positive sense, if the associated triple $(P^* Q^* R^*)$ belongs to $\mathscr{S}_2$, the negative sense class of the absolute line.

The choice of the sense class of l in the definition just given is logically arbitrary, but we shall see in Exercise 1 below that the choice of $\mathscr{S}_2$ is necessary if in $\overrightarrow{A_2}$ a positively oriented triple of lines and a positively oriented triple of points are to be related in the familiar manner.

Let $\mathbf{P}, \mathbf{Q}, \mathbf{R}$ be matrix representations (2.3a) of the points P, Q, R. The following theorem is an immediate consequence of equation (2.12).

THEOREM 5.6. *The function* sgn det $(\mathbf{P} \quad \mathbf{Q} \quad \mathbf{R})$ *is an invariant under* G_6^+.

THEOREM 5.7. *In* $\overrightarrow{A_2}$, *the ordered triple of points, P, Q, R is positively oriented if and only if* sgn det $(\mathbf{P} \quad \mathbf{Q} \quad \mathbf{R}) = +1$.

Proof. Consider in A_2 the triple consisting of the three points $O{:}(0, 0)$; $A{:}(1, 0)$; and $B{:}(0, 1)$. The associated triple is O^*, A^*, B^* with projective representatives $(1, -1, 0)^T$, $(0, 1, 0)^T$, and $(1, 0, 0)^T$, respectively, and by the corollary to Theorem 4.8 and Definition 5.4, $(O\,A\,B)$ is positively oriented. Since sgn det $(\mathbf{O} \quad \mathbf{A} \quad \mathbf{B}) = +1$, by Theorem 5.6 $(P\,Q\,R)$ is positively oriented if and only if sgn det $(\mathbf{P} \quad \mathbf{Q} \quad \mathbf{R}) = +1$.

COROLLARY 5.1. $\{P\,Q\,R\} = \{P'\,Q'\,R'\}$ *if and only if*

$$\text{sgn det}\,(\mathbf{P} \quad \mathbf{Q} \quad \mathbf{R}) = \text{sgn det}\,(\mathbf{P}' \quad \mathbf{Q}' \quad \mathbf{R}').$$

Let us next consider the problem of orienting the lines of A_2. If P, Q are two points and R^* is the absolute point of their line, we denote by $\{P\,Q\}$ the set of all ordered pairs of points $(P'\,Q')$ such that P', Q' lie on $P \oplus Q$ and $(P'\,Q'\,R^*)$ belongs to the sense class $\{P\,Q\,R^*\}$ of the (image) line $P \oplus Q$. Although the set of triples $(P'\,Q'\,R^*)$ is a proper subset of one of the sense classes of the projective line, we can show, by methods similar to those used in the formulation of the concepts of the affine sense classes earlier in this section, that the classes $\{P\,Q\}$ are preserved by G_6. We are thus justified in calling them the *sense classes of a line* in A_2. A line in A_2 possesses two sense classes; if $\{P\,Q\}$ denotes one, the other is $\{Q\,P\}$.

DEFINITION 5.5. If P, Q are distinct points of A_2, $\overrightarrow{PQ}$ denotes the pair of elements: the line $P \oplus Q$ and the sense class $\{P\,Q\}$. This pair of elements is called a *directed line*.

THEOREM 5.8. *Under* G_6, *directed lines are mapped onto directed lines.*

We leave the proof to the reader.

So far we have followed the pattern established in developing orientation of pencils and of noncollinear triples of points. We might expect next to try to show that a transformation of G_6^+ that leaves a given line fixed, leaves its sense classes fixed. But this is not true, as can be seen from the following counterexample. The point reflection $x_1' = -x_1$, $x_2' = -x_2$ and the proper dilation $x_1' = 2x_1$, $x_2' = 2x_2$ both belong to G_6^+, both transform the line $x_2 = 0$ onto itself, but the first interchanges the sense classes of this line, while the second leaves them fixed. Thus the transformations of G_6^+ have no predictable effect on the sense classes of a line.

What has gone wrong? Should we seek some other definition of sense classes of an affine line? Surely we would want any definition to be such that there are just two sense classes, each determined by an ordered pair of points. Consider the ordered pair of points $(0, 0)$ and $(1, 1)$. The opposite transformation $x_1' = -x_1 + 2x_2$, $x_2' = x_2$ leaves this ordered pair fixed. Since every opposite transformation can be obtained as the product of a given opposite one and some direct transformation, there can be no kind of object determined by this pair of points which is invariant under G_6^+, but not under G_6. Our definition is not at fault; the situation is inherent in the structure of $\overrightarrow{A_2}$.

We can direct each line, but we cannot in $\overrightarrow{A_2}$ define a *positive sense* for all lines simultaneously as we did for pencils. Nevertheless the directed line $\overrightarrow{PQ}$—the line PQ with an arrow affixed—is as much a part of the structure of A_2 as the undirected line, and the concept of directed lines, both in A_2 and $\overrightarrow{A_2}$, leads to new relations from which we can develop new concepts.

THEOREM 5.9. *The points P and Q lie on the same side of the line $Y \oplus Z$ if and only if $\{P\,Y\,Z\} = \{Q\,Y\,Z\}$.*

We leave the proof to the reader (see the corollaries to Theorem 2.7 (page 286) and Theorem 5.7).

THEOREM 5.10. *If $P_1 P_2 P_3 P_4$ is a parallelogram, the sense classes in A_2, $\{P_1 P_2 P_3\}$, $\{P_2 P_3 P_4\}$, $\{P_3 P_4 P_1\}$, and $\{P_4 P_1 P_2\}$ all coincide.*

Proof. Since $P_1 \oplus P_4$ is parallel to $P_2 \oplus P_3$, P_1 and P_4 lie on the same side of $P_2 \oplus P_3$, and by Theorem 5.9, $\{P_1 P_2 P_3\} = \{P_4 P_2 P_3\} = \{P_2 P_3 P_4\}$. The remainder of the theorem is obtained by advancing the indices cyclically.

THEOREM 5.11. *Let A, B, C, D be four collinear points, and let P be a point not on their line; then $\{A\,B\} = \{C\,D\}$ if and only if $\{P\,A\,B\} = \{P\,C\,D\}$.*

Proof. If the triples $(P\,A\,B)$ and $(P\,C\,D)$ belong to the same sense class in A_2, their associated triples $(R\,B'\,A')$ and $(R\,D'\,C')$ belong to the same class of l (Figure 5.3). The triples $(A'\,B'\,R)$ and $(C'\,D'\,R)$ both belong to the other sense class of l, and $\{A'\,B'\,R\} = \{C'\,D'\,R\}$. The perspectivity with center at P from l to $A \oplus B$ transforms the sense class $\{A'\,B'\,R\} = \{C'\,D'\,R\}$

into the sense class $\{A\,B\,R\} = \{C\,D\,R\}$. Hence $\{AB\} = \{C\,D\}$. We leave the proof of the converse to the reader.

In $\overrightarrow{A_2}$, we call the set of points X for which $(X\,A\,B)$ is positively oriented, the positive side (or half-plane) of $\overrightarrow{AB}$.

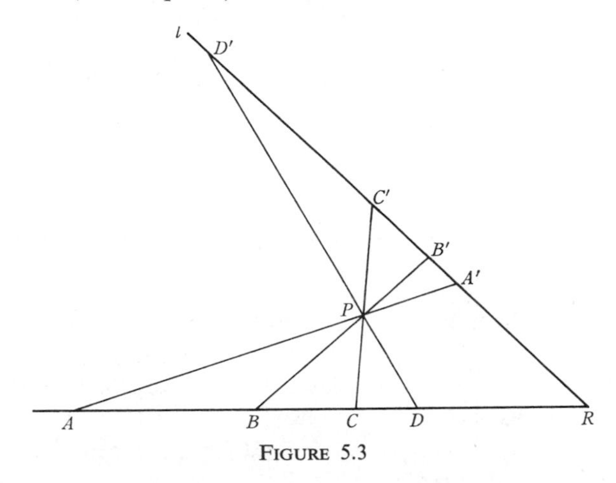

FIGURE 5.3

THEOREM 5.12. *If $(P\,Q\,R)$ is positively oriented, the interior of the triangle PQR is the intersection of the positive sides of $\overrightarrow{PQ}$, $\overrightarrow{QR}$ and $\overrightarrow{RP}$.*

Proof. If $(P\,Q\,R)$ is positively oriented, sgn det $(\mathbf{P}\quad\mathbf{Q}\quad\mathbf{R}) = +1$, and hence sgn det $(\mathbf{X}\quad\mathbf{Q}\quad\mathbf{R}) = +1$ for all points X on the positive side of $\overrightarrow{QR}$. If $\mathbf{X} = \lambda\mathbf{P} + \mu\mathbf{Q} + \nu\mathbf{R}$, det $(\mathbf{X}\quad\mathbf{Q}\quad\mathbf{R}) = \lambda$ det $(\mathbf{P}\quad\mathbf{Q}\quad\mathbf{R})$, and X lies on the positive side of $\overrightarrow{QR}$ if and only if $\lambda > 0$. A similar conclusion holds for each of the other sides, and therefore the inequalities $\lambda > 0$, $\mu > 0$, $\nu > 0$ represent the intersection of the positive sides of $\overrightarrow{PQ}$, $\overrightarrow{QR}$, and $\overrightarrow{RP}$. But by (2.16), these inequalities represent the interior of the triangle PQR.

Although no simultaneous orientation of all the lines of A_2 exists, we feel intuitively that we can direct all the lines of a parallel pencil "the same way." We shall show that it is possible to give mathematical substance to this concept. For this purpose we consider the group of translations

$$x_1' = x_1 + a_1, \qquad x_2' = x_2 + a_2, \qquad -\infty < a_i < \infty. \tag{5.3}$$

A line and its transform under a translation are necessarily parallel. If L and L' are given parallel lines, there are many translations that map L onto L', for we can specify the map of a given point of L. If $\mathscr{S}$ is a sense class on L, how does $g\mathscr{S}$ vary as g varies over all the translations such that $gL = L'$? We can show by the following geometric argument that $g\mathscr{S}$ is the same sense class on L' for all such g. Suppose $L \neq L'$; we select points

A, B on L so that $\{AB\} = \mathscr{S}$; let g_1, g_2 be any two translations that map L onto L'; let $A_i = g_i A$ and $B_i = g_i B$ $(i = 1, 2)$ (Figure 5.4). Then AA_1B_1B and AA_2B_2B are parallelograms, and by Theorem 5.10, $\{AA_1B_1\} = \{B_1BA\}$ and $\{AA_2B_2\} = \{B_2BA\}$. Since $L' \parallel L$, B_1 and B_2 lie on the same side

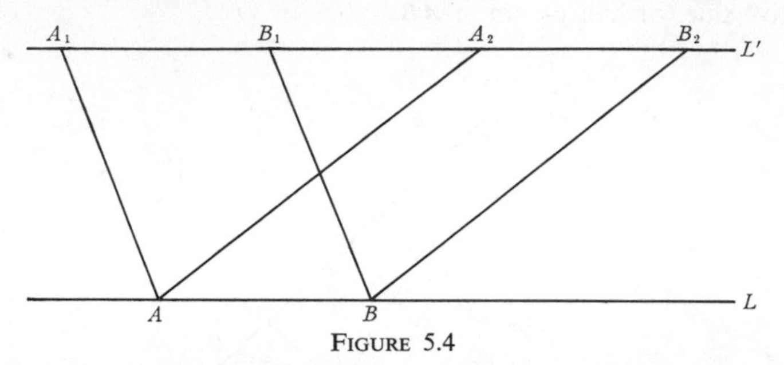

FIGURE 5.4

of $A \oplus B$, and by Theorem 5.9 the right members of these two equations are equal. Hence the left members are equal, and by Theorem 5.11, $\{A_1B_1\} = \{A_2B_2\}$. Since the translations g_1, g_2 are affine transformations, they map the sense class $\mathscr{S} = \{AB\}$ onto $\{A_1B_1\}$ and $\{A_2B_2\}$, respectively. Thus $g_1\mathscr{S} = \{A_1B_1\} = \{A_2B_2\} = g_2\mathscr{S}$, and $g\mathscr{S}$ is independent of the choice of g. We leave it to the reader to show that the conclusion is valid even if $L = L'$.

Thus if we start with two directed parallel lines $\vec{L}$ and $\vec{L'}$, either all the translations that map L onto L' map $\vec{L}$ onto $\vec{L'}$, or none of them do.

Let $\{\overrightarrow{AB}\}$ be the class of all directed lines that are equivalent, under the group of translations, to $\overrightarrow{AB}$. Then every directed line parallel to $A \oplus B$ belongs to one and just one of the two classes $\{\overrightarrow{AB}\}$ and $\{\overrightarrow{BA}\}$, and each class is determined by any one of its members. Are the classes of directed lines that we have described part of the structure of the affine plane, that is, are they preserved by all affine transformations?

THEOREM 5.13. *The class $\{\overrightarrow{AB}\}$ is mapped by any affine transformation onto the class $\{\overrightarrow{A'B'}\}$ determined by A', B', the maps of A, B, respectively.*

Proof. Let g be an arbitrary affine transformation, and let $gA = A'$, $gB = B'$. Since directed lines transform into directed lines, $g\overrightarrow{AB} = \overrightarrow{A'B'}$, Any directed line $\vec{L}$ of the class $\{\overrightarrow{AB}\}$ can be transformed into $\overrightarrow{AB}$ by some translation h. Its map under g, $g\vec{L}$, is transformed into $\overrightarrow{A'B'}$ by ghg^{-1}. But since ghg^{-1} is a translation (see Theorem 3.8), $g\vec{L}$ belongs to $\{\overrightarrow{A'B'}\}$. Hence the maps of all the directed lines of $\{\overrightarrow{AB}\}$ belong to $\{\overrightarrow{A'B'}\}$. By reversing the argument, we find that all the directed lines of $\{\overrightarrow{A'B'}\}$ are the maps of directed lines of $\{\overrightarrow{AB}\}$, and therefore $\{\overrightarrow{A'B'}\} = g\{\overrightarrow{AB}\}$.

The reader should compare this proof with the proof of Theorem 4.2. He will find that in both cases the substance of the argument depends on the fact that the subgroup in question is an invariant subgroup. If G is any group, and H is any invariant subgroup of G, essentially the same argument that appears in these two proofs can be used to show that a class of objects that are equivalent under H define a structural element with respect to G.

In the present case we must give a name to the new structural element, the class $\{\overrightarrow{AB}\}$, that we have discovered.

DEFINITION 5.6. The class $\{\overrightarrow{AB}\}$ of all directed lines that are equivalent to a given directed line $\overrightarrow{AB}$ under the group of translations is called a *direction.* Any two directed lines that belong to a given direction are *properly parallel.* Two directed lines that are parallel and not properly parallel are *improperly parallel,* and their directions are *opposite.*

Although there exists no intrinsic orientation of the lines of A_2, it is convenient to refer to the direction determined, in a given coordinate system, by the points $(0, 0)$, $(1, 0)$ as the positive direction, with respect to that coordinate system, of the pencil $x_2 = \text{const.}$ Similarly we refer to the direction determined by $(0, 0)$, $(0, 1)$ as the positive direction, with respect to the given coordinate system, of the pencil $x_1 = \text{const.}$

We can complete the definition of directed segments mentioned earlier (page 298). A *directed segment* (or ray) is the point set of a segment (or ray) together with one of the two sense classes. We can write seg $\overrightarrow{PQ}$ for the directed segment with end points P, Q and sense class $\{P\,Q\}$. Clearly a directed segment is determined uniquely by specification of its *initial* and *terminal* points. Segments and rays on a directed line are *directed positively* by choosing their sense class to be that of the directed line. Thus the positive ray on $\overrightarrow{PQ}$ with end point P is the directed ray whose point set is defined by $\{P\,X\} = \{P\,Q\}$. Parallel segments (or rays) can be properly or improperly parallel according as their directions coincide or are opposite.

Relative length is a measure of directed segments, and the reader can show that relative length is positive or negative according as the segments have the same or opposite directions. Analogously, relative area is a measure of oriented triangles, and is positive if and only if the two triangles have the same orientation.

EXERCISES

1. Prove: If in $\overrightarrow{A_2}$, $\{P\,Q\,R\}$ is the positive sense class of three points P, Q, R, and if $X \in \text{seg } QR$, the ordered triple of lines $P \oplus Q$, $P \oplus X$, $P \oplus R$ belong to the positive sense class of the pencil at P.

2. Let P, Q, Y, Z be four collinear points in A_2; show that $\overrightarrow{PQ} = \overrightarrow{YZ}$ if and only if the affine ratios $\lambda = PY/PQ$, $\mu = PZ/PQ$ satisfy $\mu - \lambda > 0$.

3. Prove that for all points $X \in \operatorname{seg} PQ$, $\{P\,X\} = \{X\,Q\} = \{P\,Q\}$. Derive the analogous property of the rays of $P \oplus Q$, stated in the text.

4. If P, Q, R are independent points, show that the sense class $\{P\,Q\,R\}$ is unaltered when Q is replaced by any point on the positive ray from P of $\overrightarrow{PQ}$.

5. Let R' be a point in the interior of triangle PQR. Prove that $\{P\,Q\,R\} = \{P\,Q\,R'\}$.

6. Prove:

(a) All points of a ray lie on the same side of a line through the end point of the ray and not containing the ray.

(b) Any two properly parallel rays lie on the same side of the line joining their end points.

7. Prove:

(a) In $\overrightarrow{A_2}$ the positive side of $\overrightarrow{AB}$ is the negative side of $\overrightarrow{BA}$.

(b) If two lines are properly parallel, one lies on the positive side of the other, which in turn lies on the negative side of the first.

(c) If $\overrightarrow{L_1}$ and $\overrightarrow{L_2}$ are properly parallel lines, and if $\overrightarrow{L_1}$ lies on the positive side of $\overrightarrow{L_2}$, then the positive side of $\overrightarrow{L_1}$ is contained in that of $\overrightarrow{L_2}$, and the negative side of $\overrightarrow{L_2}$ is contained in that of L_1.

8. Prove:

(a) A transformation g in G_6 that leaves a directed line fixed is direct or opposite according as it leaves fixed or interchanges the two sides of the line.

(b) A transformation g in G_6 that maps a directed line onto the oppositely directed line is direct or opposite according as it interchanges the two sides or leaves them fixed.

9. Prove Theorem 5.4.

10. Fill in the necessary details for the definition of sense classes of a line and prove Theorem 5.8.

\# **11.** Develop the theory of sense classes in a one-dimensional affine space by considering the affine group $x' = ax + b$ $(a \neq 0)$, and the normal subgroup defined by $a > 0$.

\# **12.** Discuss the theory of sense classes for the lines of a parallel pencil (a) from the projective point of view, and (b) from the point of view of one-dimensional affine geometry (see Exercise 11).

\# **13.** If A, B, P, Q are four points of a line in A_2, the relative length PQ/AB can be defined in terms of one-dimensional affine geometry. Do so, apply your conclusions to a pencil of parallel lines in A_2, and thereby given mathematical content to a statement such as one of three parallel lines is twice as far from the second as from the third (see Exercises 11 and 12).

14. Prove: If G is any group and H is an invariant subgroup of G, and if G' is a subgroup of G that contains H, then H is an invariant subgroup of G'.

15. Prove that every $g \in G_6^+$ is the product of two line reflections and a dilation.

6 One-dimensional Hyperbolic Space

In this section and the next, we shall develop the geometry of one-dimensional hyperbolic and elliptic spaces as subgeometries of one-dimensional projective geometry. When we define these geometries, we shall see that each is the geometry of a line of the corresponding two-dimensional space defined in Section 1. These geometries have many points of similarity; for example, in each a given involution on $S_1(\mathsf{R})$ plays a decisive role in determining the group of the geometry. Again, in these two geometries, we shall develop a metric, that is, an invariant determined by two points that plays the role of distance between them. The metric of the elliptic line is necessary to our later development of Euclidean geometry. In spite of their many similarities, the two geometries are sufficiently different to warrant separate treatment.

DEFINITION 6.1. Let S be an open segment of the one-dimensional projective space $S_1(\mathsf{R})$, and let $G(S)$ be the subgroup of $G_3(\mathsf{R})$ that leaves S invariant. We denote by $\Gamma(H_1, G(H_1))$ a geometry isomorphic to $\Gamma(S, G)$; such a geometry is called (real) one-dimensional *hyperbolic geometry*. The point set H_1 of $\Gamma(H_1, G(H_1))$ is called a *hyperbolic line* (one-dimensional space), and its group $G(H_1)$ the one-dimensional *hyperbolic group*.

The involution on $S_1(\mathsf{R})$ that has the end points of S as its fixed points is called the *absolute* involution and is denoted by σ. Clearly $\sigma \notin G(S)$, for it interchanges the two segments of $S_1(\mathsf{R})$.

We embed a given hyperbolic geometry, $\Gamma(H_1, G(H_1))$ in $S_1(\mathsf{R})$ in accordance with Definition 1.7. Since two hyperbolic geometries are isomorphic (see Exercise 1 below), the embedding in $S_1(\mathsf{R})$ can be interpreted as the identification of H_1 with S and of $G(H_1)$ with $G(S)$. Although we shall make this identification, we shall generally write H_1 and $G(H_1)$, reserving S and $G(S)$ for those occasions when we wish to emphasize elements of the projective structure. The reader should further note that although $g \in G(H_1)$ has H_1 as its natural domain, an element of $G_3(\mathsf{R})$ is determined uniquely by its restriction to S.

It is not absolutely necessary to introduce the involution σ in order to develop $\Gamma(H_1, G(H_1))$. However, if H_1 is considered as a line of the hyperbolic plane, the absolute involution exists as the involution induced on the (image) line in $S_2(\mathsf{R})$ by the polarity of the absolute conic. Moreover, as we develop the geometry of elliptic space in the next section, we shall be better able to appreciate the exact nature of the similarities and differences between the two geometries if we introduce the involution σ and keep in mind its relationship to H_1.

We recall that $G(\sigma)$, the group of σ, is the group that leaves σ invariant (see IV, 10). What is the relationship between $G(\sigma)$ and the hyperbolic group $G(H_1)$? A projectivity $\pi \in G(\sigma)$ either leaves fixed each of the two segments determined by the fixed points of σ or it interchanges them. In either case $\pi g \pi^{-1} \in G(H_1)$ for all $g \in G(H_1)$, $\pi \in G(\sigma)$. Hence $G(H_1)$ is an invariant subgroup of $G(\sigma)$.

A *ray* (or *half-line*) in H_1 is a set whose projective image is a segment with one end point an end point of S and the other in S; a *segment* in H_1 has for its projective image a segment with both end points in S. Clearly a point of H_1 separates H_1 into two disjoint rays, and two points of H_1 determine two rays and a unique segment. We leave it to the reader to describe the separation properties. We denote rays and segments as we did in A_2 (see page 281).

On H_1, we define a sense class $\{A\,B\}$ as the set of all ordered pairs $(P\,Q)$ of H_1 such that, in $S_1(\mathsf{R})$, $(P\,Q\,\sigma P)$ belongs to $\{A\,B\,\sigma A\}$. By Theorem 4.7 $\{A\,B\,\sigma A\} = \{A\,B\,\sigma B\} \neq \{B\,A\,\sigma B\}$, so that every ordered pair of distinct points in H_1 belongs to one and just one of the two sense classes $\{A\,B\}$ and $\{B\,A\}$. If, in H_1, $(A\,B) \in \{P\,Q\}$, then in $S_1(\mathsf{R})$, $(A\,B\,\sigma A) \in \{P\,Q\,\sigma P\}$. We can show that $G(H_1)$ maps a sense class of H_1 onto a sense class as follows. Let $g \in G(H_1)$, $A' = gA$, $B' = gB$, $P' = gP$, $Q' = gQ$. We can let g act on the points of $S_1(\mathsf{R})$; then $g\sigma = \sigma g$, and by Theorem (4.2), $\{P\,Q\,\sigma P\}$ is mapped by g onto $\{P'\,Q'\,\sigma P'\}$. Hence the map of $(A\,B\,\sigma A)$, namely $(A'\,B'\,\sigma A')$, belongs to $\{P'\,Q'\,\sigma P'\}$, and, in terms of sense classes on the hyperbolic line, $(A'\,B')$ belongs to $\{P'\,Q'\}$. By reversing the argument we show that every pair belonging to $\{P'\,Q'\}$ is the transform of a pair belonging to $\{P\,Q\}$, and thus g transforms sense classes into sense classes, and the sense class determined by an ordered pair of points into the sense class determined by the transformed pair. We can regard the sense class $\{A\,B\,\sigma A\}$ of $S_1(\mathsf{R})$ as the (extended) image, under the embedding, of the sense class $\{A\,B\}$ of H_1.

We denote the subgroup of $G(S)$ consisting of direct projectivities, that is, $G(S) \cap G_3^+$, by $G^+(S)$, and the corresponding subgroup of $G(H_1)$ by $G^+(H_1)$. If $g \in G^+(S)$, $\{P\,Q\,\sigma P\} = \{gP\,g\,Q\;g\sigma P\} = \{gP\;gQ\,\sigma gP\}$; in H_1, $\{P\,Q\} = \{gP\;gQ\}$. Hence the direct group $G^+(H_1)$ acts as the identity on the two sense classes of H_1. We can show similarly that opposite hyperbolic transformations interchange them. In $S_1(\mathsf{R})$, $g \in G(S)$ interchanges the end points of S if and only if it interchanges the sense classes; hence the group $G^+(S)$ is the subgroup of $G(S)$ that leaves each of the end points of S fixed.

We can orient H_1 by specifying a sense class $\mathscr{S}_1$ either in H_1 or in $S_1(\mathsf{R})$. We denote an oriented H_1 by $\overrightarrow{H_1}$; the geometry of an oriented hyperbolic space of dimension one is, in our usual notation, $\Gamma(H_1, G^+(H_1))$.

To coordinatize H_1, we choose coordinates in $S_1(\mathsf{R})$ so that the end points of S are $(1, \pm 1)^T$, and so that $A_2:(0,1)^T$ is a point of S. We can describe this choice completely by saying that the absolute involution σ and its quadratic form Q have the representation

$$(6.1) \qquad \sigma: \quad x_1 x_1' - x_2 x_2' = 0, \qquad Q = x_1^2 - x_2^2,$$

and the points of S have coordinates that satisfy

$$(6.2) \qquad S: \quad -1 < x_1/x_2 < 1.$$

On the oriented $S_1(\mathsf{R})$, we can distinguish between the end points of S, since each of them is left fixed by $G^+(S)$. We label them R_1 and R_2 so that the triple $(R_1 A_2 R_2)$ belongs to $\mathscr{S}_1$, and we impose the further requirement on our coordinate system that R_1 have coordinates $(1, -1)^T$ and R_2, $(1,1)^T$, that is,

$$(6.3) \qquad \mathscr{S}_1 = \{R_1 A_2 R_2\} = \{A_1 A_2 D\} \quad \text{with} \quad R_1:(1,-1)^T; R_2:(1,1)^T.$$

Coordinates that satisfy (6.1) and (6.2) will serve as coordinates for H_1. We call such coordinates *special projective coordinates.* Since $x_2 \neq 0$, we shall frequently use the nonhomogeneous coordinate $x = x_1/x_2$. For $\overrightarrow{H_1}$, we adjoin the condition (6.3). We note that condition (6.3) identifies the positive orientation on $\overrightarrow{H_1}$ as the direction of increasing x.

On $\overrightarrow{H_1}$, special projective coordinates are determined uniquely by the choice of a point O as the origin ($x = 0$): for then, in $S_1(\mathsf{R})$, we let $A_2 = O$, $A_1 = \sigma O$, and we let the unit point D be that fixed point of σ for which $\{A_1 A_2 D\} = \mathscr{S}_1$. On H_1, two coordinatizations with a given origin exist; if x is one, $x' = -x$ is the other.

We could at this point obtain equations for the groups $G(S)$ and $G^+(S)$ and proceed to find invariants under them. However, we already know that cross ratio is an invariant under both groups (since they are subgroups of the group of projectivities), and we shall use this invariant to develop a metric in terms of which we shall later express the groups $G(S)$ and $G^+(S)$.

On $\overrightarrow{S_1}(\mathsf{R})$, the cross ratio $(R_2 R_1, YZ)$ is a function of the *two* points Y, Z which is invariant under $G^+(S)$. This function is not a satisfactory metric, since $(R_2 R_1, YY) = 1$, $(R_2 R_1, YZ)(R_2 R_1, ZY) = 1$, and $(R_2 R_1, XY)(R_2 R_1, YZ)(R_2 R_1, ZX) = 1$ (see II, 3, Exercise 4). But we have only to write these equations to recognize that $\log (R_2 R_1, YZ)$ possesses some of the properties commonly associated with distance. Fortunately, $(R_2 R_1, YZ) > 0$ for all points Y, Z of S (see III, Theorem 5.2), so that $\log (R_2 R_1, YZ)$ is a (single-valued real) function on $S \times S$. On the unoriented line, R_1 and R_2 may be interchanged by a transformation of $G(S)$; hence the cross ratio $(R_2 R_1, YZ)$ is not an invariant of the points Y and Z under G, but the absolute value of the logarithm of the cross ratio is such an invariant.

DEFINITION 6.2. The function $d_H(Y,Z)$ of two points given by†

$$d_H(Y,Z) = \tfrac{1}{2} \log (R_2 R_1, YZ) \tag{6.4}$$

is called the *directed hyperbolic distance* from Y to Z for the orientation (6.3). The absolute value of $d_H(Y,Z)$ is called the *distance* between Y and Z on either the oriented or unoriented line and will be denoted by $D_H(Y,Z)$.

THEOREM 6.1. *If A, B, C are three points of an oriented hyperbolic line, their directed distances satisfy the following conditions:*

$$\begin{aligned} &\text{(a) } d_H(A,B) = -d_H(B,A); \\ &\text{(b) } d_H(A,B) + d_H(B,C) + d_H(C,A) = 0. \end{aligned} \tag{6.5}$$

We leave the proof to the reader.

We shall find it convenient to use the following abbreviated notation:

$$d = d(x) = d_H(O,X), \qquad O:(0,1)^T, \quad X:(x,1)^T, \qquad -1 < x < 1. \tag{6.6}$$

THEOREM 6.2. *The nonhomogeneous special projective coordinate $x = x_1/x_2$ is the hyperbolic tangent of d, the directed distance from $(0,1)^T$ to $(x_1, x_2)^T$.*

Proof. From (6.6), $d = \dfrac{1}{2} \log \dfrac{1+x}{1-x}$ or $x = \dfrac{e^d - e^{-d}}{e^d + e^{-d}}$, that is,

$$x = \tanh d. \tag{6.7}$$

COROLLARY 6.1. *In nonhomogeneous special projective coordinates,* $d_H(Y,Z) = \tanh^{-1} z - \tanh^{-1} y$.

COROLLARY 6.2. $d_H(Y,Z) > 0$ *if and only if* $\{YZ\}$ *is the positive sense class.*

Equation (6.7) establishes a map between the real intervals $-1 < x < 1$ and $-\infty < d < \infty$. Since this map is one-to-one, we can represent the points of a hyperbolic line by means of a variable d which takes on all real values ($-\infty < d < \infty$) and which is, for a chosen orientation, the directed distance from a chosen origin. The map (6.7) is order-preserving, that is, $y < z$ if and only if $d(y) < d(z)$; consequently the sense class $\{YZ\}$ determined by two points Y and Z is the positive sense class if either the x coordinate or the d coordinate of Z is greater than the corresponding coordinate of Y.

† The reader might ask why the factor 1/2 in (6.4)? Actually we can use in place of 1/2 an arbitrary positive constant. Different constants would establish on the hyperbolic line different metrics. Any two of these metric geometries are isomorphic, and under the isomorphism, corresponding distances are in constant ratio. Examples of two-dimensional hyperbolic geometries with different metrics arise naturally in the study of surfaces in Euclidean three-dimensional spaces; two such surfaces are as alike and as different as two spheres of different radii. The choice of the factor 1/2 rather than 1 is primarily a matter of convenience.

In its inner structure, the hyperbolic line is isomorphic to the Euclidean line (with a chosen unit of length), but its relation to the hyperbolic plane is quite different from that of the Euclidean line to the Euclidean plane.

We are now ready to obtain representations of the hyperbolic group in terms of the distance coordinate d.

THEOREM 6.3. *The direct hyperbolic group can be represented, in terms of directed hyperbolic distance d given by* (6.6), *by*

$$d' = d + a, \qquad a \in \mathsf{R}; \tag{6.8}$$

the set of opposite transformations can be represented by

$$d' = -d + a, \qquad a \in \mathsf{R}. \tag{6.9}$$

Proof. By (II, Theorems 5.6 and 5.7) the group $G^+(H_1)$ can be represented by the conditions

$$(R_2 R_1, X X') = k, \qquad k > 0. \tag{6.10}$$

As k runs through all positive values, $\log k$ takes on all real values, and hence a representation of $G^+(H_1)$ equivalent to (6.10) is

$$d_H(X, X') = a, \qquad a \in \mathsf{R}. \tag{6.11}$$

By Theorem 6.1, $d_H(X, X') = d_H(O, X') - d_H(O, X)$, so that

$$d' = d_H(O, X') = d + a.$$

The projectivities of G that interchange R_1 and R_2 are expressible as the product of a transformation (6.8) and the transformation

$$x' = -x, \qquad \text{or} \qquad d' = -d.$$

Hence the opposite transformations of $G(H_1)$ are represented by (6.9).

The transformations (6.8) are called *translations*, and those represented by (6.9) are called *point reflections*. Under a point reflection,

$$d_H(A, X') = -d_H(A, X),$$

where A is the point $d = a/2$.

THEOREM 6.4. *A tranformation of the hyperbolic group is either a point reflection or the product of two point reflections.*

We leave the proof to the reader.

The hyperbolic distance between two points is an invariant under the hyperbolic group. The following theorem shows that the invariance of distance characterizes the group.

THEOREM 6.5. *A point transformation of H_1 onto itself that leaves distance invariant is necessarily a transformation of the hyperbolic group.*

Proof. Let us denote by ϕ the given transformation, and by ψ the translation that maps ϕO onto O, so that $\psi\phi$ preserves distance and leaves O fixed. Let $X' = \psi\phi X$; we then have that $|d(x')| = |d(x)|$, so that $d(x') = \eta d(x)$, where η is a function of x that takes on at most the two values ± 1. We shall show that η is independent of x (except for $x = 0$, where the value of η is immaterial). Suppose that there exist two points Y, Z distinct from O, such that

$$d(y') = d(y), \qquad d(z') = -d(z). \tag{6.12}$$

Then by Theorem 6.1,

$$d_H(Y', Z') = d_H(Y, Z) - 2d_H(O, Z),$$

and

$$d_H(Y', Z') = d_H(Z, Y) - 2d_H(O, Y).$$

Since we must have either that $d_H(Y', Z') = d_H(Y, Z)$ or $d_H(Y', Z') = d_H(Z, Y)$, it follows that at least one of the distances $d(z)$ or $d(y)$ vanishes. Therefore there cannot exist points Y and Z distinct from O satisfying (6.12), and η must be constant. Hence $\psi\phi \in G(H_1)$, and therefore $\phi \in G(H_1)$.

In any space in which a distance function exists, a transformation that preserves distance is called a *motion* or an *isometry*. Thus the group of isometries of H_1 is $G(H_1)$.

A topology in an arbitrary space is determined by defining convergence. In H_1, there appear to be two natural approaches. We could base a definition of convergence on convergence in $S_1(\mathsf{R})$, saying that a sequence of points Y_i in H_1 converges if and only if the sequence of projective images (under an embedding) converges to a point contained in the open segment S. The alternative procedure would be to define convergence in terms of the hyperbolic metric, requiring that the condition $Y_i \rightarrow Y$ be equivalent to the condition (on real numbers) $d_H(Y_i, Y) \rightarrow 0$. We leave it to the reader to show that in view of Definition 6.2, convergence in either sense implies convergence in the other. It is customary to say that the topology induced in H_1 by the projective topology and the topology in H_1 based on its metric are *equivalent*.

EXERCISES

1. Prove that any two hyperbolic geometries are isomorphic.

2. Prove that the two rays in H_1 with end point P are characterized by the conditions $\{P X\} = \mathscr{S}_1$ and $\{P X\} = \mathscr{S}_2$, where $\mathscr{S}_1$ and $\mathscr{S}_2$ are the two sense classes.

3. Characterize a segment in H_1 in terms of sense classes.

4. Prove Theorem 6.1.

5. Prove that $\{P Q\} = \{P R\}$ if and only if sgn $d_H(P, Q) =$ sgn $d_H(P, R)$.

6. Prove Theorem 6.4.

7. Prove that the two $\overrightarrow{H_1}$'s carried by a given H_1 are isomorphic, and that under the isomorphism corresponding directed distances are in the ratio -1.

8. Define cross ratio of four points of H_1, and express it in terms of directed distances.

9. A finite set of distinct points P_i $(i = 1, 2, \ldots, n)$ in H_1 are said to be in hyperbolic order $\langle P_1 P_2 \ldots P_n \rangle$ if the sequence of real numbers $d(P_1, P_i)$ is strictly monotonic. Prove that every finite set of points possesses two hyperbolic orders. How are they affected by $g \in G(H_1)$?

10. Relate hyperbolic order (see Exercise 9) and projective order (see III, Definition 5.3).

***11.** Let the quadratic form of the absolute involution σ be given by $\mathbf{X}^T\mathbf{B}\mathbf{X}$ where $\mathbf{B} = \mathbf{B}^T$ is of order 2, and $\mathbf{X} = (x_1, x_2)^T$. Prove that $\cosh^2 d_H(Y, Z) = (\mathbf{Y}^T\mathbf{B}\mathbf{Z})^2/(\mathbf{Y}^T\mathbf{B}\mathbf{Y})(\mathbf{Z}^T\mathbf{B}\mathbf{Z})$.

12. Show that sense classes in H_1 can be defined in strictly hyperbolic terms by considering the group $d' = \pm d + a$ and its invariant subgroup.

13. Write up careful definitions of the limit of a sequence of points in H_1 from the two points of view cited in the text, and establish their equivalence.

14. Is H_1 compact (see III, Theorem 7.1)?

7 One-dimensional Elliptic Space

From Definition 1.5 and (III, Theorem 6.6a) we see that, in the elliptic plane, the subgroup that leaves a line fixed induces on the line the subgroup of $G_3(R)$ that leaves invariant an elliptic involution on the line.

DEFINITION 7.1. Let σ be an elliptic involution on $S_1(\mathsf{R})$, and let $G(\sigma)$ be the group of σ. Let S be the point set of $S_1(\mathsf{R})$. We denote by $\Gamma(L_1, G(L_1))$ a geometry isomorphic to $\Gamma(S, G(\sigma))$; we call such a geometry a (real) *elliptic geometry* of dimension one. We call its point set, L_1, an elliptic one-dimensional space (or line), and its group $G(L_1)$ the one-dimensional elliptic group. The involution σ is the *absolute* involution.

Unlike the situation on H_1, σ is an element of $G(L_1)$. We shall leave it to the reader to show that any two elliptic geometries are isomorphic. We shall frequently identify the points of L_1 with those of S, and elements of $G(L_1)$ with those of $G(\sigma)$ as was done earlier in the affine plane and in the hyperbolic space H_1.

The elliptic line differs from the hyperbolic and affine lines in that its point set can be identified with the full point set of $S_1(\mathsf{R})$. Hence we can define sense classes of L_1 as the classes of triples of points whose images constitute a sense class in $S_1(\mathsf{R})$. Nevertheless on L_1, as on both the hyperbolic line and affine line, a sense class is determined by two points: Let us denote by $\{PQ\}$ the sense class $\{PQ\sigma P\}$ for $P, Q \in L_1$, $Q \neq \sigma P$. By (V, 4, Exercise 5), $\{PQ\sigma P\} = \{PQ\sigma Q\}$ so that $\{PQ\sigma P\}$ and $\{QP\sigma Q\}$ are the two sense classes of L_1. Hence if Y, Z are distinct nonconjugate points of L_1, we have either that $\{YZ\} = \{PQ\}$, or $\{YZ\} \neq \{PQ\}$ and $\{YZ\} = \{QP\}$. Since σ commutes with every $g \in G(L_1)$, g maps the class $\{PQ\}$ onto the class $\{gP\, gQ\}$. Thus $\{PQ\}$ and $\{QP\}$ are structural elements of elliptic geometry. If we embed L_1 in $S_1(\mathsf{R})$, we naturally define the image of $\{PQ\}$ to be the sense class in $S_1(\mathsf{R})$ determined by the image points. When we identify the points and transformations of elliptic space with their projective images under the embedding, we identify the elliptic sense class $\{PQ\} = \{PQ\sigma P\}$ with its image, the projective sense class $\{PQ\sigma P\}$.

We denote by $G^+(L_1)$ the subgroup of $G(L_1)$ whose elements g satisfy $\{PQ\} = \{gP\, gQ\}$. Then the projective image of g is a direct projectivity, and conversely every direct projectivity belonging to $G(\sigma)$ is the projective image of some g in $G^+(L_1)$.

We denote by $\overrightarrow{L_1}$ the pair: the point set L_1 and a specified sense class $\mathscr{S}_1$ of L_1. Then $\Gamma(\overrightarrow{L_1}, G^+(L_1))$ is called *oriented* one-dimensional elliptic geometry, and $\overrightarrow{L_1}$ an *oriented* or *directed* elliptic space.

To coordinatize L_1, we choose coordinates in $S_1(\mathsf{R})$ so that the absolute involution σ and its quadratic form Q are given by

$$\text{(7.1)} \qquad \sigma\colon\ x_1 x_1' + x_2 x_2' = 0, \qquad Q = x_1^2 + x_2^2.$$

On $\overrightarrow{L_1}$, we require further that the ordered reference elements of the coordinate system $(A_2 A_1 D)$ belong to the given sense class $\mathscr{S}_1$ of $\overrightarrow{L_1}$, so that

$$\text{(7.2)} \qquad \mathscr{S}_1 = \{A_2 A_1 D\} = \{A_1 D\}.$$

We call these coordinates *special projective coordinates*. As on $\overrightarrow{H_1}$, special projective coordinates on $\overline{L}_1$ are determined uniquely by assigning to any chosen point of L_1 the role of A_1. Then we select $A_2 = \sigma A_1$; to fix D, we recall that σ and the involution that leaves both A_1 and A_2 fixed possess a unique common pair (see II, 6, Exercise 10). If either one of the points of this pair is selected as $(1, 1)$, the other is $(1, -1)$, and (7.1) holds. Since the pair lie on different segments joining $A_1 A_2$, they determine with A_1, A_2 different sense classes, and hence the choice of the unit point is determined uniquely by (7.2).

We cannot define distance on the elliptic line in quite the same way that we did for the hyperbolic line, since in L_1 the absolute involution has no fixed points. But we can embed $S_1(\mathsf{R})$ in a complex space $S_1(\mathsf{C})$ by allowing the coordinates to range over all complex values. In $S_1(\mathsf{C})$, σ possesses two fixed points R_1, R_2; can we, following the procedure suggested by our earlier treatment, obtain a real function of real points Y, Z by equation (6.4)? Not quite, but in terms of special projective coordinates

$$(7.3)\quad (R_2 R_1, YZ) = \left(\frac{z_2 + iz_1}{z_2 - iz_1}\,\frac{y_2 - iy_1}{y_2 + iy_1}\right)^{\pm 1} \quad \text{for } R_1:(1, \mp i)^T, R_2:(1, \pm i)^T.$$

Hence $(R_2 R_1, YZ)$ is a complex number of absolute value one, and its logarithm, multiplied by i is real. But $\log u$, for u complex, is infinitely many-valued, two determinations differing by an integral multiple of $2\pi i$. Hence there exists a *unique* real function of real points Y, Z, satisfying

$$(7.4)\qquad D_L(Y,Z) = (i/2)\log(R_2 R_1, YZ), \qquad 0 \leqq D_L(Y,Z) \leqq \pi/2.$$

DEFINITION 7.2. The function $D_L(Y,Z)$ defined by (7.4) is called the *elliptic distance* between Y and Z.†

We shall show later (Theorem 7.8) that elliptic distance can be defined without resort to $S_1(\mathrm{C})$.

Clearly $D_L(Y,Z) = D_L(Z,Y)$; $D_L(Y,Z) = 0$ if and only if $Y = Z$; and $D_L(Y,Z) = \pi/2$ if and only if $Z = \sigma Y$. As Z traces either of the two segments determined by Y and σY, D_L increases from 0 to $\pi/2$.

Matrix representatives of $g \in G(L_1)$ in terms of special projective coordinates are obtained from earlier results (see IV, (10.3) and (10.4) with $\gamma = -1$). They are

$$(7.5)\qquad \mathbf{A} = \begin{pmatrix} a & -b \\ b & a \end{pmatrix}, \qquad \mathbf{A}^* = \begin{pmatrix} a & -b \\ -b & -a \end{pmatrix},$$

where $\mathbf{A}$ represents the pencil of direct projectivities, and $\mathbf{A}^*$ the pencil of opposite involutions. As projectivities in $S_1(\mathrm{C})$, the direct group leaves both R_1 and R_2 fixed, whereas the involutions interchange them.

Consequently on $\overrightarrow{L_1}$, the directed line, we can dispose of the ambiguous signs in (7.3); we define

$$(7.6)\quad d_L(Y,Z) = (i/2)\log(R_2 R_1, YZ), \qquad 0 \leqq d_L(Y,Z) < \pi, \quad \text{for } R_1:(1,-i)^T, R_2:(1,i)^T.$$

As before, $d_L(Y,Z)$ is a real single-valued function of the points Y and Z.

DEFINITION 7.3. On $\overrightarrow{L_1}$, with the orientation (7.2), the function $d_L(Y,Z)$ defined by (7.6) is called the *directed elliptic distance* from Y to Z.

Clearly the conditions $d_L(Y,Z) = 0$, $D_L(Y,Z) = 0$ and $Y = Z$ are equivalent, and the conditions $d_L(Y,Z) = \pi/2$, $D_L(Y,Z) = \pi/2$, and $Z = \sigma Y$ are equivalent.

† As earlier, the choice of the factor 1/2 in (7.4) is arbitrary. See footnote to Definition 6.2.

As in Section 6, we adopt the abbreviated notation

$$d = d(X) = d_L(A_1, X). \tag{7.7}$$

THEOREM 7.1. *The homogeneous class* $[x_1, x_2]^T$ *of special projective coordinates is equal to* $[\cos d, \sin d]^T$, *where* d *is the directed distance from* A_1 *to* X.

Proof. From (6.7) and (6.8) we have that

$$d = \frac{i}{2} \log \frac{x_1 - ix_2}{x_1 + ix_2}, \quad \text{or} \quad ix_1(e^{id} - e^{-id}) + x_2(e^{id} + e^{-id}) = 0,$$

that is,

$$[x_1, x_2] = [\cos d, \sin d]. \tag{7.8}$$

THEOREM 7.2. *The triple* $(P\,Q\,R)$ *belongs to the positive sense class* $\mathscr{S}_1$ *if and only if* $d_L(P, R) > d_L(P, Q)$.

Proof. We can choose coordinates with $A_1 = P$. By (V, 4, Exercise 4), if $\{A_1\,Q\,R\} = \mathscr{S}_1$, $q_1/q_2 > r_1/r_2$, and from (7.8) $\cot d(Q) > \cot d(R)$, so that $d(R) > d(Q)$. Since $d(Q) = d_L(A_1, Q) = d_L(P, Q)$ and $d(R) = d_L(P, R)$, we have $d_L(P, R) > d_L(P, Q)$. We complete the proof by reversing the argument.

THEOREM 7.3. *If* P, Q, R *are three distinct points of* $\overrightarrow{L_1}$, *their directed distances satisfy the following conditions*:

$$d_L(P, Q) + d_L(Q, P) = \pi, \tag{7.9a}$$

$$d_L(P, Q) + d_L(Q, R) + d_L(R, P) = \begin{cases} \pi & \text{for} \quad \{P\,Q\,R\} = \mathscr{S}_1, \\ 2\pi & \text{for} \quad \{P\,Q\,R\} \neq \mathscr{S}_1. \end{cases} \tag{7.9b}$$

Proof. As in the proof of Theorem 6.1, the sum of the directed distances must be equal to some determination of $(i/2) \log 1 = n\pi$ $(n = 0, \pm 1, \ldots)$. From Definition 7.3 the left side of (7.9a) is positive and less than 2π, and hence must be π. Similarly the left side of (7.9b) is positive and less than 3π and hence must be π or 2π. To see whether both of these values are possible, we note that if $\{P\,Q\,R\} = \mathscr{S}_1 = \{Q\,R\,P\}$, from Theorem 7.2, $d_L(Q, R) < d_L(Q, P)$, and from (7.9a), $d_L(Q, R) < \pi - d_L(P, Q)$, so that $d_L(P, Q) + d_L(Q, R) < \pi$; thus the left side of (7.9b) is less than 2π, and the value 2π is inadmissible in this case. On the other hand, if $\{P\,Q\,R\} \neq \mathscr{S}_1$, $\{P\,R\,Q\} = \mathscr{S}_1$, so that $d_L(P, R) + d_L(R, Q) + d_L(Q, P) = \pi$; by using (7.9a), we obtain the second conclusion in (7.9b).

COROLLARY 7.1. *For three points* P, Q, R,

$$d_L(P, Q) + d_L(Q, R) = d_L(P, R) + n\pi,$$

where $n = 0$ *or* 1 *according as* $\{P\,Q\,R\}$ *is or is not* $\mathscr{S}_1$.

By choosing A_1 to be P in this corollary, we have

$$\begin{aligned}\cos d_L(Q, R) &= \cos(d(R) - d(Q) + n\pi) \\ &= \pm(\cos d(R) \cos d(Q) + \sin d(R) \sin d(Q)) \\ &= \lambda(r_1 q_1 + r_2 q_2), \qquad \lambda \in \mathsf{R}, \lambda \neq 0.\end{aligned}$$

A similar computation for $\sin d_L(Q, R)$ shows that

$$[\cos d_L(Q, R), \sin d_L(Q, R)] = [q_1 r_1 + q_2 r_2, q_1 r_2 - q_2 r_1]. \tag{7.10}$$

The reader can verify that equation (7.10) between homogeneous classes holds also if any two (or more) of the three points coincide. From (7.10) we obtain values for $\cos d_L(Q, R)$, $\sin d_L(Q, R)$ by choosing a representative of the right side of (7.10) for which the sum of the squares of the two elements of the representation is 1 and for which the second element of the representation is nonnegative. Or if $R \neq \sigma Q$,

$$\tan d_L(Q, R) = \frac{q_1 r_2 - q_2 r_1}{q_1 r_1 + q_2 r_2}. \tag{7.11}$$

Equation (7.10) and the following lemma enable us to describe the relation between distance and directed distance on $\overrightarrow{L_1}$.

LEMMA 7.1. *The sense class* $\{Q\,R\}$ *is the positive sense class of* $\overrightarrow{L_1}$ *if and only if*

$$\operatorname{sgn}(r_2 q_1 - r_1 q_2)(r_1 q_1 + r_2 q_2) = +1.$$

Proof. We note that σQ is the point $(q_2, -q_1)^T$ and the result follows from equation (7.2) and the corollary to Theorem 4.8.

THEOREM 7.4. *Let* P, Q *be distinct nonconjugate points of* $\overrightarrow{L_1}$; *then* $d_L(P, Q) = D_L(P, Q)$ *if* $\{P\,Q\}$ *is the positive sense class of* $\overrightarrow{L_1}$, *and* $d_L(P, Q) = \pi - D_L(P, Q)$ *if* $\{P\,Q\}$ *is the negative sense class of* $\overrightarrow{L_1}$.

We leave the proof to the reader.

We have already obtained matrices (equations (7.5)) for the transformations of the elliptic group in terms of special projective coordinates. We now express these transformations in terms of the directed distance d.

THEOREM 7.5. *The direct group can be represented, in terms of directed elliptic distance* d *given by* (7.7), *by*

$$d' = d + \alpha \pmod{\pi}; \tag{7.12}$$

the set of opposite transformations can be represented by

$$d' = -d - \alpha \pmod{\pi}. \tag{7.13}$$

Proof. In the matrices **A** and **A*** of (7.5), we can choose for the homogeneous pair $[a, b]$ the representative $(\cos\alpha, \sin\alpha)$ for $0 \leqq \alpha < \pi$. Thus $G(L_1)$, expressed in terms of special projective coordinates, has the matrix representations

$$(7.14) \qquad \mathbf{A} = \begin{pmatrix} \cos\alpha & -\sin\alpha \\ \sin\alpha & \cos\alpha \end{pmatrix}, \qquad \mathbf{A}^* = \begin{pmatrix} \cos\alpha & -\sin\alpha \\ -\sin\alpha & -\cos\alpha \end{pmatrix}.$$

We obtain (7.12) and (7.13) from (7.8) and (7.14).

As on the hyperbolic line, we call the transformations of the direct group *translations*, and the opposite transformations *point reflections*. We note that a point reflection has two *centers*, the fixed points of the reflection.

For completeness we state the following theorems. Their proofs, which can be carried out along lines similar to the proofs of the analogous Theorems 6.4 and 6.5, are left to the reader.

THEOREM 7.6. *A transformation of the elliptic group is either a point reflection or the product of two point reflections.*

THEOREM 7.7. *An isometry of the elliptic line onto itself is necessarily a transformation of the elliptic group.*

The elliptic line, like the projective line and unlike the hyperbolic line, is closed and compact. Because of the closure, addition of distances, given by (7.9a, b), is a more complicated relation than the corresponding relation on the hyperbolic line. Because of (7.9a) we say that the length of an elliptic line is π.

The directed distance $d = d_L(A_1, X)$ can serve as a metric coordinate on $\overrightarrow{L_1}$; by means of it we map the points of L_1 onto the real interval $0 \leqq d < \pi$. This mapping is one-to-one, but it is not continuous: considering, for example, the sequence of points P_n $(n = 1, 2, 3, \ldots)$ for which $d(P_n) = (n-1)\pi/n$, we see that $\lim_{n\to\infty} d(P_n) = \pi$, while $d(\lim_{n\to\infty} P_n) = 0$ since $\lim_{n\to\infty} P_n = A_1$. Similarly the description of order or sense, either in terms of (x_1, x_2) or of d, is more complicated than is the case on the affine or the hyperbolic line. The sense class determined by the two points Y, Z for which $d(Y) < d(Z)$ may be either the positive or the negative sense class of $\overrightarrow{L_1}$. We might look for some other coordinatization of the elliptic line that would not have these disadvantages; but the search would be futile. The above disadvantages of the metric coordinate are inherent in the structure of the elliptic line; special projective coordinates (7.8) and the normalized representative $(\cos d, \sin d)^T$ are the best we can do.

The method we followed for the development of the elliptic metric was suggested by the analogous procedure in H_1. It has however the inelegance of presenting fundamental concepts of real elliptic geometry as if its logical structure required the existence of complex entities. This is not the case; we could have defined elliptic distance without going beyond the real field. To do so we would use the following theorem.

THEOREM 7.8. *In* $S_1(\mathsf{R})$ *let* Q *be the nonsingular quadratic form* $[\mathbf{X}^T\mathbf{B}\mathbf{X}]$, *and* $G(Q)$ *its group* (*see* IV, 10). *Then the function*

$$f(Y,Z) = \frac{(\mathbf{Y}^T\mathbf{B}\mathbf{Z})^2}{(\mathbf{Y}^T\mathbf{B}\mathbf{Y})(\mathbf{Z}^T\mathbf{B}\mathbf{Z})} \tag{7.15}$$

is invariant under $G(Q)$.

Proof. If $g:\mathbf{X}' = \mathbf{A}\mathbf{X}$ belongs to $G(Q)$, we have that $\mathbf{B} = \rho\mathbf{A}^T\mathbf{B}\mathbf{A}$ (see IV, (10.2)). It follows immediately that $f(gY, gZ) = f(Y,Z)$.

If Q is definite, its involution σ is elliptic. We leave it to the reader to show that then $f(Y,Z)$ satisfies the inequality $0 \leqq f(Y,Z) \leqq 1$. We could define $D_L(Y,Z)$ by the conditions

$$\cos^2 D_L(Y,Z) = f(Y,Z), \qquad 0 \leqq D_L(Y,Z) \leqq \pi/2. \tag{7.16}$$

With such a development, we would use Theorem 7.4 to define directed distance.

Elliptic geometry is very closely related to the Euclidean geometry of pencils and bundles of lines. For the reader who has already developed Euclidean geometry on a logically sound basis we can summarize the results of this section in the theorem that we state below. For the reader who has not studied the foundations of Euclidean geometry, the results of this section will be used in the next section where we define Euclidean geometry in projective terms.

THEOREM 7.9. *Elliptic geometry of dimension one is isomorphic to the Euclidean geometry of a pencil of lines. Elliptic distance between two points is equal to the Euclidean angle between the image lines in the pencil, and orientation of the elliptic line corresponds to a choice of positive sense in the pencil. The absolute involution corresponds to the involution of orthogonal lines, elliptic translations to Euclidean rotations, and elliptic reflections to reflections in lines of the pencil.*

In Figure 7.1., we represent L_1 by the points, in E_2, of the circle of radius 1/2; A_1, A_2, D are the reference elements corresponding to the lines $y = 0$, $x = 0$, $x - y = 0$ of the pencil. The orientation given by (7.2) corresponds to the counterclockwise sense of rotation in E_2. The directed elliptic distance $d(P)$ is equal to the angle d from the x-axis to the corresponding line of the pencil. On the circle, d is actually the directed arc length from A_1 to P.

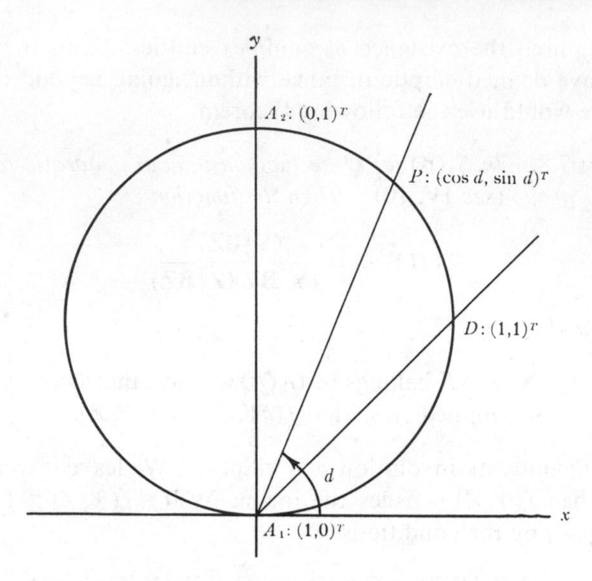

FIGURE 7.1

EXERCISES

1. Prove that any two one-dimensional elliptic geometries are isomorphic.

2. Prove the statement in the text that every g in $G_3^+ \cap G(\sigma)$ is the projective image of a direct elliptic transformation.

3. Prove Theorem 7.4.

4. Prove that in L_1 two points have two midpoints.

5. Prove that the two segments in L_1 with end points P, Q are characterized by the respective conditions

$$\text{(a) } 0 < d_L(P, X) < d_L(P, Q), \qquad \text{(b) } d_L(P, Q) < d_L(P, X) < \pi.$$

6. Define cross ratio of four points of L_1, and express it in terms of elliptic distance.

7. Prove Theorem 7.6.

8. Prove Theorem 7.7.

9. Let P_i $(i = 1, 2, \ldots, n)$ be a finite set of points in $\overrightarrow{L_1}$ in elliptic (that is, projective) order $\langle P_1 P_2 \ldots P_n \rangle$ (see III, Definition 5.3). Prove that the sum of directed distances

$$d_L(P_1, P_2) + d_L(P_2, P_3) + \ldots + d_L(P_{n-1}, P_n) + d_L(P_n, P_1)$$

is equal to π or $(n-1)\pi$ according as $\{P_1 P_2 P_3\}$ is or is not the positive sense class.

***10.** Prove the assertion in the text that (7.16) could be used to define directed elliptic distance.

11. Prove that two oriented elliptic spaces of dimension one are isomorphic, and determine the relation between corresponding directed distances.

8 The Euclidean Similarity and Metric Planes

In this and the next section we shall study the relationship of Euclidean geometry to projective geometry. Historically, Euclidean geometry is both a similarity geometry and a metric geometry. We shall distinguish between these two aspects of the Euclidean plane, devoting most of this section to the former. We begin with the following definition.

DEFINITION 8.1. Let S be the set of points of $S_2(\mathsf{R})$ not on a given line l, let σ be a given elliptic involution on l, and let G be the group of collineations that leave σ invariant. The geometry $\Gamma(S, G)$, or any geometry isomorphic to $\Gamma(S, G)$, is called *Euclidean similarity geometry* (of dimension two) or, for brevity, similarity geometry. The point set of such a geometry is called the *similarity plane*, and the group the *similarity group*. We shall denote a similarity geometry by $\Gamma(K_2, G_4)$.

If l is oriented and $\mathscr{S}_1$ is its positive sense class, we denote the subgroup of G that leaves $\mathscr{S}_1$ invariant by G^+, and our definition of an oriented similarity plane, $\Gamma(\overrightarrow{K_2}, G_4^+)$, parallels our earlier definitions of oriented spaces.

We call the involution σ the *absolute involution*, and the line l of $S_2(\mathsf{R})$ the *absolute line* (or the ideal line, or the line at infinity) of the embedding of K_2 in $S_2(\mathsf{R})$.

It can be shown that any two similarity geometries are isomorphic, and therefore we can identify the points of K_2 with their images in $S_2(\mathsf{R})$ under a given embedding, and the transformations of G_4 with the image collineations in G_8, as we have done in analogous situations earlier.

To coordinatize K_2 we choose a reference frame $A_1 A_2 A_3 D$ in $S_2(\mathsf{R})$, where A_3 is any point of S, A_1 is any point of l, and $A_2 = \sigma A_1$. We choose D on $A_3 \oplus D_3$, $D \neq A_3, D_3$, where D_3 is one of the two points satisfying $(A_1 A_2, D_3 \sigma D_3) = -1$ (σD_3 is the other, by II, 6, Exercise 10). Then D_3 and σD_3 have coordinates $[1, 1, 0]^T$ and $[1, -1, 0]^T$ respectively, l is given by $x_3 = 0$, and σ by $x_1 x_1' + x_2 x_2' = 0$. If l is oriented, we require further that the sense class of its reference elements, $\{A_1 D_3 A_2\}$ be $\mathscr{S}_1$, the positive sense class on l.

Thus we can represent the points of K_2 by nonhomogeneous coordinates (x_1, x_2), and the point of $S_2(\mathsf{R})$ that corresponds to (x_1, x_2) under the embedding by $\mathbf{X} = (x_1, x_2, 1)^T$. The special nonhomogeneous projective coordinates that we have introduced in the similarity plane are called (rectangular) *Cartesian coordinates.*

Sets that are equivalent under the similarity group are called *similar*; similar sets that are equivalent under the direct group are *directly* similar, and otherwise they are *oppositely* (or *inversely*) similar.

Similarity geometry occupies a middle position between two-dimensional elliptic and hyperbolic geometries: let us consider the pencil of quadratic forms, in line coordinates,

$$Q = u_1^2 + u_2^2 - \gamma u_3^2 .$$

For any positive value of γ, Q determines a hyperbolic polarity which, by Definition 1.4, can be taken as the absolute polarity of hyperbolic geometry. For negative γ, Q determines an elliptic geometry (see Definition 1.5). If $\gamma = 0$, the conic $Q = 0$ is a singular line conic, of rank 2, consisting of just one real line, $x_3 = 0$. Although the polarity of Q in this instance is singular, it induces on the line $x_3 = 0$ a nonsingular involution (use the dual of (IV, Corollary 6.2)), and this involution coincides with σ. Furthermore we could show that the collineations of $S_2(\mathsf{R})$ that leave σ invariant coincide with the collineations that leave invariant the singular line form $[u_1^2 + u_2^2]$ (see Exercise 2 below).

From equation (7.14) and Section 2 we obtain the following representation of G_4, in terms of Cartesian coordinates,

$$\mathbf{X}' = \begin{pmatrix} a\cos\alpha & -a\sin\alpha & e \\ \varepsilon a\sin\alpha & \varepsilon a\cos\alpha & f \\ 0 & 0 & 1 \end{pmatrix} \mathbf{X}, \tag{8.1a}$$

where $\varepsilon = \pm 1$, $a \neq 0$, $0 \leqq \alpha < \pi$. We can take $a > 0$, since otherwise we replace α by $\alpha - \pi$. Hence G_4 can be represented by (8.1a) where

$$\varepsilon = \pm 1, \qquad a > 0, \qquad -\pi < \alpha \leqq \pi, \qquad -\infty < e, f < \infty. \tag{8.1b}$$

Clearly the similarities for which $\varepsilon = +1$ constitute the direct group, while those for which $\varepsilon = -1$ are opposite.

Similarity geometry is a subgeometry of affine geometry; consequently affine invariants are similarity invariants. Thus lines and directed lines, properly and improperly parallel lines, central and noncentral conics, segments, half-lines and half-planes are examples of strictly affine concepts, all of which are part of the structure of K_2. Beyond all this, we note that in $S_2(\mathsf{R})$ the group G establishes on l an elliptic structure, and we define *angle between lines* in K_2 as the elliptic distance between the absolute points of the image lines in $S_2(\mathsf{R})$. The orientation of the similarity plane is simply the orientation of the affine plane, and since the latter is induced by the orientation of l, we can define the directed angle from one line to a second as the directed elliptic distance from the absolute point on the first line to the absolute point of the second. Furthermore, K_2 carries two isomorphic oriented similarity planes.

As in the affine plane, there exists no intrinsic orientation of the lines of the plane, but directed lines are mapped onto directed lines, and for an ordered pair of directed lines in $\overrightarrow{K_2}$ we can define a further invariant, an angle that takes into account their orientation. If two directed lines are properly parallel (see Definition 5.6), we define the angle from one to the other to be zero; if they are improperly parallel, we define the angle to be π. If they intersect, we let X be the point of intersection, Y and Z points on the positive ray from X on the first and second lines respectively. We can denote the given directed lines by $\overrightarrow{XY}$ and $\overrightarrow{XZ}$; we recall (see V, 5, Exercise 4) that the sense class $\{X\,Y'Z'\}$ in A_2 is the same for all $Y' \in r(X, Y)$ and $Z' \in r(X, Z)$, so that the sense class $\{X\,Y\,Z\}$ is determined by the given ordered pair of directed lines. According as $\{X\,Y\,Z\}$ is, or is not, the positive sense class on the oriented plane, we define the *angle from* $\overrightarrow{XY}$ *to* $\overrightarrow{XZ}$ to be the directed angle, or the directed angle decreased by π, from the unoriented line $X \oplus Y$ to the unoriented line $X \oplus Z$.

Thus the range of the angle from one directed line (or directed half-line) to another is the half-closed interval $(-\pi, \pi]$.†

Coordinates of the absolute points Y^*, Z^* of $\overrightarrow{XY}$ and $\overrightarrow{XZ}$ are $\mathbf{Y}^* = (y_1 - x_1, y_2 - x_2, 0)^T$ and $\mathbf{Z}^* = (z_1 - x_1, z_2 - x_2, 0)^T$, respectively. We refer to Lemma 7.1, we note that $y_1^* z_2^* - y_2^* z_1^* = \det\,(\mathbf{X}\quad \mathbf{Y}\quad \mathbf{Z})$, and we recall that the cosine of the elliptic distance $d_L(Y^*, Z^*)$ is positive if and only if $\{Y^* Z^*\}$ is the positive sense class. Hence the angle θ from $\overrightarrow{XY}$ to $\overrightarrow{XZ}$ satisfies the following conditions

$$
\begin{aligned}
&\operatorname{sgn}\sin\theta = \operatorname{sgn}\det\,(\mathbf{X}\quad \mathbf{Y}\quad \mathbf{Z}), \\
&\operatorname{sgn}\cos\theta = \operatorname{sgn}\,(\overline{y_1 - x_1}\;\overline{z_1 - x_1} + \overline{y_2 - x_2}\;\overline{z_2 - x_2}).
\end{aligned} \tag{8.2}
$$

It follows that the proportionality factor in (7.10) must be positive, and therefore θ is given by

$$
\begin{aligned}
\rho\cos\theta &= (y_1 - x_1)(z_1 - x_1) + (y_2 - x_2)(z_2 - x_2), \\
\rho\sin\theta &= (y_1 - x_1)(z_2 - x_2) - (y_2 - x_2)(z_1 - x_1),
\end{aligned} \tag{8.3}
$$

$$
\rho = \sqrt{(y_1 - x_1)^2 + (y_2 - x_2)^2}\sqrt{(z_1 - x_1)^2 + (z_2 - x_2)^2}, \quad -\pi < \theta \leqq \pi.
$$

† That is, the interval $-\pi < \theta \leqq \pi$.

If we let X be the origin, so that $\mathbf{X} = (0, 0, 1)^T$, and if $\mathbf{Y} = (1, 0, 1)^T$, (8.3) reduces to the usual formula for the directed angle from the positive x_1-axis to the directed line $\overrightarrow{OZ}$,

$$(8.4) \qquad z_1 = \rho \cos \theta, \qquad z_2 = \rho \sin \theta, \qquad \rho = \sqrt{z_1^2 + z_2^2}.$$

We have thus identified our measurement of angles with the usual intuitive measurement of angle used in elementary analytic geometry.

Notation. We shall usually denote the directed angle from a line p to a line q by $\theta(p,q)$, and the directed angle from $\vec{p}$ to $\vec{q}$ by $\theta(\vec{p},\vec{q})$.

THEOREM 8.1. *If* $g \in G_4^+$,

$$\theta(gp, gq) = \theta(p, q), \qquad \theta(g\vec{p}, g\vec{q}) = \theta(\vec{p}, \vec{q});$$

if g is opposite,

$$\theta(gp, gq) = \pi - \theta(p, q), \qquad \theta(g\vec{p}, g\vec{q}) = -\theta(\vec{p}, \vec{q}).$$

Proof. The first equation of each pair is a consequence of the elliptic structure of the absolute line (see (7.9a)), and the second is obtained from the first by recalling that G_4^+ leaves fixed the two sense classes of K_2, whereas an opposite similarity interchanges them.

DEFINITION 8.2. If $P_1 P_2 P_3$ is a triangle, and if $\{P_1 P_2 P_3\}$ is the positive sense class, the *interior angles* of the triangle are defined to be $\theta(\overrightarrow{P_i P_j}, \overrightarrow{P_i P_k})$, where i, j, k is a cyclic permutation of $1, 2, 3$.

THEOREM 8.2. *The sum of the interior angles of a triangle is* π.

Proof. Letting the associated triple (see page 314) be $(P_1^* P_2^* P_3^*)$, we note that the angle at P_i is the directed elliptic distance $d_L(P_k^*, P_j^*)$. Since $\{P_1^* P_2^* P_3^*\}$ is the negative sense class on l, $\{P_3^* P_2^* P_1^*\}$ is the positive one, and the sum is π by Theorem 7.3.

We have seen that a one-to-one map of A_2 onto itself which maps lines onto lines belongs to G_6, so that a collineation need not preserve the structure of K_2. We would expect that collineations in K_2 which preserve angle would belong to G_4. It turns out however that a weaker hypothesis is sufficient for the conclusion.

THEOREM 8.3. *A one-to-one map of the similarity plane onto itself which preserves collinearity and orthogonality is a similarity transformation.*

Proof. Let $\mathscr{E}$ be an embedding of K_2 in $S_2(\mathsf{R})$. The hypothesis that the map, say γ, is one-to-one implies that two lines l_1, l_2 are parallel if and only if $\gamma l_1, \gamma l_2$ are parallel. Consequently we can define (see III, Theorem 10.3) a map γ^* from $S_2(\mathsf{R})$ onto itself which coincides with $\mathscr{E}\gamma$ on $S_2(\mathsf{R}) - l(\mathscr{E})$, which preserves collinearity, and which is one-to-one. Hence γ^* is a collineation (see III, Theorem 8.6). From the hypothesis that λ preserves orthogonality, we conclude that γ^* preserves the elliptic involution on $l(\mathscr{E})$ (see IV, Theorem 10.2), and therefore that γ belongs to the similarity group.

We turn next to a discussion of the similarity group. In $S_2(\mathsf{R})$, a harmonic homology with center on the absolute line l leaves σ invariant if and only if its center and the absolute point on its axis are conjugate in σ. Hence, in K_2, a line reflection is determined by its axis, the invariant pencil of the reflection being the pencil orthogonal to the axis.

THEOREM 8.4. *A direct similarity is the product of a proper dilation with chosen center and two line reflections. An opposite similarity is the product of a proper dilation and three line reflections.*†

Proof. Clearly the group of dilations is a subgroup of G_4. If $g \in G_4^+$, we choose a dilation h so that $\det h = \det g$. Then $\det h^{-1}g = 1$. If $h^{-1}g$ is a translation or point reflection, we can apply Theorem 3.5 using line reflections that belong to G_4. If $h^{-1}g$ were a shear, its restriction to l would be parabolic. But $G(\sigma)$ contains no parabolic projectivities. Can we apply Theorem 3.7 to $h^{-1}g$ in the remaining cases, imposing the further condition that in the factorization only line reflections in G_4 are admissible? Yes, for we can write $(h^{-1}g)_l = \tau\tau'$,‡ where τ is defined as the involution with fixed points F (as described in the earlier proof) and $F' = \sigma F$. Then $\tau \in G(\sigma)$, and since $(h^{-1}g)_l \in G(\sigma)$ so is τ'; the rest of the proof follows the pattern of that of Theorem 3.7.

If g is opposite and r an arbitrary line reflection, rg (and gr) is direct and the second part of the theorem follows from the first.

THEOREM 8.5. *A direct similarity which leaves two points fixed is the identity; an opposite one is the reflection in the join of the two points.*

Proof. Let $g \in G_4$, $gP = P$, $gQ = Q$. Then in $S_2(\mathsf{R})$, g leaves fixed the absolute point F on $P \oplus Q$, so that $gX = X$ for all $X \in P \oplus Q$. If g_l is the identity, g is the identity. Otherwise g_l must be a hyperbolic involution (see Theorem 7.5) and σF its other fixed point. Hence in $S_2(\mathsf{R})$, g is a harmonic homology with center σF and axis $P \oplus Q$.

THEOREM 8.6. *Let A, B and P, Q be two pairs of distinct points; there exists just one direct similarity (and just one opposite one) which maps A, B onto P, Q respectively.*

† The dilation may, in either case, be the identity; the product of three line reflections may reduce to a single line reflection.

‡ We replace σ, σ' used in the proof of Theorem 3.7 by τ, τ' since we are here using σ for the absolute involution.

Proof. If two like ones, g_1 and g_2, existed, the product $g_2^{-1}g_1$ would be direct and, by the preceding theorem $g_2^{-1}g_1 = I$, so that $g_1 = g_2$. To show that at least one of each kind exists, we let t be the translation determined by $tA = P$ (Figure 8.1), and let $tB = Q'$. There exists a reflection r such that

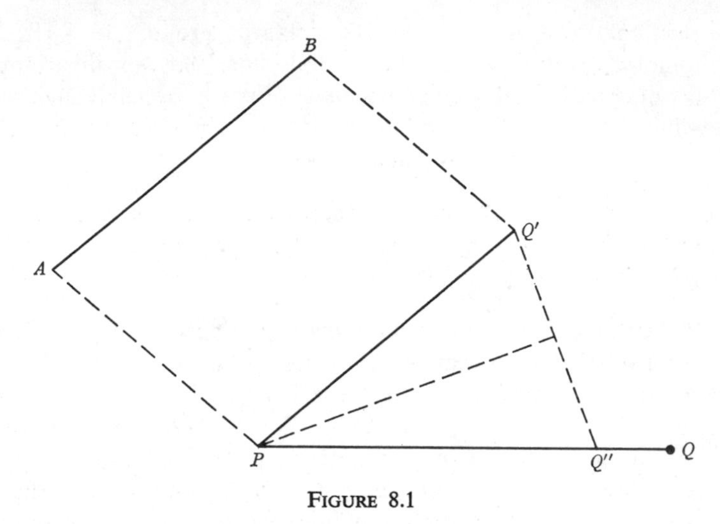

FIGURE 8.1

$r(P \oplus Q') = P \oplus Q$. Let $rQ' = Q''$, and let h be the dilation $hP = P$, $hQ'' = Q$. Then hrt is an opposite similarity which maps A, B onto P, Q. If we now reflect in $P \oplus Q$ we obtain the desired direct similarity.

THEOREM 8.7. *A direct similarity, not a translation, possesses one fixed point.*

Proof. The set of fixed points and lines of collineations in $S_2(\mathsf{R})$ is a self-dual set (see III, 11). Since the absolute line l is fixed, and g_l is not parabolic, the conclusion follows from our earlier classification of collineations in $S_2(\mathsf{R})$.

DEFINITION 8.3. We call the fixed point the *center* of the similarity.

If C, the center of a direct similarity g, is taken as the origin of the coordinate system, (8.1) becomes

$$\begin{aligned} x_1' &= a(x_1 \cos\alpha - x_2 \sin\alpha), \\ x_2' &= a(x_1 \sin\alpha + x_2 \cos\alpha), \end{aligned} \qquad 0 < a, \quad -\pi < \alpha \leqq \pi. \tag{8.5}$$

The numbers $a = \sqrt{\det g}$ and α in these equations will be seen to have geometrical significance; actually they are real-valued functions with domain G_4^+, for if g is a translation we define $a(g) = 1$, $\alpha(g) = 0$.

We call a the *magnification ratio*, and α the *angle*, of g.

THEOREM 8.8. *If $g \in G_4^+$ is not a translation, if C is its center, and α its angle,*

$$\theta(\overrightarrow{CX}, \overrightarrow{CgX}) = \alpha, \qquad \textit{for } X \in K_2, \quad X \neq C.$$

This is easily proved by using (8.3) and (8.5); an alternative proof could use the definition of directed angle and (7.12).

COROLLARY 8.1. *A direct similarity with center is determined uniquely by its center, its angle, and its magnification ratio.*

We shall return to a consideration of the magnification ratio on page 344.

DEFINITION 8.4. The product of two line reflections with intersecting axes is a *rotation.*

THEOREM 8.9. *Let r_p and r_q be reflections with axes the intersecting lines p, q, and let $\theta(p,q) = \omega$. Then the angle of the rotation $g = r_q r_p$ is 2ω (within an additive multiple of 2π).*

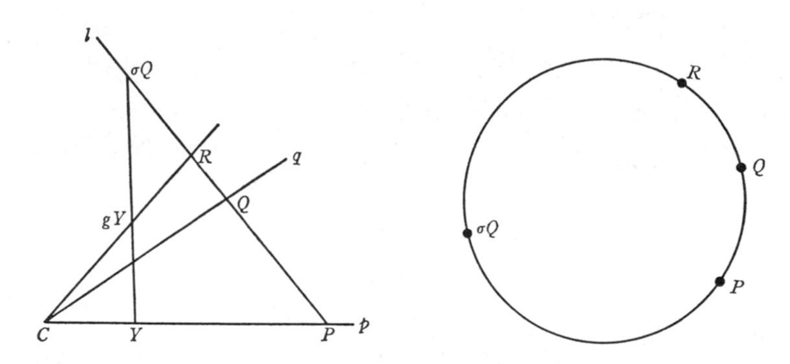

FIGURE 8.2

Proof. Let $C = p \cap q$, and select Y, not C, on p (Figure 8.2). Then $gY = r_q Y$, and the angle of g is $\theta(\overrightarrow{CY}, \overrightarrow{CgY})$. Let $P, Q, R, \sigma Q$ be the absolute points on $p, q, C \oplus gY$, $Y \oplus gY$ respectively. Then, in $S_2(\mathsf{R})$, $\sigma Q \notin \text{seg } PQR$ (see III, 6, Exercise 8), and therefore on l, $\{P\,Q\,R\} \neq \{P\,\sigma Q\,R\}$.

We note that on l, R is the (elliptic) reflection of P in Q (or σQ). If $\omega < \pi/2$, $\{P\,Q\,R\}$ is the positive sense class, and by Theorem 7.3, the directed elliptic distances satisfy $d_L(P,R) = d_L(P,Q) + d_L(Q,R) = 2\omega$. Then in $\overrightarrow{K_2}$, $\{C\,Y\,gY\}$ is the positive sense class, and $\theta(\overrightarrow{CY}, \overrightarrow{CgY}) = 2\omega$.

On the other hand, if $\omega > \pi/2$, $\pi - \omega < \pi/2$; we can carry through the above argument by interchanging positive and negative sense classes. We obtain that the oppositely directed distance from P to R is $2\pi - 2\omega$, so that, for the given orientation, $d(P, R) = \pi - (2\pi - 2\omega) = 2\omega - \pi$. Now the sense class $\{C\,Y\,gY\}$ in $\overrightarrow{K_2}$ is the negative sense class, and, by definition,

$$\theta\{\overrightarrow{CY}, \overrightarrow{CgY}\} = 2\omega - 2\pi.$$

THEOREM 8.10. *The product of a finite number of line reflections with dependent axes is a translation, a rotation, or a line reflection.*

We leave to the reader the proof of this theorem and of its corollary.

COROLLARY 8.2. *If r_1, r_2, r_3 are line reflections with concurrent or parallel axes, their product is a line reflection, and there exist line reflections r_4, r_5 such that*

$$r_1 r_2 = r_3 r_4 = r_5 r_3.$$

Of special interest are the conics in K_2 whose projective images induce on the absolute line involutions which coincide with the absolute involution. We call any such conic a *circle*.

THEOREM 8.11. *In K_2 there exists a unique circle with given center and containing a given point distinct from the center.*

We shall prove instead the following projective generalization.

THEOREM 8.12. *Let l be a line in $S_2(\mathsf{F})$, σ an involution on l, and C, P two points not on l. There exists a unique conic $\mathscr{C}$ satisfying the following conditions:*

(i) *$P \in \mathscr{C}$;*
(ii) *C and l are pole and polar in $\mathscr{C}$;*
(iii) *the involution of conjugate points on l, with respect to $\mathscr{C}$, coincides with σ.*

Proof. Let $Q = (C \oplus P) \cap l$, and let P' be defined by $(PP', CQ) = -1$ (Figure 8.3). If $\mathscr{C}$ exists, $P' \in \mathscr{C}$. Let $X \in l$, $Y = (P \oplus X) \cap (P' \oplus \sigma X)$, and $M = (P \oplus X) \cap (C \oplus \sigma X)$; $(PP', CQ) = -1$ implies that $(P\,Y, M\,X) = -1$ since the two quadruples are perspective from σX. Since the polar of X is $C \oplus \sigma X$, $(P\,Y, M\,X) = -1$ implies that $Y \in \mathscr{C}$. Hence $\mathscr{C}$ must contain the set of intersections $(P \oplus X) \cap (P' \oplus \sigma X)$ of corresponding lines, $P \oplus X$ and $P' \oplus \sigma X$, of two projective pencils; this set is the set of points of a unique conic. Since $PYP'Y'$, where $Y' = (X \oplus P') \cap (P \oplus \sigma X)$, is an inscribed quadrangle with $CX\sigma X$ its diagonal triangle, this conic satisfies the given conditions.

When a space is acted on by a group of transformations, the group is said to be *transitive* on the space if for any points Y, Z, there exists an element g of the group satisfying $gY = Z$. Thus $G_8(\mathsf{F})$ is transitive on $S_2(\mathsf{F})$, and G_6 is transitive on A_2. If a group is not transitive, the set of points gY for a fixed Y and all g in the group is a proper subset of the space. This subset is called the *orbit* of Y, under the group. Clearly, the orbit of a point Y is the orbit of every point in the orbit of Y (see Exercise 15 below).

In K_2, the set of rotations with given center is a nontransitive Abelian subgroup of G_4.

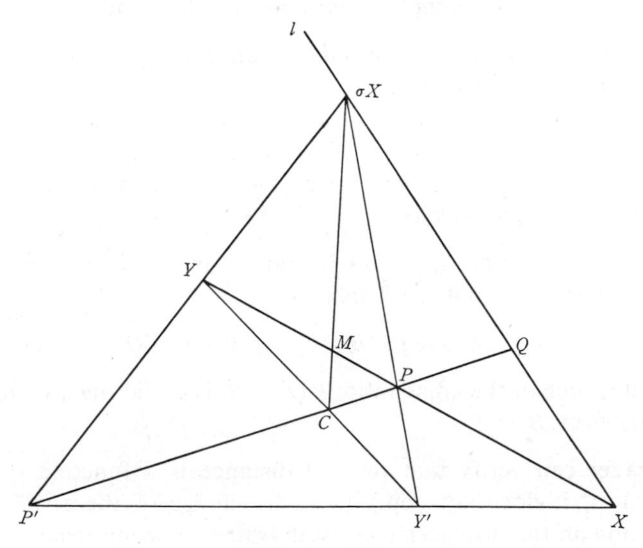

FIGURE 8.3

THEOREM 8.13. *The orbit of a point P under the group of rotations with center a given point C, not P, is the circle through P with center C.*

Proof. Let g be a rotation with center C; we can write $g = r_2 r_1$, where r_1 is the reflection with axis $C \oplus P$. In $S_2(\mathsf{R})$, let X be the center and $C \oplus \sigma X$ the axis of the harmonic homology corresponding to r_2. Referring to Figure 8.3, we can conclude that in K_2, $r_1 P = P, gP = r_2 P = Y$. By the argument used in the proof of Theorem 8.12, Y is on the conic, and therefore in K_2 the orbit of P is contained in the circle.

Conversely, if Y is on the circle, we let X be the absolute point on $Y \oplus P$. Referring to Figure 8.3, we note that in $S_2(\mathsf{R})$ the harmonic homology with axis $C \oplus \sigma X$ and center X maps P onto Y. Hence in K_2, we can find a rotation with center C which maps P onto Y, and every point of the circle belongs to the orbit of P.

The similarities which can be expressed as products of line reflections comprise a subgroup of G_4 which we shall denote by M. If $m \in M$, det $m = 1$ or -1. Those similarities which are the product of an even number of line reflections, that is, the rotations and translations, have determinant 1; we denote their group by M^+. Both M and M^+ are invariant subgroups of G_4, and therefore equivalence under these groups determines further elements in the structure of K_2.

DEFINITION 8.5. M is called the group of *displacements* of K_2, and M^+ the group of direct displacements. Equivalence under M (M^+) is called *congruence* (direct). We denote congruence by the symbol $\cong$.

Since M and M^+ contain the group of translations, our present definition of congruence does not violate Definition 3.1.

We know that K_2 is not a metric space, for by Theorem 8.5, any metric defined in K_2 would be trivial. Nevertheless we can extend the affine concept of relative length of parallel segments, and in K_2, define relative distance of any two point pairs.

DEFINITION 8.6. Let A, B, P, Q be points in K_2 with $A \neq B$, and let A', B', Q' be collinear points such that

$$\text{seg } AB \cong \text{seg } A'B', \qquad \text{seg } PQ \cong A'Q'.$$

The absolute value of the affine ratio $A'Q'/A'B'$ is called the *distance between P, Q relative to A, B.*

The reader can verify that relative distance is a function of the four points, that is, it does not depend on the choice of the auxiliary points A', B', Q', nor on the displacements establishing the congruence.

Unlike relative length of parallel segments in A_2 (which is a directed length), relative distance in K_2 must be nonnegative because congruent segments in K_2 are congruent in more than one way, and in particular, seg $\overrightarrow{AB}$ and seg $\overrightarrow{BA}$ are congruent.

THEOREM 8.14. *All radial segments of a circle are congruent.*

This follows directly from Theorem 8.13.

THEOREM 8.15. *If $a(g)$ is the magnification ratio of a direct similarity g, the distance between gP, gQ relative to P, Q is $a(g)$.*

Proof. Since $a(g) = \sqrt{\det g}$, $a(g_1 g_2) = a(g_1)a(g_2)$, and by Theorem 8.4, it suffices to prove the theorem for the dilation $x_1' = ax_1$, $x_2' = ax_2$. By Theorem 3.9, the affine ratio $gP\, gQ/PQ = a$, so that the relative distance is the absolute value of a, which is the magnification ratio.

If g is an opposite similarity, we can define the magnification ratio as $\sqrt{-\det g}$, and Theorem 8.15 remains valid. But opposite similarities do not possess an angle.

We can now define E_2, the Euclidean metric plane, by adjoining to the defining structure of $\Gamma(K_2, G_4)$ a pair of points A, B, in K_2. We call any segment congruent to seg AB a unit segment, and we define the *distance* between any two points of the new structure E_2, to be their distance in K_2, relative to A, B. The group of E_2, the subgroup which maps a unit segment onto a unit segment, is M. The reader can now identify E_2 as thus defined with our earlier definition (I, 6).

Our final theorem of this section is related to this definition of E_2. We shall leave its proof to the reader (Exercise 26).

THEOREM 8.16. *The similarity plane carries infinitely many distinct Euclidean metric planes. Each two of these are isomorphic, and corresponding distances under the isomorphism are in constant ratio.*

We close this section with a few comments on conics. We saw that in the affine plane any two hyperbolas are affinely equivalent; however, two hyperbolas need not be similar, and in general are not, for if the absolute points of the hyperbola are P, Q, the elliptic distance $D_L(P, Q)$ is a similarity invariant. This invariant does not characterize similar hyperbolas; it is preferable to introduce the two midpoints of the points P, Q on l, and to let M_1 be the midpoint interior to the conic. Then the value of

$$\omega = D_L(M_1, P) = D_L(M_1, Q)$$

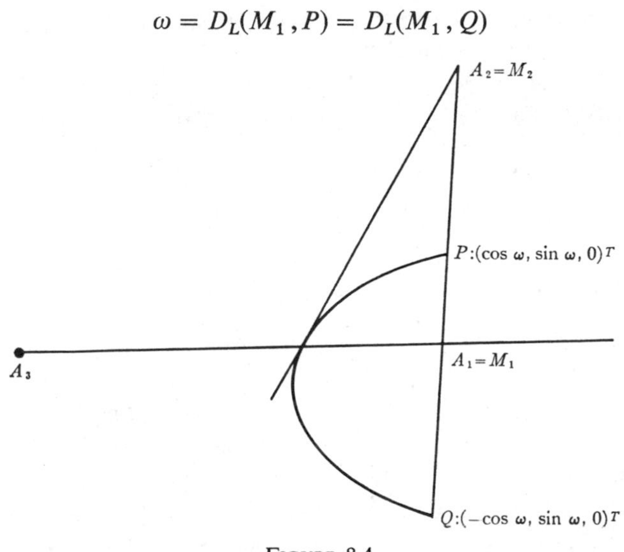

FIGURE 8.4

can be seen to characterize all similar hyperbolas: Since the midpoints $M_1, M_2 = \sigma M_1$, are the fixed points of the elliptic reflection that interchanges P and Q, $(M_1 M_2, P Q) = -1$, so that M_1 and M_2 are conjugate with respect to the conic. If we choose coordinates with triangle of reference $A_1 = M_1$, $A_2 = M_2$, A_3 the pole of l (that is, the center of the conic), and if we choose the unit point on a tangent to the conic from A_2, the equation of the conic will be $ax_1^2 + bx_2^2 - cx_3^2 = 0$, where a, b, c are chosen so that $(1, 0, 1)$ and $(\cos \omega, \sin \omega, 0)$ satisfy the equation. We find that $a = c$ and $b/a = -\cot^2 \omega$, so that the equation in Cartesian coordinates becomes

$$x^2 - y^2 \cot^2 \omega = 1,$$

and ω is, as we expected, the half angle of the sector bounded by the asymptotes and containing the curve.

If we try to apply the above procedure to the ellipse, we run into difficulties since P and Q do not exist. But the above points A_1, A_2 are conjugate both in σ and in the involution induced on l by the polarity of the conic, and such a pair is unique except when the two involutions coincide. Hence for a given ellipse in the similarity plane, we can find a self-conjugate triangle $A_1 A_2 A_3$ in $S_2(\mathsf{R})$ such that $A_2 = \sigma A_1$, and if we choose the unit point on a tangent to the conic from A_2, we obtain the canonical equation $x^2 + b^2y^2 = 1$.

The lines joining A_1 and A_2 to the pole of l are called the *axes* of the conic. Hence the axes are a pair of orthogonal conjugate diameters. They are unique except if the conic is a circle, in which case any pair of conjugate diameters are orthogonal.

If we embed the real projective plane in the complex plane, we can describe some of the relations considered above in the historically customary terms. Then the absolute involution possesses the fixed points $(1, \pm i, 0)^T$; these points are called the *circular points at infinity*, and a (nonreal) line joining a real point to either of the circular points is called a *minimal line* (or an isotropic line). If p, q are any two real lines, and if i_1, i_2 are the minimal lines through their intersection, the angle ω between p, q is given by a suitable determination of

$$\omega = \pm(i/2) \log (i_1 i_2, p\, q). \tag{8.6}$$

Two lines are perpendicular if and only if they separate harmonically the minimal lines through their intersection. A nonsingular conic is a circle if and only if it contains the circular points. We can define the foci of a conic to be (the images of) the points of intersection of isotropic tangents; under an embedding in $S_2(\mathsf{C})$ a parabola will have as its image a conic with two isotropic tangents that have one real point of intersection, and hence a parabola has one real focus. A central conic has as its image a conic with four isotropic tangents which intersect in four points (other than the circular points); two of these points are real, and hence a central conic has two real foci. The directrices are the polars of the foci. However we should note that in terms of the point of view of this book the concept of a real point in $S_2(\mathsf{C})$ is without content, and the approach we have just outlined would require mathematical clarification. We shall consider analogous questions in $S_1(\mathsf{C})$ in Section 10.

EXERCISES

1. Prove that any two similarity geometries are isomorphic.

2. Show that the group G of Definition 8.1 coincides with the group of a singular line form $\mathbf{UBU}^T$ of rank 2, whose conic consists of just one line.

3. Prove that two Cartesian coordinatizations of K_2 are related by (8.1) for a suitable choice of a, e, f, θ.

4. Prove that if the interior angles of a triangle ABC are respectively equal to the interior angles of the triangle $A'B'C'$, there exists a unique similarity g satisfying $gA = A'$, $gB = B'$, $gC = C'$. When will g be direct?

5. Let $g \in G_4^+$, let V and W be intersecting lines, and let r_L, for any line L, be the reflection with axis L. Prove that there exists a translation t such that $r_{gW} r_{gV} = t r_W r_V$. When is t the identity?

6. Prove Theorem 8.10 and Corollary 8.2.

7. Prove that the angle of the product of two direct similarities is the sum (mod 2π) of the angles of the factors.

8. Prove that if g is an opposite similarity, g^2 is a dilation.

9. The product of three line reflections whose axes do not belong to a pencil is called a glide reflection.† Prove that a glide reflection is the product (in either order) of a line reflection and a translation in the direction of the axis of the reflection.

10. Prove that if $g \in G_4$ and if $\det g = -1$, then g is either a line reflection or a glide reflection (see Exercise 9).

11. Prove that if g is a glide reflection (see Exercise 9) the midpoint of seg XgX lies on the axis of g, for all $X \in K_2$.

12. Discuss the factorization of an opposite similarity.

#**13.** Determine whether it is possible to characterize the projective image of a glide reflection in terms of its set of fixed points and lines in $S_2(\mathsf{R})$. If not, what else is needed?

14. Prove Theorem 8.14.

15. Let $\mathcal{O}(P)$ be the orbit of P under some group G. Prove that $Q \in \mathcal{O}(P)$ implies that $\mathcal{O}(Q) = \mathcal{O}(P)$.

16. State the projective generalization of Theorem 8.13.

#**17.** The proof of Theorem 8.12 together with Figure 8.3 suggests several elementary properties of circles. Find them.

18. Let L be a line in $S_2(\mathsf{R})$, σ an involution on L, and P, Q, R three noncollinear points, none incident to L. Prove that there exists a unique conic on P, Q, R whose involution of conjugate points on L is σ.

#**19.** Prove that if a triangle is self-polar with regard to a circle in K_2, the center of the circle is the point of intersection of its altitudes.

20. A triangle PQR is allowed to rotate freely about its vertex P, and a second triangle $P'Q'R'$ rotates about P' so that $(P \oplus Q) \cap (P' \oplus Q')$ is incident to a given line L. Find the locus of $X = (P \oplus R) \cap (P' \oplus R')$.

† See Coxeter, *Introduction to Geometry*, New York, John Wiley & Sons, Inc., 1961, p. 43.

21. Prove that the axes of homothetic conics are parallel.

22. The sectors determined by different pairs of intersecting lines need not be similar. How can they be characterized?

#**23.** Define rectangular hyperbola, and prove that a pencil of point conics which contains two rectangular hyperbolas consists exclusively of rectangular hyperbolas. Would this conclusion be valid in a complex similarity plane?

#**24.** Prove that the rectangular hyperbolas circumscribing a triangle constitute a pencil of type I (see IV, (11.12)), and that all contain the orthocenter† of the triangle.

#**25.** The *nine-point circle* of a triangle is the circle which contains the midpoints of the sides, the feet of the altitudes, and the points midway between the orthocenter† and the vertices. Show that this circle exists, by considering the locus of the centers of the rectangular hyperbolas circumscribing the given triangle (see IV, Corollary 11.3).

26. Prove Theorem 8.16.

9 The Hyperbolic Plane

We defined two-dimensional hyperbolic geometry earlier in this chapter (Definition 1.4) as a geometry isomorphic to the geometry of the interior of a nonsingular conic in $S_2(\mathsf{R})$ under the subgroup of G_8 that leaves the conic invariant. In this section we develop this geometry.

We shall denote a hyperbolic plane by H_2, and its group by $G(H_2)$ An embedding of H_2 in $S_2(\mathsf{R})$ determines the *absolute conic* and its interior, which we denote by $\mathscr{C}$ and S respectively. Generally we shall identify the points of H_2 with their images in $S_2(\mathsf{R})$ under the embedding, and the elements of $G(H_2)$ with the image collineations in $S_2(\mathsf{R})$, although we shall need to distinguish between the two roles played by these identified points and transformations.

We have already seen (Section 6) that H_2 induces on its lines a one-dimensional hyperbolic structure. Hence a point of a line in H_2 determines two half-lines (or rays), and two points determine two half-lines and a segment which possess the separation properties of their analogues in A_2. Furthermore H_2, unlike A_2, is a metric plane: We can define the distance between two points of H_2 as their distance in the one-dimensional hyperbolic geometry of their line, and we can direct distances along a line. Clearly $g \in G(H_2)$ implies that g is an isometry of H_2.

The reader can verify that in $S_2(\mathsf{R})$ an interior line of a conic separates

† The orthocenter of a triangle is the point of intersection of its altitudes.

the interior; consequently a line in H_2 is the bounding line of two disjoint half-planes whose union, together with the bounding line, is H_2.

We have already noted the existence in H_2 of three types of pencils of lines, corresponding to pencils in $S_2(\mathsf{R})$ which have as vertex an interior point of the absolute conic, a point of the absolute conic, or an exterior point. We call these concurrent, parallel, and ultraparallel pencils respectively.

THEOREM 9.1. *The inner structure of a pencil of lines in H_2 is that of a one-dimensional elliptic, affine, or hyperbolic space according as the pencil is concurrent, parallel, or ultraparallel.*

Proof. In $S_2(\mathsf{R})$ an interior point of a conic is not self-conjugate, and the polarity of the conic induces an elliptic involution on the lines of a pencil with vertex an interior point. The subgroup of $G(H_2)$ that leaves fixed a point P of H_2 must preserve this elliptic involution. Conversely, we can see by the dual of (IV, 10, Exercise 7) that every transformation of the one-dimensional elliptic group acting on the lines of the pencil with vertex P is the restriction to the pencil of at least one element of $G(H_2)$. Hence the subgroup of $G(H_2)$ that leaves P fixed is isomorphic to the one-dimensional elliptic group.

We leave to the reader the proofs of the remaining two assertions.

DEFINITION 9.1. We define the *angle* between two intersecting lines in H_2 to be their elliptic distance as elements of the one-dimensional elliptic space, their pencil. We define the angle between two parallel lines to be zero.

If $\theta(L_1, L_2)$ is the angle between intersecting (or parallel) lines L_1, L_2, we have that $\theta(gL_1, gL_2) = \theta(L_1, L_2)$, for all $g \in G(H_2)$. Two lines in H_2 are *orthogonal* (or perpendicular) if their angle is $\pi/2$, and hence the projective image of two orthogonal lines is a pair of lines conjugate with respect to the absolute. We note that in H_2 orthogonality is symmetric.† The lines orthogonal to a given line are represented in $S_2(\mathsf{R})$ by lines incident to the pole of the given line. Hence we have the following conclusions.

THEOREM 9.2. *A given point of H_2 is incident to exactly one line orthogonal to a given line. The set of lines orthogonal to a given line is an ultraparallel pencil, and every ultraparallel pencil determines uniquely a line which is orthogonal to all the lines of the pencil.*

We note that the lines of a parallel pencil (or of a concurrent pencil) possess no common orthogonal line.

† For examples of geometries in which orthogonality is not symmetric (that is, $L_1 \perp L_2$ does not imply $L_2 \perp L_1$) the reader may consult Herbert Busemann, *The Geometry of Geodesics*, New York, Academic Press Inc., 1955, p. 103.

We can obtain algebraic formulas for distance and angle in terms of arbitrary projective coordinates. Let $\mathscr{C}$ be given by $\mathbf{X}^T\mathbf{B}\mathbf{X} = 0$ ($\mathbf{B} = \mathbf{B}^T$, $\det \mathbf{B} \neq 0$). If $X \in Y \oplus Z$, where Y, Z are two points of H_2, $\mathbf{X} = \lambda\mathbf{Y} + \mu\mathbf{Z}$, and $[\lambda, \mu]^T$ is a projective coordinatization of $Y \oplus Z$. In terms of these coordinates, the one-dimensional quadratic form of the involution induced by the polarity of $\mathscr{C}$ is given by

$$Q = (\mathbf{Y}^T\mathbf{B}\mathbf{Y})\lambda^2 + 2(\mathbf{Y}^T\mathbf{B}\mathbf{Z})\lambda\mu + (\mathbf{Z}^T\mathbf{B}\mathbf{Z})\mu^2. \tag{9.1}$$

Since the λ, μ representatives of Y, Z are $(1, 0)^T$, $(0, 1)^T$, we have that $D_H(Y, Z)$, the undirected hyperbolic distance between Y and Z, is given by (see V, 6, Exercise 11)

$$\cosh^2 D_H(Y, Z) = \frac{(\mathbf{Y}^T\mathbf{B}\mathbf{Z})^2}{(\mathbf{Y}^T\mathbf{B}\mathbf{Y})(\mathbf{Z}^T\mathbf{B}\mathbf{Z})}, \qquad D_H(Y, Z) \geqq 0. \tag{9.2}$$

The dual quadratic form of $\mathscr{C}$ is $\mathbf{U}\mathbf{B}^{-1}\mathbf{U}^T$, and the pencil of lines $\lambda\mathbf{V} + \mu\mathbf{W}$ determines the form†

$$Q^* = (\mathbf{V}\mathbf{B}^{-1}\mathbf{V}^T)\lambda^2 + 2(\mathbf{V}\mathbf{B}^{-1}\mathbf{W}^T)\lambda\mu + (\mathbf{W}\mathbf{B}^{-1}\mathbf{W}^T)\mu^2. \tag{9.3}$$

Hence the undirected angle between lines V and W is given by (see V, 7, Exercise 10)

$$\cos^2 \theta(V, W) = \frac{(\mathbf{V}\mathbf{B}^{-1}\mathbf{W}^T)^2}{(\mathbf{V}\mathbf{B}^{-1}\mathbf{V}^T)(\mathbf{W}\mathbf{B}^{-1}\mathbf{W}^T)}, \qquad 0 \leqq \theta(V, W) \leqq \pi/2. \tag{9.4}$$

If we choose projective coordinates so that $\mathscr{C}$ is given by

$$x_1^2 + x_2^2 - x_3^2 = 0, \tag{9.5}$$

S, the interior of $\mathscr{C}$, is the set $x_1^2 + x_2^2 - x_3^2 < 0$, so that $x_3 \neq 0$ in S. Hence we can introduce nonhomogeneous coordinates,

$$x = x_1/x_3, \qquad y = x_2/x_3, \tag{9.6}$$

where

$$x^2 + y^2 - 1 < 0.$$

Interpreting (x, y) as rectangular cartesian coordinates in E_2, we observe that we have mapped H_2 one-to-one onto an open disc (the interior of a circle) in E_2. If $P \in E_2$ has polar coordinates (r, ϕ) $(-1 < r < 1)$, the inverse image X in H_2 is given by

$$\mathbf{X} = (r\cos\phi, r\sin\phi, 1)^T = (0, 0, 1)^T + r(\cos\phi, \sin\phi, 0)^T.$$

† If Y, Z are interior points of $\mathscr{C}$, (9.1) is an indefinite form, and the right side of (9.2) is greater than one. Thus (9.2) determines $D_H(Y, Z)$ uniquely. Similarly, if the vertex of the pencil $\lambda\mathbf{V} + \mu\mathbf{W}$ is an interior point, (9.3) is a definite form, and the right side of (9.4) is nonnegative and less than one. Thus (9.4) determines $\theta(V, W)$ uniquely. Moreover, (9.2) and (9.4) are valid if $Y = Z$ and $V = W$.

It follows that r is a special projective coordinate on the hyperbolic line (see (6.7)), and therefore that

$$r = \tanh d_H(A_3, X), \tag{9.7}$$

where $A_3 : (0, 0, 1)^T$ and d_H is the directed distance on $A_3 \oplus X$ corresponding to the orientation determined by A_3 and a point X for which $r > 0$.

The dual form of (9.5) is $u_1^2 + u_2^2 - u_3^2$, which becomes $u_1^2 + u_2^2$ for the pencil with vertex A_3. This is also the quadratic form defining angle in E_2, and therefore the hyperbolic angle between lines intersecting at A_3 is equal to the Euclidean angle between their images. We can arrive at this conclusion geometrically by recalling that at the center of a circle in E_2 the involution of conjugate lines coincides with the involution of orthogonal lines. Moreover a chord of the circle and an orthogonal diameter lie on lines conjugate in the circle; hence they are the images of two orthogonal lines in H_2. By recalling that there exists a projective coordinatization in which $\mathscr{C}$ is given by (9.5) and in which a preassigned interior point of $\mathscr{C}$ is A_3, we can state our conclusions as follows.

THEOREM 9.3. *There exists a one-to-one map from the hyperbolic plane onto an open unit Euclidean disc possessing the following properties*:

(i) *The inverse image of the center of the disc can be preassigned.*

(ii) *Hyperbolic lines map onto Euclidean segments.*

(iii) *The Euclidean angle between lines intersecting at the center of the disc is equal to the hyperbolic angle between their inverse images, and a line and an orthogonal diameter in the Euclidean metric represent orthogonal lines in the hyperbolic metric.*

(iv) *The Euclidean distance from the center of the disc is the hyperbolic tangent of the corresponding hyperbolic distance.*†

Although equations (9.2) and (9.4) determine distance and angle in H_2 only as undirected measures, we can introduce directed measures as well. It will turn out that in H_2, as in A_2, K_2, and E_2, there exist simultaneous orientations of all pencils of lines but not of all lines. We shall see that H_2, like our earlier planes, carries two isomorphic oriented planes, and that an orientation of H_2, just as that of the planes considered previously, can be defined in terms of either projective or hyperbolic concepts. However we shall relate our development to our earlier work in such a way that we shall be able to conclude that the map of Theorem 9.3 identifies the two orientations of H_2 with those of E_2. For this we need the following projective theorem.

† We could have introduced a constant k, called the absolute constant of hyperbolic space, by defining distance (see (6.4)) as $(k/2) \log (R_2 R_1, YZ)$. Had we done so, we should need to modify some of our later formulas, for example (9.8) to (9.16), by replacing each distance by its ratio to k.

THEOREM 9.4. *Let $\mathscr{D}$ be a nonsingular conic in $S_2(\mathsf{R})$, L a line such that $\mathscr{D} \cap L$ is empty, π_A the projection from $\mathscr{D}$ onto L with center $A \in \mathscr{D}$, and $\mathscr{S}_1, \mathscr{S}_2$ the two sense classes of $\mathscr{D}$. Then $\pi_A \mathscr{S}_i$ $(i = 1, 2)$ are the two sense classes of L, and $\pi_A \mathscr{S}_i$ is independent of A.*

Proof. Since $\mathscr{D}$, in its inner structure, is an $S_1(\mathsf{R})$, and π_A a projectivity, it follows from Theorem 4.2 that $\pi_A \mathscr{S}_i$ are the two sense classes of L. If $B \in \mathscr{D}$, $B \neq A$, the map $\pi_B^{-1}\pi_A$ is a projectivity on $\mathscr{D}$. This projectivity is elliptic, since the contrary hypothesis implies that a fixed point Y satisfies

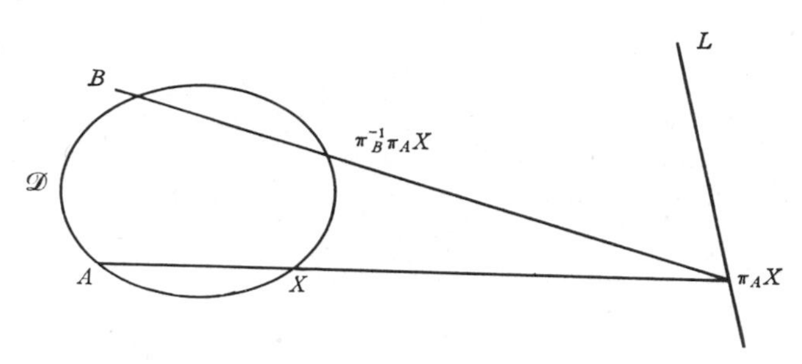

FIGURE 9.1

$\pi_A Y = \pi_B Y$, and therefore that $Y \in \mathscr{D} \cap L$. Since an elliptic projectivity is direct, the restriction of $\pi_B^{-1}\pi_A$ to the sense classes of $\mathscr{D}$ is the identity, and therefore $\pi_A \mathscr{S}_i = \pi_B \mathscr{S}_i$.

Thus the specification of a preferred sense class on $\mathscr{D}$ determines a preferred sense class on L. Conversely, we can show (by using $\pi_B \pi_A^{-1}$) that the roles of L and $\mathscr{D}$ are interchangeable. We thus have the following affine theorem.

COROLLARY 9.1. *In $\overrightarrow{A_2}$, there exists a simultaneous orientation of all ellipses. Conversely, A_2 can be oriented by orienting a single ellipse.*

In orienting the hyperbolic plane from the projective point of view, it is natural to take as the point of departure the two sense classes of the absolute conic. The preceding corollary identifies the orientations of H_2 with the induced orientations of an affine plane, which in turn can be identified with those of E_2. Thus an independent development of the orientation properties of H_2 is unnecessary; they are simply the inverse images of the orientation properties of E_2 under the map of Theorem 9.3.

We are now able to show how to develop hyperbolic trigonometry. Let us denote the lengths of the sides and the angles of a hyperbolic triangle ABC by a, b, c and α, β, γ in the usual order. We map H_2 onto E_2 with A

mapping onto the origin and $A \oplus C$ onto the x-axis of a Cartesian coordinate system. Using (iii) and (iv) of Theorem 9.3 we find that in a right triangle with $\gamma = \pi/2$, we have (Figure 9.2(a)) that

$$\tanh c \cos \alpha = \tanh b. \tag{9.8}$$

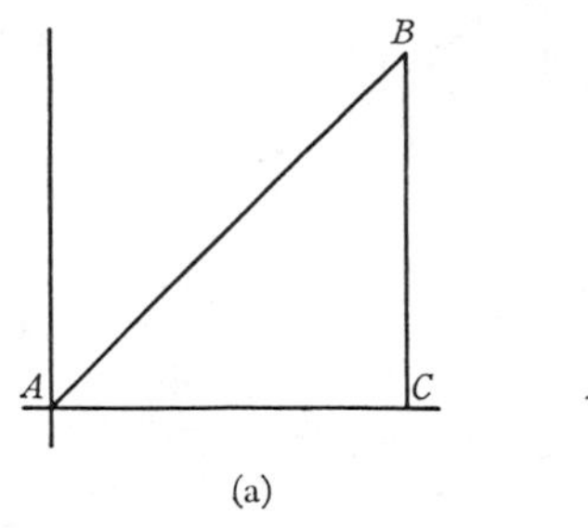

(a)

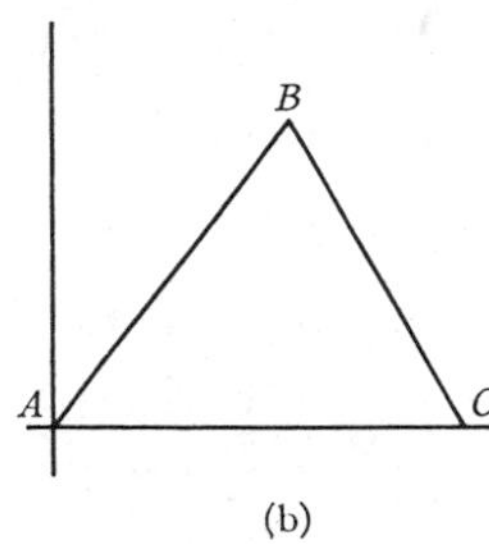

(b)

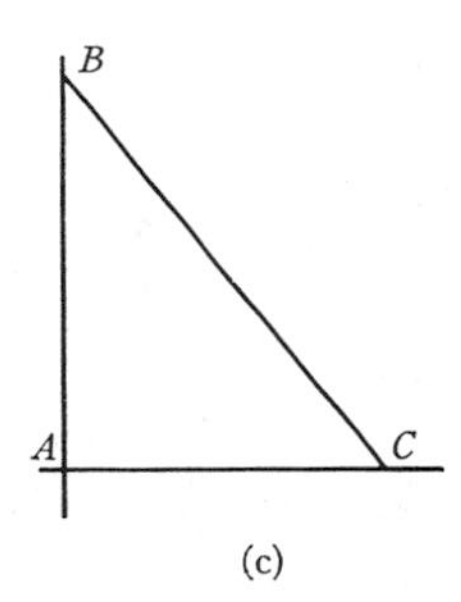

(c)

FIGURE 9.2

Hence we conclude the following:

In a right triangle in H_2, the two remaining angles are acute, and the cosine of either is the ratio of the hyperbolic tangent of the adjacent side-length to that of the hypotenuse.

For a general triangle (Figure 9.2(b)), we can let

$$r = \tanh c, \qquad s = \tanh b. \tag{9.9}$$

Then we have the following projective representatives:

$$C:(s, 0, 1)^T, \qquad B:(r \cos \alpha, r \sin \alpha, 1)^T,$$
$$C \oplus B:(r \sin \alpha, s - r \cos \alpha, -rs \sin \alpha), \qquad C \oplus A:(0, 1, 0).$$

To compute $a = D_H(B, C)$, we use (9.2) for the form (9.5) and the points B, C. We find

$$\cosh^2 a = \frac{(1 - rs \cos \alpha)^2}{(1 - r^2)(1 - s^2)}. \tag{9.10}$$

From (9.9) we have that $\cosh^2 c = 1/(1 - r^2)$, and therefore we obtain after taking positive square roots,

$$\cosh a = \cosh b \cosh c - \sinh b \sinh c \cos \alpha. \tag{9.11}$$

Similarly, we use (9.4) for the lines $C \oplus A$, $C \oplus B$. We obtain

$$\cos^2 \gamma = N/D,$$

where

$$N = (s - r \cos \alpha)^2, \qquad D = r^2 + s^2 - 2rs \cos \alpha - r^2 s^2 \sin^2 \alpha.$$

Hence

$$D - N = r^2(1 - s^2) \sin^2 \alpha.$$

We can rewrite D,

$$D = (1 - rs \cos \alpha)^2 - (1 - r^2)(1 - s^2),$$

or, using (9.10),

$$D = (1 - r^2)(1 - s^2) \sinh^2 a. \tag{9.12}$$

Since $(D - N)/D = \sin^2 \gamma$, we find that

$$\sin \alpha/\sin \gamma = \sinh a/\sinh c. \tag{9.13}$$

Formulas (9.11) and (9.13), valid for any triangle in H_2, are the analogues of the Law of Cosines and Law of Sines in E_2. From (9.11), with $\alpha = \pi/2$, we find the hyperbolic form of the Pythagorean Theorem

$$\cosh a = \cosh b \cosh c, \tag{9.14}$$

or, in words,

In any right triangle in H_2, the hyperbolic cosine of the hypotenuse is the product of the hyperbolic cosines of the other two sides.

If $\alpha = \pi/2$ (Figure 9.2(c)), we obtain from (9.8) and (9.14) that

$$\cos \beta = \frac{\tanh c}{\sqrt{(1 - \operatorname{sech}^2 b \operatorname{sech}^2 c)}}, \qquad \cos \gamma = \frac{\tanh b}{\sqrt{(1 - \operatorname{sech}^2 b \operatorname{sech}^2 c)}} \tag{9.15}$$

We can readily verify that these formulas remain valid in the limit, when b is infinite so that $\operatorname{sech} b = 0$. Then we have two parallels L, L' cut by the transversal $A \oplus B$ perpendicular to L. Denoting the second interior angle by ω (Figure 9.3), we have from (9.15) that

$$\cos \omega = \tanh D_H(A, B). \tag{9.16}$$

The angle ω was called the *angle of parallelism* by Lobachevsky, and (9.16) is a classical formula of hyperbolic geometry.†

We ask the reader to verify (Exercise 10 below) that when P is a given point and X a variable point on a given line, $\min D_H(P, X) = D_H(P, Y)$, where Y is the foot of the perpendicular from P to the given line.

Since $\cosh (b + c) = \cosh b \cosh c + \sinh b \sinh c$, we see from (9.11) that $\cosh a < \cosh (b + c)$, and since the hyperbolic cosine is strictly increasing for positive argument, we have that $a < b + c$. Thus hyperbolic distance satisfies the triangle inequality (see (6.5), page 324),

$$D_H(X, Z) \leqq D_H(X, Y) + D_H(Y, Z) \tag{9.17}$$

† A historical account of hyperbolic geometry is found in *Non-Euclidean Geometry*, Stefan Kulczycki, translated by S. Knapowski, vol. 16, International Series of Monographs on Pure and Applied Mathematics, New York, Pergamon Press, 1961.

for any three points X, Y, Z, and the equality in (9.17) holds if and only if $Y \in \text{seg } XZ$.

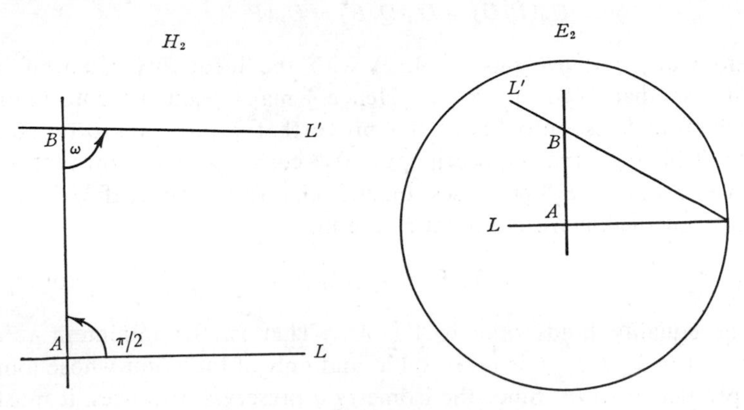

FIGURE 9.3

DEFINITION 9.2. A set W and a real-valued function d whose domain is $W \times W$ (that is, the set consisting of pairs of elements of W) is said to be a *metric space* with *metric d* if the function d satisfies the following conditions:

1. $d(X, X) = 0$ for $X \in W$.
2. $d(X, Y) > 0$ for $X, Y \in W$, $X \neq Y$.
3. $d(X, Y) = d(Y, X)$ for $X, Y \in W$.
4. $d(X, Z) \leqq d(X, Y) + d(Y, Z)$ for $X, Y, Z \in W$.

Thus H_2, with its metric D_H, is a metric space in the above sense. A point transformation g of a metric space W is said to *preserve the metric* if $d(gX, gY) = d(X, Y)$ for all X, Y in the domain of g. If both the domain of g and the range of g coincide with W, the transformation is called a *motion* or an *isometry* of W.

We note that $Y \neq Z$ implies that $d(Y, Z) > 0$, and $d(gY, gZ) > 0$ implies that $gY \neq gZ$. Hence an isometry is one-to-one; it possesses an inverse which is likewise an isometry. The set of all isometries of a space is clearly a group.

Our definition of H_2 and of D_H and the properties of the group of a quadratic form in $S_2(\mathsf{R})$ imply that every g in $G(H_2)$ is an isometry of H_2. We shall prove the converse of the last assertion.

THEOREM 9.5. *The group of isometries of H_2 is $G(H_2)$.*

Our proof will use two lemmas of interest in themselves.

LEMMA 9.1. *An isometry of H_2 maps lines onto lines, and orthogonal lines onto orthogonal lines.*

Proof. Let g be the isometry, and let P, Q, R be three collinear points, named so that $Q \in \operatorname{seg} PR$. Then

$$D_H(P, Q) + D_H(Q, R) = D_H(P, R). \tag{9.18}$$

Therefore gP, gQ, gR satisfy (9.17) with the inequality replaced by an equality, so that $gQ \in \operatorname{seg} gP\, gR$. Hence g maps segments onto segments, and therefore lines onto lines. To prove that g preserves orthogonality, we use (9.14) (and the implication $x > 0 \Rightarrow \cosh x > 1$) to show that orthogonality in H_2 (as in E_2) possesses a metric characterization: If M is the foot of the perpendicular from a point P to a line l,

$$D_H(P, M) \leqq D_H(P, Y) \qquad \text{for all } Y \in l, \tag{9.19}$$

and the equality holds only if $Y = M$. That is, the minimum value of $D_H(P, Y)$ for $Y \in l$, $P \notin l$, is taken on at and only at the point whose join to P is perpendicular to l. Since the isometry g preserves distances, it must preserve minimum distance and consequently, orthogonality of lines.

LEMMA 9.2. *An isometry of H_2 maps a pencil of lines onto a pencil of the same kind.*

Proof. A pencil of ultraparallels possesses a common perpendicular, and the map, under the isometry, of a pencil possessing a common perpendicular must be, by Lemma 9.1 and Theorem 9.2, a pencil of ultraparallels. We leave the rest of the proof to the reader.

We now turn to the proof of Theorem 9.5. We denote a given isometry of H_2 by γ. We embed H_2 in $S_2(\mathsf{R})$, and we denote the image of γ under the embedding by γ^*,† so that γ^* maps S, the interior of $\mathscr{C}$, the absolute conic, one-to-one onto itself. The central idea in our proof is to construct a map g of $S_2(\mathsf{R})$ onto itself in such a way that g restricted to S coincides with γ^* and g preserves collinearity in $S_2(\mathsf{R})$. It then will follow (see III, Theorem 8.6) that g is a collineation leaving S (and $\mathscr{C}$) fixed, and therefore that $\gamma \in G(H_2)$.

We define g as follows. If X is a point of $S_2(\mathsf{R})$, the pencil with vertex X contains a set $\mathscr{W}$ of segments interior to $\mathscr{C}$; $\gamma^*\mathscr{W}$ exists and determines uniquely a point X', the vertex of the pencil which contains $\gamma^*\mathscr{W}$. We define g by the condition $gX = X'$. From Lemma 9.2, $gX \in S$ if and only if $X \in S$, and then $gX = \gamma^*X$; furthermore Lemma 9.2 guarantees that $gX \in \mathscr{C}$ if and only if $X \in \mathscr{C}$, and gX is exterior to $\mathscr{C}$ if and only if X is exterior to $\mathscr{C}$. The range of g is $S_2(\mathsf{R})$ because, among other facts, γ^* possesses an inverse. It thus follows that g is one-to-one and onto. To prove that g preserves collinearity, we consider first three collinear points P, Q, R exterior to $\mathscr{C}$.

† If $\mathscr{E}$ is the embedding, $\gamma^* = \mathscr{E}\gamma\mathscr{E}^{-1}$.

They are the vertices of pencils whose images in H_2 are ultraparallel pencils, with common perpendiculars which are three lines of a pencil. In view of Lemma 9.2, the polars of gP, gQ, gR are concurrent and the points are collinear. We can treat three collinear points not all exterior to $\mathscr{C}$ in an analogous manner, and we conclude that g preserves collinearity. Hence g is a collineation, and since $g\mathscr{C} = \mathscr{C}$, g belongs to the group of $\mathscr{C}$ and $\gamma \in G(H_2)$.

A critical evaluation of the proof that we have just completed may suggest to the reader the possibility of finding a stronger theorem (see Exercises 21 and 22 below).

We now turn our attention to a classification of motions in H_2 in hyperbolic terms. We have already seen that the group of a polarity in $S_2(\mathsf{R})$ is generated by the harmonic homologies whose centers and axes are pole and polar in the polarity (IV, Theorem 10.4). Of special interest are the harmonic homologies with centers exterior to the absolute conic, so that the axis exists as a line in H_2. Let g be such a harmonic homology with axis L and center O (Figure 9.4). Then $gX = X$ for $X \in L$, and for $X \notin L$, g inter-

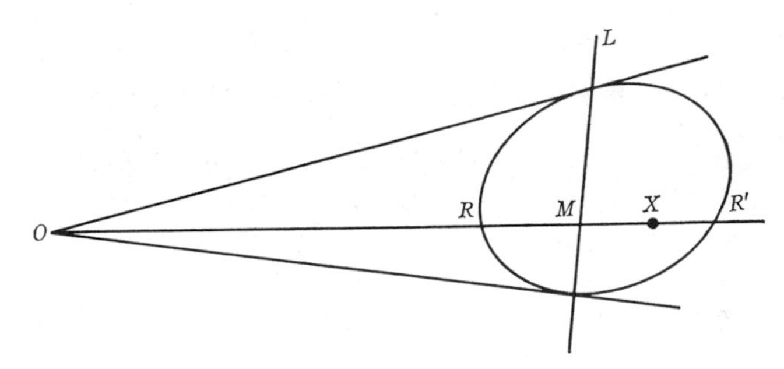

FIGURE 9.4

changes the two points of intersection of $O \oplus X$ with the absolute. If we denote these by R, R', and if $M = (O \oplus X) \cap L$, we have $(RR', MX) = (R'R, MgX)$. If we direct $X \oplus X'$ and let d_H denote directed distance (see Section 6), we have $d_H(M, X) = -d_H(M, gX)$. Hence the axis L bisects seg XgX, and the line $X \oplus gX$ is orthogonal to L. For obvious reasons, we call the transformation in H_2 a *line reflection.*

If g is a harmonic homology with center an interior point of $\mathscr{C}$, the corresponding motion in H_2 is called a *point reflection.* We leave it to the reader to show that a point reflection g in H_2 possesses a center which bisects the segment with end points X, gX.

LEMMA 9.3. *Every point reflection in H_2 is the product of two line reflections whose axes are any two orthogonal lines incident to the center.*

We leave the proof to the reader.

THEOREM 9.6. *Every hyperbolic motion g is either the product of two line reflections or the product of three.*†

Proof. By (IV, Theorem 10.4), g is the product of two reflections. If $g = s_1 s_2$, where s_1 and s_2 are point reflections with distinct centers O_1, O_2, we can write $s_1 = r_1 r_2$, $s_2 = r_2 r_3$, where r_2 is a line reflection with axis $O_1 \oplus O_2$, and r_1, r_3 are line reflections with axes orthogonal to $O_1 \oplus O_2$ and incident to O_1, O_2 respectively. Then $g = r_1 r_3$. The rest of the proof should be evident to the reader.

Since a harmonic homology in $S_2(\mathsf{R})$ induces an involution on any conic it leaves fixed, and since an involution in $S_1(\mathsf{R})$ is sense-preserving if and only if the involution is elliptic, it follows that a motion of H_2 is direct and leaves fixed the two orientations of H_2 if and only if the motion is the product of an even number of line reflections.

We shall classify only the direct motions. Let $g \in G(H_2)$, and let $g = r_1 r_2$, where r_1, r_2 are line reflections with axes L_1, L_2 respectively, and let $g_{\mathscr{C}}$ be the restriction to $\mathscr{C}$, the absolute conic, of g regarded as a collineation in $S_2(\mathsf{R})$. Then the axis of g is the join of the centers of the involutions $(r_1)_{\mathscr{C}}$, $(r_2)_{\mathscr{C}}$, that is, the polar of $L_1 \cap L_2$. Hence $g_{\mathscr{C}}$ is elliptic, hyperbolic, or parabolic according as (in H_2) L_1 and L_2 intersect, are ultraparallel, or are parallel.

We consider the first of these three classes of motions, and we let $Z = L_1 \cap L_2$. Clearly $gZ = Z$. We call these motions *rotations* with center Z. If we map H_2 onto a Euclidean disc as described in Theorem 9.3 with Z mapping onto the center of the disc, the hyperbolic reflections r_1, r_2 correspond to Euclidean reflections of the disc with axes diameters of the disc. The product of the two Euclidean reflections is a Euclidean rotation. Hence a hyperbolic rotation g, like a Euclidean rotation, maps a point X not the center Z onto gX, where $D_H(Z, X) = D_H(Z, gX)$ and where the directed angle from the ray $r(Z, X)$ to the ray $r(Z, gX)$ is independent of X. Either of its two values, corresponding to the two orientations of the plane, is called the *angle of the rotation* for the corresponding orientation.

The set of all hyperbolic rotations with given center is a one-parameter group, isomorphic to the comparable Euclidean group. We define the hyperbolic circle with center Z through a point Y to be the orbit of Y (see page 343) under the group of rotations in H_2 with center Z. Since circles in E_2 concentric with and contained in the disc are the images, under the map of Theorem 9.3, of hyperbolic circles, and since a pencil of concentric circles is a pencil of type IIIa (see IV, (11.23)), hyperbolic circles with center Z are represented by

$$k\mathbf{X}^T\mathbf{B}\mathbf{X} + (\mathbf{Z}^T\mathbf{B}\mathbf{X})^2 = 0, \tag{9.20}$$

† The product of two line reflections may be the identity, and the product of three may be a line reflection.

where $\mathbf{X}^T\mathbf{B}\mathbf{X} = 0$ represents the absolute conic, and where k is restricted to real values satisfying $\operatorname{sgn} k = -\operatorname{sgn} \mathbf{Z}^T\mathbf{B}\mathbf{Z}$, for Z an interior point of the absolute. Alternatively, (9.20) can be obtained directly from the condition $D_H(Z, X)$ is constant.

We turn next to those motions which are the product of two reflections with ultraparallel axes. Let g be such a motion, and let L_1, L_2 be the axes of the reflections (Figure 9.5). Then L, the common perpendicular of

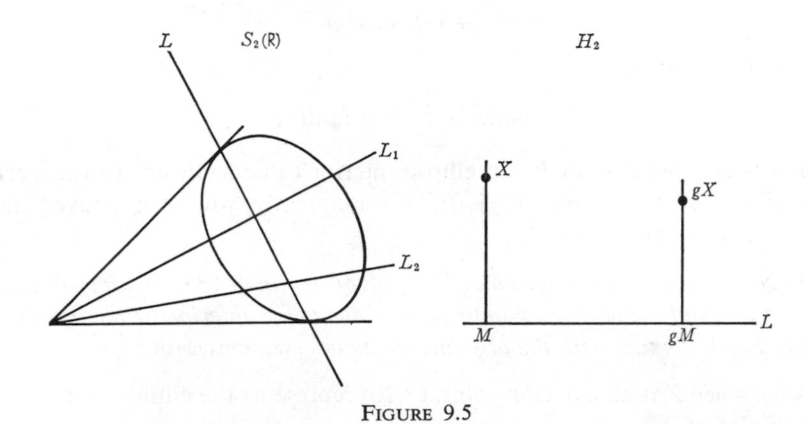

FIGURE 9.5

L_1, L_2, is left fixed by g, and g_L, the restriction of g to L, is a one-dimensional translation (Theorem 6.3). Conversely, g is determined when L and g_L are specified: If M is the foot of X on L, gX lies on the perpendicular to L at $g_L M$, X and gX lie on the same side of L, and the two distances $D_H(M, X)$, $D_H(gM, gX)$ are equal. We call these motions (hyperbolic) *translations*, and the associated line L the *axis* of the translation. In $S_2(\mathsf{R})$, L is the axis of $g_{\mathscr{C}}$, the induced projectivity on the absolute.

THEOREM 9.7. *The set of all hyperbolic translations with a given axis is a one-parameter Abelian group.*

The proof is a consequence of the conclusion that the set of translations in H_1 is a one-parameter Abelian group (see (6.8)) and of the construction of gX given in the preceding paragraph.

DEFINITION 9.3. An orbit under the group of translations with given axis L is called an *equidistant* curve of L.

As with a pencil of concentric circles, that is, the orbits of the group of rotations with given center, the set of equidistant curves of a given line cover the plane exactly once. To discover their projective characterization, we note that in the map of Theorem 9.3, we can preassign the inverse image of the x-axis. Then from Figure 9.2(a), letting (x, y) be Cartesian coordinates of B, we have

$$x^2 + y^2 = r^2 = \tanh^2 c = 1 - \operatorname{sech}^2 c. \tag{9.21}$$

By the Pythagorean Theorem in H_2, equivalent to (9.14), we have

$$\begin{aligned}\operatorname{sech}^2 c &= \operatorname{sech}^2 b \operatorname{sech}^2 a \\ &= (1 - \tanh^2 b) \operatorname{sech}^2 a \\ &= (1 - x^2) \operatorname{sech}^2 a.\end{aligned}$$

Hence (9.21) becomes

$$x^2 \tanh^2 a + y^2 = \tanh^2 a. \tag{9.22}$$

Clearly 9.22 represents in E_2 an ellipse interior to and tangent to the circle $x^2 + y^2 = 1$ at the points $(\pm 1, 0)$. Consequently we have proved the following theorem.

THEOREM 9.8. *Under an embedding $\mathscr{E}$ of H_2 in $S_2(\mathsf{R})$, the set of equidistant curves of a line L map onto the set of conics, interior to the absolute, having double contact with the absolute at its intersections with $\mathscr{E}L$.*

Thus when Z is an exterior point, (9.20) represents the equidistant curves of the polar of Z.

The third class of direct motions in H_2 consists of products of two reflections with parallel axes. Such a motion induces on the absolute a parabolic projectivity. Since the set of parabolic projectivities in $S_1(\mathsf{R})$ with a given fixed point is isomorphic to the group of translations of a Euclidean (or hyperbolic) line, the set of all hyperbolic motions each of which is the product of two reflections in lines of a given pencil of parallel lines is a one-parameter Abelian group. This subgroup of $G(H_2)$ is not transitive. Can we determine its orbits?

It will be instructive to consider this question by methods different from those used for hyperbolic rotations and translations, and we shall digress briefly to present an apparently unrelated problem. In E_2, the sequence of rotations $\{r_n\}$ with centers $(n, 0)$ and angles $1/n$ are represented by

$$\begin{aligned}x' &= n(1 - \cos 1/n) + x \cos 1/n - y \sin 1/n, \\ y &= -n \sin 1/n + x \sin 1/n + y \cos 1/n.\end{aligned} \tag{9.23}$$

For $P \in E_2$, $\{r_n P\}$ is a convergent sequence of points, and we can define a transformation r by the equation $rP = \lim_{n \to \infty} r_n P$. From (9.23), it is clear that r is the translation $x' = x$, $y' = y - 1$. Similarly in $S_1(\mathsf{R})$, the sequence of projectivities $\{\pi_n\}$, with

$$\pi_n\colon \quad x' = (1 + 1/n)x + 1$$

(in terms of a nonhomogeneous coordinate), clearly possesses the property that $\lim_{n\to\infty} \pi_n X$ exists for all $X \in S_1(\mathsf{R})$, and if we define π by the condition $\pi X = \lim_{n\to\infty} \pi_n X$, we find that π is a parabolic projectivity, whereas π_n is, for all n, hyperbolic. It would seem that the third class of hyperbolic motions might be captured as limits of motions of the other classes, and the orbits as the limits of circles and equidistant curves. If we turn to (9.20), we note that for $Z \in \mathscr{C}$, (9.20) represents a conic having four-point contact with $\mathscr{C}$ at Z.

In order to justify this approach, we should need to formulate a definition of the limit of at least a sequence of curves, something that we have done so far only for straight lines (see p. 140 and III, 7, Exercises 4–7). It is considerably more simple merely to verify that our guess is correct.

If a collineation g in $S_2(\mathsf{R})$ leaves fixed a conic $\mathscr{D}$, and if $g_{\mathscr{D}}$ is a parabolic projectivity, g possesses one fixed point and one fixed line. The matrix of g must have a characteristic value of multiplicity 3 (see III, (11.11)), and corresponding rank 2. We can choose coordinates so that the fixed point is $(0,0,1)^T$, the fixed line is $x_1 = 0$, and $\mathscr{D}$ is the conic $x_1 x_3 - x_2^2 = 0$. Then g possesses a representation of the form

$$(9.24) \qquad x_1' = x_1, \quad x_2' = ax_1 + x_2, \quad x_3' = bx_1 + cx_2 + x_3, \qquad ac \neq 0.$$

Since

$$x_1' x_3' - x_2'^2 = (b - a^2)x_1^2 + (c - 2a)x_1 x_2 + x_1 x_3 - x_2^2,$$

$g\mathscr{D} = \mathscr{D}$ if and only if $b - a^2 = c - 2a = 0$. Hence g is given by

$$(9.25) \qquad x_1' = x_1, \qquad x_2' = ax_1 + x_2, \qquad x_3' = a^2 x_1 + 2ax_2 + x_3,$$

with $a = 0$ representing the identity. We can show that (9.25) leaves fixed not only $\mathscr{D}$, but every conic having four-point contact with $\mathscr{D}$ at $(0,0,1)^T$, that is, every conic of the pencil

$$(9.26) \qquad \lambda(x_1 x_3 - x_2^2) + \mu x_1^2 = 0.$$

A point $Y \neq A_3$ is incident to exactly one conic of the pencil (9.26), and that conic is the orbit of Y under the group (9.25). We have thus verified our earlier guess.

DEFINITION 9.4. Products of an even number of reflections in H_2 with parallel axes are called *infinite rotations*, and the lines parallel to the axes are called the *diameters* of the rotation.

THEOREM 9.9. *The set of all infinite rotations with a given pencil of diameters is an Abelian group isomorphic to the group of translations on a Euclidean line.*

We leave the proof to the reader.

DEFINITION 9.5. An orbit under the group of infinite rotations with given diameters is called a *horocycle* (or a limiting circle), and the diameters are called the *diameters* of the horocycle. Two horocycles with the same diameters are said to be *concentric.*

Thus the projective image of a pencil of concentric horocycles is the set of conics interior to the absolute and having four-point contact with the absolute at the vertex of the pencil of diameters.

DEFINITION 9.6. A curve in H_2 which is a straight line, a circle, an equidistant curve, or horocycle is called a *cycle.*

If C is a cycle, there exists a one-parameter group of motions which leaves C fixed and whose restriction to C is transitive on C.

When the Euclidean concept of curvature of curves is generalized to H_2, it develops that cycles are the curves of constant curvature and therefore the only orbits of continuous one-parameter groups with transitive restrictions to each orbit.†

EXERCISES

Unless otherwise specified, the problems below relate to H_2.

1. Complete the proof of Theorem 9.1.

2. Two ultraparallel lines, as elements of a one-dimensional hyperbolic space, possess an invariant, their hyperbolic distance. Find a geometrical interpretation for this invariant in terms of the metric of H_2.

3. Theorem 9.3 asserts that the inverse image of the center of the disc can be preassigned. Show that a stronger conclusion is possible without weakening the rest of the theorem.

4. Is parallelism of lines transitive?

5. Let $r(O, A)$ be the half-line with end point O and containing A, and let $\{P_n\}$ be a sequence of points such that $P_n \in r(O, A)$ and $D_H(O, P_n) = n$. Let $B \in H_2$, $B \notin O \oplus A$. Prove that the angle between $O \oplus A$ and $B \oplus P_n$ converges to zero.

6. Prove that the tangent lines at two points of a circle of radius r are orthogonal if and only if the two points subtend at the center of the circle an angle ω satisfying $\cos \omega = \tanh^2 r$.

7. If an absolute unit k is introduced (see footnote, page 351), the Pythagorean Theorem for a right triangle ($\gamma = \pi/2$) becomes $\cosh c/k = \cosh a/k \cosh b/k$. Show that the Euclidean theorem $c^2 = a^2 + b^2$ is the limiting form obtained by letting k become infinite.

8. Find the limiting forms of the hyperbolic laws of sines and cosines, when $k \to \infty$ (see Exercise 7).

† After studying the next section, the reader could consult E. Cartan, *Leçons sur la théorie des espaces à connexion projective*, Paris, Gauthier-Villars, 1937, pp. 28–42.

9. Prove that the sum of the angles of a right triangle is less than π, and extend the result to arbitrary triangles.

10. Let L be a line, P a point, and M the foot of P on L (that is, the unique point of L for which $P \oplus M \perp L$). Show that $D_H(P, X)$ for $X \in L$ assumes its minimum at M, and is strictly increasing on each of the rays of L with end point M.

11. Projective coordinates in $S_2(\mathsf{R})$ of points in the interior of the conic $x_1^2 + x_2^2 - x_3^2 = 0$, can be normalized by choosing a factor of proportionality (in two ways) so that $x_1^2 + x_2^2 - x_3^2 = -1$. Corresponding coordinates in H_2 are called *Weierstrass coordinates.* Show that these coordinates are related to the coordinates (x, y) determined by the map of Theorem 9.3 by the equations

$$(x_1, x_2, x_3)^T = \pm(\cosh D)(x, y, 1)^T,$$

where D is the hyperbolic distance from the origin to the point (x, y).

12. Use Exercise 11, (9.8), and (9.13) to prove that if u, v are directed distances from two given orthogonal lines L, L' to a variable point X, and D the distance between $L \cap L'$ and X, then $\pm(\sinh u, \sinh v, \cosh D)^T$ are Weierstrass coordinates in H_2.

13. Prove that there exist triangles the sum of whose angles is arbitrarily small (see Exercise 5).

14. Prove that the three altitudes of a triangle belong to a pencil of lines (use IV, Theorem 6.10)

15. If the absolute conic is given by $\mathbf{X}^T\mathbf{B}\mathbf{X} = 0$, show that the circle with center at Y and radius r is given by

$$(\mathbf{Y}^T\mathbf{B}\mathbf{Y})(\mathbf{X}^T\mathbf{B}\mathbf{X}) - (\mathbf{Y}^T\mathbf{B}\mathbf{X})^2 \operatorname{sech}^2 r = 0.$$

16. In E_2 two circles possess a radical axis unless they are concentric. In H_2 we can define the radical axis of two circles as a line belonging to a singular conic of their pencil. Show that although nonconcentric circles need not possess a radical axis, if each two of three circles do possess a radical axis, the three radical axes belong to a pencil.

#**17.** The point set of E_2 is metrized by defining the distance between the origin and a point of $\mathscr{D}$, the curve $x^4 + y^4 = 1$, to be one, and the distance between any two points P, Q to be the ratio of their Euclidean distance to the Euclidean length of the radius of $\mathscr{D}$ parallel to $P \oplus Q$. Show that with this metric the point set is a metric space in the sense of Definition 9.2. (This is an illustration of a Minkowski plane.†)

#**18.** An illustration of a Hilbert geometry† (other than hyperbolic) is obtained by metrizing the interior of $\mathscr{D}$ (Exercise 17) by defining the distance between points P, Q to be $\log (R_1 R_2, P Q)$, where $(P \oplus Q) \cap \mathscr{D} = R_1 \cup R_2$.

† See H. Busemann and P. J. Kelly, *Projective Geometry and Projective Metrics*, New York, Academic Press Inc., 1953, pp. 133, 156.

Show that the resulting geometry is a metric geometry in the sense of Definition 9.2.

19. Prove that the set of all isometries of a metric space is a group.

20. Prove that the set of all isometries of a metric space $\mathscr{W}$ which map a given subset $\mathscr{M}$ of $\mathscr{W}$ onto itself is a subgroup of the group of isometries of $\mathscr{W}$.

#**21.** In $S_2(\mathsf{R})$ let γ be a one-to-one map of the interior S of a conic $\mathscr{C}$ onto itself, and let γ map collinear points of S onto collinear points, and segments in S which lie on lines conjugate in $\mathscr{C}$ onto such segments. Prove that there exists a unique collineation $g \in G_8(\mathsf{R})$ whose restriction to S is γ.

#**22.** Prove the following theorem: A one-to-one map of H_2 onto itself which maps lines onto lines and orthogonal lines onto orthogonal lines is an isometry.

23. Prove Theorem 9.7.

24. A translation g leaves fixed a line parallel to and distinct from the axis of g. Prove that g is the identity.

25. Let g be a rotation with center C, L any line incident to C, and r the reflection with axis L. Prove that there exist line reflections r_1, r_2 such that $g = rr_1 = r_2 r$. Extend this result to other direct motions.

#**26.** Show that the product of two rotations may be a rotation, a translation, or an infinite rotation.

#**27.** Prove that every rotation is the product of two infinite rotations, and that the diameters of one of these may be selected arbitrarily.

#**28.** Prove that H_2 satisfies the axiom of free mobility. (This axiom asserts that the group of motions is transitive on the set of half-lines, with end points mapping onto end points.)

#**29.** Show that any two horocycles are congruent, and discuss the analogous question for other cycles.

#**30.** Show that a cycle has infinitely many axes of symmetry, and these axes are the lines of a pencil.

#**31.** Prove that the lines orthogonal to a line L are orthogonal to the equidistant curves of L.

#**32.** Generalize the conclusion of Exercise 31 by proving that every cycle is an orthogonal trajectory of a pencil of lines, and conversely.

10 The Inversive Plane

In a Euclidean plane E_2, let $\mathscr{C}$ be a circle with center C and radius a. We define *inversion* in $\mathscr{C}$ to be the point transformation g, with domain $E_2 - C$, such that for $P \in E_2 - C$, gP is the point of intersection of $C \oplus P$ and the polar of P with respect to $\mathscr{C}$ (Figure 10.1). We call $\mathscr{C}$ the circle of inversion, C the center of inversion, and a the radius of inversion. Clearly an inversion is involutory ($g^2P = P$), it maps a line incident to the center into itself, and it leaves fixed each point on the circle of inversion. The restriction of g to a line $C \oplus P$ is the Euclidean image of a projective involution with fixed points $(C \oplus P) \cap \mathscr{C}$. Hence the product of the directed distances from C to the points P and gP is equal to a^2 (see II, (6.4)). Therefore in terms of polar coordinates (r, θ), with pole at C, g is given by

$$r' = a^2/r, \qquad \theta' = \theta. \tag{10.1}$$

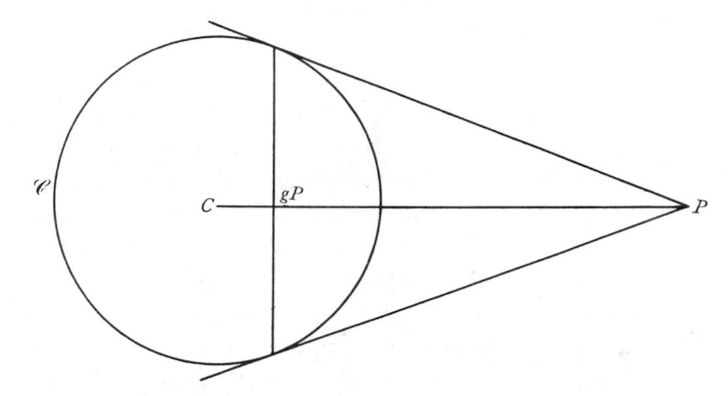

FIGURE 10.1

An equivalent form, in terms of Cartesian coordinates is

$$x' = a^2x/(x^2 + y^2), \qquad y' = a^2y/(x^2 + y^2), \tag{10.2}$$

and another, in terms of the complex variable $z = x + iy$ ($i^2 = -1$) is

$$z' = a^2/\bar{z}, \tag{10.2'}$$

where $\bar{z}$ is the complex conjugate of z. From these equations, we note that g maps the set of points defined by the equation

$$A(x^2 + y^2) + Dx + Ey + F = 0 \tag{10.3}$$

into the set defined by

$$F(x^2 + y^2) + a^2Dx + a^2Ey + a^4A = 0. \tag{10.4}$$

These equations yield the following theorem.

THEOREM 10.1. *An inversion in E_2 leaves fixed any line incident to the center, it maps any circle not incident to the center onto another such circle, and it interchanges lines not incident to the center with circles incident to the center.*

Again from (10.3) and (10.4) we note that g maps two parallel lines into two circles (or a circle and a line) which are tangent at the center of inversion, and that their common tangent is parallel to the two original lines. If $\theta = \theta(l_1, l_2)$ is the directed angle from a line l_1 to a line l_2, which we suppose intersect in a point P, then θ is also the directed angle from gl_1† to gl_2 at the center of inversion, C. Since gl_1 and gl_2 intersect again in gP, a reflection in the perpendicular bisector of seg CgP shows that the angle from gl_1 to gl_2 at gP is the supplement of $\theta(l_1, l_2)$. We thus have the following theorem.

THEOREM 10.2. *Inversion is oppositely conformal, that is, magnitudes of angles are preserved while their sense is reversed.*

In developing the theory of inversion it would seem desirable to modify the Euclidean plane by adjoining a "point at infinity" to serve as the map of the center of an inversion. Such a structure would be called the inversive plane, and its group would be the smallest group that contains all inversions. We shall describe such a structure later in this section in a formal way. For the present let the plane $\mathscr{P}$ mean the point set obtained from E_2 by the informal adjunction of one point at infinity, and let circles in $\mathscr{P}$ mean both ordinary circles and straight lines. Thus in $\mathscr{P}$ inversion is one-to-one and maps circles onto circles. We note that the plane $\mathscr{P}$ is the the domain normally used in the study of functions of one complex variable.

An intuitive justification for adjoining a "point at infinity" to E_2 can be found as follows. We recall (II, 1, Illustrations 4 and 5) that a sphere may serve as a concrete representation of the point set of the plane $\mathscr{P}$ since a stereographic projection (Figure 10.2) maps the plane $\mathscr{P}$ one-to-one onto a sphere, or vice versa. If g is an inversion with center C in $\mathscr{P}$ and τ a stereographic projection from $\mathscr{P}$ to a sphere $\mathscr{W}$ (with north pole N), τ maps a pair of inverse points P, $P' = gP$ onto τP, $\tau P'$, a pair which correspond under the map σ, with domain $\mathscr{W}$, defined by

$$\sigma Q = \tau g \tau^{-1} Q, \qquad Q \in \mathscr{W}, \quad Q \neq N, \quad Q \neq \tau C,$$
$$\sigma N = \tau C, \qquad \sigma \tau C = N.$$

σ is clearly one-to-one from $\mathscr{W}$ onto $\mathscr{W}$, and involutory. Moreover we can show that σ is continuous at all $Q \in \mathscr{W}$. To prove this at $Q \neq N$, $Q \neq \tau C$ involves no special considerations; the proof of continuity at N and at τC rests on the following facts:

1. If we are given in $\mathscr{P}$ a neighborhood $\mathscr{N}_\infty$ of ∞ (that is, the exterior of a circle), there exists a neighborhood $\mathscr{N}_C$ of C such that $gP \in \mathscr{N}_C$ for all $P \in \mathscr{N}_\infty$, and vice versa.
2. Given in $\mathscr{P}$ a neighborhood $\mathscr{N}_\infty$ of ∞, there exists a neighborhood $\mathscr{N}_N$ of N (in the metric of $\mathscr{W}$) such that $\tau P \in \mathscr{N}_N$ for all $P \in \mathscr{N}_\infty$, and vice versa.

† Strictly speaking, gl_1 is a circle (or line) with one point missing, and the angle is the angle from $C \cup gl_1$ to $C \cup gl_2$.

Thus the image, under stereographic projection, of inversion in E_2 is a transformation on the sphere which can be completed to be one-to-one, onto, and continuous. We call a map σ *inversion* on the sphere.

We shall need two further properties of stereographic projection.

THEOREM 10.3. *Stereographic projection is conformal, that is, it preserves angles.*

Proof. It is clear (Figure 10.2) that a line in $\mathscr{P}$ maps onto a circle on $\mathscr{W}$ incident to N with tangent line at N parallel to the given line. Hence two parallel lines map onto tangent circles, and the angle between two intersecting lines equals the angle between the circles into which they are mapped.

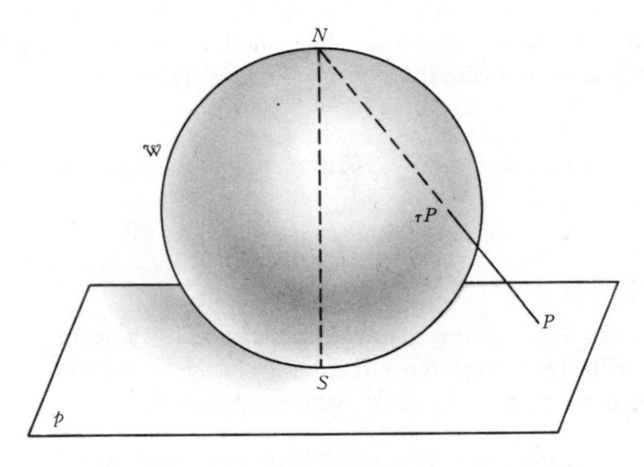

FIGURE 10.2

Before proceeding to the second property, we note that $N \oplus \tau P$ and $S \oplus \tau P$ are perpendicular, and therefore the product of directed distances from N to P and to τP is constant and equal to the square of the diameter of $\mathscr{W}$. We define inversion in a sphere in E_3 analogously to inversion in a circle, by requiring that a point and its inverse be collinear with the center and that the product of their directed distances from the center be the square of the radius of the sphere. Thus the stereographic projection τ is the restriction to $\mathscr{P}$ of the inversion in the sphere with center N and radius NS (Figure 10.2).

We can write the extension to three dimensions of equations (10.2), (10.3), and (10.4), and thereby obtain a generalization of Theorem 10.1, and in particular, that inversion in a sphere maps spheres not through the center of inversion onto such spheres. A circle is the intersection of a plane and a sphere, and hence inversion in a sphere maps circles onto circles (or possibly lines). Since a stereographic projection is, as we have seen, the restriction of an inversion in a sphere, we have outlined the proof of the following theorem.

THEOREM 10.4. *Stereographic projection maps the set of circles of the plane $\mathcal{P}$ onto the set of circles of the sphere.*

With this brief summary of inversion and stereographic projection, we can turn our attention to $S_1(\mathsf{C})$, a projective space over the complex field C. Although $S_1(\mathsf{C})$ is a space of complex dimension one, it can be thought of as a space of real dimension two. For we have already seen that we can map $S_1(\mathsf{C})$ one-to-one onto either a sphere in E_3, or onto the plane $\mathcal{P}$. We shall let $G(\mathsf{C})$ denote the group of $S_1(\mathsf{C})$, that is, the group of complex projectivities $[\mathbf{Z}'] = [\mathbf{AZ}]$, det $\mathbf{A} \neq 0$, where all the matrices have two rows and their elements are in C. We shall frequently use a nonhomogeneous projective coordinate $z = z_1/z_2$, and refer to the point $[1,0]^T$ as $z = \infty$.

DEFINITION 10.1. If A, B, C are three points of $S_1(\mathsf{C})$, the set of points $\mathcal{M}_{ABC}$ defined by

$$\mathcal{M}_{ABC} = A \cup \{X \mid (AB, CX) \in \mathsf{R}\}$$

is called a *chain.*

Clearly g in $G(\mathsf{C})$ maps chains onto chains. In terms of projective coordinates with ABC as reference frame, $X \in \mathcal{M}_{ABC}$ if and only if X possesses a real representation, $\mathbf{X} = (x_1, x_2)^T$, where $x_1, x_2 \in \mathsf{R}$.

LEMMA 10.1. *Any two chains are projectively equivalent.*

Proof. Let the chains be $\mathcal{M}_{ABC}$ and $\mathcal{M}_{A'B'C'}$. Define $g \in G(\mathsf{C})$ by $gA = A', gB = B', gC = C'$. Then for $X \in S_1(\mathsf{C})$, $(AB, CX) = (A'B', C'gX)$. Hence $X \in \mathcal{M}_{ABC}$ if and only if $gX \in \mathcal{M}_{A'B'C'}$.

LEMMA 10.2. *The inner structure of a chain of $S_1(\mathsf{C})$ is that of an $S_1(\mathsf{R})$.*

Proof. If we take the points A, B, C of $\mathcal{M}_{ABC}$ to be the reference elements of a projective coordinatization of $S_1(\mathsf{C})$, the projectivities g in $G(\mathsf{C})$ that map $\mathcal{M}_{ABC}$ onto itself possess real representations, and every such projectivity leaves $\mathcal{M}_{ABC}$ fixed.

LEMMA 10.3. *A chain is determined by any three of its points; two distinct chains have two or fewer points of intersection.*

Proof. We can coordinatize $S_1(\mathsf{C})$ so that a given chain is the set of points which possess real representatives; if any three distinct points of the chain are taken as the reference frame of another such coordinatization, the two coordinatizations will be related by $[\mathbf{X}'] = [\mathbf{AX}]$, where $[\mathbf{A}]$ possesses a real representative, and it follows that the given chain and the chain on the three points coincide.

Clearly, $\mathcal{M}_{ABC}$ and $\mathcal{M}_{ABD}$, for $D \notin \mathcal{M}_{ABC}$, are two chains with two points of intersection.

When we represent $S_1(\mathsf{C})$ on a sphere or on the plane $\mathcal{P}$, chains are represented by certain classes of curves. The following theorem identifies these classes.

THEOREM 10.5. *When $S_1(\mathsf{C})$ is represented by the plane $\mathcal{P}$, the set of chains of $S_1(\mathsf{C})$ maps onto the set of circles in the plane $\mathcal{P}$.*

Proof. If z is a nonhomogeneous projective coordinate in $S_1(\mathsf{C})$, $\mathcal{M}_{ABC}$ is given by

$$\frac{z-a}{z-b}\frac{c-b}{c-a} = t, \tag{10.5}$$

where a, b, c are the (complex) coordinates of A, B, C respectively,† and t is a real parameter (with $t = \infty$ being admissible). We can eliminate t from (10.5) by equating the left side to its complex conjugate. Using an overbar to denote complex conjugates, we obtain an equation reducible to

$$\alpha z\bar{z} + \bar{\mu}z + \mu\bar{z} + \delta = 0, \tag{10.6}$$

where α, δ are real. If $\alpha \neq 0$, we can write (10.6) as

$$(z + \mu/\alpha)(\bar{z} + \bar{\mu}/\alpha) = (\mu\bar{\mu} - \alpha\delta)/\alpha^2, \tag{10.7}$$

and if $\alpha = 0$, as

$$\bar{\mu}z + \mu\bar{z} + \delta = 0. \tag{10.7$'$}$$

Since (10.6) is satisfied by $z = a, b, c$, we must have

$$\alpha\delta - \mu\bar{\mu} < 0, \tag{10.8}$$

and in the plane $\mathcal{P}$ the locus of (10.6) is a circle. Conversely, an equation (10.6) has an empty locus in $\mathcal{P}$ if $\alpha\delta - \mu\bar{\mu} > 0$, and it represents a point (null circle) if $\alpha\delta - \mu\bar{\mu} = 0$. Otherwise (10.6) represents a circle in $\mathcal{P}$ and a chain in $S_1(\mathsf{C})$, for all choices of projective coordinates in $S_1(\mathsf{C})$.

We note that in $S_1(\mathsf{C})$ the coefficient α of $z\bar{z}$ in (10.6) vanishes if and only if the first vertex of the reference frame, $(1, 0)^T$, is a point of the chain (10.6).

By using homogeneous coordinates and matrix notation, (10.6) and (10.8) can be written

$$(z_1, z_2)\mathbf{B}(\bar{z}_1, \bar{z}_2)^T = 0, \qquad \det \mathbf{B} < 0, \tag{10.9}$$

† If one of the points A, B, or C is $z = \infty$, (10.5) would need to be modified slightly, but (10.6) would hold.

where $\mathbf{B}$ is a 2×2 matrix satisfying the conditions

$$(\mathbf{B})_{ij} = b_{ij} = \bar{b}_{ji}. \tag{10.10}$$

A matrix whose elements are complex numbers satisfying (10.10) is called a *Hermitian* matrix, and the corresponding form (10.9) a *Hermitian* form.

Although our present topic is closely related to the theory of binary and ternary Hermitian forms we shall not emphasize this point of view. It is however convenient to note that in the plane $\mathscr{P}$ inversion in the circle (10.7) is given by

$$(z' + \mu/\alpha)(\bar{z} + \bar{\mu}/\alpha) = (\mu\bar{\mu} - \alpha\delta)/\alpha^2,$$

so that the corresponding transformation in $S_1(\mathsf{C})$ determined by the chain (10.9), (10.10) is given by

$$(z_1', z_2')\mathbf{B}(\bar{z}_1, \bar{z}_2)^T = 0. \tag{10.11}$$

When the chain in $S_1(\mathsf{C})$ is given by (10.6) with $\alpha = 0$, $\mu \neq 0$, the transformation (10.11) becomes

$$\bar{\mu}z' + \mu\bar{z} + \delta = 0. \tag{10.11$'$}$$

It can be verified that this transformation is represented in $\mathscr{P}$ by a reflection in the line (10.7′). Thus although in $S_1(\mathsf{C})$, all chains are projectively equivalent, their images in E_2 may be circles or straight lines; in the latter case inversion in the chain appears as a reflection in the line (see Exercise 8 below).

Some of the properties of chains now follow from our knowledge of circles and lines in E_2 and from properties of $S_1(\mathsf{R})$ and of $S_1(\mathsf{C})$. Thus, for example, two chains may have 0, 1, or 2 points of intersection, and two points on a chain are end points of two segments. A chain separates $S_1(\mathsf{C})$ into two half-spaces and every chain incident to two points in different half-spaces intersects the given chain in exactly two points, one on each of the two segments determined by the given points.

A circle in $\mathscr{P}$ possesses a projective structure induced by its relation to conics (or straight lines) in $S_2(\mathsf{R})$. Is this structure identical with the projective structure induced on it when it is considered as a chain of $S_1(\mathsf{C})$? Surprisingly enough, the answer is in the affirmative.† It will suffice to verify this for the unit circle $x^2 + y^2 = 1$, which as a conic in $S_2(\mathsf{R})$ possesses the projective parametrization (see IV, (3.3))

$$x = (1 - t^2)/(1 + t^2), \qquad y = 2t/(1 + t^2),$$

where t is real. For a point z of the circle, we have

$$z = x + iy = \frac{1 - t^2 + 2it}{1 + t^2} = \frac{1 + it}{1 - it}. \tag{10.12}$$

† The reader might note that in $S_1(\mathsf{R})$ if we let $[x_1', x_2'] = [x_1^3, x_2^3]$, we obtain two coordinatizations of $S_1(\mathsf{R})$ which determine distinct projective structures.

When t takes on all complex values (with $t = \infty$ admissible), (10.12) yields a new projective coordinatization of $S_1(\mathsf{C})$ in terms of which the chain $z\bar{z} = 1$ is represented by real values of the coordinate t. Thus t is also a projective coordinate on the chain, and the two projective structures coincide.

We turn next to a fundamental theorem in this development.

THEOREM 10.6. *A one-to-one map of $S_1(\mathsf{C})$ onto itself which maps chains onto chains is either an element of $G(\mathsf{C})$ or the product of such an element and the map $z' = \bar{z}$.*

Proof. Let σ be the given map, and let π in $G(\mathsf{C})$ be defined by $\pi\sigma A = A$, $\pi\sigma B = B$, $\pi\sigma C = C$, where A, B, C are three chosen points of $S_1(\mathsf{C})$. Then the map $\gamma = \pi\sigma$ satisfies the hypothesis of our theorem and leaves A, B, C fixed. Now we choose coordinates in $S_1(\mathsf{C})$ with ABC as reference frame, and we map $S_1(\mathsf{C}) - A$ onto K_2 (or E_2) by mapping $[z_1, z_2]$ onto the point with Cartesian coordinates (x, y) where $z_1/z_2 = x + iy$. The image of γ in K_2 is a one-to-one map of K_2 onto itself which maps straight lines onto straight lines, and circles onto circles. Furthermore γ preserves the number of intersections of two chains in $S_1(\mathsf{C})$, and consequently the image map in K_2 maps parallel lines onto parallel lines. Finally we note that in K_2 orthogonality is preserved: If l_1, l_2 are two orthogonal lines, we can select a rectangle with l_1, l_2 as two of its sides. The transformed rectangle must be a parallelogram with concyclic vertices, that is, a rectangle, and hence orthogonal lines in K_2 map onto orthogonal lines. By Theorem 8.3 and Theorem 8.5, γ is either the identity or the inversion $z' = \bar{z}$. Since $\gamma = \pi\sigma$, either $\sigma = \pi^{-1}$ or σ is the product of π^{-1} and the map $z' = \bar{z}$.

Although in $S_2(\mathsf{R})$ the homogeneous linear group coincides with the group of transformations that map lines onto lines, this is not so in other projective planes. In particular if F is a field possessing an automorphism η, not the identity, the map $X \to X'$ in $S_2(\mathsf{F})$, where $\mathbf{X}' = \eta\mathbf{X} = (\eta x_1, \eta x_2, \eta x_3)^T$, is one-to-one, onto, and line-preserving. The group of line-preserving maps of $S_2(\mathsf{F})$ is given by $\mathbf{X}' = \mathbf{A}\eta\mathbf{X}$, where η varies over the group of automorphisms of F. The complex field C possesses two automorphisms, the identity and the map $z \to \bar{z}$, and hence in $S_2(\mathsf{C})$ the maps $\mathbf{X}' = \mathbf{A}\overline{\mathbf{X}}$ preserve collinearity. The analogous maps in $S_1(\mathsf{C})$, $\mathbf{X}' = \mathbf{A}\overline{\mathbf{X}}$ (where the matrices have row order 2, $\det \mathbf{A} \neq 0$) are called *antiprojectivities*. Theorem 10.6 thus asserts that it is this larger group consisting of projectivities and antiprojectivities that maps chains in $S_1(\mathsf{C})$ onto chains.

We are now ready for a formal definition of the inversive plane and of inversive geometry.

DEFINITION 10.2. Let $\mathscr{W}$ be a set of points in one-to-one correspondence with the point set of $S_1(\mathsf{C})$, and let $G(\mathscr{W})$ be a group isomorphic to the group of projectivities and antiprojectivities of $S_1(\mathsf{C})$. We require also that the isomorphism preserve the correspondence. The geometry $\Gamma(\mathscr{W}, G(\mathscr{W}))$ is called (two-dimensional) *inversive geometry*, and $\mathscr{W}$ is called an *inversive plane*.

Thus $\mathscr{W}$ can be coordinatized by the homogeneous classes $[\mathbf{Z}] = [z_1, z_2]^T$, $z_1, z_2 \in \mathsf{C}$, and $G(\mathscr{W})$ can be represented by the union of the two sets of transformations

$$[\mathbf{Z}'] = [\mathbf{AZ}], \qquad [\mathbf{Z}'] = [\mathbf{A}\overline{\mathbf{Z}}], \qquad \det \mathbf{A} \neq 0.$$

We shall frequently identify the points of $\mathscr{W}$ with those of $S_1(\mathsf{C})$, and $G(\mathscr{W})$ with the projectivities and antiprojectivities of $S_1(\mathsf{C})$.

We have seen that chains in $S_1(\mathsf{C})$ possess a real one-dimensional projective structure. We naturally ask whether this structure is preserved by the larger group $G(\mathscr{W})$. In fact, $G(\mathscr{W})$ need not preserve cross ratio, for if A, B, C, D are four points of $\mathscr{W}$ and if h is the antiprojectivity $z' = \bar{z}$, the two cross ratios $(A\,B, C\,D)$ and $(hA\,hB, hC\,hD)$ are complex conjugates of each other. It follows, however, that if $(A\,B, C\,D) \in \mathsf{R}$, $(A\,B, C\,D) = (gA\,gB, gC\,gD)$ for all $g \in G(\mathscr{W})$. Thus the restriction of g in $G(\mathscr{W})$ to a chain is a projectivity from the chain to its map under g, and the real projective structure of chains is preserved by $G(\mathscr{W})$.

A projective characterization of angle between intersecting chains, although possible, would take us far afield. Instead, we recall that g in $G(\mathsf{C})$ is the product of two involutions, and that a given involution in $G(\mathsf{C})$ can be expressed, in terms of suitably selected coordinates, by $z' = -z$. In E_2, $z' = -z$ is the product of two line reflections, and therefore an involution in $G(\mathsf{C})$ is the product of two inversions. Hence every g in $G(\mathsf{C})$ is the product of an even number of inversions, and similarly, every antiprojectivity is the product of an odd number of inversions. Since inversions are oppositely conformal, we can define angle between chains in $\mathscr{W}$ (or in $S_1(\mathsf{C})$) as the angle determined in E_2 (or $\mathscr{P}$, or a sphere) by the image lines or circles. Then $G(\mathsf{C})$ is the subgroup of $G(\mathscr{W})$ which is directly conformal, whereas the antiprojectivities preserve magnitudes of angles while reversing their sense (see Theorem 10.2).

Theorem 10.6 has considerable import for Euclidean geometry. Briefly, it asserts that circle-preserving transformations are conformal, and that every such transformation is the product of a finite number of inversions. More precisely, we have the following theorem.

THEOREM 10.7. *Every one-to-one circle-preserving map of a sphere in* E_3 *onto itself is conformal, and the group of such maps is finitely generated by inversions.*

Thus the relation of the inversive plane to a sphere is somewhat analogous to that of the affine plane to a Euclidean plane. In both cases, the original metric structure is destroyed and a new structure is derived by means of a group that preserves a prescribed class of curves.

In E_2 two circles are orthogonal if and only if the sum of the squares of the radii is the square of the distance between their centers. Applying this criterion to the chain (10.6) and to a second chain with coefficients denoted by primes, we obtain the necessary condition for orthogonality,

$$\mu\bar{\mu}' + \bar{\mu}\mu' - \alpha\delta' - \delta\alpha' = 0. \tag{10.13}$$

We shall agree that a null circle, that is, the locus of (10.6) with $\alpha \neq 0$, $\alpha\delta - \mu\bar{\mu} = 0$, is orthogonal to any proper circle that contains the one point of the null circle. The reader can verify that if (10.13) holds for two circles in $\mathscr{P}$ (null or not), the circles are orthogonal. Naturally (10.13) may hold even though (10.6) fails to represent a circle ($\alpha\delta - \mu\bar{\mu} > 0$).

Although we shall not develop in detail the geometry of the inversive plane, it is useful to apply earlier methods to new problems. Furthermore a great deal of our analysis can be regarded as being carried out either in E_2 or K_2, or in the plane $\mathscr{P}$, and it frequently will be convenient to call the chains of $\mathscr{W}$ circles. The condition that a point in $\mathscr{W}$ lie on a circle (10.6), or that two points be inverse in a circle, is linear in the coefficients $\alpha, \mu, \bar{\mu}, \delta$ of (10.6). But from (10.10) we note that linear combinations of Hermitian matrices are Hermitian if and only if the coefficients of combination are in R. Hence the circles satisfying two independent linear conditions belong to a real pencil,† and a pencil of circles in $\mathscr{W}$ corresponds to a pencil in $\mathscr{P}$. If two circles intersect, their points of intersection belong to all the circles of their pencil, and if points P, Q are inverse in two circles, they are inverse in every circle of the pencil determined by the two. For analogous reasons, we conclude from (10.13) that if a circle is orthogonal to two circles, it is orthogonal to every circle in the pencil of the two.

An inversion clearly leaves fixed any circle orthogonal to the circle of inversion; the restriction of the inversion to the orthogonal circle is a hyperbolic involution with fixed points the points of intersection of the two circles. Conversely, a circle left fixed by an inversion is either the circle of inversion itself, or it is orthogonal to the circle of inversion. Consequently two nonnull circles are orthogonal if and only if one contains a pair of points inverse to the other.

Two distinct points P, Q determine the pencil $\mathscr{L}_1$ consisting of all circles incident to P and Q, and a second pencil $\mathscr{L}_2$, consisting of all circles orthogonal to the circles of the first pencil. Clearly P, Q are inverse in any nonnull circle in $\mathscr{L}_2$, and, as null circles, P and Q constitute a basis for $\mathscr{L}_2$. A third type of pencil is obtained by taking as its basis a proper circle and a null

† As with quadratic forms in S_1(R) or S_2(R), a linear combination of two Hermitian forms (10.9) may vanish only on an empty set of points.

circle orthogonal to the first. Then the proper circles in the pencil are mutually tangent at the same point. The orthogonal pencil in this case is a pencil of the same kind. According as one of two orthogonal pencils has 0, 1, or 2 base points, the other has 2, 1, or 0 base points and 0, 1, or 2 null circles, respectively.

The following theorem establishes the central role that inversion plays in $\mathscr{W}$.

THEOREM 10.8. *If points P, Q are inverse in a circle $\mathscr{C}$, and if $g \in G(\mathscr{W})$, then gP and gQ are inverse in $g\mathscr{C}$.*

Proof. Every circle incident to P, Q is orthogonal to $\mathscr{C}$, and since g is conformal and circle-preserving, we have that every circle on gP and gQ is orthogonal to $g\mathscr{C}$. Hence gP and gQ are inverse in $g\mathscr{C}$.

It follows that the center of a circle has no significance in $\mathscr{W}$.

We saw earlier that the directly conformal elements in $G(\mathscr{W})$ are projectivities, and hence cannot interchange two points unless they are involutions. The analogous conclusion is not valid for antiprojectivities. Instead we have the following theorem.

THEOREM 10.9. *If an antiprojectivity in $\mathscr{W}$ interchanges two points, it is either an inversion or the product of inversions in three circles the first two of which are orthogonal to the third circle and incident to the two points.*

Proof. By choosing coordinates so that the given points are $z = 0, \infty$, the antiprojectivity becomes $z' = k/\bar{z}$, where $k \in \mathrm{C}$. By writing $k = a^2 e^{i\theta}$ ($a \in \mathrm{R}$) we can factor the given antiprojectivity π into the product $\pi_1 \pi_2$, where

$$\pi_1\colon \quad z' = a^2/\bar{z}; \qquad \pi_2\colon \quad z' = e^{i\theta} z.$$

In E_2, π_2 is a rotation with center the center of the inversion π_1. We factor π_2 into the product of two line reflections, with axes orthogonal to the circle of inversion of π_1. The transformations in E_2 can be completed, and in $\mathscr{W}$, π is the product of three inversions as described.

We shall need the following theorem.

THEOREM 10.10. *The projectivities in $\mathscr{W}$ that leave a chain fixed leave both sides of the chain fixed if and only if the projectivity restricted to the chain is direct.*

Proof. If we choose coordinates so that the given chain is $z = \bar{z}$ (that is, the axis of reals), the projectivities in question can be expressed by

$$(10.14) \qquad z' = \frac{az + b}{cz + d}, \qquad ad - bc \neq 0, \quad a, b, c, d \in \mathrm{R}.$$

If we write $z = x + iy$ and $z' = x' + iy'$, we find from (10.14) that

$$y' = \frac{(ad - bc)y}{(cx + d)^2 + c^2y^2}.$$

The conclusion follows by noting that $\operatorname{sgn} yy' = \operatorname{sgn}(ad - bc)$ (for $y \neq 0$), and recalling that $\operatorname{sgn}(ad - bc) = 1$ if and only if (10.14) induces a direct projectivity on the axis of reals.

The reader will find further properties of $\mathscr{W}$ in the exercises below.

We now turn our attention to the hyperbolic plane. We have seen (Theorem 9.3) that it can be represented by an open Euclidean unit disc, with Euclidean segments representing hyperbolic lines and with the hyperbolic metric D_H given by (Figure 10.3(a))

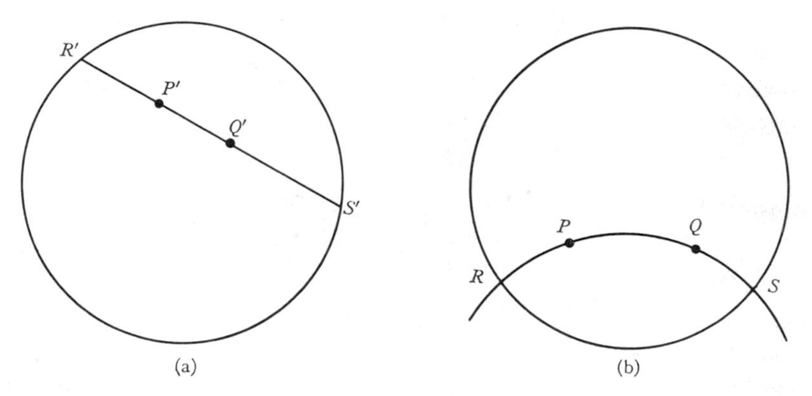

FIGURE 10.3

(10.15) $$D_H(P', Q') = \tfrac{1}{2}k \log (R'S', P'Q').$$

In this representation $G(H_2)$ is isomorphic to the group of collineations of $S_2(\mathsf{R})$ that map the interior of $x^2 + y^2 = 1$ onto itself, or, as we saw earlier, $G(H_2)$ is isomorphic to $G_3(\mathsf{R})$, the group of $S_1(\mathsf{R})$ (see IV, Theorem 10.6). On the other hand the subgroup of $G(\mathsf{C})$ that leaves a chain invariant is isomorphic to $G_3(\mathsf{R})$. Hence we might expect to find a representation of hyperbolic geometry in terms of circles and circle-preserving transformations. This is actually the case, and to obtain such a representation we first map the disc $x^2 + y^2 < 1$ in E_2 onto the hemisphere of radius one, tangent to the disc at its center, by a projection orthogonal to the x,y plane (Figure 10.4); straight line segments map onto semicircles orthogonal to the equator. Next we project the sphere stereographically from N back into E_2, mapping the hemisphere onto an open disc ($x^2 + y^2 < 4$). A proper dilation with center the center of the disc maps the disc onto a new disc with preassigned radius. We thus obtain the Poincaré representation of H_2, on an open Euclidean disc with hyperbolic lines represented by segments of circles orthogonal to the boundary circle of the disc (Figure 10.3b). We shall refer to the boundary as the *absolute* (circle) of the representation.

How are hyperbolic distance and angle measured in the Poincaré representation? What are the motions of H_2? By interpreting an orthogonal projection from E_2 onto a tangent hemisphere projectively, and by noting that in

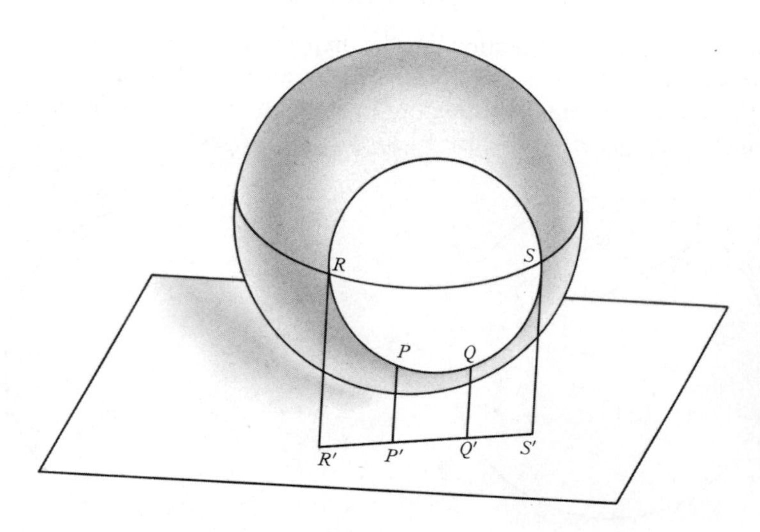

FIGURE 10.4

$S_2(\mathsf{R})$ the point $(t_1, t_2)^T$ of the conic $\mathbf{X} = (t_1^2, t_1 t_2, t_2^2)^T$ projects from $(0, 1, 0)^T$ onto the point $X': (t_1^2, 0, t_2^2)^T$ on the line $x_2 = 0$ (Figure 10.5), we find that

$$(A_1 A_3, X' Y') = (A_1 A_3, X Y)^2.$$

Consequently (Figure 10.4)

$$(R' S', P' Q') = (R S, P Q)^2.$$

From (10.15),

$$D_H(P, Q) = k \log (R S, P Q). \tag{10.16}$$

We have seen that cross ratio obtained by regarding a circle in E_2 as a conic in $S_2(\mathsf{R})$ is identical with cross ratio obtained by regarding the circle as a chain in $S_1(\mathsf{C})$. Stereographic projection, which identifies a representation of $S_1(\mathsf{C})$ on the sphere with that in E_2, does not change cross ratio, and hence in the Poincaré representation of H_2, $D_H(P, Q)$ is given, to within a numerical factor, by the logarithm of the cross ratio (RS, PQ), where R, S are the intersections with the absolute of the unique circle on P, Q orthogonal to the absolute (Figure 10.3(b)).

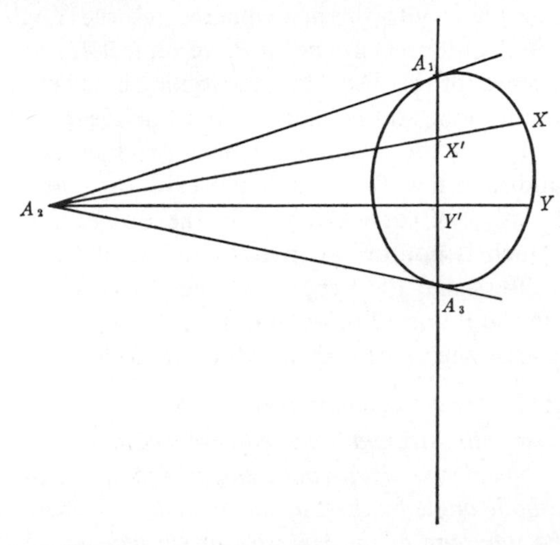

FIGURE 10.5

To identify the motions of H_2, in the Poincaré representation, we note that in $\mathscr{W}$ an inversion in a circle orthogonal to a circle $\mathscr{C}$ has the following properties:

1. Its restriction to $\mathscr{C}$ is a hyperbolic involution, and therefore it interchanges the two sense classes on $\mathscr{C}$.
2. It leaves fixed each side of $\mathscr{C}$.
3. It maps a circle orthogonal to $\mathscr{C}$ onto another such circle.
4. If P, Q are two points (not on $\mathscr{C}$), and if the unique circle on P, Q orthogonal to $\mathscr{C}$ intersects $\mathscr{C}$ in R, S, it leaves the cross ratio (RS, PQ) unchanged.

Clearly, when $\mathscr{C}$ is the absolute in a Poincaré representation, the above inversion represents a line reflection in H_2, and conversely, a line reflection in H_2 is represented by such an inversion. More generally, if $g \in G(\mathsf{C})$, $g\mathscr{C} = \mathscr{C}$, and $g_{\mathscr{C}}$ is direct,† then g preserves cross ratios, and therefore g represents a direct motion of H_2. Conversely, if $h \in G^+(H_2)$, its representation in $\mathscr{W}$ can be completed in a unique way so that the completion g satisfies $g \in G(\mathsf{C})$, $g\mathscr{C} = \mathscr{C}$, and $g_{\mathscr{C}}$ is direct. Thus the group of hyperbolic motions is represented by the subgroup of $G(\mathscr{W})$ which leaves fixed each side of a given chain.

† As earlier, $g_{\mathscr{C}}$ is the restriction of g to $\mathscr{C}$.

Our question concerning representation of angles has an unexpectedly simple answer. The Poincaré representation of H_2 is conformal, that is, the hyperbolic angle is equal to the Euclidean angle. It is trivial to verify this for angles at the center of the disc (Figure 10.4), since the orthogonal projection from the plane onto the hemisphere preserves angle at the center. If two lines V, V' in H_2 intersect in a point P, we subject H_2 to a motion g that maps P onto the center of the disc; the hyperbolic angle between V and V' is unchanged by the motion, and is equal to the Euclidean angle between gV and gV'. We carry out the two maps whose product yields the Poincaré representation, and note that these maps preserve angle at the center of the original disc. Finally, we carry out g^{-1} in the Poincaré representation, a transformation which is conformal in both the Euclidean and hyperbolic geometries. It follows that the hyperbolic angle between V and V' is their Euclidean angle in the Poincaré representation.

We can summarize the preceding results in the following theorem.

THEOREM 10.11. *The hyperbolic plane can be mapped one-to-one onto an open Euclidean disc with straight lines corresponding to segments of circles orthogonal to the boundary. Hyperbolic distance is given by the cross ratio* (10.16), *and hyperbolic angle by the Euclidean angle. Hyperbolic motions are represented by the subgroup of the inversive group leaving the disc fixed.*

The essence of the above result can be stated as follows.

THEOREM 10.12. *The geometry of a given side of a given chain in the inversive plane $\mathscr{W}$ under the subgroup that leaves the given side fixed is isomorphic to hyperbolic plane geometry.*

We shall close this section with two illustrations. First let us identify infinite hyperbolic rotations (page 361) in the Poincaré representation of H_2. If g in $G(H_2)$ is an infinite rotation, $g_{\mathscr{C}}$ is a parabolic projectivity either in the map of Theorem 9.3 or of Theorem 10.11. In $S_1(\mathsf{C})$, a parabolic projectivity can be represented by $z' = z + 1$. In E_2, $z' = z + a$ ($a \in \mathsf{R}$) leaves fixed each line $y = \text{const.}$, and permutes the lines $x = \text{const.}$ Hence in $S_1(\mathsf{C})$, a parabolic projectivity leaves fixed each circle in one pencil of mutually tangent circles, and permutes the circles of the orthogonal pencil. It follows that concentric horocycles are represented by the circles tangent to the absolute at one point.

For our second illustration we prove the classical theorem that the sum of the angles of a hyperbolic triangle is less than π, For if ABC is a given triangle (Figure 10.6(a)), we can without loss of generality suppose that B', the inverse of B in the absolute, is the point $z = \infty$. Then B is the center of the absolute, and the hyperbolic lines $A \oplus B$ and $C \oplus B$ have Poincaré representations which are Euclidean straight segments (Figure 10.6(b)). Thus the hyperbolic angle α at A is the Euclidean angle between $A \oplus B$ and the circular segment AC, and since the Euclidean line segment AC is not contained in the interior of the hyperbolic triangular region, $\angle BAC > \alpha$. Thus the sum of the three angles of the hyperbolic triangle ABC must be less than the sum of the angles of the Euclidean triangle with the same vertices.

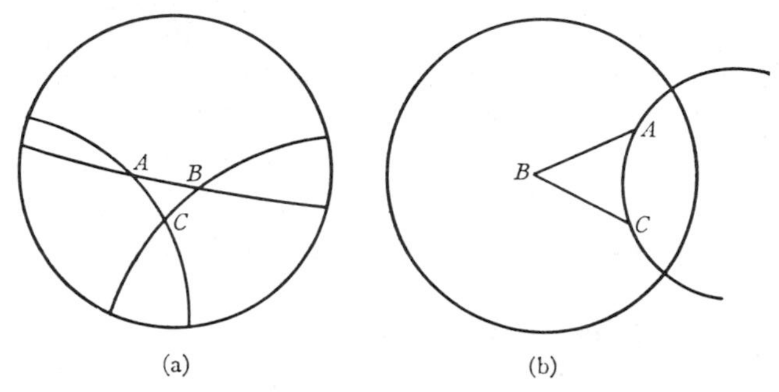

FIGURE 10.6

EXERCISES

The plane of Exercises 1–10 *is* E_2.

1. Use Theorem 10.2 to prove that two circles are orthogonal if and only if one contains (at least) one pair of points inverse in the other.

2. Prove that there exists an inversion which maps the circles incident to two points onto a pencil of concurrent lines.

3. Prove that there exists an inversion that maps all circles in which two given points are inverse onto a pencil of concentric circles.

4. Prove that the set of circles mutually tangent at a given point can be inverted into a pencil of parallel lines.

5. Prove by means of the preceding exercises that a pencil of circles determines a second pencil such that each two circles in different pencils are orthogonal.

6. Use Exercise 1 to prove that if P and Q are inverse in a circle C and if g is any inversion, gP and gQ are inverse in gC.

7. Find canonical equations in E_2 of two mutually orthogonal pencils of circles.

8. Verify that (10.11′) represents the line reflection whose axis is $\bar{\mu}z + \mu\bar{z} + \delta = 0$.

9. Let $\mathscr{A}$ be the pencil of circles with base points A_1, A_2 $(A_1 \neq A_2)$, and let $\mathscr{B}$ be the orthogonal pencil. A point $X \neq A_1, A_2$ is incident to exactly one circle of each pencil, and the two circles through X intersect again in a point, say X'. The map g defined by $gX = X', gA_i = A_i$ is called the Möbius involution determined by A_1, A_2. Prove that a Möbius involution is the product of inversions in any two orthogonal circles in the pencil $\mathscr{A}$.

10. Prove that a map $z' = (az + b)/(cz + d)$, $ad - bc \neq 0$, is the product of two Möbius involutions ($a, b, c, d \in \mathsf{C}$).

11. Prove that a nonparabolic projectivity in $S_1(\mathsf{C})$ can be represented in the plane $\mathscr{P}$ by a rotation, a dilation, or the product of two such transformations.

12. Show that a nonparabolic projectivity in $S_1(\mathsf{C})$ with characteristic k satisfying $|k| = 1$ permutes the circles on the fixed points and leaves fixed every circle of the orthogonal pencil.

13. Generalize Exercise 12 for projectivities with $|k| \neq 1$.

14. Find the fixed pencils of circles in a parabolic projectivity.

15. Show that every projectivity in $S_1(\mathsf{C})$ is the product of at most four inversions.

16. Derive (10.13), the condition for orthogonality.

17. Let $\mathbf{A}$ be an arbitrary 2×2 nonsingular matrix, and let $\mathbf{B}$ be Hermitian (see (10.10)). Prove that $\mathbf{A}^{-T}\mathbf{B}\bar{\mathbf{A}}^{-1}$ and $\rho\mathbf{B}$ for $\rho \in \mathsf{R}$ are Hermitian.

18. Show that an antiprojectivity which interchanges two points is not necessarily involutory.

19. Give a matrix proof of Theorem 10.8, using Exercise 17.

20. Show that an involutory antiprojectivity either possesses a chain of fixed points and is an inversion, or it possesses no fixed points and is the product of three inversions in three mutually orthogonal circles.

21. Prove that two inversions in mutually orthogonal circles commute, and, conversely, that the circles of inversion of two commutative inversions intersect orthogonally.

22. Prove that a Möbius involution is the product of two commutative inversions.

#**23.** Let three circles, mutually tangent at A, be intersected again by a circle on A orthogonal to the three in points B, C, D. Prove that the cross ratio (AB, CD) is independent of the choice of the common orthogonal circle through A.

#**24.** Prove that every projectivity in $\mathscr{W}$ that leaves fixed each side of a given chain is the product of two inversions.

25. Prove the statement in the text (page 377) that the representation in $\mathscr{W}$ of $h \in G^+(H_2)$ can be completed in a unique way so that the completion satisfies the stated conditions.

#**26.** Identify the set of hyperbolic circles with given center, in the Poincaré representation of H_2.

#**27.** Reformulate properties of translations and equidistant curves in H_2 in terms of circles, by means of a Poincaré representation of H_2.

#**28.** Interpret Exercises 24 and 25 of the preceding section in terms of circles and their properties.

11 The Elliptic Plane

We defined real elliptic geometry earlier as the geometry of the point set of $S_2(\mathsf{R})$ under the subgroup of $G_8(\mathsf{R})$ that preserves a given elliptic polarity (see Definition 1.5, and IV, Theorem 10.5). In this section we present some properties of this geometry.

We denote both the point set and the geometry of an elliptic plane by L_2, its group by $G(L_2)$, and the absolute polarity by σ. Since the points of L_2 and the lines of L_2 are in one-to-one correspondence with the points and lines of $S_2(\mathsf{R})$, the separation properties of $S_2(\mathsf{R})$ previously noted are valid in L_2. For example, the lines of L_2 are closed nonbounding curves, two points of a line are end points of two segments, a line does not separate L_2, L_2 is compact, etc. Thus the topological properties of L_2 (and $S_2(\mathsf{R})$) are quite different from those of H_2, A_2, E_2, and K_2. Clearly L_2 induces on its lines a one-dimensional elliptic structure. Therefore we can introduce directed distance on any line, and the length† of any line is π.

Another major difference between L_2 and the planes just mentioned is that the theorems on duality in $S_2(\mathsf{R})$ are valid in L_2.

THEOREM 11.1. *The structure of the space of lines of L_2 is that of a two-dimensional elliptic geometry.*

Proof. Let the quadratic form of σ be

$$[Q] = [\mathbf{X}^T\mathbf{B}\mathbf{X}], \tag{11.1}$$

and let g in $G(L_2)$ have the representation $\mathbf{X}' = \mathbf{A}\mathbf{X}$. Then (see IV, (10.2))

$$[\mathbf{B}\mathbf{A}^{-1}] = [\mathbf{A}^T\mathbf{B}]. \tag{11.2}$$

In line coordinates $\mathbf{U}$, g is given by $\mathbf{U}' = \mathbf{U}\mathbf{A}^{-1}$, and (11.2) is both necessary and sufficient that $\mathbf{U}' = \mathbf{U}\mathbf{A}^{-1}$ preserve the dual form

$$[Q^*] = [\mathbf{U}\mathbf{B}^{-1}\mathbf{U}^T].$$

Thus our definition of $G(L_2)$ is self-dual, and since the set of points and lines of L_2 is likewise self-dual, the theorem follows.

If $g \in G(L_2)$, the map σg (equal to $g\sigma$) interchanges points and lines of L_2 while preserving the structure of the plane. It can be regarded as a transformation effecting duality. In particular, a pencil of lines is an L_1; we can define angle between two lines as one-dimensional elliptic distance, and we can direct a pencil so that the concept "the angle from one line to a second" has meaning. However, we shall see that L_2 is nonorientable and that we cannot direct all pencils in L_2 simultaneously, as we could in A_2 and H_2.

† As in H_2, we can introduce an absolute constant k in the definition of distance (see footnote, page 351).

In terms of (11.1), elliptic distance D_L between points, and elliptic angle θ_L between lines are determined by† (see (7.4), (9.2), and Exercise 10, page 335)

$$\cos^2 D_L(Y, Z) = \frac{(\mathbf{Y}^T\mathbf{B}\mathbf{Z})^2}{(\mathbf{Y}^T\mathbf{B}\mathbf{Y})(\mathbf{Z}^T\mathbf{B}\mathbf{Z})}, \qquad 0 \leqq D_L \leqq \pi/2, \tag{11.3}$$

$$\cos^2 \theta_L(V, W) = \frac{(\mathbf{V}\mathbf{B}^{-1}\mathbf{W}^T)^2}{(\mathbf{V}\mathbf{B}^{-1}\mathbf{V}^T)(\mathbf{W}\mathbf{B}^{-1}\mathbf{W}^T)}, \qquad 0 \leqq \theta_L \leqq \pi/2. \tag{11.4}$$

We can choose projective coordinates in $S_2(\mathsf{R})$ so that $\mathbf{B}$ in (11.1) is the unit matrix; then

$$[Q] = [\mathbf{X}^T\mathbf{X}], \tag{11.5}$$

and we can normalize representatives $\mathbf{X}$ of $[\mathbf{X}]$ so that

$$\mathbf{X}^T\mathbf{X} = 1. \tag{11.6}$$

Then σ possesses the normalized representation

$$\mathbf{U}' = \mathbf{X}^T, \tag{11.7}$$

and (11.6) implies that line coordinates given by (11.7) satisfy the analogous normalizing condition

$$\mathbf{U}\mathbf{U}^T = 1. \tag{11.8}$$

In L_2 these normalized special projective point coordinates are called *Weierstrass coordinates* (see V, 9, Exercise 20). In terms of such coordinates, (11.3) and (11.4) become

$$\cos D_L(Y, Z) = \pm\mathbf{Y}^T\mathbf{Z}, \qquad \cos \theta_L(V, W) = \pm\mathbf{V}\mathbf{W}^T. \tag{11.9}$$

From these equations we note that the distance between two points in L_2 is the angle between their polars.

Every collineation in $S_2(\mathsf{R})$ possesses a representative matrix $\mathbf{A}$ which satisfies

$$\det \mathbf{A} = 1. \tag{11.10}$$

In terms of Weierstrass coordinates and of the normalization (11.10), (11.2) implies that $\rho\mathbf{A}^{-1} = \mathbf{A}^T$, or $\rho^3 = \det^2\mathbf{A} = 1$, so that (11.2) becomes

$$\mathbf{A}^{-1} = \mathbf{A}^T. \tag{11.11}$$

† In an elliptic space with absolute constant k, we would replace $D_L(Y, Z)$ in (11.3) by $D_L(Y, Z)/k$. In considering angles, we can take $k = 1$, although as in E_2, the total angle swept out by a *directed* line rotating about a point is 2π, corresponding to the choice $k = 2$.

We note that if $g \in G(L_2)$ has the normalized representation $\mathbf{X}' = \mathbf{AX}$, where $\mathbf{A}$ satisfies (11.10) and (11.11), $\mathbf{X}'$ satisfies (11.6) whenever $\mathbf{X}$ does.

DEFINITION 11.1. A matrix over R satisfying (11.11) is called an *orthogonal* matrix.

We note from (11.11) that orthogonal matrices $\mathbf{A}$ satisfy $\det \mathbf{A} = \pm 1$. In $S_2(\mathsf{R})$, however, the normalization of $\mathbf{A}$ for which (11.10) holds is unique, and we have the following theorem.

THEOREM 11.2. *$G(L_2)$ is isomorphic to the multiplicative group of* 3×3 *orthogonal matrices over* R *of determinant* 1.

One canonical interpretation for the multiplicative group of orthogonal matrices is in terms of Euclidean geometry. For the moment let $(x_1, x_2, x_3)^T$ denote (rectangular) Cartesian coordinates in E_3. The equation

$$a_1 x_1 + a_2 x_2 + a_3 x_3 = 0$$

represents a plane through the origin, say α, and the condition

$$a_1^2 + a_2^2 + a_3^2 = 1,$$

equivalent to the condition that the coefficients a_i are direction cosines of the normal to α, implies that the function

$$d(X, a) = a_1 x_1 + a_2 x_2 + a_3 x_3$$

is the directed distance from α to the point $X:(x_1, x_2, x_3)^T$. Hence in E_3 we can interpret the equation $\mathbf{X}' = \mathbf{AX}$, where $\mathbf{A}$ is orthogonal, as defining a coordinate transformation from one Cartesian system to another with the same origin. If $\det \mathbf{A} = -1$, the determinant of the product transformation, of $\mathbf{X}' = -\mathbf{X}$ and $\mathbf{X}'' = \mathbf{AX}'$, is plus one. Although we have not discussed orientation in E_3, it is intuitively clear that if $\mathbf{X}' = -\mathbf{X}$ the $\mathbf{X}$-system and the $\mathbf{X}'$-system are oppositely oriented, and therefore we would expect that in E_3, condition (11.10) (together with (11.11)) implies that the two coordinatizations determine the same orientation. It is beyond the scope of this book to develop three-dimensional Euclidean geometry with the logical completeness that the reader should seek; instead we shall formulate as a definition the substance of our heuristic discussion interpreted in terms of Euclidean motions.

DEFINITION 11.2. If $\mathbf{X} = (x_1, x_2, x_3)^T$ is a Cartesian coordinatization of E_3, the point transformation in E_3 defined by

$$\mathbf{X}' = \mathbf{AX} + \mathbf{C}, \tag{11.12}$$

where $\mathbf{A}$ is an orthogonal 3×3 matrix and $\mathbf{C}$ is 3×1, is called a *motion*. The motion is *direct* or *opposite* according as $\det \mathbf{A} = 1$ or $\det \mathbf{A} = -1$.

A direct motion in E_3 which possesses a fixed point is called a (space) *rotation* with center the fixed point. Choosing such a point as the origin implies that in (11.12) $\mathbf{C} = 0$, and therefore the set of rotations in E_3 with given center can be represented by the same matrices that represent $G(L_2)$.

THEOREM 11.3. *Let $\mathscr{P}$ be the set of lines*† *in E_3 incident to a given point, and let $G(\mathscr{P})$ be the subgroup induced by the group of Euclidean motions that maps $\mathscr{P}$ onto itself. The geometries $\Gamma(\mathscr{P}, G(\mathscr{P}))$ and $\Gamma(L_2, G(L_2))$ are isomorphic.*

In this isomorphism, $X \in L_2$ corresponds to a line in the bundle $\mathscr{P}$, and a line in L_2 corresponds to a pencil of lines in $\mathscr{P}$, that is, a plane. The elliptic distance between points in L_2 is the Euclidean angle between the image lines in $\mathscr{P}$, and the angle between elliptic lines is the Euclidean angle between the corresponding planes. The absolute polarity of L_2 appears in $\mathscr{P}$ as the map from a given $p \in \mathscr{P}$ to the plane orthogonal to p.

We should note that in E_3, the point reflection $\mathbf{X}' = -\mathbf{X}$ is the identity in $\mathscr{P}$, as in L_2.

Although we might use Theorem 11.3 to develop elliptic geometry from three-dimensional Euclidean geometry, from the point of view of logical completeness it is preferable for us to use the theorem the other way.

As a metric space, L_2 is *bounded*, that is, $D_L(Y, Z)$ is a bounded function on $L_2 \times L_2$. The distance between points conjugate in σ is the upper bound $\pi/2$, and dually the angle between conjugate lines is $\pi/2$. In L_2 one refers to points (or lines) that are conjugate in σ as *orthogonal* or *perpendicular*. Weierstrass coordinates can be defined in elliptic terms by selecting a reference triangle, $A_1 A_2 A_3$, with side-lengths $\pi/2$ (or, equivalently, with angles $\pi/2$) and taking as the unit point D one of the four points equidistant from the vertices of the reference triangle. Letting X be any point, and letting X_i, D_i be the projections on $A_j \oplus A_k$ from A_i (i, j, k unequal) of X, D respectively, we define $\mathbf{X}$ (to within a factor ± 1) by taking as one value of $\mathbf{X}$ that given by

$$x_i = \cos D_L(A_i, X), \quad \text{or} \quad x_i = -\cos D_L(A_i, X), \tag{11.13}$$

according to $X_i \in \operatorname{seg} A_j D_i A_k$ or $X_i \notin \operatorname{seg} A_j D_i A_k$. Line coordinates satisfying (11.8) can be defined dually, and the usual formulas of elliptic (and spherical) trigonometry are consequences of (11.6), (11.9), and (11.13). In particular, the reader can derive the Pythagorean Theorem for right triangles,

$$\cos c = \cos a \cos b \qquad (\gamma = \pi/2), \tag{11.14}$$

and the Law of Cosines for arbitrary triangles,

$$\cos c = \cos a \cos b + \sin a \sin b \cos \gamma. \tag{11.15}$$

† The set of all lines in E_3 incident to a given point, and the set parallel to a given line are called *bundles* of lines.

For P a point and l a line ($l \neq \sigma P$), it follows from (11.14) that $D_L(P, X)$ for $X \in l$ assumes its maximum value ($\pi/2$) only at $l \cap \sigma P$, and its minimum value only at the foot of the perpendicular to l from P, $(P \oplus \sigma l) \cap l$. The reader can use (11.15) to show that L_2 with the metric D_L is a metric space (see Definition 9.2).

The set of points at a given distance from a given point is called an (elliptic) *circle*, with *center* at the given point, and with *axis* the polar line of the center. In terms of the special projective coordinates for which (11.5) holds, the equation of the circle with center at Y and radius a is

$$(11.16) \qquad (\mathbf{Y}^T\mathbf{Y})(\mathbf{X}^T\mathbf{X}) \cos^2 a - (\mathbf{Y}^T\mathbf{X})^2 = 0.$$

Thus the set of circles in L_2 with a given center corresponds in $S_2(\mathsf{R})$ to a pencil of conics of type IIIa (IV, (11.23)); the common axis of the circles of the pencil is the singular conic in the pencil of rank 1.

Dually, the set of lines in L_2 intersecting a given line at a given angle envelop a circle whose center is the pole of the given line. If the angle is $\pi/2$, the circle degenerates into a point circle consisting solely of the center.

Another obvious conclusion is that a line in L_2 is a circle of maximum radius ($a = \pi/2$), with center the pole of the line.

If we take $Y = A_3{:}(0, 0, 1)^T$, (11.16) becomes

$$(x_1^2 + x_2^2) \cos^2 a - x_3^2 \sin^2 a = 0.$$

If $a \neq \pi/2$, $X \notin \sigma A_3$ and we can map the points of this circle one-to-one onto the real interval $0 \leqq \phi < 2\pi$,

$$(11.17) \qquad x_1 = \sin a \cos \phi, \qquad x_2 = \sin a \sin \phi, \qquad x_3 = \cos a.$$

These x's are the Weierstrass coordinates for which $x_3 > 0$ when $X \notin \sigma A_3$. Points on σA_3 do not determine ϕ uniquely; σA_3 is traversed twice when $a = \pi/2$, and ϕ traverses its range. The mapping $X \to (a, \phi)$ (for $0 < a < \pi/2$, $0 \leqq \phi < 2\pi$) constitutes a polar coordinatization of $L_2 - A_3 - \sigma A_3$. For any $X \in L_2 - A_3 - \sigma A_3$, a is the directed distance from A_3 with $\{A_3 X\}$ the positive sense class on $A_3 \oplus X$, and ϕ will turn out to be the directed angle from the directed line $A_3 \oplus A_1$ (with $\{A_3 D_2\}$ the positive sense class) to the directed line $A_3 \oplus X$ (with $\{A_3 X\}$ the positive sense class). If $Y \in A_3 \oplus X$ and $\{A_3 Y\} \neq \{A_3 X\}$, the angle coordinates of X and Y differ by π. We can expect (11.17) to be useful in verifying that a pencil of directed lines possesses a one-dimensional elliptic structure, and that directed angle in such a pencil represents the elliptic system of measurement with the choice of $k = 2$ for the absolute constant (see footnote page 382).

Turning our attention to isometries of L_2, we would expect to prove the analogue for L_2 of Theorem 9.5.

THEOREM 11.4. *The group of isometries of L_2 is $G(L_2)$.*

Actually however the hypothesis implicit in this statement is stronger than we need.

THEOREM 11.5. *A one-to-one map of L_2 onto itself which maps lines onto lines and orthogonal lines onto orthogonal lines is an isometry and belongs to $G(L_2)$.*

Proof. From the projective point of view, the map is a collineation (see III, Theorem 8.6) which preserves conjugate lines in σ. The conclusion follows from the dual of (IV, Theorem 10.2).

This theorem has obvious import for E_3.

THEOREM 11.6. *A map, from the lines in E_3 of a bundle of intersecting lines onto the lines of such a bundle, which maps pencils of lines in the bundle onto pencils, and orthogonal lines in the bundle onto orthogonal lines is the restriction to the bundle of a Euclidean motion.*

We leave the proof to the reader.

In comparison with the several types of direct motions in E_2 and H_2 and the existence there of opposite motions, $G(L_2)$ has an unexpectedly simple structure. Since every element in $G_8(\mathsf{R})$ possesses at least one fixed point (III, Theorem 11.2), we can choose Weierstrass coordinates so that a given $g \in G(L_2)$ leaves fixed $A_3:(0,0,1)^T$ and $\sigma A_3: x_3 = 0$. The elements a_{ij} of the normalized matrix $\mathbf{A}$ of g satisfy (see (11.11))

$$a_{i3} = a_{3i} = 0, \quad i = 1, 2; \qquad a_{33} = \pm 1.$$

The restriction of g to σA_3, $g_{\sigma A_3}$, is either direct or opposite. If opposite, it possesses two fixed points which can be taken to be the vertices A_1, A_2 of the reference triangle. Then g is given by $x_1' = \pm x_1, x_2' = \mp x_2, x_3' = -x_3$. Either choice of sign leads to the conclusion that g possesses a unique fixed point on whose polar g induces a direct isometry. Thus we can suppose that the fixed points have been labeled so that $g_{\sigma A_3}$ is direct. Then we have

$$a_{11}a_{22} - a_{12}a_{21} = 1, \qquad a_{33} = 1. \tag{11.18}$$

The orthogonality condition (11.11) (see (7.5) and IV, (10.8)) implies that there exists a unique $\alpha \in \mathsf{R}$, $0 \leqq \alpha < 2\pi$, in terms of which $\mathbf{A}$ is given by

$$\mathbf{A} = \begin{pmatrix} \cos\alpha & -\sin\alpha & 0 \\ \sin\alpha & \cos\alpha & 0 \\ 0 & 0 & 1 \end{pmatrix}, \qquad 0 \leqq \alpha < 2\pi. \tag{11.19}$$

We note that we must choose an interval of length 2π for the range of α because values a_{ij} and $-a_{ij}$ $(i, j = 1, 2)$ determine distinct isometries in L_2 even though their restrictions to σA_3 coincide.

It is clear that g in $G(L_2)$ possesses a unique point $C(g)$ which plays the role of A_3. We call g a *rotation* with *center* $C(g)$, and *angle* α. We shall presently determine the geometric significance of α. However, we note now that a rotation of angle π is simultaneously a point reflection and a line reflection. Moreover, the product of two line reflections, with orthogonal axes, is the line reflection whose axis is the join of the centers of the two given reflections. Therefore, in L_2, there can be no distinction between the product of an even number of line reflections and the product of an odd number. Furthermore, we observe from (11.19) that in L_2, unlike E_2, a line reflection can be embedded in a continuous family of rotations that includes the identity ($\alpha = 0$).

We determined α in (11.19) analytically, in terms of a particular coordinatization, and we cannot conclude that α is determined by the rotation g. In fact, we shall show that $2\pi - \alpha$ is an alternative value for the angle of g. In obtaining (11.19), we selected A_1, A_2 as an arbitrary pair of orthogonal points on σA_3. Had we chosen coordinates $\mathbf{X}^*$ related to our actual choice by the equations

$$(11.20) \qquad x_1^* = x_2, \qquad x_2^* = x_1, \qquad x_3^* = x_3,$$

the matrix of g in the $\mathbf{X}^*$-coordinates would be given by $\mathbf{A}^* = \mathbf{CAC}^{-1}$, where $\mathbf{C}$ is the matrix of (11.20). We find by direct computation that $\mathbf{A}^*$ is $\mathbf{A}$ with α replaced by $2\pi - \alpha$. We leave it to the reader to show that the two angles correspond to the two orientations of σA_3. Hence we conclude that the angle of a rotation is defined only with respect to a chosen sense class on the axis of the center, or equivalently, in the pencil of lines with vertex the center.

We summarize the preceding discussion in the following theorem.

THEOREM 11.7. *Every isometry of L_2 is a rotation, with a unique center and with an angle in $[0, 2\pi)$ which is determined with reference to a chosen sense class in the pencil of lines with vertex at the center.*

In E_2 (or K_2) we defined the directed angle from one directed line (or segment) to another in terms of an orientation of the plane. We could however have used less of the structural properties of E_2 (or K_2) than we did, and these alternatives are available in L_2.

We note that if $P \in L_2$ and $\vec{l}, \vec{l}'$ are directed lines on P, there exists a unique rotation g with center P such that $g\vec{l} = \vec{l}'$. We define the directed angle from $\vec{l}$ to $\vec{l}'$ as the angle of g for the chosen orientation of the pencil at P. Then it follows that in terms of polar coordinates (a, ϕ) with origin at P (see (11.17)) the rotation with center P and angle α is given by

$$a' = a, \qquad \phi' = \phi + \alpha \pmod{2\pi},$$

and that ϕ in (11.17) is indeed the directed angle.

It is also possible to introduce the concept of directed angle from one directed line to another by showing that under $G(L_2)$, circles in L_2 (of radii less than $\pi/2$) possess one-dimensional elliptic structures, and that these impart the identical elliptic structure to the set of directed half-lines through a point.

We have spoken of a continuous family of rotations. Although it is necessary in more advanced work to define continuity in very general types of spaces it is sufficient for our purposes to refer to a set of isometries in L_2 as a *continuous* family if the elements of a normalized matrix representation are continuous functions of one real parameter over an interval in R, or of several real parameters in a suitably defined subset of $\mathsf{R} \times \mathsf{R} \times \ldots \times \mathsf{R}$. Thus (11.19) are matrices of a continuous family of isometries in L_2 in an interval $0 < a \leqq \alpha \leqq b < 2\pi$. Analogously, we could exhibit continuous families of isometries in other spaces, for example in E_2, H_2, etc.

Although we have spoken of the continuity in an interval of the rotations with matrices (11.19), it is more illuminating to say that the set of all rotations with a given center is a continuous family with domain a directed elliptic line. For if $\overrightarrow{L_1}$ is such a line and if H is the set of rotations with given center, we can define a one-to-one map from $\overrightarrow{L_1}$ onto H by writing $\alpha = 2d$ in (11.19), where d is a directed distance on $\overrightarrow{L_1}$; then if $h_X \in H$ corresponds to $X \in \overrightarrow{L_1}$, $\lim_{X \to Y} h_X = h_Y$.

We have previously asserted that L_2 is nonorientable. Although we shall not define this concept mathematically, we shall derive two properties of L_2 that are strongly suggestive of its nonorientability. In the pencil with vertex A_1 let $\mathscr{S}$ be the sense class defined by the ordered pair of lines: $x_2 = 0$, $x_2 - x_3 = 0$ (Figure 11.1). Let g_α be the rotation with matrix (11.19).

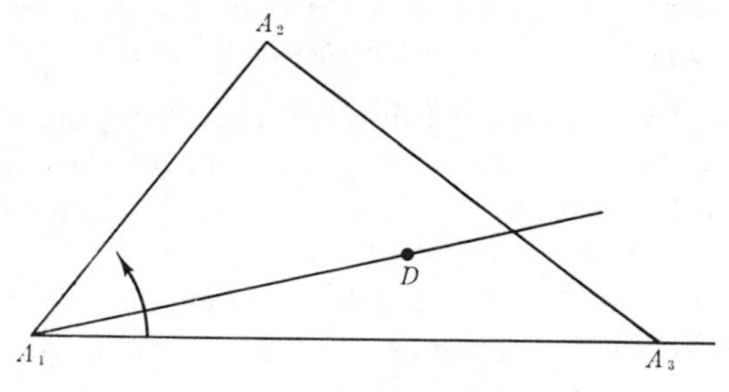

FIGURE 11.1

The set g_α, for $0 \leqq \alpha < 2\pi$, is the set of all rotations with center A_3. The reader can verify that this set is a group. For any $P \in L_2$, the orbit of P, that is, the set of points $g_\alpha P$ for $0 \leqq \alpha < 2\pi$, is the circle through P, center at A_3. Similarly, $g_\alpha \mathscr{S}$ is a set of sense classes in the pencils whose vertices $g_\alpha A_1$

traverse the line $A_1 \oplus A_2$. In the interval $0 \leqq \alpha \leqq \pi$, $g_\alpha A_1$ traverses $A_1 \oplus A_2$ just once, and $g_\pi A_1 = A_1$. But $g_\pi \mathscr{S} \neq \mathscr{S}$, as is easily verified from (11.19); the directed pencil with vertex at A_1 returns to its starting point with its orientation reversed. Thus if a directed pencil of lines is *transported rigidly* from a point P to a point Q, the orientation of the terminal pencil at Q varies with the choice of the segment (with end points P, Q) along which the pencil is transported.

An analogous conclusion holds for continuous families of rotations. We introduce the matrix

$$\mathbf{D} = \begin{pmatrix} \cos\omega & 0 & -\sin\omega \\ 0 & 1 & 0 \\ \sin\omega & 0 & \cos\omega \end{pmatrix},$$

which we can interpret as the matrix of a coordinate transformation which assigns to A_3 the new coordinates $(-\sin\omega, 0, \cos\omega)^T$. Then the motion

$$\text{(11.21)} \qquad \mathbf{X}' = \mathbf{A}^*\mathbf{X}, \qquad \mathbf{A}^* = \mathbf{DAD}^{-1},$$

for given α, ω is a rotation with center $C{:}(-\sin\omega, 0, \cos\omega)^T$ and angle α (with respect to a chosen orientation of the pencil at C). As ω varies over the interval $0 \leqq \omega \leqq \pi$, C traverses $A_1 \oplus A_3$ just once, starting at and returning to A_3 (for $\omega = 0, \pi$). However the two rotations (11.21) for $\omega = 0, \pi$ do not coincide, and are in fact inverses. Thus to say that a rotation is *transported rigidly* by letting its center move from a point P to a point Q does not suffice to determine the terminal rotation at Q. Such a phenomenon cannot occur in the other metric planes that we have studied.

Despite these striking differences between L_2 and E_2, we shall show that it is possible to identify the orientation relations of the two planes on a *local* scale. Let $\mathscr{R}$ be an elliptic disc of radius $a < \pi/2$ and center C,

$$\mathscr{R} = \{X \mid D_L(C, X) < a, X \in L_2\}, \qquad 0 < a < \pi/2,$$

and let $\mathscr{D}$ be its bounding circle

$$\mathscr{D} = \{X \mid D_L(C, X) = a, X \in L_2\}.$$

The selection of a positive sense class on $\mathscr{D}$ determines a positive sense class on σC, the axis of $\mathscr{D}$ (see Theorem 9.4 and Corollary 9.1), and the latter sense class determines (as in the affine plane) a positive sense class on every pencil of lines with vertex in $\mathscr{R}$, and the positive orientation of $\mathscr{R}$. On the other hand we can map $\mathscr{R} \cup \mathscr{D}$ onto a closed Euclidean disc (see page 97); in terms of polar coordinates, (u, ϕ) in L_2 and (r, θ) in E_2, this map can be given by (see (11.17))

$$\tau\colon \quad r = \sin u, \qquad \theta = \phi, \qquad 0 \leqq u \leqq a.$$

Clearly τ maps the sense classes of $\mathscr{D}$ onto those of $\tau\mathscr{D}$, and therefore τ preserves orientation relations.

In E_2, the determinant of a continuous family of motions is a continuous function, and therefore a continuous family of motions in E_2 cannot contain both direct motions (with determinant 1) and opposite motions (with determinant -1). The space of motions of E_2 is not a connected space in that two of its motions cannot necessarily be joined by a continuous family of motions. The space of elliptic motions, $G(L_2)$, is quite different.

THEOREM 11.8. *The space of isometries of L_2 is connected.*

Proof. Let $g_1, g_2 \in G(L_2)$, and let C_1, C_2 be their centers, and α_1, α_2 their angles referred to specific orientations of the pencils at C_1, C_2. For definiteness, let us suppose that $\alpha_1 \leqq \alpha_2$. Intuitively, we can increase the angle of g_1 continuously until it is equal to α_2, and we can then let the center trace that one of the two segments with end points C_1, C_2 along which the directed pencil at C_1 becomes the directed pencil at C_2. In a formal way, we can coordinatize the plane so that g_1 is given by (11.21) with $\alpha = \alpha_1$, $\omega = 0$, and g_2 is given by (11.21) with $\alpha = \alpha_2$, and $\omega = \omega_0$. If we define

$$\begin{aligned} &\alpha(t) = \alpha_2 t + \alpha_1(1-t), \qquad && \omega(t) = 0 \qquad && \text{for} \quad 0 \leqq t \leqq 1, \\ &\alpha(t) = \alpha_2, && \omega(t) = (t-1)\omega_0 && \text{for} \quad 1 \leqq t \leqq 2, \end{aligned}$$

we see that $\alpha(t)$ and $\omega(t)$ are continuous functions of t in $0 \leqq t \leqq 2$, and for these values of $\alpha = \alpha(t)$, $\omega = \omega(t)$, (11.21) represents a continuous family of isometries with g_1, g_2 corresponding to $t = 0$, $t = 2$ respectively.

We turn next to another property of $G(L_2)$ which is not shared by many of the more elementary transformation groups. To discuss this property we need to consider the limit operation on transformations more carefully than we have heretofore. Two examples suffice to indicate the more important possibilities. If π is a parabolic projectivity in $S_1(\mathsf{R})$, with representation $x' = x + a$ in terms of a nonhomogeneous projective coordinate, π^n is given by $x' = x + na$ $(n = 1, 2, 3, \ldots)$, and the sequence of points $\{\pi^n X\}$ converges for every $X \in S_1(\mathsf{R})$ (see page 138). However the map $X \to X'$, where $X' = \lim_{n\to\infty} \pi^n X$ is not a projectivity, since all points X are mapped onto one point, the fixed point of π. On the other hand, if we define $\tau_n \in G_3(\mathsf{R})$ by

$$\tau_n\colon \quad x' = x + 1 - 1/n,$$

we note that the sequence $\{\tau_n X\}$ converges for every $X \in S_1(\mathsf{R})$, and the map $X \to X'$ where $X' = \lim_{n\to\infty} \tau_n X$ is a projectivity. In both of these cases we say that the sequence of projectivities converges, even though the limit map in the first case is not a projectivity.

In considering limits of transformations the essential ingredient is that we are dealing with spaces in which convergence of points is defined. If this is the case, and $\{g_n\}$ is a sequence of maps, we say that the sequence $\{g_n\}$ converges to the map g, and we write

$$g = \lim_{n\to\infty} g_n,$$

provided that

$$gX = \lim_{n\to\infty} g_n X$$

for all points X in the given space.

The following theorem gives a remarkable property of the elliptic group of motions.

THEOREM 11.9. *Every infinite set of isometries in $G(L_2)$ contains a convergent sequence, and the limit is an isometry.*

Proof. The set of centers contains a convergent sequence because L_2, like $S_2(\mathsf{R})$, is compact (see III, Theorem 7.1). Let $\{C_n\}$ denote this sequence, let $C = \lim_{n\to\infty} C_n$, and let $\{g_n\}$ be a sequence of isometrics in the given set with the center of g_n the point C_n. We do not exclude the possibility that the C's coincide for n larger than some integer. We can suppose (after discarding a finite number of C's at the beginning) that all C_n lie inside some small circle $\mathscr{C}$, center at C. For definiteness, we can take the radius of $\mathscr{C}$ to be one-half, although any radius less than $\pi/4$ would serve. We can choose a positive direction on $\mathscr{C}$ and thereby orient its interior. Let α_n be the angle of g_n, referred to this orientation. Then there exists a subsequence of $\{\alpha_n\}$ that converges, and therefore a sequence of isometries in the given set of which both the centers and angles converge. Let us change our notation slightly, using the index i for the new sequences

$$\alpha = \lim \alpha_i, \qquad C = \lim C_i, \qquad i = i_1, i_2, \ldots.$$

Let g be the rotation with center C and angle α (mod 2π). To finish the proof we need to show that the sequence of points $\{g_i X\}$ converges for all $X \in L_2$, and that $\lim g_i X = gX$.

It is clear from (11.17) that a sequence of points $\{Y_i\}$ where Y_i has polar coordinates (a_i, ϕ_i) will converge if $\lim a_i$ and $\lim \phi_i$ exist, and that $\lim Y_i$ is then the point determined by (11.17) for $a = \lim a_i$, $\phi = \lim \phi_i$.

By the triangle inequality, we have

$$D_L(C_i, g_i X) - D_L(C, C_i) \leqq D_L(C, g_i X) \leqq D_L(C_i, g_i X) + D_L(C, C_i).$$

Since g_i is a rotation with center C_i, $D_L(C_i, g_i X) = D_L(C_i, X)$, and since distance is a continuous function on $L_2 \times L_2$, $D_L(C, C_i)$ converges to 0, and $D_L(C_i, X)$ to $D_L(C, X)$. Hence the sequence of real numbers $\{D_L(C, g_i X)\}$ converges to $D_L(C, X)$, that is, to $D_L(C, gX)$.

If $X \in \sigma C$, the sequence of lines $\{C_i \oplus X\}$ converges to $C \oplus X$ (see III, 7, Exercise 6). Since $\alpha_i \to \alpha$, the sequence $\{C \oplus g_i X\}$ converges to the line whose angle from $C \oplus X$ is α. Hence $g_i X$ converges to the point with polar coordinates $(\pi/2, \phi + \alpha)$ so that $g_i X \to gX$. If $X \notin \sigma C$, let $\vec{l}_i$ be the directed segment of length $\pi/2$, with initial point C_i and containing X, and let $\vec{l}$ be defined similarly, with initial point C. Then $\{C_i \oplus X\}$ converges to $C \oplus X$, and only a slight extension of earlier results permits the conclusion that $\lim \vec{l}_i = \vec{l}$. Since $\theta(\vec{l}_i, g\vec{l}_i) = \alpha_i$, and $\lim \alpha_i = \alpha$, $\lim g\vec{l}_i$ exists, and is $g\vec{l}$, the unique directed half-line whose angle from $\vec{l}$ is $\alpha \pmod{2\pi}$.† Thus $\lim g_i X$ exists and is the point gX, so that $g = \lim g_i$.

We say‡ that $G_2(L)$ is *compact*.

In L_2, as in E_2 and H_2, every rotation is the product of two line reflections; the product is not commutative, and the angle from the axis of the first reflection to that of the second is one-half the angle of the rotation. Letting A, B, C be three independent points, and r_{AB} the reflection in $A \oplus B$, etc., we have

$$r_{AB} r_{AC} r_{CA} r_{CB} r_{BC} r_{BA} = I.$$

The product $r_{AB} r_{AC}$ is a rotation with center A and angle twice the angle from $A \oplus C$ to $A \oplus B$. Hence we have the following theorem which is valid in E_2 and H_2 as well as in L_2.

THEOREM 11.10. *The product of rotations about the vertices of a triangular region with angles twice the directed interior angles of the region is the identity.*

We close this section with a few comments on the realization of elliptic and hyperbolic geometries in E_3. We have already seen that a region on the sphere that contains no two antipodal points can be mapped isometrically onto a subset of the elliptic plane. Although the two-dimensional metric structure induced on a surface in E_3 by the metric of E_3 can be of a more general type than any that we have considered, there exist large classes of surfaces in E_3 with the property that reasonably generous portions can be mapped isometrically on subsets of H_2 or L_2. In order to relate our work to further studies by the reader in the area of differential geometry, we need to introduce the concept of a line element. In E_2, we find arc length of differentiable curves from the forms

$$ds^2 = dx^2 + dy^2, \qquad ds^2 = dr^2 + r^2 d\theta^2, \tag{11.22}$$

† Here we are using the property that directed angle from one directed segment to another is a continuous function for segments which intersect inside $\mathscr{C}$. In view of our orientation-preserving map of the interior of $\mathscr{C}$ onto a Euclidean disc, it would suffice to prove this in E_2.

‡ See Olmsted, *op. cit.*, p. 334.

valid respectively in Cartesian and polar coordinates. Similarly, in E_3, we have

$$\begin{aligned} ds^2 &= dx^2 + dy^2 + dz^2, \\ ds^2 &= dr^2 + r^2 d\phi^2 + r^2 \sin^2 \phi \, d\theta^2, \end{aligned} \tag{11.23}$$

in Cartesian and spherical coordinates, respectively. More generally, a metric space in which the square of the differential of arc of an arbitrary curve is a quadratic form in the differentials of the coordinates, with coefficients functions of the coordinates, is called a *Riemannian space*, and the form is called the *line element*, or more precisely, the representative of the line element for the given coordinate system. Thus (11.22) and (11.23) are line elements of E_2 and E_3, respectively.

We can find the line elements of H_2 and L_2 by an elementary calculation. Let $\mathbf{X} = \mathbf{X}(t)$ represent a curve $\mathscr{D}$, either in H_2 or L_2, and let $Y = Y(t_0)$ be one of its points. If $\mathbf{B}$ is the matrix of the absolute polarity, the function $f(t)$ (see (9.2) and (11.3)), where

$$f(t) = (\mathbf{X}^T\mathbf{B}\mathbf{Y})^2/(\mathbf{X}^T\mathbf{B}\mathbf{X})(\mathbf{Y}^T\mathbf{B}\mathbf{Y}),$$

is a function of the distance between X and Y. By writing $\mathbf{X} = \mathbf{Y} + \Delta\mathbf{Y}$ and expanding the matrix products, we find that

$$\lim_{t \to t_0} \frac{f(t) - 1}{(t - t_0)^2} = \left\{ \left(\mathbf{X}^T\mathbf{B} \frac{d\mathbf{X}}{dt} \right)^2 - (\mathbf{X}^T\mathbf{B}\mathbf{X}) \left(\frac{d\mathbf{X}^T}{dt} \mathbf{B} \frac{d\mathbf{X}}{dt} \right) \right\} \Big/ (\mathbf{X}^T\mathbf{B}\mathbf{X})^2. \tag{11.24}$$

Since $f(t) - 1 = \sinh^2 D_H(X, Y)$, or $-\sin^2 D_L(X, Y)$, and since $\lim_{\alpha \to 0} (\sin \alpha)/\alpha = \lim_{\alpha \to 0} (\sinh \alpha)/\alpha = 1$, the hypothesis that $\mathscr{D}$ possesses an arc parameter s and that the ratio of the arc length between Y and X to the distance between Y and X converges to 1 as X tends to Y along $\mathscr{D}$ implies that the left side of (11.24) is $\pm (ds/dt)^2$. If we normalize the projective coordinates so that $\mathbf{X}^T\mathbf{B}\mathbf{X}$ equals 1 (in L_2) or -1 (in H_2), it follows that $\mathbf{X}^T\mathbf{B}\,d\mathbf{X} = 0$, and we find in either case that

$$ds^2 = d\mathbf{X}^T\mathbf{B}d\mathbf{X}. \tag{11.25}$$

It is convenient to replace $\mathbf{X}$ by polar coordinates (u, ϕ). In L_2, for $\mathbf{B} = \mathbf{I}$, we have (see (11.17))

$$\mathbf{X} = (\sin u \cos \phi, \sin u \sin \phi, \cos u)^T,$$

and (11.25) becomes

$$ds^2 = du^2 + \sin^2 u \, d\phi^2. \tag{11.26}$$

In H_2, when the absolute conic is given by (9.5) we have

$$[\mathbf{X}] = [\tanh u \cos \phi, \tanh u \sin \phi, 1]^T,$$

so that the normalized representative $\mathbf{X}$ is given by

$$\mathbf{X} = (\sinh u \cos \phi, \sinh u \sin \phi, \cosh u)^T.$$

In this case

$$ds^2 = du^2 + \sinh^2 u \, d\phi^2. \tag{11.27}$$

The line elements (11.26) and (11.27) have constant Gaussian curvature (equal to ± 1), and there exist classes of surfaces in E_3 with these line elements; such surfaces possess local isometric maps into L_2 or H_2, according as the Gaussian curvature is $+1$ or -1.†

EXERCISES

1. Prove that a matrix is orthogonal if and only if

(a) the sum of the squares of the elements of each row is 1, and

(b) the sum of the products of corresponding elements of distinct rows is 0.

2. Prove that the rows of a matrix satisfy conditions (a) and (b) of Exercise 1 if and only if the columns satisfy the analogous conditions.

3. Prove that the tangent line to a circle in L_2 is perpendicular to the radius through the point of contact.

4. Find the locus of points in L_2 at a given distance from a line.

#**5.** Prove that the three points in L_2, one on each side of a triangle, orthogonal to the opposite vertex, are collinear, provided that no side of the triangle is the polar of the opposite vertex.

6. Verify that two circles in L_2 may have four points of intersection.

7. Interpret Exercise 6 in E_3.

8. Prove (11.14) and (11.15).

9. Interpret Weierstrass coordinates in E_3.

10. Prove Theorem 11.6.

11. Find the relation between two Weierstrass coordinate systems in L_2.

12. Prove, using stereographic projection, that the sum of the angles of a triangle in L_2 exceeds π.

#**13.** Define convergence of a sequence of points of L_2

(a) in terms of an embedding of L_2 in $S_2(\mathsf{R})$ and of convergence in $S_2(\mathsf{R})$, and

(b) in terms of the elliptic metric.

Show that the two natural definitions lead to the same concept of convergence.

14. Let $\{Y_i\}$ be a convergent sequence of points in L_2, and let $\{l_i\}$ be a sequence of lines l_i in the bundle $\mathscr{P}$ such that l_i corresponds to Y_i under an isomorphism of Theorem 11.3. Let $\{Z_i\}$ be a convergent sequence of points

† See D. J. Struik, *Lectures on Classical Differential Geometry*, Cambridge, Mass., Addison-Wesley Publishing Co., 1950, pp. 147–153.

in E_3, with $Z_i \in l_i$; prove that $\lim Z_i \in \lim l_i$. Conversely, if $Z \in \lim l_i$, there exists $Z_i \in l_i$ such that the sequence $\{Z_i\}$ converges to Z.

15. Prove that every direct motion in E_3 that possesses a fixed point is a rotation about a line.

16. Under the group of rotations in L_2 with a given center, the orbit of the vertex of a directed pencil of lines is a circle. When the vertex first returns to its initial point does the directed pencil return to its initial directed pencil? (Suppose that the radius of the circle is less than $\pi/2$.)

17. Is $G(H_2)$ connected? Is $G^+(H_2)$ connected?

#**18.** Is the set of all rotations in H_2 compact?

19. Use (11.26) and (11.27) to find the lengths of circles, in L_2 and H_2, of given radii.

#**20.** Investigate the representation of rotations in L_2 by means of quaternions.†

† See Coxeter, *Non-Euclidean Geometry*, Toronto, University of Toronto Press, 1957, pp. 122–126.

Notation and Symbols

The letters and symbols listed below denote concepts whose meaning is amplified in the text on the pages referred to.

$\mathbf{A}$	Square matrix	67, 97
A_2	Affine plane	273, 280
$\overrightarrow{A_2}$	Oriented affine plane	311
$A_1\ A_2\ A_3\ D$	Reference frame	100
$\mathbf{B}$	Square matrix	67, 97
C	Complex field	26
d, D	Euclidean distance functions	19, 20
d_H, D_H	Hyperbolic distance functions	324
d_L, D_L	Elliptic distance functions	329
$\mathscr{E}$	Embedding	80, 163, 275
E_n	Euclidean metric space ($n = 1, 2, 3$)	13, 44, 344
F	Field not of characteristic two	26
F_p	Field of residues mod p	26
G_3, G_3^+	Projective group in S_1, direct subgroup	67, 308
G_4, G_4^+	Similarity group, direct subgroup	335
G_6, G_6^+	Affine group, direct subgroup	12, 273, 312
G_8, $G_8(\mathsf{R})$, $G_8(\mathsf{F})$	Projective group in S_2	97
$G(H_n), G^+(H_n)$	Hyperbolic groups ($n = 1, 2$)	321, 322, 348
$G(L_n)$, $G^+(L_1)$	Elliptic groups ($n = 1, 2$)	327, 328, 381
$G(\sigma)$	Group of an involution or polarity	246
H_n, $\overrightarrow{H_n}$	Hyperbolic spaces ($n = 1, 2$)	321, 322, 348
K_2, $\overrightarrow{K_2}$	Similarity planes	335
$\mathscr{L}$	Pencil of quadratic forms	254

$l(\mathscr{E})$	Absolute line (line at infinity)	163, 280
L_1, $\overrightarrow{L_1}$, L_2	Elliptic spaces	327, 328, 381
M, M^*	Euclidean metric group	12, 44
Q	Quadratic form	85, 182, 209
$r(A, B)$, $r(A/B)$	Half-line (ray)	281
R	Real field	26
$\mathscr{S}$	Sense class	305, 313, 314
S_n, $S_n(\mathsf{F})$, $S_n(\mathsf{R})$	Projective space of dimension n, over F, R	67, 97
$\overrightarrow{S_1}$	Directed (or oriented) $S_1(\mathsf{R})$	309
seg, seg*	Segments	121
seg $\overrightarrow{ABC}$	Directed segment	310, 319
sec	Sector	131
sgn	Signum function	196
$\mathbf{U}$, $\mathbf{V}$	Row matrices	102
$\mathbf{X}$, $\mathbf{Y}$, $\mathbf{Z}$	Column matrices	64, 66, 96
$\Gamma(S, G)$	Geometry of S under G	271
$\Sigma_2(\mathsf{F})$	Space of lines of $S_2(\mathsf{F})$	107
Ω_n	Set of nonzero homogeneous classes	61
$\in$, $\subset$, $\times$	Membership, inclusion, Cartesian product	13
$\cup$, $\cap$, $\oplus$	Union, intersection, join	43, 103
$\parallel$	Parallelism	280
$\{X \mid \ldots\}$	Specification of a set	43
$\{P\ Q\}$, $\{P\ Q\ R\}$	Sense classes	306, 314, 322
$\infty(\mathscr{E})$	Absolute point	80
$[\quad]$	Equivalence class under scalar multiplication	61, 209
$(A\ B, C\ D)$	Cross ratio	74, 80, 82, 115
$(A\ B, C\ D)_X$	Cross ratio	199
$(A\ B, C\ D)_{\mathscr{C}}$	Cross ratio	238
AC/AB	Affine ratio	281

Index

References are to page numbers